TAMMY, TELL ME TRUE

Books by Cid Ricketts Sumner:

Tammy, Tell Me True

by
CID RICKETTS SUMNER

the NEW *Bobbs-Merrill* COMPANY, INC.
AN ASSOCIATE OF HOWARD W. SAMS & CO., INC.
Publishers • INDIANAPOLIS • NEW YORK

14590

COPYRIGHT © 1959 BY CID RICKETTS SUMNER

Printed in the United States of America

First Edition

Library of Congress Catalog Card Number: 59-14300

This book is a work of fiction and any
resemblance between the characters in it
and persons living or dead is coincidental.

TAMMY, TELL ME TRUE

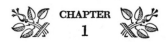

CHAPTER
1

TAMMY went running through the garden, out toward the south field where the sound of a tractor told her that Pete was at work. She had to find him, she had to know if it was true, what she had just heard. She had been down on her knees, pulling up grass from Miss Renie's verbena bed, and at first she had paid no heed to the murmur of voices from the dining room. She had just been thinking what a contrary thing it was—all this grass flourishing like the green bay tree regardless of the long dry summer while Pete's crop was dying in the field for lack of rain.

It had been the sound of her own name spoken that caught her attention. Not that she meant to eavesdrop, but the spoken words struck her dumb and motionless, the way a run-down rabbit might halt and freeze before a mortal enemy. It was Pete's ma and pa talking, mostly his ma, who was a great one for palavering about this and that.

Pete always said, "Oh, just pay her no mind, honey" and laughed off her fussing and fidgeting. But this was different, she was in dead earnest now and arguing Professor Brent down to no more than an occasional sputter.

"But, Joel, I am not interfering. You know I never interfere with Peter's plans. I am just trying to help. Now Tammy is welcome to stay here as long as she needs a home and dear knows Aunt Renie is getting more and more eccentric every day and really will need a companion after we go back to town. And I do want to go soon—my club meeting——"

"But the wedding, my dear——"

"Never mind that. Peter's come around to my way of thinking at last. I've done my best with that child—and she is still a child, say what you will. I've taught her to use a knife and fork properly, but I despair of her language. Really, Joel——"

"Now, Ena, wait a minute. Is that really important compared to other things? After all, Tammy and her grandfather saved Pete from drowning in the river. That is a debt we can never repay and——"

"I do not forget. Nor that her grandfather is now in jail——"

"My dear, Mr. Dinwoodie is in jail, as you insist on calling it, entirely at his own request. He finds it more comfortable than living on that shanty boat on the river where Tammy grew up and I can't say I blame him for refusing to leave the jail when his term was up."

There was a hint of laughter in his voice and Tammy clenched her fists, hearing it. He was laughing at Grandpa. Even Professor Brent who was always kind when he wasn't too wrapped up in books to know what was what, even Professor Brent was making fun of Grandpa.

"Indeed," he went on now more soberly, "I believe he has been made some sort of assistant chaplain and surely that is a most respectable——"

"Respectable, my foot! He was taken up for moonshining in the swamp as you well know and the fact that he is a kind of preacher—never properly ordained, I'm sure—has nothing to do with it. The point is that I don't want anything to interfere with this new plan of Peter's. . . ."

At that Tammy dropped the handful of grass she was still clutching in her fist and set out as fast as she could run, looking

8

for Pete. It couldn't be true. Why, the wedding day was named and set and Pete was as eager as she. Or was he? She stopped dead in her tracks while little things he had said came back to her. Pete, wishing he knew more about stock-raising and then sending off for all those catalogues of what he called agricultural colleges. Most of all Pete saying nothing when she or Miss Renie mentioned the wedding day, or Pete seeming worried and uneasy and sometimes sunk in a kind of gloom that all her wiles and talk could not dispel.

She moved slowly across to the fence now and rested her arms on the top rail, seeing Pete far off at the other end of the field, backing and turning the tractor round, then when it stalled, jumping down to fiddle it into going again.

"Pete, Pete, my darling," she whispered through tears, "my own true love, working so hard all spring and now plowing the crop under because somehow or other the government might pay for it. What are you thinking inside yourself, what are you planning now?"

Pete was always going from one thing to another. He had had the notion of making a fortune on hickory chairs with cowhide seats. All now left of that plan was six chairs that stood with their backs to the side porch wall, empty and forlorn, for all the world like a row of last year's birds' nests. For the price of hides had gone up and by the time he had spent hours carving out the hickory by hand, he had to ask so much money for the chairs that nobody would buy. People seemed to want things made fast by machinery and costing little and breaking soon so that more had to be bought. So in the end it was all just a notion Pete had had, like the notion of raising a new kind of tomato never seen before in all the land, and then the wind and the hail had come and cut down the tender plants. It had been like the great wind from the wilderness that smote the four corners of Job's house so it fell.

Was Pete a man like unto Job, bound to be pestered with one thing and then another? In the end, of course, Job had

9

more than ever before and died being old and full of days. But she didn't want to wait till Pete was old and full of days. She didn't mind his changing from one thing to another—that was just the way Pete was and she loved him whole, good and bad alike. Only she wanted to be with him the while, through all his waverings and changes. And now—what was it his ma was egging him on to do, or not to do?

She was about to climb the fence and run to him when he got the tractor engine started, turned to mount it and saw her. He was a far-off figure at the bottom of the field, but when he waved, it was as if he were close beside her, and she was eased of her first blind panic. Besides, she decided, this was no moment to pester Pete with questions. He was all hot and worn out with trying to get that engine going. She would wait till he left off work for the day. Yes, in the cool of the evening they would walk in the garden and she would ask him what his mother meant saying never mind the wedding, saying nothing must interfere with his plans. The very sight of Pete was reassuring but as she turned away now, moving slowly, eyes downcast, other words returned to her and she heard again, as if it might be now, Mrs. Brent's voice saying, "I've tried to teach her . . . a child . . . her language, oh dear me . . . jail . . . moonshining."

Under the big oak tree back of the barn a nanny goat stood, looking as lost and hurt as Tammy felt. It was Nan who had been her one friend and playmate on the river, it was Nan who had walked by her side all the way through the swamp and here to Brenton Hall after Grandpa got found out by the revenuers and so had to send her traipsing the road to Pete's house. For she could not live alone on the river and Pete had said that she would always have a home here on the plantation if need arose. It was out of gratitude he had said that, she thought with sadness. But surely it had been out of love that he spoke the last day of the Pilgrimage visitors to Brenton Hall, the day she sang for them and he hearkened to the last verse of her song, and kissed her, and sang it back to her and said he meant the words for true.

Tammy climbed the fence and sat perched there for a while, plucking a splinter from the sole of her bare foot. Then she pushed back her sweat-damp hair and spread her faded blue skirts as if it might be for some fine gathering of human beings and sang the song as she had sung for the Pilgrimage tourist folk:

> "I come walking by yonders gate
> Feelin' mighty disconsolate
> Had some eggs stowed in my bonnet
> Bonnet hangin' on my arm
> I come up the long driveway
> Singin' a mighty mournful song"

Tammy looked across at Nan. "This here's the song I sung," she said and smiled a little, being cheered by the recollection.

> "Where is my dear one
> I ask of a star
> Do you see him comin'
> Afar, afar?
> Where is my dear one
> I call to the moon,
> Will I find him
> Find him soon?
> Does he come ridin'
> To light an set,
> Does he come stridin'
> To lift my kiverlet?
> Does he come sailin'
> From over the sea
> Or does he lie ailin'
> In a far countree?

"Then I see Pete standing by and I make up a make-up song. Like Grandpa always said, if you got no song to suit the occasion, make one up to fit. So this here's it, and a mighty bold one, too."

11

Nan seemed to nod her agreement, and Tammy sang:

"Is it my dear one
Standin' there,
Black the color of his hair?
Is it my dear one
Standin' there
With such a noble
Lordly air?
Why does he give me
Such a frown?
Doesn't he like my linsey gown?
Got no slipper
Got no shoe
But he would find me
Fond and true.

"So I come singin' to the big house door
And he like to look me into the floor.
Will ye buy fresh eggs this mornin', sir
Or maybe a pullet for Sunday dinner?
The young man looked me up and down
Me a-standin' in my linsey gown.

"Then here's the young man's song in answer:

"I'll take the eggs
I'll take the bonnet
The linsey gown
An all that's in it.

"I'll make you lady
Of my land
I'll put a ring
Upon your hand
I'll take you for
My lovin' bride
An keep you ever
At my side.

"An that's how I come to be ladyfied
That's how I lived happy till I died."

Tammy slid down from the top of the fence. She ran to Nan and dropped on her knees, cheek close against the soft flank.

12

"Nan, oh, Nan, won't I ever get ladyfied? Won't I ever live happy till I die?"

Nan answered never a word, but the feel of her was sweet and comforting and she slobbered a little, rubbing her head against Tammy's shoulder as much as to say, "Where's my sugar lump?"

"Nary a thing have I for you," Tammy said, "just my love." She scratched behind the soft small ears and rubbed the swollen stomach. "Never mind, Nanny dear, you'll be having some little ones soon to keep you company. Only I wisht it was me." For when she and Pete got married, she meant to have a whole raft of babies. Might be they would keep Pete contented and not always going from one notion to another. Pete's ma didn't believe in big families. She'd just had Pete and left off right there.

"We know better, don't we, Nan?" And Nan nodded her head for all the world like as if she understood, Tammy thought. And with that she rose and set out for the house, comforted yet not quite knowing why she should be.

Osia was in the kitchen at the end of the ell, cooking supper. Miss Renie was yonder on the ell gallery giving Roots his drawing lesson. What was it Mrs. Brent had called her? Eccentric, that was it. Well, anyway, she was a wonder. Nobody would guess she was pushing seventy, for she was one that life didn't die down in. She was like a kettle pushed to the back of the stove by life and time but now and then boiling up and rattling the lid. She was still planning, if she ever got the money, to take off for New Orleans and lead what she called a Bohemian life, painting pictures and making batiks. Right now she was bending over Roots's easel, her dark eyes flashing, one lock gray hair fallen across her cheek and the little black bow tie she always wore at the neck of her white shirtwaist all awry. She was saying, "That's splendid, Roots, and I want you to draw this bust of Shakespeare sideways, and hindside, too."

"Yessum," Roots said. Roots was Osia's grandson, dark as the

13

dark of the moon but bright as a silver dollar and ever since a visiting artist at the Pilgrimage had said he had talent but needed discipline, Miss Renie had been giving him discipline along with his drawing lessons. Tammy moved slowly on, unseen.

Once she had asked Osia how-come Roots was named Roots. Osia had answered that he was born in hard times, a time of root-hog-or-die and that was how he came by his entitlement. Tammy's own name came out of a book and she was proud of that because it showed her own little ma, who had died so young, had at least known how to read. It was Grandma who had taught Tammy to read and taught her the Bible and common sense as well. That was all a girl needed to know, she had said. But now, as Tammy passed on round the corner of the house, she wondered. Seemed like there was a sight more one needed when she got out into the world.

On the driveway she paused beside the circular rosebed and looked up at the house with its tall columns and wide veranda and open double doors to the long central hall. It was a elegant house in spite of Pete's saying it was run-down and needing paint. She liked its being gray and worn, for it matched the gray moss that hung from the live oaks of the drive, and right now their shadows, cast by the westering sun, lay like dark lace across its face. How could Pete think it poor and plain?

It was really so fine that those who lived there had maybe got into the way of being cushioned against life. So much was ready to hand, the house with its size and roomage, its richness of furnishing with silver and dishes and many acres of land—land-poor, Pete called it—and all the heavy work being done by others, the whole putting a distance between self and the real. Pete was used to living at that remove. Cousin-once-removed, the phrase came to her out of remembered talk of kin. Pete was a cousin-once-removed from reality and now he maybe wanted to become still more removed through new ways and learning, making the plantation bring forth more than the

14

needed living, making it a means to money and to fame and such-like things that were a feather bed to real living.

It was the realness which she missed here, the closeness to what a body had to have in order to keep on living and breathing. It was the making-do with what was at hand—a dress from meal sacks, not boughten from a store, it was the daily known need of fish caught from the river, of ground sown with seed against hunger, not just for sale. It was the mending of a roof to keep out the rain, the cutting of wood for warmth in time of winterly cold, and besides all that, it was knowing the river ways and swamp life and the year's changes with spring returning ever, it was the living and dying of animals and humankind, each at the end of his season. Like Grandma, lying now in the little old graveyard atop the bluff by the river, her life rounded round, ends tied up together so it was all brought neatly about from being born out of the unknown and growing up and loving Grandpa and borning children to live and die, and then coming at last to her own dying into the unknown again.

Tammy drew a long sigh. For a fact, she was homesick for the *Ellen B.* and the life there. But this was Pete's home—that is, it would be when Miss Renie left it to him—and this was where she was going to live happy till she died, like the song said. Maybe. She hung a maybe to the end of her hope as one hangs a horseshoe over the door for luck, or a rabbit's foot round the neck on a string. Then she mounted the steps and went into the house.

The library was deserted most of the time now because Professor Brent had finished with what he called his research and he had all his books and papers spread on the table in the dining room where he was writing out his lectures for some new course he was to give in town at the college where he taught. Tammy pushed back the sliding doors and went in. It was dark in there after the bright afternoon light outside, the books in their sober bindings holding the shadows and seeming more than ever a mystery, unread. The old oak mission chairs merged

15

with the brown of the carpet as wild things of the swamp might crouch, motionless and unseen in the midst of like-colored underbrush. There was a special smell here, too, the smell of learning maybe, and there was a holy stillness as if the wise were sleeping. She took a book from the shelves without bothering to read its title, seeing only that it was an old one. All summer in spare moments she had been reading in secret, hoping to catch up with Pete in learning and she had thought to begin with old books and work up to newer ones.

This was called *Jay's Sermons* and she felt straightway at home with it because Grandpa was always practicing his sermons on her and she thought likely she knew more about sermons than anybody in the world save those that wrote or preached them. She opened at random to the Twenty-fifth Discourse, as it was called, and the text was the one about the tree of life planted on either side of the river, the tree of life that bore twelve manner of fruits and yielded her fruit every month of the year.

That was the kind of tree Pete ought to have, Tammy thought. Then he wouldn't ever have to worry about crops. What a wonder that would be! She read on for a little, but this sermon was not half as lively as Grandpa's, so after a bit, she dozed. The far-off *chug* of the tractor died away, the hot August sun went down and when she woke Pete was calling her to come to supper.

CHAPTER
2

As ALWAYS, supper was on the ell gallery, a little south wind smoothing and soothing the heat of the day as the sun went down. As always Miss Renie and Mrs. Brent talked, one without seeming to hear what the other said, or only out of politeness not speaking till there came a lull. Each was intent on her own way, not openly hostile, yet finding no common meeting ground. They were like two beasties of alien kind. Miss Renie talked about a new manner of painting she was going to make, a poem made by brush and oil out of the words it came in. There would be a piper piping songs and a bold lover and a heifer lowing to the skies, "And all his flanks with garlands drest." Tammy thought it must be like to the way she bedizened Nan at Christmas with berries and green mistletoe because there were no flowers blooming in the swamp in winter time.

Mrs. Brent talked about the paper she had to read before her club. It had a high-sounding, far-reaching title but no more yet writ, she said, and she worrit about getting it done in time. The title was "Trends in Southern Literature Since the Civil War" and she did hope no one would expect her to mention someone who seemed to go by the name of Faulkner. His grandpa had written a real sweet story about the White

Rose of Memphis, but there hadn't been anything else respectable come out of the family since.

Professor Brent had left his mind in the dining room with his lectures and as for Pete, he ate and said never a word save to ask Osia for more of her buttermilk-and-sody battercakes. But when he had mopped up the last smear of molasses from his plate and topped it off with the last bite of grits and sausage, he asked, "Did anybody get the mail?"

"I plumb forgot it," Tammy said.

"Not 'plumb,' Tammy dear," Mrs. Brent said, butter as usual not melting in her mouth. "Rather say—'I completely forgot,' or 'it quite escaped my mind.' "

"Yessum, thanky—I mean thank you."

"That's better." Then as if sharpness had boiled up in her and had to spout out somehow, she turned to Pete. "Peter, I hope this is the last time you will come to the table looking like a field hand."

Tammy looked at him, trying to see with Mrs. Brent's eyes. She saw him, tall and bronzed and healthy seeming, collar open at the throat showing fair the skin no sun had touched, saw dark hair still damp from his before-supper brushing. He looked just the way a proper man that was a man should look. Oh, she would never speak up in her own behalf, but for Pete—her lips parted, then she choked back the words.

For Pete was laughing, leaning to put a light kiss on his mother's cheek and saying, "Don't worry, honey, this is my last day in the field." Then, rising, he gave Tammy his quick warm glance and caught her hand in his, pulling her up beside him, saying, "Come on, Tammy, let's go down to the letter box."

Here was the time and the chance Tammy had been waiting for. They went through the hall and across the wide front gallery, down the steps to the drive. Then he put his arm around her. "How's my girl? You've been mighty quiet this evening."

"Oh, I'm all right." For now, walking close beside him down the dusk-filled drive, hearing the last hot-bug of the day giving

18

his last farewell to the heat, seeing the moon just coming over the roof of the house to silver the upper leaves, her fears quietened and she had no heart for shattering this lovely moment. That was the magic Pete had. She could be fair in a frenzy over something and then he would come along. She would go giddy at his touch and forget everything save that he was near. "You mean you've finished plowing the south field under?"

"I've finished." Then quickly he added, "Race you to the letter box. Last one there's a rotten egg. One, two, three, go!" And away they went, down the curving drive and out the gate that stood always open, across the road to the letter box.

"No fair, you slowed up for me," Tammy cried.

Pete just laughed and reached into the box. One letter was all there was. "Keep your fingers crossed, sugar," he said and tore it open.

"You can't read in the dark," Tammy said.

He moved out of the shadows so that a slash of moonlight coming between the trees fell on the printed page like a shining sword. Tammy, standing in the darkness under the big beech that guarded the gate, saw his face brighten, heard the quick indrawing of his breath, and for the moment that he stood there unmoving, letter in hand, she felt as if he were gone from her, far gone beyond her reach and beyond her knowing.

She ran to him, crying, "Come back, come back!"

He slid the letter into a trouser pocket and put his arms around her. "Why, goosey, goosey, I'm right here. What's the matter?"

"J-just a rabbit run acrost my grave, I reckon." She clung to him while he patted her and smoothed her hair back from her forehead and made her look up at him.

"A rabbit over your grave!" he scoffed. "Really, Tammy, you must get over silly superstitions like that."

She stiffened and drew away from him. There was a time when her sayings out of olden time had amused and pleased him. Of late he had stopped laughing and seemed like he was turning more and more into the ways and the mind of his ma, wanting her to be different. But if he didn't like her the way she was, how could he have loved her in the first place?

"Do you love me, Pete?"

"Of course, child. What's got into you?"

She hung her head. Child. That's what Mrs. Brent called her when she was the most put out.

"I don't know, Pete. I just——" Then as they moved through the gate and up the drive, she asked, "Was it good news your letter brung you?"

"Brought. Yes, it brought me good news. Good and bad both."

"How can that be?"

"I'll tell you," and he quickened his steps as if the very thought of it set him stirring. But he did not tell her right away. Instead he began to talk about the crops being ruined by the drought and mostly plowed under now, though it was maybe too late to get money from the government for that. He said he was thinking he maybe ought to go into raising cattle. There was money in cattle nowadays.

Tammy broke in to say, "I reckon I could milk a sight of cows. Anybody can milk a goat wouldn't have no trouble——"

"Not dairy cows, it's beef cattle I would be raising, and I could manage all right with no help but Roots and his father, and it looks as if they're the only ones I can keep on the place."

He talked on and on, saying it took more learning now than it used to, to raise cattle. There were new methods a body had to know and if he was going to make a success of it . . .

All this had brought them along the drive to the end of the gallery.

"So you see, Tammy," he said, turning at the top of the steps to face her for the first time, "if I want to keep on living here at Brenton Hall—and I do—I've simply got to study so I'll know all these new ways of doing things. You do understand, don't you?"

20

"Yes, Pete." The moonlight was bright as a new tin bucket pouring white water on bush and tree. The shadows lay in liquid blackness that one might wade in up to the knees and over, so deep it seemed. "Yes, Pete," Tammy said again, not turning her eyes from the scene before them. "I been seeing you studying over all them catalogues. Only didn't seem like you could be learning much, just reading lists of studies and names of professors alongside them."

"Of course not," he said with impatience. "I was trying to see where I should apply to get the best, and my letter tonight tells me I can go to the very one I thought was best of all. So Tammy, darling, you see—" he had a desperate note in his voice that made her turn quickly to him—"I don't know how to say it——"

"Oh Pete, did you think I'd be mad? Why, I think it is wonderful. Don't look so worrit. You know I don't care the least smidgin of a little bit where we are or where we go." She was fair dancing up and down in the sudden easement of hearing at last the what and wherefore of his plans. "I'd traipse the road forever with you, if that was what you were wanting. You're the silly one to have been worriting about that. I'll write Grandpa to come straightway for the wedding and we'll light out for the furtherest college in Christendom, if that's what you're wanting. And might be I could get me some schooling there at the same time. Oh, not in the way a man gets it, but in a womanly way," she added quickly, seeing the shake of his head.

"But, Tammy, you couldn't get into any college. You've never been to school a day in your life. Don't be ridiculous."

"Oh?" She drew back from him and stood very still, saying in a small voice, "Ridiculous, is it?"

"Of course. Not that I blame you, darling, but living all your life on a shanty boat, how could you——"

The "darling" gave her a mite of courage, just enough to say, "There might be a lower-down school in the same town——"

At that Pete stood silent, his face turned away from her. In

21

that silence all the joy of the brief moment, all the gloriation of the moonlight went away. Of a sudden on this warm summer night, it came on to be cold. Nothing said, but a doom stood in the shadows waiting. Tammy moved from him then, she leaned her back against one of the tall pillars of the gallery and looked up into the bright moon till her eyes were blinded and all the cold boding that stood in the shadows gathered round her.

"Maybe . . . maybe you don't truly want to marry me, Pete," she said at last, and the words came out as small and fearful as the peep of a young bird downfallen from its nest.

"For heaven's sake, Tammy—" he whirled on her as if a fury had caught him—"why do you have to go leaping to conclusions? Just because I want to go away and study so I can do better with the plantation. And why do I do it? So I can make more than the bare living that is all I can get from it just farming. You ought to be able to see that. Oh, Tammy, darling." He came and put his arm around her, drew her toward the front door. "Don't let's fight. We'll talk in the morning. I'm all in tonight. That sun was really hot today, and I started for the field before seven this morning. Honestly, I've got to turn in. Don't be mad."

"All right, Pete. I won't be mad."

He kissed her good night and went up the wide curving stairs, yawning as he went and giving her a sleepy wave of the hand as she passed down the hall on the way to the studio room in the ell which she shared with all Miss Renie's painting and Picasso, the tortoise-shell cat. She saw Professor and Mrs. Brent in the dining room as she went by and would have said good night but they seemed busy with their books and papers and besides she wanted to get away by herself and ponder on what she did not understand. She had not yet figgered things out. Pete still was of a mind to marry her, he said, and yet there was something more unspoken.

She lay awake for a long time, going over and over in her

22

mind every word Pete had said and puzzling over what he had almost said. For now, thinking back, seemed as if there had been something slippery about Pete tonight, seemed as if he had slithered away from something in his talk. What could it be? For now she knew his plan that his ma was making such a to-do about, talking to his pa. But there was something more, else why had he said they would talk in the morning? Poor dear, he had been tired and sleepy tonight. She'd ought to make allowance for that.

As she drifted off to sleep at last, she heard the wind rising and then the patter of rain on the roof. Rain at last, but too late to help Pete's crops. Was that the way things happened always, out in the world, that by the time you got what you wanted, you were done with wanting it?

After a restless night, Tammy woke and knew she had overslept. Rain was still falling in a fine gray drizzle but she could tell by the light that it was late in the morning. A sad-colored day, she thought as she rose and went to the washstand in the corner behind Miss Renie's cat screen. There were dozens of cat faces on it—her best friends, Miss Renie said, and she thought people's souls went into cats when they died and that was why she treated them with such loving kindness. Every cat she had ever owned had its painted portrait here and it was enough to scare the living daylight out of a body that woke to a dim dawn and took them for real.

Tammy washed and dressed quickly and she brushed her hair with care, leaving it loose on her shoulders because Pete liked it that way instead of in braids. When she went out to the ell gallery, there was no sign of breakfast, only Miss Renie at her easel, humming a snatch of song to herself. "Oh, I was born with an itching foot, a knapsack in my hand——"

"Humph, thought you were going to sleep all day." Miss Renie's speech was like to be sudden when she was in the throes, as she called it. But her heart was right in spite of her queerness, and from the first she had been kind, giving Tammy welcome and not a bit afraid of what folks might say about somebody off the river come to stay.

"I like to have slept all day," Tammy said.

Miss Renie bent over so her tall thin body was like a strung bow, she put in a stroke of her crayon and snapped herself upright again. "See? I've just blocked in the main lines. But the priests, where shall I put them?"

She stood back from her drawing, head cocked to one side, eyes, that must have been beautiful when she was young, squinting as if to dim the lines she had drawn and make room for the dream of what she wanted to draw.

"You've got a sight of folks already," Tammy said, for there were men and ladies and every last one of them naked as a jay bird. Luckily there was a plenty of trees and bushes to mostly cover their private parts. "Are you going to put clothes on them?"

"Clothes?" Miss Renie gave a big snort. "Clothes! This is art."

"Oh," Tammy said and went on to the kitchen where Osia was just finishing the breakfast dishes. "Don't stop for me," Tammy said. "I'll get my own coffee."

"Yessum. And there's biscuit keeping hot in the oven."

"Thanky, ma'm." Tammy helped herself and sat down at the kitchen table.

"Miss Tammy, how many times I got to tell you it ain't fitting for you to be ma'm-ing me."

"Well, I just naturally say ma'm to anybody older than me. So why shouldn't I?"

"Come to think of it thataway, ain't no reason, excepting the color of my skin. That's plenty why for lots of things."

"Don't make sense to me. My, but this is good coffee."

Osia's hands were motionless for a moment among the dishes. Then she said, "Miss Tammy, I declare, look like you come into this world with a fresh brain."

"Maybe it's fresh, but it's too empty, Osia. There's lots I've got to learn."

24

Osia stood the last of the dishes in the rack. "Just don't you onlearn what you knows aready because that's a sight more than some folks ever learn." She was pouring the dishwater down the sink when there came a high-pitched voice calling from upstairs somewhere. "Osia, Osia! I'm waiting for you!"

"Yessum, I'm acoming, Miz Brent." Then she added, "Got to go help her pack her clothes."

"Pack? Is she going somewheres?"

"Going home, her and the professor, both the two of them."

"But—Pete and me—the wedding . . ." She stared at Osia's broad back and for a moment could not swallow the last bit of her biscuit.

Osia moved slowly toward the door, not looking round. "I reckon as how they figger on coming back for that, if and when."

"What do you mean, if and when?"

"I don't mean nothing, Miss Tammy. 'Cepting I'd ought to keep my big mouth shut." At the door she turned. "Miss Tammy, I'll say this much and no more. There comes a time when a body got to put her foot down, when a body got to say what's what and nail it up on the wall like a rabbit skin to dry."

Tammy rose. "Where's Pete?"

"In the liberry figgering his head off, last I seen," Osia went on to the ell gallery and stomped up the open steps that led to the upstairs ell rooms.

Tammy went on a run. She flung back the double doors to the library and then just stood there staring at Pete. He sat at the table, papers strewn all round about. One dark lock of hair had fallen across his forehead and he had a half-distracted look on his face, his face that was so known and dear to her in line and shape.

"Tammy," he said, "I've been figuring and figuring till I'm about wild and there just isn't any earthly way to take you with me. The G.I. Bill isn't enough for the two of us."

After a stunned moment she said, "If it's just money, I've got money."

"You?"

"Yes, me!" she cried with spirit and crossed to stand before him, the table between. "When Grandpa got took by the reve-nuers, he told me his secret hiding place. It's the reward money he got for hauling out the floaters from the river—like you, only you were alive." She paused, remembering the dark night she and Grandpa had rowed up river to the big whirlpool where everybody who drowned this side of Vicksburg was bound to end up sooner or later. "There's lots of money, maybe as much as a hundred dollars."

Pete smiled faintly, shaking his head. "That wouldn't be a drop in the bucket. No, there's no use."

"Oh," Tammy said and the word was a plummet, dropping down, down.

She knew now, knew for sure that he was going, going soon and going alone. She walked to the window and stood with her back to the room, looking out at tree trunks wet black and gloom soaked, at gray moss that was dark and listless and drip-ping, at grass and leaf gray veiled with dampness. All feeling left her for a little and when it returned it was like the feeling a body gets in the middle of the night, waking and quavering to a hoot owl's hoot from so far away it might be no more than the memory of another hearing long gone, and because of be-ing not quite real, it doubled and redoubled its doomsomeness, gathering unknown terrors as it grew till it seemed like the end of the world. She clasped her hands together to hide their trembling.

"Well," said Pete, "you needn't sound like that. It isn't that way at all. I'll be back in June and we'll be married right away, as soon as I get here. After all, as my mother says, you're young, maybe it would be best to give you time to grow up a bit and——"

At that Tammy whirled around, wrath waxing hot against him and his ma and her voice was tight from the boiling-up within her. "I'm a woman growed already, so don't go saying I'm needing time to grow any more. Just say what's what.

26

That you're bound to go regardless, and we can't get married till the going is over and done with. I won't be holding you back." She faced him fiercely, chin high and haughty. "What's more, I don't believe one word of what all you been telling me, that you've got to learn new ways and all that. There's plenty here already. It's you that ain't satisfied, wanting to go traipsing the road, footloose and free."

"Tammy, Tammy, don't take it like that. You'll be learning, too, right here with Aunt Renie. She loves to teach. Look how she's working over Roots. And I'll get her to set you a lesson every day, grammar, history, everything——"

"So it's all arranged, is it? Well, now I see clear as day. I know why you won't take me. It's not the money, it's because you're ashamed of me, you and your ma. I know what they called me, those Pilgrimage folks, they called me that shanty boat girl come off the river. That's what your ma calls me, the river gal that's got a grandpa in jail. Oh, I see it all clear as day. You won't take me because I don't talk right, like proper folk do and I'd shame you out in the world, like I shamed your ma before the Pilgrims, and here you go putting off the wedding and I won't have it so, and I ain't agoing to let you!" She choked and could say no more. Pete sprang to his feet, but she fled before him, down the hall, out to the ell, to Miss Renie's studio room that was the only creep-hole she had to hide in. She bolted the door, flung herself across the bed and hid her face.

She heard Pete coming fast, heard him knocking on the door, heard him saying she had got it all wrong and please, please come out. The more he pleaded, the madder she got, shouting, "Go way, go way, I ain't listening," and she covered her head with a pillow so she would not be beguiled with sweet words such as spoke to the heart.

She lay there till all was still and empty seeming. If she didn't have Pete all the world would be empty, she thought with a stab of pure fright. Betwixt and between them they had managed to mess things up to a fare you well. What now?

27

What now? Overhead she heard the quick sharp click of Mrs. Brent's high heels and the slow *shuush* of Osia's easy step, as they went about packing bag and box. Then from out on the ell gallery came voices, Pete's seeming small and sad, Miss Renie's rising till it came forth like a stream of brimstone.

"Pete Brent, you're just a plain dam, dam Amsterdam simpleton without the sense you should have been born with. You might at least have told her the real reason you are going."

"But I thought she would know. And besides how could I guess she'd take it like this?"

"How else could she? You don't know one Rotterdam thing about a woman, except to wheedle and charm and expect her to know things you never tell her. How can she understand your point of view about the plantation when it seems such luxury to her as it is? And she may be right at that. Tammy's little toe is worth more than all six feet of you." Then, with one of her swift changes, Miss Renie broke into laughter. "Sounds as if you were some kind of six-footed animal. What would you call it, a sexaped?"

Pete wasn't laughing. "It's just that—well, her language is all right on the river, or even here, but one has to live in the world and—well, even she is not happy about it. Of course I know she's worth a dozen of me in everything that's important."

Miss Renie sobered at that. "Then tell her so, for heaven's sake. And furthermore, let me tell you right now I have not the slightest intention of tutoring her all the time you are gone. She's perfect the way she is, in the world or out of it, and you'll be lucky if she waits for you and doesn't change in other ways."

"Well, but—what can I do now?"

"Go and tell her you love her, if you do."

"Of course I do, Aunt Renie. Do you think I want to leave her, or that I'd dream of it if you weren't here to look after her? She's all the world to me and I'm only doing this for her sake, so I can take care of her properly. I wouldn't have hurt her feelings for a cool million."

28

Tammy was sitting on the edge of the bed, torn two ways in her mind. Pete was worrit about her manner of talking and such, but, if his going was all for her and him loving her all the time, then how wickedly she had spoken! She had spoken grievous words such as stir up strife, she had been stiff-necked and proud. By pride came destruction, the Bible said. Well she did not mean to be destructed by any such of a low-down thing as pride. With that she ran to wash her tear-stained face and smooth her hair. Then she unbolted the door and went along the passageway to the ell gallery. Miss Renie was back at her drawing and Pete was just sitting by the table with his head in his hands. The sight of him thus was more than she could bear and she ran toward him crying, "Pete——"

He sprang to meet her. "Tammy!"

Then both at once they said, "I'm sorry."

Miss Renie laid down her crayon. "Quarrels end in lovers' meeting, or something like that and I can see it's no place for a maiden lady." Then as she picked up a plate of scraps from the shelf between the posts and set out for a morning visit with her cats in the old carriage house, she looked back to see Pete holding Tammy close, and she gave him a wink and a nod. "But mind you, Tammy," she called over her shoulder, "Pete was born with an itching foot, like me, only I never got the chance to scratch mine in the open road." And with that she went her way, singing that old song she was always humming:

> "Oh, I was born with an itching foot
> A knapsack in my hand;
> Born to rove the wide world over,
> Die in a foreign land.
> But life goes by with a laugh and a sigh
> And says Oh my, what a li-ar!
>
> Oh, I was born to be a rover,
> Born to dance and sing,
> Born to play in the hay and the clover
> And to cut the pigeon wing;

Born to build a masterpiece
And set the world on fire,
But life goes by with a laugh and a sigh
And says Oh my, what a li-ar!

Sometimes I think that even yet
I'll kick over the traces;
But then I look in the looking glass
And see how old my face is.

Oh, I was born with an itching foot
A knapsack in my hand;
Born to rove the wide world over,
And die in a foreign land."

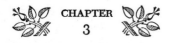

CHAPTER
3

TAMMY sat on the steps of Brenton Hall, her calico skirts spread round in a whirl as if a pale blue morning glory had fallen upside down. Behind her was the wide veranda of the house, before her was the circle of rosebushes budding toward their fall blooming, and beyond was the curving drive, held in shade by live oaks that led down to the gate and the letterbox. Tammy would not let her eyes stray in that direction because she knew very well that a watched pot never boils and if she kept looking and looking, the postman, like as not, would never come.

Elbows on knees and chin in hand, she studied one brown leaf, fallen from the sweet olive tree beside the steps. It was curled tight like a small clenched hand holding in a hurt and it fluttered in a little circle of wind that caught it up, then let it be. . . .

Like me, Tammy thought. All that lovely flurry last spring and then the sweet sap of living dried up and gone, the ache of its going all that remained. So here I be, she told herself, setting here like a broody hen awaiting for the mailman, awaiting for the winter and spring to come and go, awaiting for June to come and bring Pete home to Brenton Hall.

For Pete was gone. First his ma and pa had left and then

he took off, early, he said, because he had to find a room he could have free in exchange for tending the furnace or some such thing. They had made up all right, thank heaven. But something left over from their falling out rankled still. Like a pricker from a thistle, seemingly all plucked out yet leaving a secret prick to fester. It was not just the fact that he was gone, their wedding postponed. That was understandable to Tammy's reasoning mind. It was the knowledge that her speech and manner might shame him before the world no matter how strong the love between them. He had said as much to Miss Renie that day when he didn't know she was listening. Tammy reckoned that it was by way of loving that one was open to hurt.

She had written to him more than once but she was unskilled in the written word, and her pen was a sword at the gate of her thought and feeling, it was a hindrance to their expression. It should not be so with Pete, who had the power of words when he wished. He could write wonderful words, but he did not. She took his latest letter from her pocket, fingering it with care for it was about worn out with holdings and readings and she did not want it to go all the way to pieces because Pete had touched it, he had bent over writing it, sitting at his study table in the little room at the big far-off university he had told her about in his first letters.

This letter troubled her. It had a sparse, held-back sound, like the drip of water from the eaves after the first full rush of rain is over. The words brought no warmth with them. It was a strange thing, how a word on a page could say more than a word, or less. As if each one, passing through the mind of him who wrote, gathered up the color and flavor of that mind and so could arrive sometimes shining and savory, triumphant over time and distance. But some could come flat and dull and laden with heaviness to the one who read it on the page. A word fitly spoken—she remembered that from a Chapter learned long ago when Grandma was alive to hear her say off her morning verses—a word fitly spoken was like apples of gold in

32

pictures of silver. Those were such words as she would write were she able. But these last words of Pete's were not fitly writ, they had no scent of apples nor any shine of silver. Oh, this was no kind of a letter to be sending to a love-lass waiting and longing for a word warmed by love—such a letter as this just saying he was busy, saying he had a lot of heavy courses and that he knew he was on the right track at last.

From the hall behind her she heard the sound of Osia's broom, the long slow strokes raising more dust than they got rid of. When Osia had finished, Tammy would go and dust with a feather duster. That would be something to do, though she wished she had something more to be doing than just dusting dust, a mighty piddling business. Maybe it was wicked to set dust at naught, for the Lord made man out of dust. But not woman. Out of bone she was made. Was that so she would be strong for sweeping up the dust a man might shake from off his feet when he took leave and left her? Well, no matter how you thought about it, there wasn't much of a muchness to dust.

Then, like buzzards that circled and circled and ever returned to their unlovely feast, her thoughts came back to the knowledge that Pete wanted her different, more knowledgeable and like-minded to others in speech and manner with that kind of polishment she had seen in some who had come here in the spring to the Pilgrimage. That must be what Pete had meant when he said she needed time to grow up while he was away.

But to grow one needed firm ground to be rooted in, like a tree planted by a river of waters. Such a tree could then shoot forth in greenness unafraid and be gay and fanciful in a thousand dancing leaves. She did not feel rooted here at Brenton Hall. Where could she go, how could she learn to grow as Pete wanted her to grow? When she was living on the *Ellen B.* with Grandpa down on the river there was a sight of things to do there, real things, all needful—like cooking and mending and hoeing the salad patch and milking Nanny and running to the spring for fresh cool water. Remembering, Tammy felt a home-

33

sickness so keen it was akin to a green-persimmon bellyache.

Osia came through the door and started on the gallery, sweeping the fallen leaves with a big swish, sending them flying hither and thither like a summer whirlwind in the middle of the big road. "Looks like you got the lonesome blues, Miss Tammy," she said, stopping her flurry and leaning on the broom and peering round sideways so her eyes rolled, mostly white in her dark face.

"Oh, Osia, it's only that about the time you think you've got everything settled fine and forever, it unsettles."

"Reckon don't nothing settle long as you'se aliving, Miss Tammy. That's how it goes. And if things don't get upsot of themselves, looks like folks stir 'em up out of pure contrariness."

Miss Renie came down the hall and turned into the library. She was singing to herself, low and growing louder as she bumbled about in there—" 'Tis years since last we met and we may not meet again"— It was a mournful song but that did not mean Miss Renie was likewise. Miss Renie went by opposites in singing: the mournfuller the song, the cheerfuller she was.

Her voice was deep and quavery—"I have struggulled to forget But the strug-gul was in vain"— A great slambang interrupted her song. "Oh, dam, dam, Amsterdam!"

"Lawsy," Osia breathed and made a tut-tut sound, "what happen now? All that swearing."

"No, it's not swearing if you spell it with just three letters instead of four. It's the four-letter words that are bad."

"Well, I hope the good Lawd can tell the difference because I shore can't."

Tammy rose. "Reckon I'd better see." She went in by the wide hall and through to the library. "What's the matter, Miss Renie?"

"I'm trying to find an old book of mine, Pancoast's *English Poems,* and somebody has put all these catalogues of Pete's in here so I can't—— Oh dear, there go the rest of them." They slid to the floor in a papery whirl.

34

"I kind of cleared up after Pete left and I didn't rightly know where to put them so——"

"Here it is," Miss Renie cried, paying her no mind at all. "Now let me see, one line I've forgotten. Ah, here it is. 'What little town——' Well, I simply have no room for a town in my painting." She slammed the book down and went hurrying away.

Tammy began gathering up the scattered papers and booklets and she had almost finished when there came a call from the front gallery. "Yoohoo, Miss Tammy! Yonder come the mailman."

Tammy let things fly every which way and tore out and down the steps to jump a rosebush and take a short cut to the drive. Her thoughts ran faster than her feet. Maybe Pete had changed his mind, maybe he had figgered out some way so she could go up yonder and they could get married and live in that little room of his. Oh, it wouldn't matter how little, and while Pete was studying about raising tomatoes and breeding them like horses to get the best agrowing, she could maybe get some book-learning somehow so she could hold her head high in the world because of all she had in it and be like everybody else so Pete would never be ashamed of her nor Pete's ma either and nobody would dare say she was quaint or call her that shanty boat girl.

Long before she got to the gate she was shouting, "I'm coming, I'm coming," for all the world like old black Joe, and she had come so far in her thinking and hoping that it seemed she was shouting not to the mailman but to Pete way off up yonder a thousand miles and more. "I'm coming, I'm coming!"

The mailman leaned out the car window and grinned at her hurry. "Ain't no need of running your feet off, Miss Tammy. I don't aim to leave you." He handed her a postal card. "It's for Miss Renie."

Tammy stared at him as if she had forgotten there was such a thing as a mailman living and breathing on this earth, she looked down again at the card and turned it over. Miss Renie Brent. Yes, that's what it said. All the life went out of her and she felt as limp as a rope flung to the ground. "Ain't there anything more than this?"

"That's all. But don't give me that look out of your pretty blue eyes—like a stuck hawg—you'll have better luck next time, maybe. Lord, I could write me a book about folks on this route, always wanting something they ain't got, only it would be such a bookful of sadness as would brim over and spill out to the four corners of the world." He roared up the engine and went down the road in a cloud of yellow dust.

Tammy stood looking after the car. The dust was so thick and golden in the sun that the old rattletrap might have been a chariot wrapped in fire and swooping down for Elijah to bear him to the skies. Only this one was bearing away her hopes. Had Pete forgotten all about her? Couldn't he take time to write her a line? Just a picture post card like this one somebody had sent to Miss Renie would have been something fair to see. It wouldn't even need to have a picture on it or a lot of fine writing. "Love from Pete" would have been enough. Slowly she turned and went back through the gate and along the drive under the oaks.

Sometimes loving another could lift one high as on the wings of the morning, she thought. Other times, like now, it was a burden to bow one low, hard as stone and weighty as sand. And it came to her mind as she went slowly toward the house that humans had to pay for good times with bad. Though who would keep the books on that? It would not be like the Doomsday Book with good and evil set down against the day of doom. Must be this was the devil's own private account book, kept for the pure pestering of folks. She would have to ask Grandpa about that next time he came.

Grandpa was mighty wise in the ways of the world, the flesh and no doubt the devil too, for all he was just a kind of off-and-on preacher, though he was more on than off lately what with his having been invited down to live at the big state prison to help out the regular one there. Chaplain, he was called. Grandpa had written her a letter about that, feeling proud to be asked, feeling easy about her, settled here at Brenton Hall. "They say I got a way with the wayward," he wrote. "They say I can scrape away the callouses of sin and get right down close to touch flesh and nerve."

It was good that Grandpa had found him a calling. That was what everyone needed. Maybe it was what Pete was seeking by way of studying things like plant pathology and soil conserving. Miss Renie did not have a regular calling but she was all the time making up one. Osia had a solid one—cleaning, cooking, washing. Roots had drawing, his pa and ma had the work of the fields. "I reckon I'm the only one got no place in this world," Tammy said aloud, kicking a big brown magnolia leaf with her bare foot.

When she got back to the house, she remembered the card in her hand and went through to the ell porch calling Miss Renie.

"In my studio, Tammy. But don't bother me now. I'm in a fine, fine frenzy. Don't speak, don't breathe."

Tammy laid the card on a chair, taking care not to disturb Picasso who was balled up in a curl on a cushion there. Then she went back to the library.

Her hands lingered over the catalogues that Pete had sent off for when he was deciding where to go. Throw them out? She hesitated, because touching them, smoothing the ruffled pages, she could see again how Pete sat over there by the table studying them. Once she had thought he might be going to decide on the college that was nearby, just down the river a way, and costing little because it belonged to the state. That would have been good, for sure, because then they could have gotten married and floated the *Ellen B.* down and tied her up alongside of the school and they would have had a place to live together in at small cost of cash money. But it seemed Pete

37

figgered the farthest-off place was fairest, and he had set his mind on distance. That was his manner of thinking.

Tammy was about to put that booklet back on the shelf with the rest when the notion struck her like something sent down from heaven. All in a lantern-puff it came to her that the Lord had caused Miss Renie to scatter these books a-purpose. It was maybe one of the wondrous ways Grandpa was always saying He worked in. So now it had come to pass that when she was puzzling and wondering how to improve herself, here came this, ready to hand, telling her as if it spoke with the tongues of angels, "This here's the place for you to go, Tammy Tyree, here's where you could get you some book-learning and make out how to be like other folks." But how much money would it take? Was there enough in Grandpa's secret hiding place up in the graveyard atop the bluff by the river?

She moved slowly back to the big chair and sat down to find out if it might be possible. She read and read, turning page after page till at last she came to a place that said STUDENT EMPLOYMENT, and that held her. She read how many students earned their way doing work, they earned their food and their keep so all they had to pay was for the lessons. She read all it had to say about that, and then best of all, read how some might come who had no preparation, just to learn.

With this she rose up and went straight to Miss Renie's studio. "Miss Renie," she said, holding back the excitement that kept getting in the way of her words, "Miss Renie, I been thinking about my education, and all this waiting time, waiting for Pete to come home. Seems like it would be just sensible for me to get me some learning whilst I've got the chance."

Miss Renie went right on with her drawing. "Well, Tammy, if you're the one that's set on it, not just Pete, I might lay out a lesson each day and——"

"No'm, though that's mighty kind of you. But I got a notion of going off . . ." and as she went on to explain, getting more and more breathless as she spoke, Miss Renie caught excitement like some catching disease, then she calmed down a bit and said, "When does it open? You'll need money——"

Tammy broke in to explain about the hidden money, and she could hitch her way, she said, and right off, too, for the opening date was next week.

"But clothes, child——"

"I've got the two dresses I brought from the *Ellen B.* besides the meal sack ones I left there. And that's all, I reckon."

"Not enough. Of course you could take that party dress that belonged to my grandmother Cratcher, for parties."

"Oh no, Miss Renie, I won't be going to such. I'm going for education. Besides, I couldn't go to a party without Pete."

"Serve him right if you did," Miss Renie muttered.

"I'll go this minute and wash out every stitch I've got to my name." Tammy whirled around and was at the door when Miss Renie's voice stopped her.

"Tammy, wait. Hold your horses. You've taken me so by storm and I'm so excited over everything, I just haven't been using my wits. See here, child, I can't let you go off among strangers like this. What would Pete say?"

"Pete don't say nothing. That's one reason I go to be doing something and not just setting round the rest of my life pining for a word from him——" Tammy choked, then went on, "Don't you see, Miss Renie? Don't you understand I can't just be waiting, waiting——"

"Don't I understand!" Miss Renie's tone was bitter. "It's what I've been doing all my life. But, why should you go off down there for your education when there is Pete's father, his own father, a professor at Fairhaven College. You could just go and live there. Ena could give you Pete's old room and——"

Tammy stopped her right there. "Miss Renie, I can't. Mrs. Brent, she's ashamed of me and it would shame her to have me living in the house with her. I'd always be doing something she'd think was not proper and fitting and no matter how hard I tried I couldn't hold my tongue all the time, and—

and——" Tammy was silent, not wishing to say a word of disrespect for Pete's own ma who likely was the way she was because she couldn't help it, for nobody'd be that way a-purpose.

"Lord, don't I know! It would be pure hell living with Ena. How my poor brother has put up with it all these years."

"He loves her, that's how come. If you've got enough love in your heart you can put up with anybody ruffled on the outside so long as you know the inside is good. I reckon you can get used to most anybody by way of love. Mrs. Brent's just scared, scared of what folks will say, scared of living and dying. No, ma'm, Miss Renie, if I went there I'd be too big a thorn in her side. Besides, I got to be independent and free. I've done made up my mind."

"Ah, to be free. That's the heart's desire." Miss Renie stood with clasped hands, gazing at the painted wall of the room as if there wasn't anything there at all and she was looking into distance and a wild free time.

"I'll just write a letter to Grandpa and tell him——" Tammy began.

"Oh, your grandpa!" Miss Renie flung around. "I forgot him. Isn't there a school, couldn't you live——No, a jail's no place for you. Well, I've tried my best to be sensible. So now I'll just pitch in and help you get ready. There's an old alligator bag in the attic. You can have that to put your things in. I'll get it this minute."

"But Miss Renie, your painting——"

"Lord, child, don't you know I just do such things when there's no human interest to occupy me? It's a substitute for life." She studied Tammy for a long moment, her face intent. "I'm going to make you a dress."

"But, Miss Renie, I told you I got one to wear and one to spare and old extras for odd times or accidents like getting caught in the rain."

Miss Renie went right on as if she had not heard a word,

40

and like as not she hadn't. When she got her mind on one idea, there wasn't any turning it to something else. "An original design. Now let me see. Did you say your name had a meaning?"

Tammy could not see for the life of her what that had to do with a dress, but she answered just the same. "Yes, ma'm, it was in the little book I got named out of—'Ladies' Names and their Significance together with their Floral Emblems.' It says Tambrey, meaning immortal. Flower—the amaranth, and that's like prince-feathers, or love-lies-bleeding or—I don't like this one but the dictionary said it when I looked up amaranth—pigweed, it said. That kind of shamed me. But I reckon it just means it all depends, and you can run from princes to pigs and be whatever it's your nature to be. Don't you reckon?"

But Miss Renie had gone off into another of her spells of thinking. Composition throes, she called them. And for a fact, sometimes she did throw things around. But now she was just considering quietly. "I shall dip it first in yellow dye, make a wide full skirt with a border of prince's feathers. They will be a soft brick-red, the bodice of the same, piped in yellow. Yes, very simple in design yet full of significance. Meaningful. In short, symbolic. All is symbolism nowadays."

"Symbolism?" Tammy puzzled. "Sounds like some kind of sickness. There was a lady Grandma told about, had a symbolism in her head——"

"I can see it all so clear, very full and graceful and——"

"But, Miss Renie, I got no cloth to cut it from, even skimpy."

"Cloth? Why, child, where do you think I get all the material for my batiks? I've enough to keep me busy for the rest of my natural life if I live to be as old as Methusalah. You will take a double-bed size."

"Bed size?" Had Miss Renie gone clean out of her wits? "Miss Renie, hadn't you better rest a while? Looks like you're plumb wore out."

41

"Nonsense, I'm in the creative mood. Don't stop me." She ran to the closet, flung open the door and threw back the lid of a great old-fashioned leather-covered trunk. "All this bed linen, no sense in saving it forever. Might as well use it and not keep it for winding sheets. Ah, here's a double-bed size."

Tammy crossed the room and gave Miss Renie a hug. "You're mighty good to me, Miss Renie. I'll sure be proud to have a dress out of your head."

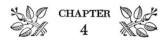

CHAPTER
4

THE DAYS that had been dragging went free-running now. For Tammy there was no more sitting on the front steps like a setting hen, waiting for the postman, letter-pining. Clothes had to be washed and ironed, and writing a letter to Grandpa took all of a morning. Tammy did not plan to write to Pete till she had arrived at her destination and found some work to do to earn her keep. She wanted to stagger him with amazement for a thing already done, she wanted to startle him by showing that she too could move about in the world on learning bent.

Miss Renie had made the dress she promised and it was a fair sight to behold, being hand cut and sewed and dyed gold with red flowers that stood proudly in a row around the full skirt. Miss Renie had found for her the alligator satchel but it was so old and rotted that the handle fell off in the lifting and one side fell out before it was half filled. Tammy was relieved to have it happen so. An alligator was an ornery beastie in life and like as not he was skinned because of his frowardness. She wanted naught to do with alligators, dead or alive. Besides, a bundle was better and a gunny sack best of all, being easier to carry.

Tammy was folding her belongings when Miss Renie came in

with a worried face. "Tammy—" she began and then stood there fingering the bedpost as if she didn't know how to say what she'd come to say—"Tammy, I've been so carried along by this notion of yours that I simply have not given it enough practical consideration."

Tammy dropped the cotton petticoat she was folding. "You mean you're thinking I hadn't ought to go?"

Miss Renie turned to face her. "I just don't want you to get there and be disappointed. You see, people who go to college have to go to school for years, preparing. I doubt if I could get in myself. They have to pass examinations in—oh, I don't know what all. And you have never been to school a day in your life." She paused at the sight of Tammy's stricken look. "I don't mean that you are ignorant altogether, you know far more than the average high school graduate in other ways. If there was any sense to education, you would have enough to enter the highest in the land. The Lord knows you know the Bible backward and forward and I daresay you were born with common sense. But I should have thought of this sooner. You have had no formal education and I'm afraid they won't——"

"Formal education?" Tammy broke in, her face brightening. "That's what it said in the catalogue you didn't have to have any of if you were an auditor. I looked that up in the dictionary and it is a listener. I'm going to learn by listening. I ain't agoing to open my mouth, just listen."

A kind of wonderment came over Miss Renie's face. "Out of the mouths of babes. Tammy, I see I am just a foolish old woman. There isn't anything that can stump you, and the Lord takes care of the innocent. So——"

"I'm not all that innocent, Miss Renie. I'm acquainted with all manner of evil, the Bible kind, and I reckon that about covers all that's been thunk up so far. It runs the gammon of human wickedness, is what Grandpa says. But it might be I'm innocent enough so the Lord will keep a weather eye out for me. That's what I'm counting on."

44

"And I suppose you have it all planned out, what you'll do when you get there?"

"Why, yessum, of course. I couldn't do anything without taking some forethought for the morrow. I'll go to the register-ating place and I'll pay what I have to pay and then I'll go to a place called the Employment Bureau, though why they call it a bureau I can't see for the life of me. Unless maybe they have one with drawers to put things in."

"Something like that, no doubt. Without the looking-glass part." Miss Renie chuckled. "Honestly, I'd like nothing better than to just float along beside you, Tammy, invisible to the world, watching to see what happens when you hit the halls of Academe. But now, back to my own drawing. I shall make a whole series of batiks out of poems. They will be a dream of artistic delight."

Tammy watched her go, then turned back to her folding and packing, a wondering look on her face. The halls of Academe? She didn't aim to be hitting any halls, and she wasn't going to Academe, she was going to the college down-river. Miss Renie was more sensible than most in lots of ways, easier to under-stand, but sometimes, like now, what she said was a puzzle-ment. However, Tammy reminded herself, that was what she was going to school for, to get enough learning to understand suchlike things. Growing up on the river she had missed a lot, maybe even come to be a mite queer compared to others in the world. But now she would be off in the morning, going out to learn. And by the time Pete got home from off up yonder, she'd be like folks, talk proper and understand, and he would take pride in her. She could hardly wait to get started, and it seemed as if months lay between this moment and the going-away time. But morning would come. That was one thing a body could count on.

She woke before sunup and lay for a while wondering what all would happen before she slept again here in Miss Renie's studio room with the walls all decorated and adorned after a fashion that had seemed so strange to her when she first came to Brenton Hall. Now she felt at home with the painted fairies that sat on toadstools in each corner, with the easel that every day had something different propped up for Miss Renie to be painting. This last one was a wonder for sure, all those naked folk leaping around trees. That was art, she had said, art to be naked. Off in the background was a priest, like the high priests in the Bible. He was leading a cow decked with flowers. But lordy, what was she doing lolling abed like this on the day of her going! With that she bounced out of bed and began to get ready, her fingers fumbling and awkward with eagerness.

Then all in a flash, breakfast was over, excitement making a lump in her stomach of what little she had managed to swallow and now it was the very moment of going. A going was truly easier and more to be desired than a staying. It had the tang of mystery to it, it held the scent of far-off places, the sound of things unheard before. Any twinge of sadness was dulled, the ache of parting given surcease and even the last good-bys made bearable. It must have been so with Pete when he left, Tammy thought, and rejoiced that already, even before arriving at college, she had increased her understanding.

Miss Renie came out on the gallery with her, Osia right behind. Tammy stood straight and bold in her clean gingham dress, the gunny sack over her shoulder. She shifted it a little so the shoes she meant to save by traveling barefoot would not be scraping her shoulder blades.

"Bless you, child," Miss Renie said and gave her a big hug. "And remember, you can always come back to Brenton Hall and welcome. Osia and I will miss you."

"That we will, ma'm." Osia nodded her head with vigor. "And here's a shoe box of lunch I fixed for you, Miss Tammy, so's you wouldn't get hunger-bit on your way."

Tammy thanked her and shook her hand. "Take good care of my nanny goat whilst I'm gone. I sure wish I could take her with me, just for company if nothing more, but coming

46

here from the river I found out how hard it is to hitch a ride if you have a goat along."

"I'll care for her like a motherless child," Osia said. "But Miss Tammy, there's just one thing I want to say before you go."

Tammy turned on the steps. "What's that, Osia?"

"Don't you let them college folk monkey round too much with your brain. Don't you let them change your manner of thinking or clutter up your mind with learning so's you can't see straight, because you was born thinking straight and that's a gift it don't pay to tamper with."

"I promise, Osia," Tammy said. "But I'm hoping to get changed in some ways—just the outside of me taking on alteration—couldn't nothing change the heart of me." She took a quick look around, for here was where Pete had been, here was where she had been happy, here was where she had been sad, and leaving such a place was leaving a part of herself. Then she turned and ran down the long curving drive between the rows of live oaks.

"Slow, now," Tammy shouted above the rattle and roar of the truck. "We're nigh on to the stopping place."

"Don't look like nothing but swamp to me," the truck driver said. "You right certain you know where you're going?"

"Sure I know. Swamp is home to me and the *Ellen B.* will be setting back in there waiting to welcome me. I'm mightily obliged to you for the ride."

He had come along before she had walked more than a mile down the big road from Brenton Hall, he had slowed down and told her to climb right in. Truly it looked like the good Lord was watching over her, bringing him along at just the right moment.

"Yonder stands the big magnolia, shiny as clear-running water. . . . Yonder's the hollow. I'd know it if I'd been gone a million years." Now she was so close, a kind of trembling came over her innards, a shiver and a whir like to a hummingbird's wings when he arrived before a chosen blossom.

The truck ground to a halt. Tammy reached down and picked up her gunny sack. "I'll leave the rest of the lunch for you because if I get hungry whilst I'm here I can catch me a catfish and fry it."

But the truck driver handed her the shoe box from the seat

49

beside him. "No, ma'm, you better take it. I got to stop when I get to the next hot dog stand and phone back to see how my little boy is feeling, so I won't need it and you might."

"All right, then, and I sure do thank you. I wisht I had something to give you for being so kind, or a pretty to send to him."

"It was a pleasure, ma'm. I been right well entertained all the way and I treasure that. Truck driving is a lonesome business."

Tammy climbed down, shouldered her gunnysack, tucked the shoe box under one arm and looked up at the big burly driver who sat looking down at her, his hairy arms resting on the steering wheel. "I sure hope your little boy'll be better. I'll send up a prayer for him. He's got a good kind pa, for sure."

"Thank you, ma'm, and good luck to you." He shifted gears and the big truck rattled away.

Tammy stood waving till it passed round the curve and she heard the hollow rumble of wheels on the bayou bridge. Then she turned and with a hop, skip and jump went down the bank, pushing aside the small sassafras bushes that blocked her way, her feet of their own knowing finding the overgrown path.

How good it was to be in the swamp again! The air was cool and damp after the heat and dust of the road and Tammy thought that if she were blindfolded she still would know where she was by the smell. It was a mixture of black earth and tangled vine, of tree roots and moist mosses and ripening muscadines. She stopped to reach up for a bunch of the rich red grapes. If she wasn't in such an all-fired hurry to be on her way, she would stop and gather some and make a few jars of jelly just for old time's sake.

Grandma had taught her jelly-making long ago. One of the pure pleasures of housekeeping, she had said, was to see the grapes bubble and hear them boil in the pot and simmer and smell up the whole kitchen with their tangy sweetness, then to watch how the juice dripped down all day and night from the jelly bag and then behold how sunlight struck through the jars of juice when they were ranged along a window ledge to jell, red as jewel rubies.

On and on she went, deeper into the swamp, the green-leaved branches overhead, a roof against the hot September sun. Redbirds whistled and gave her a welcome so now and then she had to whistle back. One bright-crested fellow followed along from tree to tree answering till Tammy thought it a shame to be leading him on when she was not one of his own kind. Then a jay bird scolded like mad, and once she stopped to watch a whole covey of quail go sashaying by. There wasn't another bird in the world could look so prim and walk so important.

When she came to the rise, she turned a little out of her way to pass the known, remembered remnant of a chimney, fallen down, yet showing still where folks long ago had had a house. Now there was no sign left save a tumble of bricks and a hearth where people once had sat and warmed their fingers or stood to toast their behinds before stretching out to sleep with their feet to the fire, one rousing now and then to toss on a log. Now there wasn't a living thing to show for them save a gnarled old chinaberry tree. But it was in its autumnly glory now, leaves turned to trembly gold and lit up like a light for ghosts at a window that wasn't there for ghosts to fret at. The berries hung in dangles, a golden brown, ripe for boiling in a pot and skinning down to the hard pits that were fluted like carven wood and could be strung for beads. Tammy wished she could tarry long enough to ready some beads for wear at the college. There was nothing dressed up a plain dress like beads. Pokeberry juice would dye them, or hickory hulls.

Down, down into the hollow then, and there, coming out from under the roots of the old sweet gum tree, was the pure spring water, just as always. Tammy knelt beside the sunken barrel that caught and held it. She bent over and saw her face and her hair hanging loose around it, self seeing self, face answering to face and saying welcome, welcome home. Once this had been her best looking glass. Now she had been a far piece and had seen herself in long mirrors out in the world. But this was her true familiar self, wavery on account of a waterbug's skimming round the edges of the barrel, and wondering, because there was so much that was still unknown to her. The world was full of things to wonder about. She bent lower and drank her fill. There was no water anywhere as good as what came like a miracle out of the side of a hill. Surely it was such water as this that came forth when Moses smote the rock with his rod and quenched the thirst of the children of Israel.

Tammy gathered up her gunny sack and the shoe box and went on. When she came to where the bayou had turkey-tailed into forks throughout the swamp, she jumped across or passed over by a beech log. The log felt smooth and lovely under her feet and where the moss had grown, she curled her toes into it, for they had been aching for the feel of it all these long months she had been away. She ran up the slope of the bluff and halted to look. Yes, the river was still there like always, though low now at the end of this long dry summer, and there in a tangle of willow branches, there was the *Ellen B.*, her chimney cocked sideways so she sat for all the world like a crook-tailed wren on the nest, the skiff a small birdling snuggled beside her. Tammy felt her bones become as water for gladness. "I didn't know how home-pining I'd been," she said aloud.

Then standing there, she felt all at once as thin and vanishing to the touch as the haze that lay on the river way off by the Louisiana shore. She was a ghost drawn back by memory, seeking in alteration something known and unchanging. The river was forever, sometimes high and brown and boiling along like mad, sometimes lazy and slow and pale, letting its silt settle, as now, yet always going, going, never gone the way a human had to be sooner or later, all gone.

Tammy gave herself a shake. What had come over her, standing here when she had so much to do, so far to go before nightfall! At that she went flying down the bank to leap the space from shore to deck and feel the *Ellen B.* rocking once more under her feet. She took the padlock key from her pocket and found the lock rusty from long disuse, but in a minute she had it turned and the door flung wide. Heavens, what a musty smell! But there everything was, just as she and Grandpa had left it the day the revenuers came and took him away. If she could have looked ahead then she would not have been all in a swivet over his going. For Grandpa started straightway preaching to them that were in jail and in the end the judge let him off easy because of that. Grandpa laughed about it now and said yes, sure, he was still in jail but being there by his own free will was a sight better than being held by compulsion of the law.

All her remembering past came to greet Tammy as she entered. Here was Grandpa's cot bed in one corner of the room, the wood stove nearby and the makeshift sink he had rigged up for her washing; here was the table with bench and chair under the window and on the shelf were tin cans with coffee and sugar and a bit of meal left over from their last breakfast. Just for old time's sake she gathered up a handful of pine knots from the wood box and started a fire in the stove. If she put the coffeepot on to boil she would have her a good cup of coffee time she got back from the graveyard and digging out Grandpa's tin can of money.

When she had hauled up a bucket of water from the river and built the fire to a good blaze and set the coffeepot on the front hole for quick boiling, she jumped ashore again, spade in hand, and hurried up the bluff and on to the graveyard. It was still up there with none near but the dead and them not stirring. Still and lonesome, so it was right companioning and cheery to see the blue woodsmoke floating up to the sky from the *Ellen B.*'s chimney, making an airy, fairy path to heaven.

First Tammy went to stand by Grandma's grave. "It's me, Grandma, Tammy come home from out in the world."

Grandma didn't say a word but it seemed as if she might be

close by somewhere feeling pleased to be remembered and taken notice of.

Tammy knelt and brushed the fallen leaves from the mound and wished there could have been a stone with name and date and maybe a Bible verse instead of just this board with painted letters already fading out, just plank board saying ELLEN B. DINWOODIE, and down below, RIP. That meant rest in peace, though when she was young and Grandma fresh dead, she had thought it meant get along fast as you can to heaven, just rip along at good speed.

The graves of the floaters Grandpa had plucked out of the river and buried here when nobody claimed them seemed lonely and sad as always, having no names, having none to mourn them. Grandpa had gotten many a body from the river. Those that were sought for and known and claimed brought him reward money, and that was what he had stored away in the can under the grave of Celeste that died on Christmas day, 1835. Tammy moved slowly toward the raised-up tomb. It didn't seem right and respectful to be digging round it, but she reckoned Celeste had been lying there so long and so quiet, it might be she would welcome a little kindly scratching down under the stone floor of the tomb—if there was any feeling or knowing left in her bones.

The grass and sticks were hard to break through, the ground being dry and hard, but at last Tommy found a spot where the earth was looser and easier to spade and the work went fast right down to where metal clanked on metal. She laid aside the spade and grabbed the dirt out with her hands, for all the world like a squirrel digging up a nut he had stored away for hard times.

It was a fair-sized can. Must be a lard can, Tammy thought, prying the lid off. Lordamussy, what a sight of greenbacks! Dollar bills and tens and fives and enough silver two-bit and four-bit pieces so there was a rattle when she reached down in. Too much, it was too much money for anybody to have all at once. She would not dare take it all lest she fall among thieves at the college. Maybe she would just take some of the big bills that she could pin on the inside of her pocket. They were reward money and she liked them better than the smaller bills that came from the sale of the corn likker Grandpa had made down in the swamp, for it was the making and selling of that had got him into the hands of the revenuers. Carefully she made a neat roll of the bills and thrust them deep in her pocket. Then she put the lid tight on the can and took up the spade to make free and clear the hiding places where the dirt had fallen in.

The spade hit something hard and hollow sounding and Tammy shivered at the sound. But it could not be Celeste's skull, for there was a new-looking board showing. Tammy cast aside the spade and knelt again. She wiggled the board loose, shut her eyes tight and reached in to feel what she might feel. Jugs! A regular little cellar of jugs neatly stored there. So this was where Grandpa hid his corn likker till what time he could take it out for selling. She drew out one jug, thinking to take it along with her. Likely Grandpa would come to see her at Christmas time and he did like a little cheer at Christmas. Then she pushed the board back and shoveled dirt in and smoothed it over so not even a rabbit would know there had ever been a hole.

Now it was time to go. She would just have her cup of coffee and sit on deck in the shade of the willow branches and take her ease for a bit, then she would be on her way, back through the swamp to the big road to hitch her way onward. When she left the graveyard and started along the rim of the bluff, she heard the *chug-chug* of a motor and there, cutting shoreward from the middle of the river was Captain Joe. She might have known he would be along on a Tuesday. That had always been his day for coming with his floating store of things to sell to folk who lived up and down the river too far from any road to get to town. Oh, it would be good to see Captain Joe again, and she set out running along the bluff and down the steep bank to the *Ellen B.*, arriving just as he drew up alongside.

"Well, howdy!" he shouted, easing the motor so it just held him against the current. "I seen the smoke coming from the chimney and I says to myself, well, old Deadwood's out of jail and home again. Whereabouts is he? Inside?"

So Tammy told him, and then she told him how she was going to the college down river to get her an education. He shook his head at that.

"You'd run into trouble sure as you's born, Tammy. The river's too low now and plumb full of snags and sandbars. You'd get stuck and the Lord knows how you'd ever get free."

"Oh, but I ain't going to——" She stopped short as the notion struck her. If she could float the *Ellen B.* down the river she would at least have a roof over her head. She could walk to her schooling every day and she could mighty near live off fish, and maybe even sell some and make money that way. "I sure wisht I could get the *Ellen B.* down there. If Grandpa was here, he could do it, easy as pie. Maybe . . . but I reckon you're right, Cap'n Joe, it would be too much pushing and poling and shoving for me all by myself. Now if there was just high water, I might——"

"Say, I tell you what. Remember the old tug *Susie* you used to wave at? Well, she's overdue, coming back this way, heading for New Orleans. I'm bound to run into her this evening or tomorrow. She's been pushing a bunch of barges up to Vicksburg. Matter of fact, I've got some supplies for old man Cheeps. I'll tell him to come by and shove you on down far as you like, and you'd better lay in some supplies, too, whilst I'm here."

Tammy didn't stop to hiver-hover over it, but chose a good lot of vittles and paid for them and then said, "You tell Mr. Cheeps for sure, and much obliged to you. Only won't he be wanting a lot of money for it?"

Captain Joe roared up his motor till it seemed to be laughing with him. "He wouldn't want money if you had a good swig of old Deadwood's corn likker to pay him with."

"The revenuers might get me."

"Ain't no law agin giving a body a present," and before she could offer him enough to wet his whistle, he was off upstream. Tammy stood watching till he passed out of sight, then she turned and danced a jig so quick and gay that the *Ellen B.* rocked and rolled, entering into her liveliness. It was like Grandpa said, for sure, Tammy thought. The Lord made straight and clear the path and sometimes even opened up new ways a body had never dared hope for. With that she went inside and poured some coffee and finished off the fried chicken and biscuit and jelly Osia had given her. Then she dug worms and set out lines. She would have fresh fish for supper and she would make some good old corn pone to go with it.

Meanwhile she must ready the *Ellen B.* for the voyage, knocking boards off windows, airing her bed out for the night, cleaning the lantern and filling it with coal oil so even if Mr. Cheeps didn't come till full dark, there would be a light to see by. And besides all that, it might be she could holler loud enough to call in from the woods the old red rooster and the dominecker hens that she and Grandpa had left when they lit out last spring, her for Brenton Hall and him for jail. Chickens went wild if you left them, but she thought the domineckers might know her voice and come running, bringing the rest. It would be mighty fine to have a few chickens in the fattening coop. She hauled it aboard and got it ready against their coming. Eggs and fried chicken some days would help out if she tired of fish. Oh, it was a grand life she would be having down-river, getting her book learning and being snug at home all at the same time.

It wasn't till she was sitting on deck, watching the round red sun dip down behind the low-lying Louisiana shore, that loneliness came over her, and a longing kin to the cry of the whippoorwill that called again and again in the coming dark.

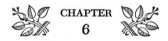

CHAPTER
6

TAMMY STOOD on the forward deck with the wind of the river in her face and the feel of motion underfoot. Mr. Cheeps had come along in his tug this morning just as the sun was touching the willows on the far side of the river. She had given him corn pone and catfish fry and coffee, but none of Grandpa's likker. She had that hidden away in the closet behind some of Grandma's clothes that still hung there and she would not give him any till the *Ellen B.* was finished with her voyage and safely tied, lest he get wobbly and uncertain and run tug and shanty boat both into a sand bar. Corn likker was liable to make a man unreliable in his motions and she didn't want any slip-up betwixt here and yonder.

They had had trouble enough getting the *Ellen B.* off—Mr. Cheeps hollering and swearing, backing and hauling—for she had settled in the low water as if forever. At one point Tammy almost gave over, shouting to him to never mind, she didn't want the *Ellen B.* tore plumb to bits. But he was a man pig-headed for finishing what he had started, a man with few words beyond cuss words of which he had a plenty, and in the end the *Ellen B.* swung free into deep water so he could come round and fasten up and start pushing. Now they were fair on their way.

In the chicken coop beside her the domineckers clucked, the rooster fussed and some young chicks kept trying to escape between the laths. They had been hatched wild in stolen nests so Tammy had to run them down to catch them. The only thing missing was the nanny goat. It would have been wonderful to have Nan running about on deck and giving milk to put on corn mush and whiten the coffee but one could not have everything, and Tammy had already been so lucky that she thought it was plumb scary.

The river spread out before her, it curved and came back, it hooked round sometimes as if it forgot all about direction or destination and just meandered. The tugboat went this way and that way too, in a wiggle and a waggle, missing a great tree trunk laid bare by the low-level water, then skirting a sand bar where driftwood was piling in a dark mass. On the right, the man-made bank of the levee rose all green and grassy with now and then some cattle grazing along its slope, or rising above it, the water tank of some small town. Once she saw a whole bunch of chimneys and treetops and a church steeple. If the river was high, a body might get a fair view of many a city. On the left there was only the high, wild bluff for mile after mile, and sometimes, to keep in the channel, they moved so close in under the bank that cottonwoods swished the side of the *Ellen B.* and a branch came nigh to scraping the stovepipe smokestack right off the roof.

With the tugboat behind and pushing, it seemed to Tammy, standing there, that she was captain, and she pretended she was heading all the way down the river and past New Orleans and the bayou country and out into the open sea, bound for foreign lands on the other side of the ocean. She wished she knew the names of all the lands that lay there, and the speech and ways of the people. They would talk with other tongues, they would go decked in strange garments, yet if they were human, she thought there was like to be more kinship than difference in the things that were most important, like living

60

and dying and begetting and loving, and sometimes even thinking the same thoughts about the world around about.

But now there was plenty to do besides dreaming. She wanted the *Ellen B.* to be all swept and garnished to make a good impression on the college when they got there. Like as not people would be coming aboard to see. They would be curious and wondering, like those Pilgrimage folk in the big boat long ago that had come close by the *Ellen B.*, tourists looking amazed at Grandpa with his chair tilted back, smoking his pipe all comfortable and easy, and pointing to Tammy saying, "How quaint!" She knew now that quaint didn't mean anything really bad, only old-timey and different from most. After she got some book-learning, nobody could call her that, for she would be neither funny-to-laugh-at nor funny-peculiar, but somebody for Pete to be proud of when he came home again.

First she trimmed the geranium plants that were nigh on to dying from neglect. The roots were alive and they would once more fill the window boxes, give them a little time. She swept away the straw and crumbs the chickens had scattered out through the sides of the coop and she sang to them as she worked:

> "Chickamy, chickamy, crany crow,
> I went to the well to wash my toe.
> When I got back my chicken was gone,
> Chickamy, chickamy, crany crow."

She dipped up a bucket of water from over the side and got to work scrubbing. Inside and outside she scrubbed the *Ellen B.* till the unpainted boards shone silver in the sun and every cobweb was shaken overboard. Then for setting-down work she brought out from the closet Grandma's brown coat that she had just grown to, all but the sleeves that needed taking up. It was a handsome coat Grandpa had sent off for, ordering it from the catalogue as a Christmas surprise. It was made of broadcloth and lined with something that might have been silk, it was so slick and shiny. Come winter, it would be a fine thing to wear, with Grandma's little gold watch that smelled like brass and wouldn't run pinned on the front of it. Nobody need know the watch didn't go. Like as not there would be clocks all over a college and Tammy thought she could keep aturning the hands to keep up with the time that everybody lived by out in the world.

Out in the world, o-u-t spells *out* and that was where she was going. She sang as she sat sewing:

> "Yier, briar, limber lock,
> Three geese in a flock.
> One flew east, one flew west;
> One flew over the cuckoo's nest,
> And O-U-T spells out."

Toward evening there began to be houses high on the bluff and smokestacks smoking and signs of people living close together, and there were boats anchored in the river, sitting high and empty, waiting to be filled with oil for foreign lands, great ships that might have swallowed up the *Ellen B.* and the tug all in a gulp had they been so minded.

On they came down the wide brown river and the sun, going down, shone on the glass windows of buildings so they seemed afire. It lighted up a white church steeple and made clearly visible the road that ran up the bluff slantwise with cars like ants scooting up and down. Tammy stood looking, lost in wonder. She wished they could stop so she could go up that road and come into the heart of the city. Mr. Cheeps called down to say it was Natchez. He was in a hurry, no time to stop, he said. He had a load of barges waiting in New Orleans to be pushed up river and he would be traveling night and day to get there.

Whilst she was still watching the last of the city go by, Tammy saw all in a little huddle below the bluff a bunch of shanty boats, true kin to the *Ellen B.*, for sure. Why, it must have been right here that the *Ellen B.* had been tied up long ago when she was no more than seven or eight years old. Here she had played with other children, jumping back and forth from deck to deck, had sung game-songs. Oh, they came back to her now! She could almost hear them, sung in high childish voices.

"Shift your feet in nimble flight;
You'll be home by candle light.
Open the gates as high as the sky
And let King George's army go by."

They must have been old songs out of far-off days when kings were common. There was another that began with kings:

"King William was King James' son,
By all the royal races run.
He wore a star upon his breast—
Go choose your east, go choose your west
Go choose the one that you love best.
If he's not there to take his part,
Choose another with all your heart.
Down on the carpet you must kneel,
As sure as grass grows in the field.
Salute your partner and kiss her sweet,
Now you may rise upon your feet."

Other songs she had heard there, for Grandpa preached of a Sunday morning to all who would listen and the sound of the hymns went up by way of the high bluff to brush the very floor of heaven. It was here she had known some show-folk who taught her how to dance and sing and wanted her to come away with them to be in what they called their act. She could copy anybody, a good mimic, they called her. But Grandpa, he reckoned he was fogy but he didn't hold with such. It was here one Saturday morning when everyone was gone traipsing the streets of the city that she heard a woman holler, and she had gone and done what she was told and so had helped born a babe into the world. And when Grandma got home to the

Ellen B. that night she'd said she was proud of a little girl not eight year old who could holp out at such a woman-time, and it was good to know about borning babes.

There had been other things Grandma did not like so well, goings-on, Tammy remembered. There was a frizzy-haired woman and it had been on account of her that Grandma said they'd better get on up the river somewheres because this wasn't any place to raise a young girl, with her not even bothering to shut her door when men come drabbing. In a way, Tammy thought, it had been real educational, living amongst people. In a different way no doubt from what it would be in a school or college. But these were root things, kept hidden deep underground in polite society, though hell's bells, there was plenty such in the Bible. Pete's ma had told her there was a lot in the Bible not fit subject for conversation and she must not speak out about them. It was mighty confusing.

The sun sank low, tree shadows crept across the river to spread like a lazy, ragged blanket over the restless water and it was full dark by the time Tammy had supper cooked. She hadn't much to do with, but Grandma had taught her never to throw anything out, so with some new-laid eggs and the scraps of fish left over from noon dinner, she made an egg-fish scramble and baked it on top of the stove in the skillet. It puffed up real pretty so she helped her own plate and took the rest of it to the stern, reaching over across to the tug, calling Mr. Cheeps to come down from his little steering house and get him something to eat.

No doubt the noise of his engine had got him discouraged about saying what nobody could hear. But when he came down and took the skillet and smelled what was in it, he said, "You're kinder a good cook, I reckon."

Tammy said Grandma had taught her, and how to sew and knit besides. He mumbled some kind of answer and went back into his pilothouse. But he had said enough to please

Tammy and she thought that when there were just a few words spoken they came to mean more than any free-flowing speech could ever amount to.

Though dark had come, it was not the heart of darkness because of the moon that rose over the bluff, all round and orange colored. The river, lapping at the sides of the *Ellen B.* and rolling back in whispering plumes of sound, was heard now as the engine slowed for night travel. Tammy sat on deck for a long time, listening, and watching the shadow of the bluff retreat before the moon and all the water turn to trembling metal. It was nigh on to bedtime when she saw lights ashore, not house lights scattered in the way of houses, but one close on to the other as if there might be great buildings with many windows. Could it be that they were passing the college all unknowing? Tammy ran to the stern and shouted to Mr. Cheeps, pointing back to the fast-disappearing lights. "Is that where I'm bound for—passed by——"

He leaned down out of his little window. "Ain't anywhere near. Won't get there afore tomorrow evening."

"What's all that back yonder?"

"That there was the state jailhouse. Wouldn't want to drap you there." He laughed and drew back his head like a turtle hauling himself into his shell.

Tammy stood looking back and seemed as if it would draw the very lights and liver out of her, for Grandpa was there, right there, so near and yet beyond all sound or reach. If she had only known she might have sent him word somehow so he could come and give her a wave of the hand or the lift of a lantern in a loving signal to wish her well. She brushed a tear from her cheek and went to bed, knowing it was high time she was learning the whereabouts of places and the ways of the world.

It was afternoon of the next day when they came round a bend and Tammy saw, far off and high above the bluff, new

65

signs of human living. Nearer and almost hidden by oak trees hung with moss were buildings of wood and brick and one white house like the house of Brenton Hall. This was how she had thought the college would be and she ran quickly to the stern and shouted to Mr. Cheeps, "Ain't that there the college?"

He shook his head. "That there's a college but 'tain't yourn. It's a nigger college. They wouldn't let you in there."

Tammy watched it fall behind, wondering. It was a mighty fine-looking place and she wished that was where she was bound for. With the *Ellen B.* tied under the bluff she could just go running up the bank to get her schooling. She would likely feel at home with colored folk, if they were like Roots and Osia. She had felt straightaway at home with them, the only such she had ever known. They had no pretending about them, they went right to the heart of things. And seeing the colored folks' school so fine and high seeming, Tammy felt a small quaver of dismay. She hoped her college wouldn't be more fine and fancy than this because then she would feel too scared and small. She stood by the rail, overcome by the doubt and misgiving that assailed her.

There was so much she did not know. At Brenton Hall the world had come to her in the shape of the Pilgrims that came and went in the weeks of the Pilgrimage. It was much more scary when she herself went out into the world, as now. Yet here underfoot was the deck of the *Ellen B.* Here were all the familiar things, known from her first remembering hour. Oh, but she was glad now that she had not come hitchhiking all this way by the road that was strange to her.

Mr. Cheeps shouted down to her, "Yonder's the city."

Slowly they swung out into midstream away from it, slanting off to the far side. There was a town on that side too, for above the levee that was mud caked and brush strewn, there rose chimneys and a silver water tank. A long line of cars was moving down the levee road to roll aboard a ferryboat tied up there. Coming nearer, Tammy could see people on deck, all bound for the big city on the other side of the river. They stared down at the shanty boat, they stared at her as if she might be a show and a sight to be seen. Mr. Cheeps roared his engine, showing off his speed, maybe, pushing the *Ellen B.* ahead so spray was flung high. He tooted his whistle and the ferryboat answered with a mighty blast.

Tammy wondered if any of those young folk aboard were bound for the college. She wondered if she might be looking at those that would some day be her friends. Some of them pointed, some laughed and called to others to come and look and one young man leaned over the rail and shouted, "Hi, Toots!"

Now that was real friendly, Tammy thought and took heart, waving back and calling "I ain't Toots, I'm Tammy," but her voice was lost in the chug of engines and the churning of the ferry as it backed away from the pier. Oh, it was a mighty fine thing, how one human being could hearten another just by a wave and a shout, seeming to say that all lived together under the blue sky, no matter if it was so big and the world beneath, so strange.

Now on the city side of the river Tammy could see turreted towers and off to the left was a queer tall structure going straight up into the sky, flat sided and graceless with window holes all the way up and a pointed top. There were great silver tanks sitting on the ground like so many crowns abandoned by giant kings. There were houses built so close together it was a wonder how people could know which was which. It was a wonder they could breathe, being so hemmed in. Low down below the bluff there were railroad tracks and engines puffing with importance. And here were more and bigger ocean-traveling boats such as might go to the uttermost parts of the earth where unknown languages were spoken and the heathen in his blindness bowed down to wood and stone. Just looking at them gave a reality to the words of the old hymn and an enlargement to the mind.

The river turned again, leaving all that behind, and now was the time to be seeking the college that lay below the city. Tammy went again to the stern. "Be we nigh?" she shouted.

Mr. Cheeps nodded. "Coming up pretty soon, now." And he gave his mind to dodging driftwood.

The sun was low in the sky when he began working his way across the river slantwise toward the eastern shore. There was nothing there save low banks and willows and cottonwoods. The water was low, though high water had left its muddy mark plain to see on every tree trunk. When the river rose and spread, having no bluff here to hold it back, then maybe the *Ellen B.* could be poled closer to the college, but now there would be a long walk back through the swamp to get there. "You sure this is the right place?"

Mr. Cheeps pointed. Far off, Tammy made out roofs and more towers and buildings than you could shake a stick at. Miss Renie would say there were the halls of Academe. But now the problem was to find a good mooring place for the *Ellen B.* and a stout tree to tie up to. Mr. Cheeps had a time of it, running close to shore more than once and having to haul back to keep from getting stuck on a sand bar. At last he nosed the *Ellen B.* in under the wide-spreading branches of a giant cottonwood and Tammy flung the stout hawser up and made it fast to a branch that hung low over the deck. Mr. Cheeps came aboard and tested the line and tightened the knot and nodded. "That'll hold." Then for the first time he showed a little curiosity concerning the wherefore of her coming. "Now what?"

"Me? I'm going over yonder to college."

He took off his grease-stained cap, scratched his baldy head. It seemed there was something he wanted to say and just couldn't get it out. Then he gave up, shook his head and turned away.

"Wait, I got something for you." Tammy ran to the kitchen and brought out the jug of likker. It was not quite full now because she had poured out some of it into a molasses jug so Grandpa could have a snort when he came visiting.

"I don't want nothing." His voice was gruff as if he might be offended at the suggestion of pay. "Told Cap'n Joe I'd shove you down here and now I done it and you ain't beholden to me."

Tammy held out the jug. "But this is some of Grandpa's best, aged and seasoned and mighty fine for them that likes it. I'd be proud to have you take it."

His eyes brightened. "I've heard tell of old Deadwood's likker all up and down the river. Much obliged." And then he added, "I wish you luck, no matter what notions you got." With that he unfastened his tug from the stern of the *Ellen B.* and chugged backwards out into midstream again.

Tammy stood waving till he was out of sight around a curve. Then she looked about her, at the low bank, the trees, the swampy earth where evening shadows were gathering. It was all strange to her, and now the tug had vanished and the sound of it had died away, there was something scary about the silence and the strangeness. Maybe when she got used to it, she would feel at home and come to know the look of the place as well as she knew the old familiar riverbank where the *Ellen B.* had been tied for so many years. After all, the *Ellen B.* was the same, and again she rejoiced that she had hearkened to Captain Joe and had brought along her own abiding place. It came to her that she was like a snail traveling hither and yon in his own snug shell.

The notion tickled her mightily, so she laughed to herself as she set about the evening chores of feeding the chickens and building up a fire to make her supper. She sang as she worked, setting new words to one of Grandpa's old country tunes, a make-up song. "If you haven't got words to suit the occasion," Grandpa always said, "then make a make-up song." And so she sang:

> "Me, I'm just a travelin snail,
> A-inching down the road.
> Wherever I go I carry along
> The house of my abode."

Before she slept that night she lay abed wondering what the next day would bring forth. A little bird, waking into moonlight called, "Pete, my sweet, my sweet," and it seemed a good sign to Tammy that all would go well.

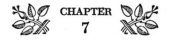

TAMMY AWOKE before dawn, hearing the faint ripple of the river against the side of the *Ellen B.* and the tentative call of swamp birds. She opened her eyes and so familiar was her dusk-filled little room that she could scarce believe she had ever been away. Surely Grandpa must be on deck baiting his jugs and the bluff must rise as always to the east with Grandma's grave atop it under the old cedar tree. All that had come to pass in the time of her absence was as a dream in the night.

She lay there blinking sleepy eyes, bemused and wondering till time and event reordered themselves into reality again. Then she knew there was no time for dawdling. She did not have a notion what hour the college woke, but she had a sight of things to do before she went to see and there was no sense lying abed dreaming of times gone or even of times to come when Pete would return and find her learned and proper spoken.

With that she sprang up and set about her morning tasks. As she worked in the night-dim kitchen, building a fire in the stove, making coffee and corncakes because they were the quickest, she kept looking out the window to see the dawn's coming. On the river side the water ran pale and delicately tinted as the inside of a mussel shell, on the land side she could

71

make out no shape of college buildings. Night lingered there, the tangle of underbrush coming up to meet the mass of cottonwoods that were black against the pale sky. She would have to seek out a path through that jungle, mark it well so she could come and go freely with no risk of getting night foundered in swampy spots.

Soon she was ready in her clean cotton dress. It was faded but who was to know it wasn't pale blue to start with, and how could strangers know but that some artist like Miss Renie had dyed the seams apurpose in darker blue where the color lingered? She tied her shoelaces together and hung the shoes around her neck—no sense in getting them all muddy, for they were harder to clean than feet.

The hens clucked at her as she hauled out the gangplank and flung one end ashore and she hesitated a moment before leaving. "If I was sure you'd find your way back and not go aroaming for some hunger-bit professor to snatch for his dinner, I'd let you go free whilst I'm gone. But you better wait till you know your whereabouts. That's what I'm going to learn for myself."

She laughed and felt in her pocket to make sure the greenbacks were still there. She looked to the west to take her sights, for night still lingered in the shadows of the swamp, and then went clattering down the plank to the shore.

It was hard going for there were boggy places aplenty where she sank to her ankles and had to pull out by what low branches she could reach. Coming back in broad daylight she would seek out a better way, down-river perhaps, for there was a rise off to the southward and the land might be dryer there. When fall rains came and the river rose, she could row ashore in the skiff.

Leaving the swamp and mounting to the top of the levee, Tammy stopped to smooth her hair and catch her breath and look the landscape over. Beyond a vine-covered wall was a great green-cut lawn with walks laid out upon it, and set back beyond that was a whole mess of houses and buildings that went on and on as far as she could see. How would a body ever learn which one to go to? But first she had to clean the mud from her feet and legs, and lucky there was not a soul in sight to see her at so lowly a task. She ran down the slope and sat on the ground close to the wall and began to wipe away the mud with a handful of leaves and grass. It was a hard job with no water and no washrag.

Resting for a moment she felt something light on the top of her head and before she could reach up to brush away the bug or bee or mosquito or whatever was tickling her, down came a netting over her face. It was white and fine-meshed as a mosquito bar and a kind of ring held it fast, circling her neck and shoulders. She sat caught in a maze of surprise.

There was a rustling behind her and a man came slithering over the wall. He was holding a long pole to which the net bag was fastened. He was slim and agile as an eel in all his motions, he turned this way and that as if seeking something lost and when his dark, far-apart eyes came to rest on Tammy, he said, "Where'd it go? I didn't catch it."

"You cotched me for fair," Tammy said through the net.

"Oh, so I did." He lifted the net from her head. "Had my eye on the butterfly." He looked at her as if she were some strange new manner of beastie he had trapped and Tammy looked back at him in wonder. He had on a shirt, not a biled shirt but one as thin and white as a lady's veil might be. His naked hide showed pinky through it and there was a patch of dark hair too plainly seen on his chest. Lucky his breeches were made of stouter stuff, Tammy thought, or he would be a sight to behold.

"A butterfly?" she said at last.

"Yes, a most unusual color. Where did it go?"

Tammy looked down, she moved one hand slowly and as the purply-blue wings closed, caught the butterfly that had lighted on her big toe. "This here the one?"

"Heavens—how did you——" He dropped to his knees and studied it.

"Just sneaked up behind. I've cotched many a one so. What for did you want it?"

Not answering, he took it from her, and bringing from his hip pocket a small brown envelope, he slipped the butterfly neatly inside and pressed it between his fingers till there was no quiver of life left.

"What for did you have to kill it?" Tammy demanded.

"It's just the colors I want to study." Then, with a glance at her face he added, "Don't be upset, though the look becomes that elfin face of yours. The butterfly has a very primitive nervous system and doesn't feel as you or I might."

"But it was a-living, and you got no right——"

"I assure you the life cycle of a butterfly is brief and hazardous at best. I should know. After all, I used to teach entomology." He sat back on his heels and studied her with a teasing expression.

"What's that?"

"My students called it *bug*-ology. In short, I taught bugs."

"Lordamighty," Tammy cried, "don't bugs already know all they need to know? That butterfly now, he knew to come out of being a grub and how to dry his wings and fly and feed on all the flowers that bloom. What more could a human teach him?"

He laughed. "Maybe that's why I gave it up."

"So what do you do now?"

"Paint. Oh, I teach a few dumb students, to make a living, but the rest of the time, I paint like mad." As he spoke his eyes went over her from the top of her head to her mud-stained legs and feet. "But *mon dieu,* what on earth have you been doing?"

There was something Frenchified in his manner of speech, like that of the bayou folk and Tammy paused to study that over in her mind before replying. She could remember such

74

out of her earliest remembering days, men with lithe, trimly built bodies, slim waisted and quick moving, quick spoken and with a certain liquid brightness of the eyes when looking at a woman. This man was like that, only more shined up and polished seeming and citified. "I stumbled into a sinkhole over yonder in the swamp. Aimed to get cleaned up before anybody laid eyes on me and I'd better hurry or it will be too dried up to scrape off." She plucked another handful of grass and got to work.

"Here, take this." He tossed her a folded, clean white handkerchief.

"Oh, that's too fine." She snatched it up, but too late, the wet mud had stained it.

"It'll wash, don't worry."

"Well, might as well use it, now it's messed, but it's a shame, such nice linen. I'll wrench it out for you. Only river water won't ever get it this white again."

"What were you doing in the swamp?"

"Just coming through."

"Coming through? From where? There's nothing beyond but the river."

"That's where I live."

He scowled and blinked. "So you won't talk." Then he added, "You're not a mermaid, not with those two legs I see before me, and very shapely they are, if I may say so."

Tammy looked up in time to catch his eyes taking measure of the shape and length of her limbs. She pulled her skirts over her knees and rose with dignity. "You've done said it, so let it lay. I thank you for the loan of your kerchief and I will return it if you'll tell me where to."

"The red brick with white trim, top-floor studio. Name's on the door, Buford Woodly." He rose too, and stood tall and narrow seeming in his height. "You might be a water nymph, of course, a daughter of old Father Mississippi. But if so, what are you doing here on the campus?"

"I've come to get me some learning and now I must be on my way, if you will be so kind as to tell me where a body goes first."

"The old building with a tower, south end of the campus. But you might at least tell me your name."

"My name is Tammy Tyree, the Tammy being short for Tambrey."

"Tambrey? What kind of name is that?"

Tammy was itching to get away. He made her fidgety, the way he looked at her, but in courtesy she answered his question. "It has a meaning of its own, unlike to all others."

"What does it mean?"

"It means immortal, and now I will say good morning to you." She made a small bow in honor of his being a teacher even though he had not the proper manner for one.

"Immortal, did you say? Hey, wait a minute——"

But Tammy, with one hand on the wall, had leaped lightly over and now she was on her way, running on tiptoe across the green-cut grass that was like to softest velvet to the touch, springy and still wet with morning dew. High wisps of cloud were turning pink in the arch of the sky, the sun would be up in a minute now and where was everybody? She slowed her steps and looked around in wonder. Not a living soul up and about. Was she the only one of all the college who hungered and thirsted after knowledge?

She went on slowly. There was a path now, dividing to left and right. Which way? A rhyme from one of the old counting games came to her and she stood pointing this way and that, saying,

> "Eeny, meeny, miney, mo.
> Catch a bugger by the toe;
> If he hollers let him go.
> Eeny, meeny, miney, mo."

There, it was settled, and she could see, far off, the building with the tower on top, deserted, night hushed and sleeping still. She would just have to wait.

76

Straight ahead she saw a great live oak with none to keep it company. It had wide-spreading branches, some crooking downward to almost touch the ground so that it made a kind of tent, all moss hung and full of mystery. It was a rare sight, one tree alone like this in a wide green lawn, a tree free grown to its own will, fulfilling every sweet fancy uncramped by other growing things, as were the trees of the swamp. In the early light, under the dawn-rosy clouds of the sky, the moss was lavender seeming, like a lady's veil might be when she first comes out of black mourning. The great trunk rose for a little way, then parted, as if it had decided overlate to be twins and someone had fixed an iron bar across from one half to the other lest it break altogether apart. Around the base was a circular wooden bench. She would sit there and wait for the college to wake up and come to life.

She crossed the grass and sat down, feeling more at home with a tree than with all the man-made buildings round about, even though it was a tree planted in the heart of a college. It pleased her to pretend that this was a tree of knowledge and if she sat still enough the leaves might whisper some sweet wisdom to her listening ears. She leaned back, looking up at small ferns that grew in the crotch, at blue-green lichens that frosted the bark. High on an upper branch an oriole flashed and as the first rays of the sun set the topmost leaves aflame, he broke into song. His high sweet call shot through all the dome of foliage as if the golden sunlight might be heard as well as seen.

At once, as if it were an agreed-upon signal waited for from the beginning of the world, the tree began to speak:

> "For we were nursed upon the self-same hill,
> Fed the same flocks, by fountain, shade, and rill.
> Together both, ere the high lawns appeared
> Under the opening eyelids of the morn,
> We drove a-field, and both together heard
> What time the gray-fly winds her sultry horn, . . ."

The voice was the sweetest that ever fell on Tammy's ears, the words akin to Bible words, having a rise and fall like music.

Poetry, that's what it was. "But hell's bells," she whispered, "trees don't talk regular talk, much less poetry." And with that she came out from the enchantment that had held her. Without a sound she stepped to the bench, put one foot in the crotch of the tree, caught the iron rod and pulled herself up, the voice continuing all the while:

"... the woods, and desert caves,
With wild thyme and the gadding vine o'ergrown,
And all their echoes, mourn:
The willows, and the hazel copses green, ..."

A small tangle of moss and leaves in the crotch of the tree, dislodged by Tammy's foot, slid down on the other side and the voice was silenced by the fall. She leaned over the bar and looked down on the top of a man's head. "Shucks," she said, "it's human. I might have knowed."

Slowly the man sitting there with a book open across his knee turned and looked up at her. "And you? Are you human, too? Or a dryad, perhaps?"

Tammy laughed at his cocked eyebrow and puckered-up lips and comical air. He was so big he was like a bear that had just left off being a beast and found it awkward to find himself in guise of a man. "What might a dryad be?"

"A sprite, a spirit, a nymph that haunts the wilds, a divinity of nature that dwells in forest or water."

"They must be powerful common hereabouts."

"Why so?"

"Well, first I got took for a river nymph and now you've mistook me for a tree one. What I took you for was the voice of this here tree speaking to me with words like music."

"You liked what I read?"

Tammy rested her arms on the iron bar, she leaned her chin on her hands, remembering the sound of it, and it put her in mind to speak to the same tune, to mimic it. "It wasn't so much the words as the voice in the speaking of them. It was a sound as smooth as molasses pouring out of a jug, it was clear as water that flows from a spring at the foot of a sweet gum tree. It made words fair and true, the way a fiddle shapes sound. No wonder I mistook it for the voice of the Lord speaking out of a live oak tree like he spoke to Moses out of the midst of the burning bush."

She leaned forward and peered down at him, finding him looking up at her with his mouth a little open, like a big fat baby bird waiting for a worm to drop in it. The sight of a grown man thus made her laugh.

"Come down, come down," he said, "so I can see you without breaking my neck. Besides, I want to make sure you are real."

Tammy jumped to the bench and to the grass, she circled the tree and sat down beside him, swinging her feet gaily to and fro till she turned to him and saw that he was not at all an old man, as she had thought at first. He was young, and of a sudden she was shy of him.

"What's the matter?" he asked.

"You ain't old."

"Did you want me to be?"

"Kind of."

"Why?"

"Seems like I can understand old folk better than young ones. Maybe on account of being raised by Grandma till she died, and then Grandpa finished me off."

"Could that account for it?"

Tammy gave him a puzzled glance, for his words, as so often happened out in the world, went along with what had been said and understood and yet all the time were meaning something else, more far reaching. "Account for what?"

"Your speech, your phrasing, your manner of thinking. Tell me some more. What are you doing here? Where have you been to school?"

"I haven't been yet. But I'm agoing, if they ever wake up and open the doors. That's why I'm here." She felt a sudden twinge of anxiety. Would he speak as Pete had spoken about her going to college, making of his mouth a sharp sword? But this man's face held naught but gentleness and a kind, encouraging look. "You don't think it's ridiculous?"

"Of course not. It's a splendid idea. Suppose you start right in and tell me all about it, how you came to think of it, everything."

"Everything?" Tammy drew a long breath. It was wonderful, having somebody willing to listen without flying off the handle or thinking her too queer to bother with the minute she opened her mouth. "Then I will tell you the story of my life. I won't start with getting borned, that's too far back. I'll begin with Brenton Hall because there is where my love life grew."

The words came slowly at first, but seeing the kindly look of interest in this big man's face that was at the same time both young and old, being young in years and old in understanding, she gathered courage. She did not say much about Pete, for the hurt of their parting was still too raw to be bared to the open air. But she tried to make him see how she had to have learning and polishment so Pete would not be ashamed to have her go with him next time he got the going-away blues and had to take off for far places. And when she had finished, she added, "Might be I erred in bringing the *Ellen B.* down. I didn't know the river would be so far away with so much swamp to come through—that's how come I muddied my legs and draggled my toes. But I thought if I come with my own lodgement, it would be free of cost to me, and besides it would be a place where I could repose my spirit and be at home with myself under my own vine and fig tree, like. So none should make me afeard. Out in the world loose I had a feeling I might get distracted from myself and scattered to the winds by being too close to other humans."

He nodded. "That is one of the problems of modern living. But I doubt if the dean of women will approve of your living there alone."

"Dean of women? It has a noble sound."

80

He chuckled. "I had not thought of it that way, but you may be right. She has the say about such things. However, there are positions which give you room and board. Indeed, I know one which might suit you." He took a small notebook from his pocket, a pencil from another, wrote and tore out the page. "Give this to her when you go to the Employment Bureau. Miss Jenks. She attends to that, too."

"I thank you, sir. And who might you be? The . . . the president, maybe?"

He laughed. "Just one of the faculty."

"There was another one back yonder way. Teaches painting, he says. Seems funny to have teachers up so soon in the morning and the learners having a little more slumber, a little more sleep. What are you professor of?"

"Speech. Public speaking, it is usually called."

"But that's just what I've come to learn! Seems like the Lord had a hand in it, bringing me straight to you afore I could go astray amidst all these buildings roundabout. Not that I want to be public in my speaking, it's just private speaking I'm after. Could you teach me that?"

"It seems to me you are already able to express yourself in an extraordinarily interesting and unique manner."

"Unique," Tammy repeated. "If that means what I think it means, it's just what I don't want to be—peculiar. I want to talk like everybody talks out in the world."

He shook his head. "I do not believe in mass production of speakers, or of anything else, for that matter. Each one should retain his own individuality and express it through speech. There I can help. I would not change your outlook or point of view, or alter many of your phrases—straight out of the early 1800's."

"But that ain't the time I'm aliving in."

"True enough. I can see your problem. Perhaps I can help you without destroying the flavor, the charm. That is, if you care to enter my class."

"I'd be proud to."

He tore another sheet from his notebook and wrote again. "Give this to your faculty adviser. He will tell you how to arrange it. But now I would like to know a little more of your background preparation."

Tammy hung her head. "I ain't never had none."

"Well, then, what do you know already—out of your life?"

"Oh, that's different." She brightened at once and swinging her legs back and forth, she told him, concluding, "So you see I know about living and I know about dying, know about being in love. I know to cook and sew and knit and patch. I know to plant taters and beets in the dark of the moon, and beans and peas and corn in the light of the moon. Know how to milk my nanny goat and tend chickens, and onct I helped born a babe. That's what I know. It's what comes in books that I don't know, excepting of the Bible. Grandpa taught me that."

"You haven't read much?"

"A little, of late. I took on reading because I was feeling lonesome. At Brenton Hall there's a whole room full of books, called the library, so I set out to read them all. That was afore I got the notion of coming here. Not having read any, I thought I would take the leather-back, old-looking ones first and read up in time."

"I'd be interested to know what you read."

"It would pleasure me to tell you. There was one called *The History of the Earth and Animated Nature* by Oliver, a goldsmith."

"Hm-mmm. What was that about?"

"It was about the universe, mines and mountains and tides and the air. There was another volume about animals, their generation, age and death. Six volumes in all so they had room to tell about human monsters and every manner of beast, like the cow-kind, the hog-kind, the cat-, dog- and hare-kind, and that's as far as I got."

"Did you read any fiction—stories?'

"Oh yes. *Rosamund.* Kind of silly, that was. Such a fuss

82

over a purple vase that wasn't really purple, just had purple-dyed water in it. There was another one called *Harry and Lucy* by the same lady, a very moral lady by the way she writes, name of Maria Edgeworth. Pretty name, ain't it? And right alongside them on the shelf was Jay's *Sermons,* short discourses to be read in families, it said, but I read them to myself, not having any family. They weren't a patch on Grandpa's sermons, not half so lively and full of meat."

"Any more?"

"Just one, and it was real entertaining, being mostly about a kind of human giant by the name of Pantagruel which means all thirsty on account of there having been a long dry spell, just like this summer."

"Rabelais. Strong medicine for a young girl."

"I reckon. A lot I couldn't understand. But I like the part where he got born because with him there come into the world camels and mules and horses and wagons full of all manner of things, all at a single borning. So no wonder it was too much for his ma, him being so big to start with all by himself, besides all that come with him. I reckon she wasn't as tough as Annie Christmas."

"Annie Christmas? Who was she?"

Tammy smiled. It pleased her to know something a professor didn't know. "That is one of Grandpa's old songs. Annie Christmas had her twelve sons at a single borning, tall as corn on a summer morning. Don't you know about her?"

He shook his head. "Can you sing it?"

"Why, yessir, of course. It's sad and funny all at the same time, like the story of Pantagruel. I specially like it where he fell in love with a great lady who would have naught to do with him for all he was fit to die of it. So he got mad and said he would make all the dogs in town go jumping her. So he found him a bitch and that's how he perfumed her. It worked, too."

"Yes, I remember. But Annie Christmas . . . could you sing that for me?"

"Now?"

"If you'd like to. You still have a bit of time before registration will open."

"All right." And swinging her legs to and fro in time with the song, she sang:

> "A fightin' woman and a crowin' hen
> Bound to come to a sorry end.
> Aree, aroo, aree, aroo.
> If she don't die by a bloody han'
> She's bound to die of lovin' a man.
> Aree, aroo, aree, aroo.

"That there is the chorus, supposed to come at the end of every verse, but I'll just sing it straight through?"

He nodded. "Please do."

> "Annie, she was ten feet tall
> And heavy as an ox,
> Stronger than the stevedores
> On all the river docks.
>
> She had her a mustache long and shiny
> Hung below her chin,
> And when she fit she rolled it up
> Upon a rollin' pin.
>
> She had her a necklace with a bead
> For every ear she chawed.
> She hung another on the string
> For every eye she clawed.
>
> She fell in love with a gamblin' man,
> Went by the name of Curly,
> Loved him like a house afire,
> Loved him late and early.
>
> And after a year or so went by
> All on a summer mornin',
> She fotched him forth a dozen sons
> All at a single bornin'.

Now Curly went to New Orleans
To gamble at roulette,
Put his money on the red
And there he let it set.

Every time the wheel went round
Winner was the red,
But when they slapped him on the back
Curly fell down dead.

When Annie heard about her man
She put on her beads and her bonnet.
She gave him a fancy buryin',
Spent all his winnin's on it.

She called her sons around her then
And told them what to do.
She put a pistol to her head
And shot a bullet through.

They laid her on a coal-black barge
Deep in the dark of the moon,
Every son in a coal-black coat
And a coal-black pantaloon.

They set them down by Annie Christmas,
Six of 'em to a side,
And floated down the Mississip
And out on the ebbin' tide.

And sometimes on a coal-black night
The river folk can hear
The singin' of the mournful song
They sung by Annie's bier."

Tammy finished the song and in the same breath asked, "Did you like it?"

"Indeed I did. I'd like to make a recording sometime."

But Tammy was not listening, for she noticed now that while she was singing the whole place had come alive, people moving to and fro, mostly in one direction. "What for are they going down there?" she demanded.

"To the cafeteria. Have you had your breakfast? I'd like you to——"

"I et too long ago to talk about."

"Well, I haven't had mine yet. I like to come out early and read a while, while I wait. But before I go, I'd like to know what else you plan to study. I might be able to help you in deciding, though of course you will have your own faculty adviser to talk it over with."

"I'm mightily obliged to you, sir. For a fact I don't know the proper names of what I want to learn about, but I'd like to get cotched up on new books. I mean on some that have been writ since the ones I read at Brenton Hall."

"Modern literature should do it." He took yet another slip of paper from his notebook and wrote down a name and a number. "What else?"

"I want to know what's going on in the world now. I already know about Bible times."

"Ah yes, current events." He wrote again and gave her the paper. "Show this to your adviser," he said and rose, taking up a walking stick that had been resting on the seat beside him, "and if there is anything else I can do—my office is in Baker, and I live in that building at the far end of the quadrangle. Bachelor faculty apartments."

"You've been monstrous kind," Tammy said, hastily putting on her shoes and rising too. Then as she looked up at him standing so big and tall beside her, she said, "You kind of put me in mind of a ba'r. Only I ain't a mite scared of you, even if you do be a professor. My name is Tammy Tyree. What might your entitlement be?"

"I've written it there for you. Thomas Freeman."

"But what's that?" She stood openmouthed in wonder, listening. The sound struck her ears in waves, one upon the heels of the other, filling her head with a delicious din.

"Just the clock tower bells striking the hour."

"They sound like bells of pure gold. I reckon it was bells

like that the Lord meant when he told Moses to put a bell and a pomegranate round about the hem of his garment. I never figgered out what the pomegranate was for. Do you know?"

He shook his head. "I wouldn't know about that. These bells were given to the college by Mrs. Call in memory of her son. At noon you will hear them ringing the changes."

"Mrs. Call?" Tammy looked at one of the slips of paper he had given her. "Is this—"

"The same. A lonely sad old woman who needs someone to stay with her. Her son was my best friend, and she was a good friend too, once. I would like to do her a good turn, and you might prove to be just that." He made a small bow. "And by the way, if her niece happens to be there, don't let her put you off. See Mrs. Call herself. I think she'll like you. Now thank you for singing for me, and for talking too. I'll see you at my first class, I hope."

"That you will and I'm powerfully obliged." She watched him move away down the walk, limping a little as he went and swinging one leg in a halting manner, helping himself along by means of the walking stick. She wondered how he had come by such an affliction. It was a pity, though maybe that was why he was so kind. Grandpa said them that were cast into the furnace of affliction were either burnt to bitterness or refined with silver, and surely this was as refined a man as she had ever met up with in all her born days.

And thinking these things she set out in the direction of the building with the tower on top.

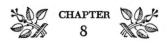

CHAPTER
8

As SHE MOUNTED the steps of the big building, Tammy moved more slowly. All these young people laughing and talking, one with another, seemed like old friends brought together after long parting and the sight of them gave her a lonesome feeling. They were so gay, so much at ease. She felt separated from them as by a great gulf, as if she might have come not only from a distance but out of a faraway time. She even felt estranged from herself so that the motion of her skirt, the placing of one foot before the other was unfamiliar to her. Maybe after many days she might feel at one with these who moved with confidence, knowing just what was fitting to be said and done. But not yet, not yet.

She slipped in behind a group that was passing through open doors to a great room with tall windows that let in the morning sun. Sun, sun, do you know who I be? This one here, I mean, the one come all alone into the halls of Academe? There was no word spoken, yet it seemed as if the long shaft of sunlight on the floor had laid itself down in surprise, in full amazement to see her, seemed as if it might be saying, "Well, I declare!" or "Well, hush my mouth!" If a sunbeam had a mouth, Tammy thought with a faint smile and an easing of the tension within her.

There were tables scattered round about in an orderly kind of irregularity and some folk sat writing. Tammy took her place at one and bent over the long sheet of paper that was lying there. She sat bowed over reading and rereading the questions writ upon it and not knowing how to answer, and having no pencil with which to write had she known. Only her name was sure, and home address—the *Ellen B.* It came over her now that they were true words Pete had spoken in his anger. Ridiculous, that's what it was, ridiculous for her to be here. She bowed her head lower and shrank up inside herself, giving no sign.

˙Some one passed, brushed her elbow. "Oh sorry," the girl said, looking down friendlywise. Then with a smile, she laid a pencil on the table before Tammy and went on without waiting for thanks.

She was a tall slim girl with no color in her cheeks, only in her bright red lips. Her black hair was drawn back as tight and plain and smooth as Grandma's ever was and it had a shine to it as if it might be polished. The most amazing thing about her, however, was the dress she wore. It was a fair mate to one of Tammy's own gunny-sack dresses, hanging as it did straight from the shoulder without form or fit and it was made of even rougher stuff than burlap. Tammy reckoned that if so proud-moving, so queenly-seeming a girl could wear such a garment, then she herself should not ever feel shame for her own shanty-boat clothes. Was this girl poor, too, this one who drew admiring glances by her manner of moving and by her air of being somebody? Maybe this was a sign sent to show her that being countrified had naught to do with one's standing in a college.

Tammy watched, fascinated, as the girl went on down the aisle to mount a slightly raised platform where there sat behind a long table, a lady with an air of great importance; the girl bent over and seemed to be consulting her about the paper of

90

questions. Tammy drew a breath of relief. If one did not understand, it was possible to ask for help. It was no disgrace to be ignorant. She wrote down her name and her address and then rose and moved slowly down the aisle, paper in hand. Behind her someone tittered, another went "Sh-sh!" Some one let out a long breathy "Whew!" and there was from here and there a shuffling of feet as if in derision.

Tammy wished she might sink through the floor. They were mocking her as the children mocked Elisha. She had always thought it mighty mean of him to call forth the she-bears to tear forty-odd of them. But now she wished she had a she-bear to loose amongst these here who laughed her to scorn. Nothing to do but turn and face them alone.

As she turned, someone sashayed past her. Ah, this was the one they were mocking. She wore a dress like to the tall slim girl's. Could it be the fashion? Only she was fat as a hog at hog-killing time. Lordymussy, Tammy thought, following along behind, she wobbled her jacobstaff in every pernimbula. No wonder there was laughter at her passing. Yet she seemed not at all dismayed, for reaching the table before Tammy, she turned and gave herself a little swish, for all the world like a plump pullet priming herself for the cock.

When Tammy's turn came, the lady said, "What's the trouble? You haven't half filled out your questionnaire." She looked up sternly through dark-rimmed glasses.

Tammy's voice was low and full of uncertainty. "I . . . all this about schools. I haven't been. I've just come."

"You have never been to school?"

"No, ma'm."

"Then how in the world . . ."

That was the way Pete had spoken, in that same tone. "The catalogue said that anyone could come and be a listener, though that wasn't the word. Auditor, that's what it said, and that's what I've a mind to be."

"Oh, that's a different matter. You don't need to do anything more here, then. But see—what do you mean, the *Ellen B.*? That's no address."

"It's where I live. It's a boat, on the river."

"Most irregular." Her glasses flashed as she looked Tammy up and down. "The dean . . ."

Tammy glanced round at all those standing behind her, waiting their turn. "To make it plain so that a wayfaring man though a stranger might understand, I would have to tell you the story of my life, and I reckon you've no time for that."

The lady smiled, she blinked her eyes and then said, "You intrigue me. Have you seen your adviser?"

"I don't know where to find him, or what his entitlement might be."

"Special students go to Dr. Dilloby. Here, I'll make a note of it for you. Room 112, Main."

"There's nothing really special about me——" Tammy began.

"What's that? Well, it's beyond me. You had better see him at once. This is the last day. Wait. Take this." She handed her a slip of paper with printing on it. "Your post office box number, and . . . here. You are expected to attend."

This card said, All students are invited to tea . . . President and Mrs. Calker's . . . "Oh, thank you ma'm," Tammy cried. "It will pleasure me mightily."

The lady stared up at her for a moment, then shook her head. "Perhaps I have just been to too many. Next, please."

Outside, Tammy looked around, wondering how to find Main 112 and her adviser. She would have to ask. She tried to stop a group of girls sauntering past her on the walk but they just looked around, said "Hi," and went right on talking amongst themselves. After a moment she came abreast of an elderly man walking slowly, his sandy-gray head bare to the morning sun, a wide-brimmed black hat in his hand.

"Excuse me, sir, but could you tell me where this might be?"
She fell in step beside him and held the card out for him to see.
He stood still, fumbled in his pocket, brought out his spectacles, set them on his nose and looked her up and down saying, "They get younger every year—and prettier, unless my eyesight is failing me, like everything else. Now what is it you want to know?"

"This. Where is it?"

"To all appearances, in your hand." Then he continued as if addressing a large church chockablock with people, "However, appearances are deceptive. We must remember that position as well as length is relative to the individual observer, and there is also the influence of motion, celestial and otherwise. Furthermore, all sense impressions are dependent upon one's mental state. Yours and mine may well differ, thus introducing another element of uncertainty. Now let me see."

As he bent closer to examine the card, Tammy sighed. What hard luck this was, running into a professor who was either crazy in the head or so learned his words ran away with his brains. "It's my adviser," she explained.

"Ah yes, your adviser. George Dilloby, a very competent young man. Main 112. As I am going in that direction, perhaps you will permit me the honor of showing you in person."

"I will permit it and much obliged to you," Tammy said and fell into slow step beside him. "Be you a professor?" she asked after a moment, giving him a shy glance.

He bowed slightly. "Emeritus."

Here was another subject she had never heard of. "Emeritus —is it something a body should study about?"

He turned his head stiffly and looked down at her with a surprised and interested air. "A most discerning question. Yes, I should say it is one subject that should be required of every student, indeed of every human being. For all who live long enough will some day have to encounter the problems of age

93

and enforced leisure. Early preparation would be a definite help, but our short-sighted makers of curricula have not yet seen the necessity. May I ask what courses you intend to pursue?"

"You may ask and I will tell you. I will pursue speaking, not so much public as private, though it is called public. I will pursue modern lit and current events." She gave a little skip full of pride that she could answer properly, thanks to the professor under the tree. "Of course," she added, "what I want most is to learn to understand—people in the world are so—so odd and peculiar."

"Congratulations!" He made her a little bow, his thin white face lighting up with pleasure. "As a wiser man than I said many years ago, 'With all thy getting, get understanding.'"

"Oh yes, I know. And if I do I will have an ornament of grace for my head and a crown of glory will be delivered to me. One of Grandpa's best sermons is about that."

"Your grandfather is a preacher?"

"Kind of. Off and on. And one thing he learned me for sure, before he got took up by the revenuers, was the Bible. He said it was a shield and buckler."

He gave her a puzzled glance, one finger tapping the side of his head. His hair fitted his head like a cap. Indeed, Tammy saw now that it was a cap, somewhat crooked over one ear and he tapped it as if to make sure it was still there. "Most curious, in this godless day. And the revenuers——"

"I think you are right curious yourself, sir, if you please," Tammy replied with some spirit. "So is nearly everybody I have met so far, but all in different ways and some curiouser than others."

"Ah yes, I have reached the same conclusion after more years than you have yet to your credit. As of course did Alice before me." He glanced around as if suddenly aware of his surroundings. "And here we are. I regret that we have so quickly arrived at the entrance of Main. It is not often I have the pleasure of such intelligent conversation."

"Isn't it? I should think that here in the midst of a college you would have nothing else but."

"You would be surprised," he replied with a small chuckle that was like a hen's cluck.

"I'm surprised right and left every minute. But I'm much obliged to you for guiding me on my way, and for saying that about my conversation. Though it seems to me that you have done most of the conversing."

"Perhaps that is one reason I have found it intelligent." He held out a hand that was as thin and papery looking as his face. "Maybe you are a good listener."

Tammy laughed as she gave his hand a hearty shake. "Oh, I do hope so, for that's what I've come to be, a listener." And with that she ran up the steps and went down one corridor and another till she came to a door marked, "GEO. DILLOBY, ASST. PROF. COME IN."

In the room there was a long row of chairs and every one of them occupied. On the far side sat a young man behind a desk playing on a small black machine that tapped briskly while a sheet of paper moved in front of him as if by magic with words appearing upon it. There had been a picture of such a thing in the catalogue, Tammy remembered, and it was called a typewriter, but to see it working in the fullness of its ease was a wonder. She stood entranced, watching the busy fingers, listening to a little bell that rang—the catalogue had not mentioned that. The young man said, "Take a seat and wait your turn," his fingers never slowing as he spoke.

At that moment someone came from an inner office, the line moved down and there was room. "Thank you and I'm much obliged," Tammy said and sat down.

The young man beside her yawned. He had a big mouth and red hair and he slumped down low in the chair till he was sitting on the middle of his spine. "It's my tired blood," he said, as if in apology.

"Puts me in mind of a chicken roost," Tammy said, not knowing how blood could be tired, "the last-come nudging himself a place and the end one falling off."

The lazy boy beside her stretched his legs yet farther out and murmured. "Some line. A real comic," and gave her a slow glance. "Or did you come that way?"

Tammy turned and studied him for a moment. This was one she did not cotton to, so she said, with dignity, "I come the way I come. How do you come?"

"Easy made and ever ready, that's how I come."

Some one down the line said, "Watch it, boy."

"No offense, baby," he said.

"None taken," Tammy replied. "Likely your tired blood can't get to the brain."

There was a little laughter by those who heard and he said no more. When her turn came, she went into the inner office and taking from her pocket the slip of paper she had been given by the professor under the tree, she laid it on the desk before the man who sat there busily writing and not looking up.

"Very good. These are excellent courses. Do you want college credit?"

"Oh no, sir. I have cash money to pay with."

He looked up then, studied her from under his heavy dark brows. "What's the idea?"

"The idea is to be a . . . a auditor, just learning those things writ there on the paper, learning by listening." She did wish people wouldn't look at her as if she were a Hottentot or a heathen or something equally rare and peculiar. "Also, I want to get some work to earn some of my keep."

"Ah, I see. I will fill out the proper slips for you." He worked busily for a moment with a catalogue before him. "You know what to do next?"

"No, sir."

"These papers go to the business office on the second floor here. Pay your fees there. The blue slips you must give your professors when you go to class. Miss Jenks, the dean of women handles the employment problems. Anything else on your mind?"

"I reckon not. Thank you, sir." She went out, through the outer office and down the hall, thinking it was lucky she'd had advice from Mr. Freeman. This adviser had sure been stingy with it.

Paying out money was a simple matter, she found. Not at all like earning it in the first place, for that was slow and hard. All she had to do now was pass the papers through a little wicket fence to a man behind an open hole and when he told her the sum of it all, reach in her pocket and hand it forth, no word being said of where it came from or how it was gathered together, no word of the floaters Grandpa had brought to shore nor of the still in the swamp and people slipping in by night for their corn likker. Just money handed out and received. "I sure hope I'll get my money's worth," Tammy said.

The man laughed, he stamped a paper with ready-made printing and handed it to her saying, "That's your risk. No refund."

The dean's office was almost empty and after a few minutes Tammy was admitted to an inner room where a lady sat behind a desk that had upon it a placard saying "Miss Jenks." She began briskly, "Well, now, let me see. Your name is——"

"Tammy Tyree and a professor by the name of Thomas Freeman told me to give you this lady's name. He thought it might be a place where I could do some work for my keep."

"Where are you staying now?"

"On the *Ellen B*. It's my home and it is my wish to keep on staying there." But when she had explained it all, Miss Jenks shook her head.

"Quite impossible, my child. Unheard of. Now I wonder . . ." She studied the name on the slip of paper, she took off her

97

glasses and chewed on one end of the earpiece. She had a narrow pale face that was fined down to the bone. Her hair was a mass of short dark curls with one gray streak rising from her forehead like a plume. "Of course I would not dream of questioning Mr. Freeman's judgment—he knows her very well indeed. But it is a difficult position. I have sent half a dozen girls there over the last year or so. But we might try, no harm in that. You could move in at once?"

"Yes, ma'm. And I don't mind hard work."

"It's not so much the work, it's the strain. The problem is . . . no, I'll call first." Miss Jenks lifted the phone that sat on her desk. "Get me Mrs. Theodore Call's house, please. . . . Yes. Della? This is Miss Jenks at the college again. Is Mrs. Call's niece still there? . . . Oh, good. . . . Miss Rook? So glad I caught you. Will you have time to see another applicant? I think we may have someone this time. Mr. Freeman, Tom Freeman, recommends her. . . . Very well, she will be right over."

Miss Jenks hung up the phone and turned to Tammy. "You will have to hurry. That was Mrs. Call's niece and she has to catch a train for New Orleans. She wants to see you at once. Now here is the situation. Mrs. Call is . . . difficult. She lives alone, though there is a cook who comes in by the day. There just has to be someone there in the house in case she is taken ill or needs something at night. You will be given room and board for being within call when you are not busy on the campus. Sounds easy, doesn't it? But the trouble is that Mrs. Call doesn't want anyone there. She resents her niece's insistence that someone is needed, and she makes it as trying as possible. One of the students I sent over left because she had to eat in the kitchen. How do you feel about that?"

"I'd be pleased to eat anywhere, so long as I got my food."

"Good. Now you must leave by the east gate. Here's a note

98

of the street and number. It's a big gray house behind an iron fence. Miss Rook, the niece, will tell you anything you need to know."

"Why doesn't she live with the old lady?"

"Her home is in New Orleans. She just comes up every six weeks or so to check on her aunt, who has no one else. Good luck to you."

Tammy thanked her. "I'll make out somehow." Then she set out for the east campus gate.

Walking quickly down a shady street of many houses set all close together, Tammy paused when she came to one with an iron fence. Yes, there was the gate, the number shaped in iron right in the middle of it and iron grapevines woven roundabout it. The shallow yard was a jumble of overgrown shrubs and the porches upstairs and down were almost hidden by vines. The house had a closed-up, forbidding look, the long windows that came down to the floor of the porch being shuttered and fastened tight.

Tammy ran up the steps. She lifted the heavy iron knocker and let it fall with a bang. Then she waited and waited. Not a sound came from within. She banged still harder and after a little while the door was opened and there stood a colored woman in white cap and apron. "Good morning, ma'm," Tammy said, politely. "I've come from the college to live with Mrs. Call, if I suit."

"Yessum, come right in." She led the way down the hall and showed Tammy into a room that seemed to be a kind of second-best back parlor. "I'll tell Miss Rook. Just take a chair."

Tammy sat down on a spindly gold-painted chair just inside the door. It creaked and wobbled so she moved over to stand by the window, hoping for a bit of fresh air, for the room was musty smelling. The shutters were closed but through the slats she could look down on a small garden that was enclosed by a high brick wall. Seated there in a rocking chair was a fat

99

little old lady knitting on a red sock. A ball of red yarn lay on a gray-painted iron settee beside her and a pale purple scarf was draped there, half falling to the bricks of the courtyard pavement. The old lady rocked back and forth in time with the motion of her needles but now and then she was still, turning a quick glance in the direction of the house. Tammy had the feeling that she was expecting someone and did not want to be found idle.

A voice came from somewhere out of sight. "Dear Auntie Ann, I'm so glad to see you with your knitting. We must keep busy, you know. That's the way to be happy and gay. I'll send you some more yarn as soon as I get home."

Heels clicked on steps and the speaker came into sight. She was a slender woman, neither young nor old as far as Tammy could see, for her longish blond hair curling up at the ends was young seeming and the lines of her face, showing through paint and powder, were old and worried. Her voice was light and sweet, almost too sweet, Tammy thought. She wore a smart gray suit with a yellow blouse that matched her gloves and a flower on her little black hat. She bent and picked up the scarf, laid it around the old lady's shoulders with little fussy tweaks and pats. "There now, darling. You must take care of yourself."

Mrs. Call went on knitting without a word, and Tammy thought she looked as sour as a green persimmon.

Her niece perched on the edge of the iron chair. "Now dearie, I do hope you will think about that house. Just off Audubon and a great bargain. With just a little money put into repairs, it will be a splendid investment, besides giving me a decent place to live. After all, I'm the only relative you have in the world, dear. And I have to be out of my apartment in six months, just time to get the house in shape. Then you could come down to visit me and I could make you really comfortable."

100

"I'm right comfortable here, thank you, Sandra."

"Yes, dear, but I worry so about you, here all alone. Now do you promise you will think about the house?"

"I'll think, Sandra."

"Good. I knew you'd do the generous thing. Now about someone to stay with you, I've another college girl to interview. Just don't you worry. I'll make all the arrangements."

"I do not need or want——" The old lady let the knitting fall to her lap and made a little hopeless gesture of her hands as much as to say, "What's the use?"

"Oh, darling, will I have to come and live with you myself?"

"Heaven forbid! I mean, you have your life to lead. Let me have mine, stupid as it may seem to you."

"Of course, dear. Don't excite yourself. I just want you to be looked after. Now I have so much to do before train time, but I'll see you before I go."

"Don't bother. I'll be having my nap."

"Well, dear, if you say so. Do send me a line now and then so I'll know you are all right." She rose and took a quick peck at her aunt's cheek.

"I'll send your allowance as usual."

"Oh, thank you, Auntie Ann. And if this college girl Miss Jenks is sending over doesn't seem just right, I'll find someone else."

"Good-by, Sandra. Don't miss your train. And thank you for coming."

She did not sound very thankful, Tammy thought. And as for her niece, she really brimmed over with airs and graces and dearies and darlings—too sweet for a steady diet. Maybe that was why the old lady seemed eager to be rid of her. Bossy, she was.

Her voice came from the hall now. "Just set my bags on the porch, will you, Della. These taximen are so unobliging. And here—I wish it were more but I'm really terribly short of money

101

right now. Mention it to my aunt if you get a chance, will you? Really she doesn't have any idea how living expenses have gone up." Then her voice sharpened. "Della! What on earth has happened to this secretary?"

"Thanky, ma'm. Wellum, about that secretary, it just kind of collapsed in the leg and I set them bricks under there so's it wouldn't topple over."

"What a shame! It's one of the best things in the house. I saw one like it on Royal Street the other day. Over a thousand dollars, it was. Della, you must get a man in to fix it, and have him do over some other pieces at the same time."

"Yessum, only Miz Call, she don't seem to care."

"Well, I care. This furniture will be coming to me before long and it should be kept in good condition. Some of it is very valuable, but not in this condition. Oh dear, I have so much to worry about. Where's that college girl?"

"Right in yonder in the back parlor, Miss Sandra. She's waiting for you."

Tammy was standing in the middle of the room when Miss Sandra appeared in the doorway. "Good morning, ma'm," she said.

"So dark in here!" Miss Sandra bumped into the table just inside the door and made the telephone that lay on it give a little ring as if in protest, then she came on saying, "Ah, there you are. Well, I have only a moment to give you, so let's get right down to business. Come, sit here." She dropped down on a small sofa and motioned Tammy to sit beside her. "My aunt, Mrs. Call, is quite well except for low blood pressure and varicose veins. But she is old, she has a tendency to dizziness and it is necessary that someone be here, especially at night. Would you be going out nights much?"

"No, ma'm, I——"

"Good. Now I must tell you my aunt does not want anyone and she makes it difficult. You understand?"

"Yes, ma'm."

102

"I've tried everything—housekeepers, companions, nurses—I've spared no expense and effort. She says they talk too much, they chew with their mouths open, oh, just anything to be rid of them. To tell the truth—I am being very frank with you—she is a little . . . how shall I say?" She tapped her forehead.

"Notional, I reckon," Tammy said. "I know about old folks. It was my grandma and grandpa raised me and I really know more about the old than I do about the young."

"Splendid. Now if I decide to have you, I want you to write me if she gets more notional, as you call it. I want to relieve her of all her business cares, just take over everything for her, but her lawyer—— Well, no matter. Just let me know if she gets any more erratic. Here is my address, and I will expect you to keep me informed." She took a card from her purse and gave it to Tammy.

"Now." She tossed back her hair and took her first good look at Tammy. "Now I've told you my side of the matter and you know all about the position and what I expect. Tell me about yourself, your family and so on." She sat back, hands folded in her lap.

"Yessum. Well, there ain't much to tell. I growed up on the river with Grandpa and Grandma till she died, and lately I been living with Pete—that's who I was thinking to marry before now, only he's gone off and so I come to get me some schooling in the meanwhile."

Miss Sandra looked as if she was going to lose her eyes from their popping right out of her head. "Living with—why, why! Oh, dear me. You . . . your grandfather let you go to live with——"

"Yessum, he likes Pete and he was real pleased to have me off his hands because he couldn't rightly look after me himself whilst he was in jail, and——"

At that Miss Sandra sprang to her feet, mumbling nobody knew what. She stood there and ruffled up like a wet hen.

"That will do," she said when she got her breath. "I don't believe you will suit, after all. Good-by, and thank you so much
for coming."

Tammy stared at her, openmouthed. "You don't want me?
B-but if it's account of Grandpa's being in jail, I can explain
that——"

"I most certainly do not want you and I do not care where
your grandfather is, nor do I care to hear any explanations.
You may go now. Go back to where you came from. Don't
you understand?" She fair spat the last words out and in the
dim-shuttered room her eyes blazed up like a cat's.

Tammy rose slowly. "You mean, go back to Miss Jenks?"

"Miss Jenks! I shall have plenty to say to her." She might
have been made of fire and hell, the way she whirled around
and snatched up the telephone from the table by the door.
"Good-by," she said over her shoulder, and gave a number into
the phone.

Tammy stumbled over a chair as she went down the hall,
too stunned and bewildered to know what she was doing.
They'd been getting along so well, then—— And if it wasn't
Grandpa's being in jail, what was it? Suddenly she found herself on a vine-covered side porch. She must have taken a
wrong turn. She went back through the hall and couldn't help
but hear Miss Sandra talking, as she passed the back parlor.

". . . simply outrageous. Is this some joke of Tom Freeman's?
I know my aunt hates the sight of him, but this is no way to
get back at a poor feeble old woman, and I consider it a personal insult. How you, Miss Jenks, of all people—or how the
college could admit such a—— No, no. I do not want another
student. I shall go on to New Orleans and send someone up
from there. What's more——"

Tammy opened the front door and went out, closing it softly
behind her. What a strange happening! Mr. Freeman was just
trying to do something nice for Mrs. Call, and here was Miss
Sandra taking it for some mean kind of joke because Mrs. Call

hated the sight of him. Miss Sandra, so sweet talking and then flying off the handle. She simply could not figger it out. One thing was certain. Miss Sandra had treated her like pure poison, downright insulting, ordering her to leave like that and now, scandalizing her name to Miss Jenks. Tammy walked faster and faster, never looking which way she went and getting madder with every step. It wasn't fair, her first chance at a job! And how could she go back to Miss Jenks and ask for another? She felt just too shamed to ever hold up her head again. If she only had Grandpa here to tell her, to explain things for her. It was all too mixed up and she could not make head nor tail of it.

When at last she became aware of her surroundings, she saw she must have come a long way into some strange part of the city where the houses were unpainted and small colored children romped around the meager yards and shouted as gaily as though they might be living in palaces. Well, she thought, the river was bound to be to the west, so she took her sights by the sun and headed toward it. At least she had the good old *Ellen B.* to go home to.

After she had walked and walked, the houses and trees began to seem a bit familiar to her and suddenly she saw the iron fence and the overgrown bushes that surrounded Mrs. Call's house. She had made a circle in her wanderings. A car stood before the iron gate and Miss Sandra was just stepping into it, Della handing her luggage in after her. Tammy slowed her step till the car had pulled away. Miss Sandra was one lady she never wanted to see again in all her born days, and as for Della—well, she was already disappearing round the corner of the street at the end of the block.

The old lady would be alone now, Tammy thought, walking on. She would be alone in that big gloomy old house. A lonely, sad old woman, Mr. Freeman had said. He had said something else, too. Tammy stopped short, remembering. "Don't let the niece put you off. See Mrs. Call herself," that was what he had said. He must have known more than he let on to her. And surely, since it was Mrs. Call's house, she ought to have the say about who, if anyone, was to live with her.

"I give up too soon," Tammy said aloud and lifting the latch, went in by the iron gate.

She knocked again and again and there was no answer. Mrs. Call, out in the garden, would never hear. Maybe there was a side gate. She went looking and found only the solid brick wall.

However, there was a big, low-branched hackberry tree beside the wall, its branches reaching over. Tammy hesitated only a moment, then she kicked off her shoes, shinnied up the trunk to the first branch, edged her way along another until she was looking down into the garden where Mrs. Call still sat in her rocking chair. It would be an easy drop from here, but Tammy hesitated, wondering if she shouldn't speak first so as not to be too startling. While she considered, she saw Mrs. Call fling the half-knitted sock into the border of chrysanthemums beside her. Then she snatched the lavender scarf from her shoulders and balling it into a tight wad, tossed it into the border of violets. "I loathe lavender," she said aloud.

"Howdy, ma'm," Tammy said.

Mrs. Call glanced upward toward the branch where Tammy was perched. She gave no sign of surprise. She looked too old and settled and solid to be surprised by anything, not even by the sight of bare legs and feet dangling down from a leafy branch. "Who are you?"

"I'm the girl from the college and my name is Tammy Tyree."

Mrs. Call sighed noisily. "I thought I would have at least till tomorrow in which to enjoy my privacy. Wasn't it so arranged by my ever-loving niece?"

"No, ma'm. She took a dislike and wouldn't have me."

"Humph! That's one thing in your favor!"

"Yessum, and I thought since you was the one that would be giving me my room and meals, that you ought to have the real sayso about it."

106

"Humph! A novel idea. 'When thou shalt be old, thou shalt stretch forth thy hands and another shall gird thee'——"

"Yes ma'm—'and carry thee whither thou wouldst not.' Only I don't want to carry you anywhere. I just come back to have you say what's what."

"My only say is NO. But who listens to that?"

"Then you don't want me, either?"

"I do not."

Tammy, near to tears, began to hunch her way along the branch toward the wall. She would have to go to Miss Jenks and say she had been ordered off twice. "But that isn't fair." She shouted the words back over her shoulder. "You haven't so much as laid eyes on me yet. You might like me, for all you know."

"I doubt it. Why should I? But come along down while you're here and let me look at you."

Tammy whirled around, nearly losing her balance. She swung down from the branch, jumped over a bush and came out on the brick pavement of the courtyard with red yarn tangled around one foot. She followed it back to where the ball lay, found sock and needles. There was a dropped stitch, so she caught it up and took a few stitches to make sure there were no more.

"So you can knit."

"Yessum. My grandma taught me."

"Do you like to knit?"

"I don't mind. If I have yarn."

"I loathe knitting. My niece sends me yarn. I knit socks and send them back to her."

"For her children?" Tammy asked, her needles clicking busily.

"She has none."

"Then what for does she——"

"Some charity, I suppose. But really to keep me busy and happy and out of mischief." She said the words with scorn.

107

"If I was here I'd do your knitting for you, and as for getting into mischief, Grandpa says the devil's got a right to a little credit now and then. If he wasn't around to tempt us into mischief, then being good would be so easy there'd be no point to it."

An odd small sound came from the old lady, like a laugh that got smothered before it was born. Tammy stuck in the needles and laid the knitting down on the iron chair beside Mrs. Call. She hesitated a moment, then as Mrs. Call said no word, "I reckon I better be going," she sighed, "I don't want to be where I ain't wanted."

"I suppose I'll have to let you out." Mrs. Call stirred as if to rise, but there was a little uncertainty in her voice.

"No, ma'm. I'll go out the way I come. Wouldn't want to be a trouble." She crossed to the overhanging branch, jumped and caught it, crooked a knee over and pulled up. She sat a moment, swinging her feet, thinking. Then she spoke her thought aloud. "Seems kind of too bad we can't jine up. They don't want you living alone because you're too old and they won't let me live alone because I'm too young. There's no pleasing people. Oh well." But before she had humped her way to the tree trunk, the old lady stopped her with a question.

"Where do you live?"

"On the *Ellen B.*"

"What's that?"

"It's home to me, the only one I ever knowed. But I reckon it's what folks call a shanty boat."

"A shanty boat? Where is it?" For the first time she spoke with quick interest, leaning forward, squinting up at Tammy with bright black eyes that were almost buried by the fatness of her cheeks.

"Out yonder on the river." What a change had come over the old woman, Tammy thought, peering down at her. She seemed almost young again for a moment. Then the life went out of her and she leaned back with a sigh.

108

Tammy suddenly felt sorry for her, wished she could do something to keep her alive and interested in living. She seemed so lost and lonely now, the moment's animation gone and age descending on her again like a weight. How would it be, to be old and alone with nobody really loving you? Grandma had lived to be old but she had been loved and cherished, and she never gave up and slumped like this poor old soul was doing. She just got a little notional about her vittles, not liking hogmeat any more and wanting catfish every day of the world. Tammy leaned down and asked, "You like catfish, fresh caught?"

"Catfish? Fried in cornmeal?"

"Yes, ma'm. I could bring you one."

"Where would you get it?"

"Catch it myself, soon in the morning."

Mrs. Call leaned forward eagerly. "I will pay you for it."

"I wouldn't take money, for it wouldn't cost me nothing. I'd be proud to bring you one, cook it too. First thing in the morning."

"Daybreak? I wake so damn early these days."

"Yes, ma'm. Or sunup at latest. Good-by for now." She moved along the branch toward the wall, hearing Mrs. Call talking to herself, saying, "Catfish for breakfast once again. Now think of that! And a shanty boat!"

The campus had a deserted look as Tammy hurried along the path. She considered stopping in to see Miss Jenks but she was still smarting from Miss Sandra's sharp words; besides, who could tell? Mrs. Call might change her mind. Passing close by one of the buildings Tammy smelled food and heard a great clatter of dishes. She peeked in a window and had a quick glimpse of many people sitting at small tables, eating. What luxury that was, to sit at a table and eat in ease! Even so, you would have to take what was brought. You wouldn't be free the way you could be on the river.

She did not enter the swamp where she had come out that

109

morning, but kept on the outskirts of the campus for a while, finding the land higher here and a neglected road slanting up the side of the levee. It led down past a log cabin and on toward the river, as if wagons might have come this way perhaps for sand. She had not gone far when the sound of voices stopped her.

A girl's voice. "I did hear someone."

The answer was no more than a low murmur, but it was a man speaking and the words were lost to Tammy's ears. She started on, then heard the girl say, "Of course, darling. I never would have come back to this lousy little college but for you."

Tammy peered through the underbrush and turned away quickly. There were times when people needed privacy. She went on, as quietly as any Indian with scarce a crackling twig underfoot. But she went sadly, too. Seeing the two of them standing close, with arms around each other, had given her a lonesome feeling. It was a new kind of lonesomeness. Long ago, not knowing, long ago on the *Ellen B.* before Pete came, there were times on moonlight nights when she had had a vague, lost, sad feeling. It came when she heard a whippoorwill that called again and again and got no answer, or in the spring of the year when a mourning dove mourned. Then she had felt a longing and a kind of emptiness. But that old sweetsad, vague feeling came of being young and unknowing. This new sadness that was upon her now came of having had something and lost it, a grown-up grief that spread into the furthermost parts of her being, keen and penetrating.

She came out on a sand bar at the river's edge and stood there a moment trying to set away from her such thoughts. Forget the couple she had glimpsed through the bushes. Though that was a curious thing the girl had said, that she never would have come back to this lousy college but for him. Could it be that there were students here who had come not to learn but for other reasons? What was the sense in having all these beautiful buildings and many wise and learned teach-

110

ers if students did not come to learn? And lousy, she had said. Well, when she got back to the *Ellen B.* she would have to sit down and search the seams of her dress. That was where lice were apt to settle.

She rounded a point and there sat the *Ellen B.* waiting for her, a pleasant sight after all the unfamiliar things she had been seeing. Except for the days of the Pilgrimage when crowds had come each day to visit Brenton Hall, she had scarcely seen so many people in all her born days. Oh, but it was exciting out in the world with things happening one right after the other, even bad things like having no luck with Mrs. Call's job, but it was better than sitting round Brenton Hall waiting for the postman, listening to Miss Renie, dusting for Osia and pining for Pete. As soon as she had fed the chickens and herself, she thought maybe she might write to Pete. She could understand now how it was that he did not write to her often. Too much was going on around him and he was too busy, as she had been all morning. She had got that bit of understanding already from being at a college.

She had thought, back before Pete came, that when a body fell in love, he just naturally gave his whole time and thought to it, that it filled up every living, breathing minute of the day and night. But that wasn't so. There were so many things in this world that had to be done, you had to put your mind on it while you were doing them, paying no mind to love. That didn't mean you loved the less, only that you could not give all your time to it. Somebody ought to tell a girl that, she thought, as she went about her tasks.

"The truth of the matter is," she said to the stove as she built up the fire to cook a midafternoon dinner, "you've got to set love on the back of the stove and just let it simmer. You know it's there and you can pull the pot forward when you get hungry. Like shoes. If you've got shoes you don't need to be wearing them all the time, showing off that you've got them."

She wanted to write to Pete and tell him all these things she

111

had been thinking. But what with washing out the handkerchief the painter had loaned her, cleaning and cooking, it was sundown before she got round to writing. She lit the hanging lantern, turned the wick back so it would not smoke the chimney and sat down with pencil in hand and paper before her. Then her thoughts which had seemed so clear and sure, became blurred and would not fit into any words, and other thoughts kept coming, such as how blue it looked outside, now the lamp was lit, and why did frogs sound louder after dark than before.

She was still at the table with the letter unwritten when there came a great shout from the shore and a light that ran across the face of the window, "Ahoy, ahoy there, the *Ellen B.!*"

Tammy sprang up and ran to the deck. It couldn't be, but it was. Grandpa! He leaped aboard and caught her in his arms, the boat rocking under his weight. For a little she could only cling to him, speechless, then she dragged him in to the light and set him down in his chair and stepped back to study him and make sure he was real.

"Big as life and getting fat. Oh, Grandpa, how in the world did you know to find me here?"

Grandpa wiped his eyes, his ruddy, gray-bearded face all smiles. "Tammy child, you are a caution. You sure give me a chase. Soon as ever I got your letter this noontime, the one you wrote before you left Brenton Hall telling me what you had in mind to do, I set right out to find you and make sure you'd got here safe. Rode down to the city with one of the jail guards that lives down this way and then I hitched a ride out to the college. Never thought to find you on the river."

Tammy sat down across the table from him, pushing aside her writing paper that lay there still blank and empty. "Oh, Grandpa, I do hope you don't think I was crazy in the head, bringing the *Ellen B.* down. It just happened like as if it was intended, when I went to get the money from under Celeste, one thing leading to another, Captain Joe coming along saying he could get me a tow—or a push, rather—and that's how come I didn't have time to tell you. But you, how in the world did you find out? Who told you?"

"Well, honey, when in doubt, always go to the top man. I made my way to the president's house. A mighty fine man he is, too, just as cordial and kind as anybody might be and powerfully interested in my work at the jail."

"But he don't know me. There's hundreds of students here. I never seen such a mess of people in all my born days."

"Oh, he managed. He telephoned round and finally got hold of one of the registrating people that looked you up in some papers they had. The minute I heard you'd set it down in writing that you lived on a boat by the name of the *Ellen B.* I knowed what you'd done and where to find you. So here I be. Now tell me what you're up to. Begin at the beginning, but be quick about it because I've got to be back in the city afore bedtime to catch my ride back."

"Can't you leastways stay the night?"

"You forget, child. Tomorrow's the Sabbath day and I'm bound to be there for the church services. Can't neglect my duties. Now get on with your story. I want to know what struck you."

While Tammy talked, she poked up the fire and set the coffee to boil. She didn't tell him about Mrs. Call and her failure there, only said the dean of women would help her get a job. She was a woman growed now, and bound to keep her worries to herself.

Grandpa grunted now and then at what she told him, saying "Onh-huh," from time to time and "Yes, child, I see," in that satisfying way he had.

When she had finished at last and he had drunk two cups of coffee, he said, "Tammy, I'm right proud you had the independence and the git-up-and-git to take things in your own

113

hands. There comes a time when it is the only thing to do."

"And you won't be worrying about me, here in a strange place and not yet knowing whereabouts I'll be living?"

"The Lord will watch over you, child, don't ever forget that. And speaking of the Lord, hand me down the Bible, will you?" Then he read the Psalm that began, "He that dwelleth in the secret place of the most High shall abide under the shadow of the Almighty," and then he said a prayer for them both.

When they rose from their knees, Tammy put her arms around him. "I feel safe now, Grandpa. I feel strong and full of courage. I could tread upon a lion and a adder, a young lion and a dragon I could trample underfoot."

Grandpa gave her a great hug, then he went ashore, sure-footed and quick, finding his way back through the swamp.

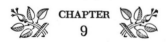

CHAPTER
9

THE OLD red rooster crowed for dawn, and dawn came to dapple the water with a pale opalescent light. With her nightgown tucked under one arm, Tammy dug some bait and set her line. Grandpa always said lie low and whisper for bass or trout, or better yet, hold your breath, but a catfish now, you had to talk to him. He was a funny, knowing critter, nigh on to being human in some ways, being half cat and half fish and three quarters pure cussedness that needed cajoling.

So now Tammy leaned over the rail saying, "Come on, you catfish down under there, here's a pretty to put in your old cat mouth and a hook to hang you on. Come on, you cat, you're going to be et by a lady living in a fine house, you're going to be rolled in meal and fried in fat and that's a most honorable end. So come along now and take the hook whilst I wash my face and brush my hair and get my clothes on." They must have been the right words, for by the time she was ready, there was a fish on the line just wiggling to be hauled in and cleaned.

This was going to be a breakfast fit for the highest in the land, Tammy thought as she made her way through the swamp, taking the roundabout route she had sought out the day before. It did not seem lonely, for the birds were awake and calling, a hoptoad hopped just in time to escape being stepped on and a cottontail went bounding across her way. "Good morning, Mr. Rabbit," Tammy said. It was a saying out of old times—never fail to give a rabbit good day when he crossed before you. That was the only way to wipe out the bad luck he left.

Grandpa said there was no such thing as luck, only chance. Not a word in the Bible about luck, he said, and chance was mentioned only twice. "Time and chance happeneth to them all," and again it was said that "by chance there came down a certain priest that way," the one that passed by on the other side. That meant the Lord didn't like the notion too much, but was willing to admit there was such a thing, leaving it as a kind of loophole a body might crawl out by when he got in a tight place.

It was his sermon on chance that got Grandpa into trouble with those that believed everything was settled from the beginning of the world, one thing leading to another without escape. He was all for the free human spirit, free to take advantage of chance and it was such surprises and unbargained-for happenings that made the world entertaining and gay for living. It was the kind of sermon that set a body to thinking about this and that. She had never thought about it much, but it might be that hearing Grandpa preach his sermons up and down the riverbank was kind of educational in a way, so maybe she did not come altogether empty-headed to college, in spite of what Pete had said.

The notion pleased Tammy, so when she came out of the swamp she went skipping along the campus path, swinging the catfish at her side. There was not a soul in sight, not even the professor under the tree reading his morning poetry. Only the buildings stood dignified and silent, no doubt full of learning from having heard so much of it spoken for all the years of their being. If a college were old enough it might be so full of learning that there would be no need of professors, and a seeker after knowledge could just breathe it in with the morning air.

With such fancies she amused herself as she left the campus by the east gate and she walked more sedately when she came out on the street. She could see ahead the gray-shuttered house of Mrs. Call, standing closed and silent and forbidding. At sight of it her spirits sagged. She was not wanted there, the house itself seemed to be echoing the words of its mistress and her niece. Maybe the next place she was sent to would be less like a jail that held one poor old sad fat lady and nothing more.

Tammy hesitated a moment before the door. It would likely wake the whole street if she knocked with that iron knocker. Better go in by the tree. Then maybe she could get the fire going before Mrs. Call knew a thing about it. Give her a surprise, for by the look of her, it had been many a long year since anybody had bothered to surprise her. She kicked off her shoes, wrapped around her wrist the string from which the fish dangled and shinnied up the trunk of the hackberry tree, moving out along the branch to drop down into the courtyard. She was coming in like a thief, for a fact. Now to find the kitchen. Maybe that room at the end of the ell porch. The door was closed but the knob turned easily and she went in. Yes, it was the kitchen, and a mighty fine one with a big white refrigerator, bigger than Miss Renie's. But where was the stove?

There seemed to be neither stove nor wood box. A funny state of affairs. Tammy searched the room. There was a coffeepot sitting on top of another white boxlike table that was stone cold to the touch. But wait, she had seen something of the sort in the catalogue. Across the front were buttons to turn. Did she dare? Gingerly, standing far back lest it blow up, she reached out, turned one button and snatched her hand away quickly. There was not a sound beyond the click of the button, no fire at all. But after a minute a flat coil of wires began to glow red hot. Pure magic, Tammy thought. Now to

117

find things. A skillet for the fish, bacon from the refrigerator, cornmeal to roll the fish in. It was an exploring party for sure, but luckily she was good at search-and-find.

There was no sign of a pump such as Miss Renie had in her kitchen. How could she make coffee without water? There was only a sink with pipes. She turned a knob and out poured clear fine water. Lordymussy, what a lot of things there were on land for the ease and comfort of people! So much time saved by not having to go to the spring for water. And so much missed too, Tammy thought, remembering the path she had so often taken. Up the bluff, down into the hollow with deep ferns to brush the morning dew from, then the log across the bayou and at last the clear pure water flowing from the foot of the sweet gum tree. Once she had surprised a deer drinking there.

Coffee was boiling and she was turning the fish in the skillet when someone spoke from the doorway. "You really did come. I didn't believe you would."

Tammy whirled round to see Mrs. Call standing in the doorway. She was wearing a long blue silky wrapper, her gray hair was in two night braids hanging down over her shoulders and she seemed wider than ever, all loose and unconfined. With her fat pale face and her little blinking black eyes almost hidden by the flesh of her cheeks she looked for all the world like on oversize baby that had just crawled out of its crib. "Yes, ma'm," Tammy said, "I'm real and I'm true. So here I be according to promise."

Mrs. Call sniffed the air. "That smell's what woke me." She waddled across the room and bent over the skillet. "Fresh caught?"

"I set the line whilst it was no more than first light this morning and I spoke beguiling words to make my catch sure. I've mixed a corn pone, too. See?"

Mrs. Call stared at Tammy instead of at the corn pone. "College students don't cook."

118

"I ain't a regular one. I'm what they call special. I'm a listener. Now if you'll tell me where the plates be . . ."

A few minutes later they were sitting across from each other at the kitchen table. The old lady ate in silence save for an occasional smacking of the lips. It was plain to see she was savoring every mouthful not only for its present flavor but for one recollected, for her eyes had a remembering look. When she had finished and Tammy had poured her a second cup of coffee, she leaned back, patted her lips with a white linen napkin and sighed, "Best food I've had in forty years."

"Can't your cook cook?"

"Oh, Della's all right, as cooks go. Luckily she never comes till ten o'clock on Sundays. It is my only free morning."

Now that was a puzzling thing to say, Tammy thought. "You ain't free in your own house? That don't make sense to me."

"Age. That's what. They think I'm in my dotage or something."

"Who is they?"

"Just one, but a regiment for getting her own way. However, I do not propose to buy her a house. My niece, all I have left, now my son is gone. Thinks she has to manage me."

"Your son?"

"Dead. Dead like all the rest."

Tammy sat silent thinking how strange and dismaying it would be to be left so, alone, not being loved or loving anybody in this world. "It's kind of like being in jail," she said after a little. "Only not a nice sociable jail like what Grandpa was in when he first got took up by the revenuers. He had his preaching and hymn-singing and the Lord's work to do."

At that Mrs. Call leaned her elbows on the table, chin in hand and began to put questions, so before Tammy knew what was what, she was telling everything about herself and Grandpa and Grandma, Pete and the *Ellen B.* "So that's the story of my life," she finished.

119

As Mrs. Call listened, her face lost its sad, drooping look, her mouth left off its discontent and her eyes grew brighter and brighter. Tammy, seeing how she could liven up when she got interested and forgot herself, felt more than ever sorry for her. She said, "I reckon it ain't so much of a muchness, after all, having all this fine kitchen and such a big house. When I was living on the *Ellen B.* with Grandpa, I was all the time wanting to be setting somewheres on dry land in a house. Oh, not a elegant house like this, just one that stayed put, with a chimney to it and a fire on the hearth and maybe scaly-bark nuts to crack and maybe somebody setting there picking out the goodies and holding out his hand saying 'Here, take this.'" Tammy gave herself a little shake and came back to the present. "But the more I get out and see folks living in suchlike places as this the better the old *Ellen B.* looks to me. It's so free and easy and lively. Spill something, you don't have to wipe it up. Runs into the river. I wisht I didn't have to leave it. It's just a notion folks have. Like the notion your folks have that you hadn't ought to be here all alone."

"They're the ones who are *non compos.* Not me," Mrs. Call said grimly.

"What's that, *non . . .*"

For answer Mrs. Call tapped her forehead with one finger.

"Well," said Tammy, "looks like you and me are in the same boat." She laughed at the words. "Same boat. Too bad we aren't, and for a fact I'd be proud to have you come and stay with me on the *Ellen B.* If you don't want me here."

The old lady sat blinking in that funny little way she had, then she began to shake all over as if the palsy had caught her. It was scary, seeing her taken like that because she was so jelly-loose in all her parts. Then motion turned into sound-laughter that had been so long deep hidden and hidebound that it broke out like a waterspout.

Tammy didn't know what to do or say, she didn't know whether to laugh along with her or to be mad at her for scoffing at her offer. So she just sat waiting to see what would come of it.

At last Mrs. Call leaned back and wiped her eyes. "It would serve them right if I did it. How many rooms have you?"

"There's two, one being the kitchen with a cot bed where Grandpa always slept, and then there's my room in back. It's real nice and it has a iron bed ordered off for out of the catalogue. That's where Grandma slept, me on a pallet beside her."

"An iron bed out of the catalogue," Mrs. Call repeated and began to laugh again.

Tammy rose with dignity and began to stack the plates. She felt right put out, having her own home so laughed to scorn. "Just because some folks have more than others doesn't mean they got a right to laugh——" she began.

Mrs. Call sobered at once. "You needn't begrudge me a little laughter. I haven't had much of it in recent years. Besides, I have to laugh to keep from crying. You've set me to remembering my own shanty-boat days, the happiest of my life."

"Your shanty boat?"

"Pour us some more coffee and I'll tell you. It wasn't mine, really," she went on when Tammy was again seated across the table from her. "It was my uncle's. There were five rooms and space for the servants in the stern, and the carriage and two horses besides. We stopped at landings all the way down from St. Louis. The horses would be hitched up and we would drive here and there along country roads or to see the sights if there was a town. Then back to the boat at night. Catfish every morning for breakfast. I was ten and my uncle and aunt and two cousins came. We floated all the way down to New Orleans. My uncle had orange groves down that way. Then we drove home overland. Took us all summer. But the shanty-boat part was the best of all." She sighed, looked again to Tammy and seemed to come back to the present. "And now here you come along with your shanty boat."

"Yessum. Only they won't let me stay there. Why, I could

holler if robbers come, or thieves in the night. But I suppose there's no use. And if you don't want me here and won't come there, I reckon we'll have to part company." She rose and began carrying the dishes to the sink.

"Wait!" Mrs. Call smacked her hand down on the table so hard the salt and pepper jumped up in the air, and Tammy almost let fall her handful of plates. "I'll do it, I'll do it!"

Tammy stared at her, not quite believing her ears. "You mean you'll come to the *Ellen B.?*"

"That's exactly what I mean. Why, I haven't done anything that was fun in the last twenty years."

"I'd be pleasured to have you, ma'm. Only—" she hesitated as the first doubt crept in—"only do you reckon you would be comfortable as you've got used to being in such a house as this?"

"Comfortable! Who cares about comfort? At my age there's no such thing either here or there and what difference does comfort make anyway? Here, leave those dishes for Della. Or no—" a crafty look came over her face so she was all of a sudden like a naughty child planning a new bit of deviltry—"no, I think you had better wash up everything but my coffee cup. No need of Della's getting mixed up in this. Nothing but a spy for them. And be quick about it, we have a lot to do." She opened the table drawer and took out pencil and pad and began to write. When Tammy had finished the dishes and put all in order as she had found it, Mrs. Call said, "Now come here. I want to tell you what to do."

Tammy sat down, folded her hands in her lap and waited. It was a wonder how the old lady had come to life. It had done her good already, just thinking about the *Ellen B.*

"What's your name, by the way. I forget." And when Tammy told her, she repeated, "Tyree? Tyree, did you say? There is an island called Tyree."

"Well, I declare, I never knowed that! Whereabouts? In the river?"

"Off the coast of Scotland, a flat windy place."

"Have you been there?"

"Yes, yes, but don't distract me now. I have other things to think about."

Tammy nodded. My, but it was going to be real educational, having somebody like Mrs. Call around, somebody traveled and knowledgesome.

"Now, Tammy," she said briskly, "there's nothing more you can do for me now. Better go on back to the river, and you needn't say a word to anybody about our little plan. Nobody's business."

"Y-yes, ma'm. But don't you want me to help you get some things together? And I'll have to show you the way. Only——"

"Only what?"

"I never thought of this. It's a mighty long walk back through the swamp, kind of hard going, too, part of it. You reckon you can——"

"Now don't worry about that. I don't propose to walk."

"But there ain't any road you could get a car through, or a horse and wagon either."

"Leave that to me. I'll be there some time late this afternoon."

"Yes, ma'm, but——"

"Don't go butting me any buts. What's the matter, getting cold feet?"

"No ma'm, my feet ain't cold. I'm used to going barefoot. It's just that I might not be there."

"No matter. I don't suppose there are many *Ellen B.*'s tied up out there. But where will you be?"

"The president invited me to some kind of a do at his house, a kind of play-party, I reckon. He's going to have tea for students, at four o'clock. I'd kind of like to go. I ain't never yet been in the house of a president."

"Ah, yes. The welcoming tea. How many times I have sat at that long table and poured thousands of cups——" Abruptly her manner changed and again a crafty look came over her face. "Listen. If you see me anywhere, not a word."

"You mean don't speak if I should meet you here or yonder?"

123

"Exactly. I don't want anybody interfering in my business. Now run along. I have enough to do without you standing round pestering me with questions." She bent over her writing pad and as Tammy moved quietly toward the door, she heard her murmuring, "Della—fare to Chicago. Note to milkman, pack, food, president's tea, taxi . . ."

Tammy did not know what to make of it. She felt a little worried about Mrs. Call. No taxi could get through the swamp. It didn't seem right to go off and leave her in such a muddle, so at the door she paused. "There's a lot I can't seem to figger out. It seems sensible, your coming to the *Ellen B.*, but the *how* of it is another matter. Still, I suppose I'd better leave something to the Lord."

"The Lord and me, child, two good managers. Now get along. Surely you have something better to do than stand there making me fidgety with your chatter."

"Oh yes, ma'm, I've got to hurry back and wash out bed sheets so they'll be dry before you want to go to bed tonight."

"Wait." She started to rise, then sat back down again. "You get them. In the hall closet. Two pair and anything more you need. I'll have enough to carry without——"

"Two pair of what?"

"Sheets, sheets for the iron bed that came out of the catalogue," and she bent over her writing, her plump shoulders shaking with laughter.

Tammy left her then, and feeling a bit like a thief, went along the ell gallery, into the back hall where she found the closet and more bedclothes than any one human had a right to. She took some pillowcases as well as sheets, an extra one for a tote bag and she put in a soft yellow blanket she spied on another shelf. Not that she didn't have a good blanket on the *Ellen B.*, but anybody used to such fine things as these might be too proud for one that had been so often washed. Grandma's best patchwork quilt, log cabin pattern, would be the only touch of real elegance she could offer. She slung the stuffed pillow

124

case over her shoulder and went down the front hall and out by the big front door.

It was a wonder, she thought, crossing the campus, a pure wonder, how things worked out. She wished she had known about Mrs. Call's coming last night when Grandpa was there. It would have eased his mind to know she was not going to have to live off the river, and like as not he would have been able to explain all those puzzling things Mrs. Call said about getting there. Could be she was coming in a airplane. When people had money, they could do anything. It was a power. Power but no glory.

Not until she was half way across the campus did Tammy remember she had left her shoes under the hackberry tree in Mrs. Call's garden. No time to go back for them now. She would just have to start early enough to go by and pick them up before the party. But it had been mighty careless of her, coming off and leaving her onliest pair. Of course they weren't rightly speaking party shoes. Would everybody else be wearing such?

The campus had come to life while she was at Mrs. Call's. Groups of students were moving toward a churchly building in the distance and they all had a dressed-up churchly look. Tammy wished she could be going too. She had never been to a real church in all her born days. But it might give her a kind of flavor of church if she walked along behind some of those going. Also she could see what the girls were wearing.

Mostly they wore cotton dresses as fine as silk, or silk that was made to look like cotton, or jackets and skirts of black or brown, and their hats—you couldn't rightly call them hats, if hats were meant to keep off the sun. For these were just little bits of ribbon and flowers. Some of the girls had their hair tied up high with a string or a ribbon so it looked for all the world like a horse's tail, or a feather duster, if it was curly. As for shoes, there were high heels, low heels and some that weren't shoes at all, being soles with straps coming round and

125

round to hold them on. Tammy was sure she could make some like that for herself, for she had some inner soles she had sent for once, hoping they would keep her feet warm in winter and they had been too big to go inside her shoes. Perforated for ventilation, the catalogue had said. Well, she could run string through some of the holes along the edges, tie them on and be in the height of style.

All these ideas had brought her to the edge of the swamp, but the sound of bells stopped her. There were many bells of different tones sending forth shafts of sound to make the tune of a hymn, one of Grandpa's favorites. "Come all ye faithful," was the way it began. She stood enchanted, listening. What a wonder it was, the sound mounting like Jacob's stairway up to heaven.

"Hey there, river nymph!"

Tammy whirled around and there, coming out of the bushes at the entrance to the swamp, was the bug-man painter, his netting trap slung over his shoulder. Tammy put one finger to her lips. "Sh-sh! Listen to the bells!"

He came toward her slowly, stopped at a little distance and waited till the last sweet echo of the bells had died away. "Church bells. Seems to me I remember a poem about a mermaid and the village church bells."

The sweet sounds were still ringing in Tammy's ears. "It's enough to put a spell on you, a holy spell. But now I've got to run or I'll never get my work done." With that she set out at a brisk trot toward the old road, jumping logs, dodging between trees and leaving him standing there saying, "Well, I'll be damned!"

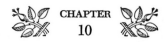
BY THE TIME the sun was slanting across the river
Tammy had made up the bed with Mrs. Call's fine sheets and,
for a decoration, had plucked some thorn branches with berries that would soon be red. She had done her ironing and
sewed up a kind of purse cut from scraps of the dyed sheet
Miss Renie had used for her best dress. It was just a bag with
strings but it matched, as did the strips of cloth she had used
to make tie-on shoes out of the old inner soles. She had never
been so matched up before in all her life and she thought that
what Miss Renie called the *toot on sombel* must be pretty fine,
even though she could not see herself whole in the little
cracked looking glass that hung above her box dressing table.
Her hair was tied up high and swished with satisfying elegance and style.

She took a last quick look around the *Ellen B.* and hoped
Mrs. Call would be pleased with everything, but how could
she help it when all was so neat and clean and decorated?
Then, just as she was leaving it occurred to her that here
she was going to the president's house and not taking a
thing with her. She had had her mind entirely on herself—
vanity, vanity, Grandpa would say—and she should have been
thinking up something to take along for a present. It wasn't

manners to go to anybody's house empty-handed. She went back into the kitchen and looked around. She might have caught a fish if she had thought of it in time. But there high on the shelf was a jar of last year's muscadine jelly, red and clear and pretty as ever. She wrapped it in paper and set it down in her little new bag alongside the painter's handkerchief. Likely he would be at the party, or she might meet him on the way. Oh, it was a wonder, how many people she had come to know in the short time she had been here.

There was no trouble knowing which was the president's house. A great line of people stretched from the gate all the way up the front steps and across the wide gallery. Tammy took her place at the end of the line, her heart beating fast with excitement. She wished she had Pete here to walk beside her. In her mind she told it over to him as it happened. "I come in the gate with the others, all party clad, roses blooming each side the walk and more people coming all the time. A elegant house with glass windows washed clean and shiny, two stories high and another gallery on top of the bottom one. That's how I come to the president's house."

A group of girls were right behind her palavering amongst themselves. Tammy looked around and said, "Howdy."

"Hey," one of them said and stared and turned away.

Tammy, inching slowly ahead in a line that was like the tail end of a lazy snake wondered if it was not good manners to speak. She wished she knew what was a blunder and what wasn't, and with that a great loneliness came over her. She thought it was a curious thing to be lonely in the midst of such a multitude. She never felt so when she was off by herself on the *Ellen B.* She gave her hair a little swish. At least she was in style.

But when she had come inside the door and could see the great crowd of people, she wondered what the style really was. Some of the girls wore dresses as straight and baggy as those she had seen the day before. She felt sorry for them, thinking

128

surely they must have nothing better or they would not come to a president's party in such as that. When two boys just ahead of her nudged each other and began to laugh, looking at them, she felt quite indignant. One of the boys turned and gave her a friendly grin. "Some bag," he said with a little whistle.

"You hadn't ought to make fun of her when it's likely all she's got."

"If she's got anything, it sure doesn't show."

The other said, "Anybody that wears a thing like that is just begging for laughs. What a style!"

"Chemise, that's what they call it."

"But that's underclothes," Tammy cried. "Nothing to be talking about out in the open, like at a party."

"She's wearing it out in the open, isn't she?"

"I don't like it," Tammy said.

"Who does?"

Before Tammy could say more, they both turned to speak to a lady standing just inside the front door. She was so stiff and straight and elegant in a low-cut black satiny dress that for a moment Tammy did not recognize her as Miss Jenks. She was saying, "Your name, please?" Then she turned and repeated it to the tall man standing beside her. The two boys shook hands and moved on down what Tammy now saw to be a whole row of folks waiting to have their hands shaken. It was like playing a game, only the game stopped before it more than got started.

"Please, you are holding up the line. Your name? Oh—you!" A troubled look came over her face.

"Yessum, it's me, Tammy Tyree. And I want to tell you it's all right. I've got a . . . a nice old lady coming to live with me. So you needn't bother——"

Miss Jenks nodded and smiled. "That's good," then she added, "See me in my office soon," and turned to the man beside her and said, "Miss Tammy Tyree."

This was likely the president, Tammy thought, for he had an air of majesty about him and a dignified stomach under his vest. The noise of talking filled the big room so it hummed and buzzed as if it might be a tree full of bees on a summer morning. Tammy wanted to tell him that Grandpa had found her all right, and she tried to get the jar of jelly out of her bag, but before she could do either one, he had shaken her hand and passed it on as if it were something on a platter, to the lady next him, saying, "My wife, Miss Tamtry."

"I hope you like jelly——" Tammy began.

"Very well, thank you," said the president's wife, looking round over her shoulder and nodding to someone else.

Tammy had the jar out of her bag now. "It might be a little sticky on the outside——"

The next in line was a short fat man who took her hand and passed it along saying, "Yes, but very pleasant in here."

"It's muscadine——"

"The dining room? Straight through the archway," said the lady next in her path, smiling and nodding and handing her to the man beyond.

Tammy began to feel quite desperate. It was like being in some foreign land where no one could understand. She wished she had not brought any jelly to the president. "Where shall I leave it?"

"I think you leave by the side door," said the last of the line, giving her hand a hearty shake and turning quickly to those who followed her.

It was truly bewildering, Tammy thought. No one said a sensible word such as one would expect to hear in a president's house. Everybody full of learning and not letting a morsel of it escape. And there was neither singing nor dancing such as there should be at a real play-party. Holding the jelly awkwardly in one hand, Tammy allowed herself to be moved along with the crowd through open double doors to the next room.

130

When she found herself next to a long sideboard lit by flaming candles, she set the jelly down there. The president would find it and be surprised maybe, after all had gone. Then she turned to look the room over.

What a sight it was! There was a long table down the middle of the room and a lady at each end, one pouring tea and the other coffee. There were bowls full of pink roses on the table and pink candles gaily lighted. You would think the president might have electric lights in his house, Tammy thought, but it looked as if he had spent all his money on food. There were great platters of sandwiches cut so small they were no more than one bite each. That did look stingy. There were little pink and white frosted cakes, very fancy and not a one of them much bigger than a thimble. Young men in white coats kept edging their way through the crowd carrying out used cups and saucers and bringing in clean ones. People were eating and talking, though no one seemed to be paying much mind to what the other said.

"How do you like the party?" A deep voice at her shoulder managed to make itself heard.

Tammy turned. "Oh. Mr. Freeman. It . . . it's a funny kind of party. Not what I thought."

"What did you think it would be like?"

"I thought there would be words of wisdom spoken, or else that it would be more of a . . . a frolic with folks more blithe-some and gay. With games, maybe."

"That would be a great improvement. If I ever got to be president, which heaven forbid, I shall change all this." Then he added more soberly, "It's just something one must attend and live through if possible. Finding you here, however, cheers me unspeakably."

"Does it?" Tammy brightened at the thought. Then she said, "Isn't anybody having a better time than they look like they're having? Which is powerful little."

He smiled down at her in his kindly twinkling way, looking more than ever like a big friendly bear. "Nobody is having a good time but me, now that you——"

He was interrupted by a crash and a small scream and a lady's voice crying "Oh my dress, it's ruined!"

Other small cries of dismay came from the group at the far end of the sideboard. Tammy wheeled around. It was her jar of jelly, smashed to bits on the polished floor. Someone demanded, "How in the world did such a thing get here?" Another cried, "Who is responsible——" and another one who had not been spattered said, "What a jolly mess!"

Tammy shrank back, she tried to get the words out—"It was me——" but could go no further.

"You? Why, you weren't anywhere near," Mr. Freeman said.

"But it was me that brought it. I thought it was fitting to bring something when invited to a party. Only I didn't know where to put it. Oh, it's true, I don't so much as know a bee from a bull's foot and I might better give up right now." She stood with bowed head, blinking back the tears, scarcely seeing the white-coated men who came with cloths and dustpans to clean up the glass and spattered jelly.

"Nonsense." Mr. Freeman patted her arm. "Come now. I think it was a delightful idea, bringing a jar of jelly. You can't help it if some awkward oaf knocked it over. You're not responsible for that. What kind of jelly was it?"

"M-muscadine."

"Have you got any more? I know it is delicious."

Tammy looked up at him gratefully. "Yessir. There's another jar or two on the shelf."

"Could you spare some for me? Muscadine is my favorite."

"Oh yes, sir, of course. Would you truly like some?"

"Of course I would, especially if you would let me come and get it. I'd like to see the *Ellen B.*"

"It would pleasure me no end."

"Meanwhile, let's have a little food." He stopped one of the waiters carrying a big platter. "Hey there, not so fast," and he told Tammy to help herself. "Nothing like food to cheer and comfort."

Tammy took a small hot roll and made two bites of it for politeness' sake. "It ain't apples, but it comforts me for sure."

"Oh yes, I remember. Comfort me with apples and stay me with flagons. Well, there are no flagons, but may I bring you tea? Or coffee?"

"You hadn't ought to be waiting on me, but coffee would be good. If you can get to the place where it is."

"I used to be tackle on the football team before this hit me." He gave his lame leg a slap and then, holding his cane before him to make a path through the crowd, he humped his way along, for all the world like a caterpillar with a feeler out to find his way.

As she stood waiting Tammy heard whispers behind her and there was something about a whisper that made it more audible than any amount of shouting above the hubbub of the crowd. "I know it's your turn, Lisa, but Mrs. Call, of all people, has turned up. We had no idea—it's been years—but she always expects to pour. Would you mind?"

"Of course not. Glad to escape the mob."

Mrs. Call? Tammy thought she must have misunderstood the name. Or it was some other Mrs. Call? Her Mrs. Call was busy packing and making ready to come to the *Ellen B.* Then Tammy saw her coming from the next room, everyone making way for her in a little wave of movement so she came on like a tugboat at full steam ahead. She was dressed with elegance, in black with beads on beads around her neck and dangling earrings from her ears and a little feathery black hat on top of her waved gray hair. Her figger was laced in and well stayed so now it just looked dignified and imposing. But what did it mean, that she was here instead of on her way to the river?

Miss Jenks herself came to settle her behind the tall teapot, others fluttered around her, as if she might be the Queen of

Sheba, Tammy thought, and all at once she understood. Mrs. Call never had had the slightest notion of coming to live on a shanty boat. She had just been having fun, making fun of river folk, having herself a little joke and that was why she had laughed so. False, false, that's what she was.

"Here you are, ma'm." It was Mr. Freeman, back with her coffee. "But——what's hit you, my dear Tammy? Why are you so troubled?"

Tammy took the cup from him and thanked him. "It's people," she said. "There is just no counting on them. Looks like I've come out in the world just to see there's no putting your trust in the best of them."

"Come now," he teased, "don't damn us all without a trial."

But for once Tammy could not respond to his humor. "There just ain't any steadfastness. Might as well face the fact and be done with it."

"I wouldn't give up so soon." Then after a keen look at her, he said, "Are you steadfast?"

The question brought her up sharp. If she had been truly steadfast, wouldn't she have stayed at Brenton Hall? Wouldn't she have done what Pete expected and just waited for him? "I don't know," she said. "It's all so mixed up."

"All you need do, my dear, is be steadfast and true to yourself, and not let others change you." He stopped another waiter with a platter. "Here, try these."

Tammy looked at the platter of small biscuits with bits of ham meat sticking out around the edges. "I've small stomach for food right now, but they do look powerful good." She took one and turned again to Mr. Freeman. "I don't know what for you are being so kind to me, there are so many fine important people around."

"Because I like you, because you interest me. There are plenty of reasons, all valid, sensible and true."

Tammy considered that as she nibbled on her biscuit. "It's mighty pleasant, having a professor take notice of me."

"Do you have to think of me as a professor? I'm only an instructor, and after all, I am human."

Tammy studied him earnestly. "I can see you be human. And you've had trouble. That makes you kind. Grandpa would say you come forth as gold from the furnace of affliction."

"I'd like to meet your grandpa some time."

"Next time he gets out from the jailhouse, maybe you'll come to see us on the *Ellen B.*"

"But you are not going to be living there, are you? What about Mrs. Call? Did you go to see her? Didn't Miss Jenks——"

"I got sent to see her."

"Well?"

"She didn't want me in her house, her nor her niece, neither."

"But wait. If she could only get to know you——"

"I know her now. There couldn't never be anything arranged between Mrs. Call and me. So you can set that down and nail it up on the wall."

He studied her with a puzzled expression. "Well, if you say so. But what happened?"

"If you don't mind," Tammy said with dignity, "I'd rather not say."

"Surely you must have misunderstood. I know she is old and rather odd, but——"

"I reckon nobody relishes being made a laughingstock, and that's what she's done. Miss Sandra too."

"That doesn't sound a bit like Mrs. Call. Why——"

Tammy shook her head, her eyes resting balefully on the imposing figure at the far end of the table. "Must be you are one of them that see neither guile nor deceit in any man. But me, I've been out in the world a mighty short time, but I see plain and clear that there be some that speak with false tongues. And she, she is one of them." She looked up at him now and was sorry she had spoken so freely and with bitterness. She felt rebuked for it, though he said never a word and only looked down at her with concern. "Never mind. I'll find some place

135

to stay. I ain't agoing to let it beat me. And now, I reckon I better be going lest I get dark-foundered going through the swamp." She set down her coffee cup on the sideboard, adding, "I'm much obliged for your kindness." Then before he could say a word, she slipped through the crowd, passing by Mrs. Call without so much as a scornful glance and going out by the side door.

She went out by the east gate, passed a long line of cars and taxis and hurried on to Mrs. Call's house. She wanted to get there and pick up her shoes before the party was over. She never wanted to meet Mrs. Call again. But when she got there, there were no shoes at the foot of the hackberry tree. She searched all around and they simply were not there. Well, she was a thief as well as a liar, that Mrs. Call. And with that, Tammy slammed the gate behind her and set out for the swamp.

Once aboard the *Ellen B.*, a measure of peace returned to her. At least she had come into some mighty fine sheets and pillowcases, not to mention the blanket. But was it honest to keep them? Just because Mrs. Call was a thief was no reason, no excuse for her to be one, Grandpa would say. So when she had ripped them off her bed, she folded them neatly and laid them on the high shelf in the closet till she could return them. Then all the strength and the indignation went out of her. She dropped down in the kitchen chair, bent over to rest her forehead on the table. Tomorrow she would have to go to Miss Jenks and say how she had been laughed at and fooled, and she would have to try again somewhere else to get a room-and-board job. No hope now of staying on the dear old *Ellen B.* She sat motionless while the sun went down and the shadow of the trees on the western shore crept slowly across the river to envelop shanty boat and swamp.

 CHAPTER
11

THE *chug-chug* of an engine roused Tammy from her gloomy thoughts. She rose and lighted the lantern that hung down from the ceiling, so no one unseeing, would run down the *Ellen B.* in the dark. Then she went on deck. A bright searchlight was playing across the water, flashing over the swamp trees, turning their green leaves a yellow green that did not look real. The light settled on the *Ellen B.,* blinding in its brightness. Tammy stood by the rail shading her eyes with one hand and trying to see who it could be. Grandpa would have shouted at sight of her. Was it robbers coming? A strange voice shouted, "Ahoy, the *Ellen B!*"

The light moved from the deck to the water now and Tammy could make out the shape of a motorboat with two people in it—a man and a large, bundled-up figure in the midst of many bundles. The boat swung alongside. Tammy leaned over, staring down unbelievingly. "Mrs. Call! Is it really you? I thought . . . I thought——"

"Never mind what you thought. Give me a hand."

It was a hard job, heaving her aboard, the boatman pushing from the rear and Tammy pulling for all she was worth, and in the midst of it, Mrs. Call laughing so she had no strength to help them with. The *Ellen B.* rocked with her weight. "Now hand over those packages and boxes," she ordered. Some were wrapped in brown paper and tied with string, some were bags filled with vegetables and oranges, apples and grapes, and there were cartons of canned goods.

When they were all aboard, Tammy said, "It's enough to feed a regiment."

"Couldn't get much at that little store on a Sunday night, but there will be more later. I don't mean to starve." Mrs. Call turned to the boatman. "Now you know what you have to do? You won't forget?"

"No, ma'm. I'll be by Wednesday, pick up your order and bring things back to you on my way home from the city."

"That's right. And not a word to anyone."

"Yessum. I mean no'm, not a word."

"Then get along now and much obliged."

The motor roared, the *Ellen B.* rocked as waves hit the side. Mrs. Call stood clinging to the rail, her feet wide apart, head thrown back and on her wide fat face, a look of triumph. "Oh, to think I feel the river under me once more. And the frogs. Listen. What a lovely sound!" Then she turned to Tammy, saying "Now let me see what the *Ellen B.* is like."

It was not until she had inspected every corner of the boat with evident delight that she was willing to sit down at the kitchen table with a cup of coffee and answer Tammy's questions as to how she had managed to get here. "I thought for sure you had just been fooling me," Tammy confessed. "When I saw you at the president's all dressed up, it just didn't seem possible you'd come here. And I don't see yet——"

Mrs. Call's laughter interrupted her. "Haven't had so much fun in a coon's age. Why, child, after you left me, I packed a few things, made a few arrangements, took my nap as usual, got dressed for the tea and called a taxi. Perfectly simple. I kept it waiting while I went in and poured tea, just long enough to throw them off my scent. I told everybody I was thinking of a boat trip for my health. Then the taxi took me to the city and the ferry boat. I crossed over, found a small shop near the dock where I got a few supplies, then got hold of this man with a motorboat, and that's all there was to it. You can do anything you make up your mind to, never forget that. And by the way, I picked up your shoes from under the hackberry tree. They're in one of those bags out there." She leaned back in her chair and yawned. "No sleeping pill tonight."

"There are pills to put people to sleep?" Tammy asked.

"And to wake you up."

"Hell's bells, that's a funny thing," and with that she went to bring in the packages and bundles that had arrived with Mrs. Call. "I hope there's some everyday clothes amongst your things," she said, as she came in with an armful, for Mrs. Call was a strange-looking figure there under the hanging lamp in all her silk and beads and her little feathery hat.

"Of course I did. Not in my dotage yet."

It was a busy evening, Mrs. Call sitting there giving directions, the kitchen shelves filling up with canned goodies and fruit brimming over the biggest platter. "Must have cost a lot of money," Tammy said as she brought in the last load. "Looks like I ought to be paying for some of it, if I'm going to be eating it."

"Nonsense. I then would have to pay for my room and there'd be no end to the whole business."

"Well, I've got money, some left over of what I brought with me, and the lady at the employment place, Miss Jenks, she said I could make more working at what she called baby sitting. Though why babies have to be taught to sit is more than I can figger out. All I ever seen just naturally started sitting when the time come for it."

Mrs. Call laughed. "You'll see." She stood up and yawned again and said she thought she would go to bed.

Tammy lighted a candle and went ahead of her into the little bedroom next the kitchen. She made up the bed again and hoped it would hold up under Mrs. Call's weight. She felt proud of the room, it was so neat and pretty with the dyed meal-sack curtains that turned a rosy yellow in the candlelight, and Grandma's log cabin quilt laid elegantly across the foot of the bed.

Mrs. Call took off her hat and handed it to Tammy. "Put that somewhere. I'll need it if I ever get back into civilization—— I mean . . ."

Tammy faced her with hat in hand. "You're thinking it ain't civilized here?"

"It's just a manner of speaking, child. Never mind me."

"We-ell," Tammy said doubtfully, "but if fixings and trimmings is civilization, this ain't it."

"Now let's get this straight once and for all," Mrs. Call said. "I'm sick of what you call trimmings and fixings. I'm here for two reasons. One, out of memories of happy days on the river. Two, because I want to get down to fundamentals, to what is really important and lasting. It is those things that make civilization, no matter where you find it." She zipped the zipper down the front of her dress, stepped out of it and handed it to Tammy. "Now hang this somewhere out of the way."

"I'll put it in Grandma's closet."

Mrs. Call laughed again and as Tammy watched with wonder, she stripped the shiny rings from her fingers, looked round the little room, then hung them one by one on the thorn branches Tammy had put in a jelly glass for a decoration. "Didn't you ever read 'The Purloined Letter'?"

"No'm, I ain't read much."

"Well, the moral is, if you want to hide something put it in plain view." And for a fact the glass stones might have been dewdrops shining.

At the door Tammy turned. "Thank you, ma'm, for saying what you did about civilization. I'm proud to have you aboard the *Ellen B.* Though when I saw how important they seemed to think you was, this afternoon at the party, I never dreamed you would really come. Can't believe it yet. I reckon you

140

could go anywhere in the world you took the notion to go to, with plenty of cash money to pay for it. I'm mighty pleased you chose to come here."

"Ah, there are lots of things money can do and don't think for a moment that I minimize its power. But this—" she gave a glance around the room—"this is just pure lagniappe and lagniappe is what no money in the world will buy."

As she washed the coffee things and got ready for bed, Tammy thought how good it seemed to have somebody sleeping in the next room. Mrs. Call might be just a dumpy little old lady, but she had plenty of spirit. Like Miss Renie. Miss Renie? Lawsymussy, she hadn't so much as sent her a line to say the journey had been safely made. So Tammy sat down at the table, her long cotton nightgown tucked up around her knees and wrote:

Dear Miss Renie, I brought the Ellen B. down. She is tied up near the college and I am going to begin learning tomorrow. An old lady, very fat and nice, though a little peculiar in some ways, is come to stay with me so they will think it proper and fitting for me to live on the river.

Have you had a letter come to me from Pete? If so, please send it to me at the college where I have a box. It has a number 270 on it.

I am well and hope you are the same. I wore the dress you made for me to the president's party, a tea, they called it only there was much more than tea to eat, all in small bites.

I miss you and Osia.

Respectfully, Tammy Tyree.

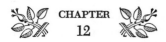 CHAPTER
12

THE DAYS CAME and went and still there was no word
from Pete. To Tammy the distance between seemed greater
than ever. Pete was set away from her not only by space but
by event, by the absorbing and exciting activities which filled
her days. She had quickly learned where her classes met, and
the hours of their meeting were known to her. She had been
to the college store and bought what books were needed, nearly
exhausting her small supply of money. The path through the
swamp was made plain and clear by her feet. Rains had come
and the river was rising, slowly spreading through the low
parts. But her roundabout way was still passable save for a few
spots where she had to watch her step. Then when she got
back to the *Ellen B.* there was Mrs. Call to talk with, and that
was a great pleasure and comfort to her. For she went to and
fro, and to her classes and home again and no word was spoken
save an occasional "Hey, there," from one who sat near her.
No one behaved unkindly, only with great indifference. It was
a most unsociable college, Tammy thought, and she might have
forgotten how to talk out loud but for Mrs. Call.

Sometimes in her mind she talked to Pete, telling over to
him what she did—real muddy in the swamp this morning but
I found me a sink hole to wash off my feet before I come out

on the green-cut grass. Got me a gunny sack hung on a syca-more branch that stands on high ground so I can clean up afore folks set eyes on me. . . . Such a lot of books in the world. I went into a store that was nothing but books and I paid a sight of money to buy what I'm bound to read if I am going to know what that professor is talking about. Modern lit is the name of that course. He is a little man with a beard cut sharp to a point and so neat in his clothes he might be cut out of the catalogue suit department, and he talks crisp and slow all at the same time. Everyone writes down what he says, but I couldn't ever keep up so I listen and stow away in my mind all I can hold. That is what I do every day in all my classes. I sit and listen and nobody says a word to me nor me to them. Bells ring every hour from a tall tower. They have a sound merry to hear and on Sundays they are sweet as honey-drip and solemn with holiness. . . .

It was easy enough, talking to him so in her mind. But to write, that was a different matter, she was dumb before the obstacle of paper and pen and she found no acceptable words. Day after day and no letter came. Never since his leaving had he gone so long without writing to her, even though it might be only a small poor word with no richness of love wrapped in it. Each day she went by the post office and turned the knob and opened the small door of the box that had been given her, and found it empty and blank.

But this morning she could see through the heavy glass that there was something there, a letter and a folded paper as well. Her fingers trembled with eagerness—twice to the left, once around the other way—then she had the door flung back and the papers in her hand. Her name was writ in a large sprawling manner, the lines curly-cueing as if to make a picture of each one of them. Miss Renie! Her disappointment was so sharp she crushed it in her hand, gave but a glance at the folded paper—baby sitting tonight and an address given—then she went across the green to sit on the bench under the live oak tree. At last she tore the envelope open. Out dropped another letter addressed to her at Brenton Hall, and this was in Pete's own known hand. "I give up too soon," Tammy whispered. It was no real letter such as she had hoped for with news and love-words. It was just one big question mark in what it had to say:

> I have a note from Aunt Renie and I can't make head nor tails of it. What is going on? She writes of unimportant things then adds a postscript saying that you are gone. You are gone??? What does she mean? What is she talking about? I know she is old and flighty but this simply makes no sense at all. Let me hear from you at once.

Two pages and saying no more than that. Tammy sat with the letter in her hand, not knowing what to think.

Maybe she should have written him. But she had not wanted to write till she was all settled—— With that she brought herself up short and sharp. That wasn't the real reason and she had better face the fact of the matter and be honest about it. The truth was, she hadn't written because she was afraid he would be mad with her. But what was it the Bible said? Perfect love casteth out fear. Then wasn't her love perfect? She buried her face in her hands and sat there lonely and troubled till she became aware that some of those passing by were looking at her curiously. Then she rose and stuffed the letter in her pocket and went running across the green and along her path to the river.

Mrs. Call was ashore, chopping wood. It was a wonder what a change had come over her in this short space of time. She had even come to look quite different, for she had lost a powerful lot of poundage, and she moved with ease instead of with a halting wobble. She had taken on a number of duties. She fished, she cooked—and what a good cook she was—and she swept and cleaned and fed the chickens. Tammy waved to her as she went aboard, then she sat down at the kitchen table to write a letter to Pete. This time she had so much to say that the words came. The knowledge that he wanted to know, that he was worried about her, seemed to release the springs of her language.

It was late afternoon and Mrs. Call had come out from her daily long nap before Tammy finished her letter. "Never mind about supper," she told Mrs. Call who was poking up the fire in the stove. "I have to mail my letter and go right on to baby sit. Only I don't know the whereabouts of this place." She took the note from her pocket and smoothed it out on the table before her. "Miss Jenks at the employment place just put this in my box."

Mrs. Call studied the slip of paper for a moment. "Why, that's just two blocks from my house, in the new development. I sold off my woodland and they chopped down my lovely trees and put up those horrid little houses all just alike except for different color trim. You can find it easily." Then as Tammy started down the gangplank, she called to her. "Wait, take this banana to eat on the way, and here's the key to my house. You will be so near you can just stop in and look in my closet, the downstairs bedroom, and get me another pair of shoes. Black, stout, thick boots. I'm always getting my feet wet in these thin-soled things."

With the key in her pocket, Tammy set out on a run. Now she had written to Pete she felt free and lighthearted as she had not felt in a long time. And when she had put a quick kiss where his fingers might touch in opening the letter, and when she had slid it through the slot at the post office, it was as if a great weight had been lifted from her heart.

It was too early to go to her first job as a baby sitter, so she went to the bench that ran around the live oak and sat there, swinging her legs and enjoying the banana Mrs. Call had given her. She was getting plumb spoiled with all the goodies Mrs. Call had the boatman bring, but it was mighty pleasant, she had to admit. And when she saw Mr. Freeman coming toward her with his swinging, halting step, she waved the banana skin

146

at him gaily and called, "Howdy! I was just wishing somebody would come along and tell me what to do with this. Don't seem right to leave it lay when everything roundabout is so apple-pie neat and every blade of grass in place."

He stopped before her, held out the tip of his cane toward her. "Hang it on here." And when she had done so, he tossed it lightly up out of sight in the crotch of the tree. "I used to be good at basketball," he said and sat down beside her. "You are looking mighty cheerful this evening. Not a bit as you were at the president's tea."

"Oh, yes." Tammy leaned back and looked up into the green canopy of branch and leaf. "That was a dark time. I thought there was no dependence on any human. Trouble was, I got disheartened too soon." Her lips parted to tell him of Mrs. Call's coming, then she remembered that she had promised to make no mention of that, she had given her word to tell no one. It was silly, but old folks were notional and had to be humored and Mrs. Call was so kind and generous, it would be mean to contrary her. "Yes," she repeated, "I'm kind of settled in my mind now." For she had been to Miss Jenks and had gotten things straightened out. Seems Miss Sandra had somehow got the notion she'd been living in sin with Pete. She was one inclined to get things all mixed up, Miss Jenks said.

Mr. Freeman studied her a moment in silence as if waiting for something more, then he said, "You have not yet made an appointment to come and have your speech recorded. I was looking forward to that. I'd like a tape of your song about Annie Christmas."

"You mean on that machine that sets down words and voice and keeps them forever even if a body up and died and couldn't ever speak any more?"

"Exactly."

"Well, I would be proud to be so recorded and set down. Maybe that's how the recording angel manages to get everything where he can put his finger on it. I always wondered how he could do it. But I haven't come because . . . well, I didn't know you meant me when you told the class they must do that."

"But you are in the class, aren't you? Of course I——"

"Oh, but I'm just a listener, so I didn't think——"

"But you must take part in everything. No matter if you are just a special student."

"You mean I could speak up and ask questions of you and of those other two I go to? I been dying to say something and every now and then I come nigh to busting loose in spite of myself."

"But your comments would be of great interest and value. Of course, in my class these first weeks I have been doing most of the talking myself, outlining my objectives and all that. But after this the class, and you, will have plenty of opportunity to talk and I only hope you will. Tell me, how do you like your modern literature?"

"In that class everybody just listens. Couldn't get in a word edgewise if you tried. It's all listening and reading. And these new books ain't the least like those old ones I was telling you about that I read at Brenton Hall. Lawsymussy, the things people write about, or maybe it's just the *way* they write it."

"What do you mean?"

"Well, there's one—hell's bells, it's about the lowest-down folks you ever heard tell of, and their carryings-on are really something to make you stop and wonder what humans is coming to. Of course there ain't anything really new about any of it. You can find plenty of sin and deviltry in the Bible, like lying and fornication and killing and all manner of whorings of strange women and harlots. The people in this book carry on like that all the time and some of them even with their own kin, like Lot's daughters when they got their pa drunk in the cave. But it seems different in the Bible. It ain't sticking its tongue out and snickering like some bad little boys don't know any better. There's a kind of dignity to it." At a sound from

148

the man beside her, she looked round and cried, "Oh, you . . . you . . . I know, I talk too free. Pete's ma was always telling me I talked too free, and now you are laughing at me."

He sobered at once, he took her hand in both of his. "My dear Tammy, if I laugh it is with delight. I love the way you talk and I love you for it. Please don't ever change. You are quite right, dignity is one of the things that seems to be missing from much of our modern literature." He released her hand and added, "Please tell me some more."

"Well," said Tammy mollified, "it's just common sense, what I've been saying. Of course a book is a kind of private thing, you read it and there is just the book and you. But a play! One of these things I been reading is a play, meant to be play-acted in a theayter right out in front of folks. Some things need a kind of privacy about them, in the saying as well as in the doing." She looked at him earnestly to see if he understood.

He nodded. "Privacy and dignity. Much modern writing lacks both."

Tammy clasped her hands together and swung her feet to and fro. "It sure pleasures me to have somebody like you think I'm sensible and not just funny-peculiar. It makes me feel I could go on talking forever. Holding converse one with the other, that's what the Bible calls it, and it's mighty sweet seeming." After a moment she went on, "There's another thing that's different in the Bible from all this I been reading. There you have to kind of pretend it out for yourself, figger out what is not set down in words. It leaves you free to think up things according to your own fancy. For instance, take David and Bathsheba. It just says she came in unto him and he lay with her. Now that reads simple and beautiful, even if it was a sin and displeasing unto the Lord. But these here books I been reading, they come out flatfooted and put so much down in words and so often that in the end you think a man and a woman laying together don't amount to a row of pins. It's

149

enough to turn your stomach and take away your appetite. Now you are laughing again," she added, giving him a reproachful glance.

"I was wishing I had a tape recording of this."

"I shall not say another word," Tammy said with dignity.

"Oh, come now. Tell me, did you find a place to stay? I went to see Mrs. Call to tell her she should jump at the chance to have you and she was not at home."

"Oh, but I'm staying on the *Ellen B.*"

"Miss Jenks will allow that? She will let you stay there alone?"

"Y-yes, that is—" she rose because she did not want to give away Mrs. Call's secret, and she might if she kept on talking to this most encouraging listener she had ever had—"that is, it's all right because I am not alone. I have . . . a old lady staying with me. And now I've got to run because I am going baby sitting and it is nigh on to time for me to be there." She was about to leave in this hasty fashion when something in his look held her. He seemed, as he too got to his feet, so large and yet at the same time helpless, needful of something he had not and lonely in the world. So she stood there, not moving, though she heard the sound of the bells from the tower beginning to mark the hour.

"May I come to see your boat sometime? And you did promise me a glass of your muscadine jelly, remember? I could come and get it. Maybe next week? On Saturday, and—"

"Of course, do come." Then she bit her lip. What of Mrs. Call? "Come after dinner, after middle of the day dinner, I mean. That's when I am free." For she had remembered just in time that Mrs. Call always had her nap then. Oh what a mix-up it was when anybody tried to keep a secret! She did not like it one bit.

He was quick to see her momentary hesitation because he said, "I have never been on a river boat and it would greatly interest me to see one. But if you would rather I didn't come——" He waited, his gray eyes under their heavy dark brows, holding her as she stood poised for flight.

"Oh, it isn't that," Tammy cried. "I'd be proud to have you. Truly."

"Then it is settled. So, till then."

Tammy made her escape. She was late for her first job and felt ashamed to have dallied so. Yet it had been pleasant, she thought as she broke into a run down the street, good to have someone to talk to that was not as old as Grandpa or Mrs. Call, someone who liked her in spite of her being not like everybody else, or maybe because of that. At any rate it made her happy to think she had a friend.

It was too late to stop by Mrs. Call's for the shoes, so she hurried down the next block to find the street and number written on her slip of paper. As she paused, searching among the houses all alike for the one with the proper number, a door opened, a blue door in a blue-shuttered house, and a young woman called, "Are you looking for 218? This is it. Do come along. You are late." A man came out on the porch with her and he nodded to Tammy while his wife beckoned her inside.

"The living room's there on the right. TV is on. There's a sandwich in the refrigerator if you get hungry. We'll be back around eleven."

"But the baby?"

"Oh, he's sound asleep and won't wake. But if he does he's in the room across the hall. Just change him and put him back. He's been fed."

"Where will I find a hippen for him?"

"A what?" She turned in the doorway and gave Tammy a startled look.

"To put on him when he wets the one he is wearing."

"Oh. Plenty on the table near his crib."

"But . . . who all is in there?" Tammy motioned toward the living room and the sound of voices.

"Just TV. I told you I left it on. But turn it off if you want to study." And with that she was gone, slamming the front door behind her.

Tammy moved cautiously toward the living room from which came sounds of yelling and banging as if murder were going on. She peered into the large, book-lined room, only vaguely aware of the fine chairs and tables, the flowered sofa and the tall lamp beside it. For there on the front side of a big box with legs was a moving picture, like the big movie Pete had taken her to once, just as perfect and real with true pictures of people stirring about. Only small. To have such a thing playing just for her and nobody else seemed almost too great a luxury and the thought came to her mind that it was she who ought to be paying for the evening instead of expecting money for coming and watching.

She sat on the edge of a chair just inside the door and stared, entranced. Not that the story was so interesting—it was just a lot of men on horseback chasing each other and shooting without ever hitting anybody and then having a fisticuff fight and knocking each other down. No, it wasn't the story, it was the wonder of it, that such a contraption as this could exist in the world and she, Tammy Tyree, be here to see and hear. After the fight was over and everyone seemed happy, there was a kind of play-acting piece and there was music with a woman singing like as if she had a terrible pain in her stomach, or maybe lice in her clothes that kept her wiggling while others were dancing and jumping around like crazy.

But what was really good, she soon discovered, was what came in between-times when the story or the singing stopped and someone just stood there talking. That was real educational. For now were made clear to her certain words and phrases she had overheard spoken by passing groups of students, or that she had picked up as she stood on the outer fringes of a small cluster of boys and girls waiting for the bell to ring and the class to begin.

Here was a kind of secret language she had been longing to know and understand. A man came out with a bottle in his hand. He held it up for all to see, a kind of medicine, and he said it would cure tired blood. Too bad that boy she had sat next to in her adviser's office didn't know about this cure for what ailed him. Then some people sang a song called "Live Modern," and she had heard that said so many times it was good to know it meant having a nice-looking man light your cigarette for you.

There was a great deal of excitement over soap and soapsuds. You wouldn't think soap could be so talked about and made so interesting, Tammy thought in wonder. One kind could be beaten up into what was called controlled suds, another kind was uncontrolled—or that might have been an automobile, for one ran into the other so it was hard to tell. The automobile that was best, one man said, had suspended animation, another had contortions and another was full of tension and nearly everything had what they called an additive with letters of the alphabet in it, especially toothpaste. Doctors came out in white coats and praised this and that but there was always one who disagreed. That made it more interesting, somehow, that only three out of four praised something. Her modern lit professor had said just yesterday that every novel or play had to have disagreeing and conflicts and now she could see how true that was.

The pictures of people's insides were mighty confusing. She had always thought human innards took after chickens' and other animals', but now it seemed they rather resembled those pipes that brought the water into Mrs. Call's kitchen sink, and when a man with a pain in his head and making an awful face about it swallowed some kind of pill, there was a great to-do in the pipes with such a lot of soap bubbles blowing up you would think it enough to give him a pain in the stomach as well as in the head. But no, a minute later he would come out and smile and say he felt fine. A sickly man, because after a lot of music and dancing, there he was again with the same old pain in his head. Tammy thought he probably was not long for this world, and she felt sad at the thought because before the evening was over she had come to feel right well acquainted with him.

Another thing much spoken of, was a filter—different kinds of filters. One perhaps was intended to keep out flies, for it was named something like flyconite, and sometimes these people, smoking as they talked, said one should have fifty thousand of them and that they worked fast, fast, fast. Others praised another kind that was slow, some were strong, some were weak, but all were wonderful. With all this, Tammy dozed a little, for she had been up and on the go since before five this morning. But all at once she was bolt upright, leaning closer in order not to miss a word. This was something important.

For here, speaking directly to her, was a lovely-looking young woman telling how to be as glamorous as she was. It was just a matter of how you washed your hair so it would be clean, clean, singing clean—though Tammy had never heard of hair that could sing unless it was the hair of horses tail strung on an old board fiddle—like the one in Grandpa's old song-story. This beautiful woman who would have been mighty pretty even if somebody had snatched her baldheaded, proved her point by showing a poor sad, dauncy-looking girl with stringy straight hair sitting all alone. Just like me, Tammy thought, and her heart went out to her. She was sitting there wishing she too could be lovely and glamorous instead of having drab dirty hair like a mouse's—though hell's bells, Tammy said to herself, most mice had a kind of sleek shiny look to them. But maybe these were city mice she was talking about. In any case, before you could blink an eye, here was this same girl back again to be admired and made much of. All in a flash she had washed her hair and it was shiny and frounced up curly and grown about two inches longer and here were all manner of handsome men to eye her and look eager as a bunch of dogs waiting for a bone. It was a miracle, for sure.

Tammy felt of her own hair, pulled a lock around to be studied and wondered over. Oh, if she could just buy some of this wash that came in a bottle and dripped out slow and shiny when the lady tipped the bottle—and what a dreadful waste that was—then Pete would be amazed for sure, he would never want to leave her again.

She leaned back in her chair and thought of Pete's coming, and how he might be bedazzled by her looks. Then she dozed a little more till the made-up story was finished. She roused up to hear about a kind of cream that came in a jar and moistured the skin so it didn't look sickly, and she learned there was something to take the stink off people without their bothering to wash themselves. The trouble was that there were so many such things. Even a man might become more beautiful, for there was a kind of grease that was not greasy that he could put on his hair and make it so slick and fine that girls came running up to rub their white-gloved hands over his head as if he might be a pet dog. It was all enough to make a body wonder how males and females ever got together in the first place before there were all these fine inventions to make them take notice of each other. In any case, Tammy resolved to take some of the money she was earning tonight and buy at least one of these magic things to beautify herself with.

As she sat thinking over all she had seen and heard, there came voices from the hall, and she sprang up. The young parents came in. "Did he wake?" the mother asked.

"Who?"

"The baby, of course," and she gave Tammy another such look as she had turned on her when she asked where the hippens were.

"Oh, him. No, ma'm, not a peep. I just set here doing nothing for him all the whole enduring time. And I'd be pleased to come again. It was real educational."

"Once a week is almost more than we can manage, but we do like to get out." She yawned and turned to her husband. "Pay her, Joe, and let's get to bed."

Tammy held the money in hand and stood looking down at it. "Seems like it's a mighty lot for the little I did."

155

"That's the current rate," the young father said and opened the door and gave her a sleepy goodnight.

Outside it was very dark between street lights and Tammy hurried along jingling the coins in her pocket to make a merry sound. Then it came to her that there might be robbers about and she had better not let them hear money rattling. She was turning toward the college when she remembered Mrs. Call's shoes. She didn't like the idea of poking around a house in the dark, but there was nobody to stop her and it might be she could find a button that would turn on a light. So feeling rather like a thief in the night, she went back down the street and in by the iron gate.

The key turned easily in the lock and after a little fumbling around on the wall just inside the door, she found the light button, and then had to stand blinking till her eyes grew accustomed to the brilliance. She opened the door on her right and went into Mrs. Call's bedroom, she found the closet, knelt down and groped around till she came upon a rack full of shoes. More shoes than any one human could possibly wear unless she was a centipede. She pulled out one heavy boot and then another, and tiptoed softly back to the hall. The silence was enough to give a body the creeps and it seemed as if all the people who had ever lived in the big empty house might be listening and waiting to pounce on her as she crossed the hall. In her hurry she dropped a boot and something clattered and spun across the floor, but she had no time to look, for the sound was echoing around her like an alarm. She clicked off the light and had her hand on the doorknob when there came a shrill scream from upstairs and words shouted in a high voice: "Who's there? Get out of here! Help! Help!" Then as Tammy fled she heard, "Operator, quick, police, police!"

Tammy ran down the steps and out the gate and down the street faster than she had ever run before. The police! Lordamussy, if they caught her, she'd go to jail for sure, and what would Pete say to that? It was bad enough, the way folks talked about Grandpa's being in jail when he went for a moral principle. What would they say about one taken for a thief? She did not slow her step till she came into the safe familiar darkness of the swamp. Then she caught her breath and thanked the Lord for her escape.

The swamp was not altogether dark. Shafts of light came from between the chinks of the little log cabin. Were people living there? Or was the place afire? Tammy stood still, wondering if she should go to investigate, though she had had about enough of poking into strange houses for one night. Then voices came to her, a man's angry, petulant and fussy, and a girl's voice answering brokenly.

Tammy moved on with silent step. There were things not meant to be heard or seen, and here was the sound of trouble. Let it remain secret and hidden. As the road curved and she passed behind the back of the cabin, she saw the brightly lighted open window, and framed in it as it might be a portrait hanging on a dark wall, the head, bare neck and shoulders of that tall slim girl she had so admired on the day she went to register. There was no pride in her now, her head was bowed, her hair hung loose across her cheeks. Tammy looked quickly away, but the picture stayed imprinted on her mind, a portrait of despair, all in black and white save for a purply-red scarf that had been hanging across the window ledge.

Well, it was none of her business, Tammy told herself and went her own way, feeling for each step after the road petered out and moving with caution till the lighter darkness of the river came into view and she saw the black bulk of the *Ellen B.* Then she was safe from pursuit by the law, safe from the turmoil of emotions that were filling and overflowing the little log cabin she had passed.

"That you, Tammy?" Mrs. Call shouted as she went aboard.

"It's me," Tammy said and no more. Let her have a good night's sleep and there would be time enough tomorrow to let her know that somebody was staying in her house. Lordy-mussy, what a night it had been!

157

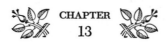

CHAPTER

13

NEXT MORNING at breakfast, sitting across the table from Mrs. Call, Tammy told how she had been taken for a burglar in the night and had had to run all the way to the swamp to escape the police.

"Did she see you?"

"Who? Her that yelled so? No, ma'm, I don't think so. I had turned the light button out before she made a sound, before I knowed or she knowed anybody was there."

Mrs. Call pushed aside her plate as if she had of a sudden lost all appetite for food. She sat twisting her hands together, making little distressful sounds and shaking her head all the while. "She's after me. Has a nose like a bloodhound. Oh, I knew she would come, that's why I covered my tracks and left that note on the hall table so she would find it."

"Is it your niece? Miss Sandra?"

"Of course, child. There's no one else, but she is a regiment in herself. Probably has detectives checking every steamship company and airline in the country." Mrs. Call's face brightened with a look of deviltry as she went on, "I threw her off the scent all right. Told her I was taking a boat for other parts, said I was going for my health and no telling when I would be back. Oh, I was clever, not telling a thing that was not perfectly true. I even said I had a young companion to look after me." She chuckled over her own cleverness.

"Meaning me?" Tammy asked.

"Of course, you. My mistake was in sending you for those boots. Not worth it. But I did not think she would be coming up for another week or so." The worried look came back to her face.

"But what can she do? And hearing a burglar in the night would not put her in mind of you. It would likely make her want to clear out and go back to New Orleans, for she was sure scared out of her wits."

Mrs. Call nodded. "That's true. But we must be careful. I've bribed the boatman so there's not much of a chance of a leak there. Maybe it will be all right." She began on her breakfast again and asked for more coffee.

Tammy filled both cups, then, thinking to turn Mrs. Call's thoughts from the subject, began to tell of all she had seen on TV the night before. Mrs. Call made no comment till she had fairly run out of words, describing the wonders of that new world which had been revealed to her. Then she said, "I wouldn't waste money on such things as they describe."

"But it wouldn't be wasted," Tammy cried. "Not if it would make me look so . . . so shining and sweet smelling and everything so that nobody would notice my clothes or how I talk. Not if it would make me like everybody else out in the world that's known all along about the wonderful things you can buy like soap and hair wash and medicine that keeps your blood from getting tired and . . ." she floundered under Mrs. Call's penetrating gaze.

The old lady leaned forward, resting elbow on table and chin in hand, regarding Tammy with an expression of mingled severity and indulgence. "Listen to me, child. You have a lovely, clear skin, your eyes have no need of drops to brighten them nor your lashes a liquid to darken them. You do not need

160

to be deodorized because you scrub with soap and water, and as for your blood's running any way but brightly through your veins, that is pure nonsense."

Tammy listened to all this and more, in silence. She did not mean to think disrespectful thoughts of the aged and perhaps the wise, but really, how could anybody as old as Mrs. Call know about such things? They were something new in the history of the world. Or were they? And she remembered the woman in the attire of a harlot who perfumed her bed with myrrh, aloes and cinnamon. But the TV had said nothing about beds.

No, this was something new and different. Grandma had not known about it, Grandpa would not be interested because he always said beauty came from the inside and worked out. He would have no patience with all these aids and lotions. But if one had to live in the modern world as it really was, then she was obliged to take advantage of what one of those people last night had called the great advances of modern science. And she had to keep up with Pete.

"However," Mrs. Call concluded, "if you must satisfy yourself and try some of those silly beauty aids, as they are called, don't go spending your money on them. Just look in my dressing case and you will doubtless find enough to keep you amused and busy for what time you care to give to carry coals to Newcastle."

Tammy could not speak for a moment, she just sat with her mouth open staring at Mrs. Call. "You mean . . . you mean that you use——"

"Of course. It is hard to buy anything else nowadays and the simplest things are advertised in those wildly extravagant terms."

"But then, I should think you would be——" She bit her lip— she had almost said beautiful and glamorous.

Mrs. Call laughed. She might be old but she was quick to

guess at meanings. "No matter what they claim, there is nothing that can make the old be young again. Now go and see what you can find and satisfy yourself once for all."

"That's mighty kind of you, ma'm, but I wouldn't want to be using up your supply. I'm going to have lots of money. Baby sitting is so profitable I shall never want for money again."

"People are always wanting money," Mrs. Call said grimly.

A few minutes later on her way to feed the chickens, Mrs. Call paused to set a little row of bottles and jars on the kitchen window ledge. "These will dry up before I use them all," she said.

So Tammy decided to prove or disprove what she had heard. She built up a big fire in the stove and heated water, one bucket for washing and one for rinsing, then she carried them to the deck and got to work on her hair. Mrs. Call, fishing pole in hand, perched on the rail and dropped in her line. Tammy rubbed and scrubbed, now and then looking through her lathery dripping hair to wonder at the change that had come over Mrs. Call.

Something stronger than beauty aids had been at work on her, and at the same time she had become more and more careless of her appearance. Tammy thought that the more she herself strove to be up-to-date, the less so Mrs. Call became. For as she lost weight, she had abandoned skirts for some of Grandpa's old seersucker pants. She wore this morning a blouse of her own, with the shirttail out, and on her head one of Grandpa's old lop-brimmed felt hats he had cut slits in around the crown to let in the air, he said. What's more, she seemed to take great pleasure and pride in getting herself up like this. Not the least like the way a body would feel who had had nothing better to wear all her days. It must be that knowing you had silks and satins and beads and decorations gave you a feeling that you could wear anything and not feel brought low thereby. She had a lot of learning, Mrs. Call did. Maybe it was with learning as it was with clothes. If you had a plenty, you didn't need to show it off all the time. "I reckon if I knowed as much as you, Mrs. Call, I wouldn't need to be going to school."

Mrs. Call turned on her quite fiercely. "Nonsense! I don't know anything. That's why I am here."

"Here? Are you learning something here?"

Mrs. Call pushed the hat back from her forehead, then she took it off and Tammy, kneeling on the deck before the bucket of suds, sat back on her heels with a little shriek. "You . . . you've cut it off!" For Mrs. Call's head was shorn of her iron gray hair, she had clipped it unevenly and brushed it up so she looked for all the world like a frizzly chicken.

"Yes, yes," Mrs. Call said. "Too much bother the other way and at my age time is too precious to waste, fooling with it. That's one of the things I have learned since I came here."

The thought went through Tammy's mind that her own niece would scarcely know her now, and that maybe that was another reason for whacking off her hair. But she only said, "It's funny, me leaving the *Ellen B.* every day, going over yonder to listen to professor talk, and you coming here to learn. It don't make sense, and I don't see what you can learn here."

"I learn myself."

Tammy soused her head into the rinsing bucket, saying between dips, "You mean you been living with yourself all your life long and ain't got any knowledge of what you are?"

"Yes, I've just been going along without stopping to consider, a boat without a rudder, at the mercy of outside forces."

Tammy soused her head in and out again. "You weren't going any whichaway at all when I climbed the hackberry tree and dropped over into your yard. You was just setting there fuming and fussing in your mind and not doing a thing about it."

"True." Mrs. Call sighed and looked away, down the river. "I was stuck on a sand bar."

163

"And now you're going somewhere?" Tammy began to dry her hair on a meal sack and moved toward the stern to get the early morning sunlight on it.

"It's a little hard to explain. It is very hard to explain. I suppose these days and nights on the river, the contact with . . . with realities, these primitive living conditions, the sound of frogs at night and the whippoorwills, water lapping at the side of the boat—all these things take me back to that little girl I once was, coming down the river with my uncle so many years ago. I was real then, myself. Now I begin to connect, to revive that little girl, the self so deeply buried under layers of fat, under the alterations of the years. I made a kind of loop of my life, I hold it up and look at it."

"Well," said Tammy, "one thing is certain. You ain't near as fat as you was, or you never could get into Grandpa's pants."

Mrs. Call laughed. "Eating was my only pleasure till I came here. Now I take pleasure in activity, cooking, scrubbing. And most of all I take pleasure in being able to face my life with all its mistakes. This is a lovely little interlude, for which I am grateful to you, child. I'll manage to repay you somehow."

"Hell's bells," Tammy cried. "You don't need to pay me for anything. It's the other way round. Look at me, living like a lady of the land with you doing everything, not to mention all the fine vittles you buy every week when the boatman comes. And besides all that, it's real companionable, having you here to talk to. Why, it's me that owes you."

Mrs. Call just smiled, and then as there came a tug on her line, she gave her attention to hauling in a fair-sized catfish. "Don't throw out your suds. Just fetch me the kitchen knife and I'll clean this beauty before I scrub the deck." Then when Tammy came back with the knife, she said, holding the flopping fish at arm's length, "I'm too old to do much with my life, and at my age it doesn't much matter. But you are young. You must stop and think before it is too late. Consider where you are going and why, look on both sides and use your head about your life. That's the mistake young people make. They just go on and never stop to think."

Tammy ran her fingers through her hair and shook it in the early morning breeze. It did feel light and soft and fine. "I reckon I got no more than one main idea in my head and that's back of everything I aim at. Look out for those fins."

"I know about fins—" she took the fish firmly by the neck, yanked out the hook—"and I know about you. You don't say much, but I can put two and two together. All you think about is pleasing that Pete of yours. Is he worth it, I wonder?"

"He's worth all the world to me," Tammy said softly, her eyes on the bright running river.

"No man is worth that, except maybe your own child." She was silent for a moment, then kneeling down on the deck, she began to clean the fish. "You are too young to be so absorbed in any other single human being. Look around, look around, and leave yourself free to see others. You wear your love for Pete like a cloak to hide behind. That's why none of these young men you see every day make any effort to come closer, to get to know you. You are insulated from them and they sense this and leave you alone. That's not right. Oh, sometimes I could give you a good shake, you provoke me so!" Her words were fierce but her glance was kind and Tammy took no offense. She had grown used to Mrs. Call's manner of speaking.

"Didn't you never feel you had to keep on loving one man till the day you die?"

"What I have felt is neither here nor there. I've made my mistakes. That's why I want to see you come out of this mishy-mashy mooning over somebody that isn't even around to give you any comfort. He's just a dream. Talk with some of these young men on the campus. Get acquainted, give them—and yourself—a chance."

"Well," said Tammy, smiling, "seems like I get on better with professors than with the young ones. There's one of them wants to come to see me—on Saturday. What's more," she added with a little triumphant swish of her skirts and a flirting of her loose hair, "I told him he could come. Of course I think it is really the *Ellen B.* he wants to see."

"But I can't have anyone coming here! I . . . who is he?"

"I told him to come after dinner so you would be having your nap. Saturday is the day and he needn't see you at all."

"Well, I suppose I can lie low. What's his name?"

"Mr. Freeman, that's who."

"Tom Freeman," she repeated and was silent for a long moment, squatting there on the deck with the fish in her hands and his insides half in and half out. "There were years when I hated the sight of him."

"But he is good and kind," Tammy cried. "He is a man that has been refined in the fires of affliction and come out pure gold. That's what I think of him."

"Hum-m." Mrs. Call got to her feet, pulling up by the rail as if of a sudden the life had gone out of her. "I hated him, because he was alive and my son was dead." She stood looking out across the swift running water. "Because it was his project, I refused to build the theater he wanted for his department. But—" she sighed—"I suppose that really was not fair. Heaven knows, he did not escape scot free. Lame for life. But he is alive, alive," she repeated with bitterness. Then, turning to Tammy she said, "They were best friends, they were together in the plane when it crashed and my son——"

"Oh," Tammy breathed. "I'm sorry I told him he could come."

"No. No, child, let him. I can see now it was wrong of me to hold against him something he could not help. That is one of the many things I have begun to see clearly since I came here to the *Ellen B.* But I will not meet him and he must not know that I am here."

"Oh no. I give you my word, didn't I?"

"Yes, yes, of course, and I do trust you." With that she went on to the kitchen.

166

A little later, setting out for her ten o'clock class, her hair shining and brushed and tied back neatly, Tammy kept feeling of it, her fingers searching out its ways. Was it all that had been promised? As she crossed the green-cut lawn, she overtook the old professor emeritus and fell in beside him. It was pleasant to know someone to say good morning to, and to have him remember her.

"You are the young lady who has come to get understanding," he said with a smile and a bow, taking off his hat and tapping his head to make sure his cap of hair had not come off with it. "And may I inquire what progress you are making?"

"You may inquire and I will tell you if I can." She walked beside him in silence for a few moments, considering. Then she said, thinking of Mrs. Call, "I have come to understand that there is more to people than what you see on the outside at first knowing, and that it is possible to keep on learning even when you are old. Right now I am trying to understand the difference between the true and the false, and it might be that you could help me."

"I would be happy to do so."

"Then would you kindly look at my hair?"

He stopped, took out his spectacles, set them on his nose and turned to her with a mystified air. "I see your hair."

"Is that all?"

"It has been a long time since I was consulted about a lady's hair and having lost my own so that I am obliged to wear a wig to keep my head warm, I cannot say that I am a great authority on the subject." He looked down at her with quizzical, amused eyes. "Just what do you want to know about your hair?"

"Is it anything special this morning? Is it singing? Is it full of glamor and enticement?"

"As far as I can see, it is neat, tidy, clean, and a very pretty shade of brown."

"That's just what I was afraid of," Tammy said with a sigh

167

as they moved along together. "I listened to a lady on TV and I washed my hair this morning with the very glamour-glow cream she said would change all my life, giving me a kind of enchantment that would draw all men toward me like a light draws bugs. But I begin to think it was false words she spoke, a snare that was set for me and I was taken."

"I see," he nodded. "Very interesting. You have had to learn that everything you hear is not true, and that is a sad awakening that comes sooner or later to us all. The moral— discriminate, and be not carried away by false promises." They had come now to a branching of the path and he said, "Here is where I must leave you. But will you allow an old man to say that you are not lacking in enchantment just as you are?"

"I will allow it and thank you, sir. But I haven't enough. Not that I would be like the strange woman that lieth in wait at the corner and leadeth the young men astray. It's just one, one special young man I am thinking of."

He smiled down at her with a look that put her in mind of Grandpa when they talked together about ideas that came out of her head. "I think you need not feel too great concern," and with that he bowed and left her.

He was kind, Tammy thought as she went on her way, kind to say such things to her. But he was old, it could be his eyes were getting dim and his desire failing him. But since he was a professor, the chances were that he spoke the truth when he found her hair no more than neat and clean and tidy. It was a great disappointment.

This was the day of her public speaking class and her spirits rose as she went down the hall toward the classroom. For one thing, Mr. Freeman was her friend, and for another, it was one of the most interesting of her classes. Now that the first lectures were over, different members of the class were being asked to stand up and make speeches about things they had done, places they had been. Some of them spoke almost as good as Grandpa, making a little rounding-about of the story

they told and never lacking for words any more than he did.
One talked about diving in his skin and what he saw down
under the water. Another spoke about working all summer in
what he called a settlement, a place with lots of poor people
in it. These talks gave her a look into the lives of her classmates and made her feel acquainted even if they had never
spoken together. For she still came and went with no more
than a "Hey, there," or a "Good morning," spoken to her. She
went in now and took her seat as usual at the back of the
room, as was fitting for a listener.

This day one of the boys spoke about the game of baseball,
naming many names all unknown to Tammy, making her feel
that she was discouragingly ignorant. The tall, dark-eyed girl,
Rita by name—the one who had given her a pencil on registration day and whom she had seen in the cabin at midnight—
stood proudly when her turn came and began, "I shall speak
today of my trip abroad."

She told of crossing the ocean by means of an airplane, and
of her travels in far lands and the strange sights she had seen.
She told of the food she had eaten—snails in France and other
unlikely things that had been set before her in Italy. She stood
straight and proud and her words came forth smooth and without fumbling such as the best of the others had at times. She
named the names of cities and rivers and she made mention
of paintings and carven statues and such like things. It was a
wonder that she could remember and give to each its entitlement.

Yet all the while she stood before the class so full of ease and
assurance, Tammy was seeing her as she had appeared, framed
by the cabin window, her smooth hair tribbling over bare
shoulders, head bowed low, face care crazed and her speech
making but a poor whinnocking sound. But such double sight
was not given to the others who looked and listened with
naught but admiration in their eyes, and when she had finished,
they made a small murmuring of pleasure over her manner of

speaking and the words said, finding no fault as they had with some of the others.

If she could only speak like that, Tammy was thinking, when she heard her own name called. For a moment she could not collect her wits enough to know that now she too must rise and walk to the front of the room and speak out for all to hear. She moved slowly into position and when she was standing beside the desk with all eyes fastened upon her, she wished she might sink right through the floor, for no thought came to her. Then she remembered that long ago those show folk who had taught her to sing and dance, had said she was a good mimic. So all she need do now was to imitate Rita in manner and tone and wordage as near as she could, telling about her own journey down the river.

She straightened up and held her head high and put on an air of being proud as Lucifer. She began "I shall speak today about my trip down the river. It was a fine sunny day when my boat was hauled away from its mooring by the bluff——" She could not keep it up all the way, but now and then by the astounded look of all who listened, she knew she had succeeded in using some phrases of Rita's or in making some like gesture. So she told of the trees she had seen, of the egg-catfish dish she had eaten, she spoke of the towers and water tanks visible over the top of the levee on the Louisiana shore. She was not half through when the bell sounded and she had to stop.

Mr. Freeman had a puzzled look on his face as he said, "We will reserve comment on this speech until the next meeting," and his voice, usually so warm and enheartening, had a clipped, cool sound.

Going out, Tammy was suddenly conscious of odd glances, she could feel their mislike of her like a chill current eddying round about her, and here and there she caught a few words. "Mean trick," and "What was the idea, do you suppose?" She paused in the corridor where other classes were coming and going. She could see Rita ahead with a group of students talking and gesticulating, then she heard what the two just in front of her were saying, "But why, why? They don't even know each other," and the other answered, "Jealousy, I'll bet."

That didn't make sense. Yet as she moved slowly toward the door, it came over her that maybe they thought she was making fun of Rita, maybe they thought she was holding her up to scorn. Rita, who had been kind that first bewildering day. With that, Tammy set out on a run, dodging through the crowd, dashing down the steps and looking everywhere for Rita. At last—yes, there she was, just waving good-by to the group and saying "Oh forget it," as she turned off by the path that led toward the post office.

In a moment Tammy had overtaken her. "Rita, listen . . . please——" she was breathless, gasping the words out——"please, it wasn't thataway, I wasn't holding you up to scorn. I was just trying to be like you. I didn't mean it like folks took it, you too, I reckon. I just——"

Rita was studying her with a strange, steady gaze, not angry so much as puzzled, saying never a word.

"Can't you understand? Me, I growed up on a shanty boat on the river. I can't talk like . . . like proper folk out in the world. It's what I come here to get learned. And when I seen you that first day, you give me a pencil, remember? Well, even then I thought I never seen anyone so proud and beautiful. So today, I was just trying to talk like you."

"Well, I'll be damned," Rita said. "Funny——"

"I know I'm funny," Tammy cried hotly. "But it's because I don't want to be that I . . . I was trying to be like you. . . ." Her voice trailed away to silence, head turned away, hair falling across her cheek.

Rita said, "Oh come on, buck up. I believe you, and after all, imitation is said to be the sincerest flattery, isn't it? So I'm just flattered. What more do you want?" Her voice was sharp sounding but true.

Tammy faced her now. "You ain't mad, then?"

"Of course not. It doesn't matter. I've got other things to worry about."

They walked side by side down the path, silent now, Tammy trying to puzzle her out and Rita seemingly lost in her own thoughts. Dark ones, by the look of her. Tammy said at last, "I wisht there was something I could do—for you, I mean—to make up for it, sort of, even if you don't hold it against me."

Rita spoke as if she had not been listening. "So you grew up on a shanty boat on the river? I wish to God I had. Then it wouldn't matter." Her mouth had given up its tight pride as she spoke and now it was crooked with sadness.

Tammy in her mind's eye saw her again through the cabin window, framed in darkness and bowed low with grief and maybe shame. "You mean you wisht you had growed up knowing what's right and what's wrong and to count on the Lord to help you in time of trouble? Didn't your folks teach you that?"

Rita gave a little laugh that had no merriment in it. "I wouldn't say they knew anything about it. Besides," she went on, her tone changing and some manner of assurance returning, "besides, who wants to be a slave to some out-of-date superstitions never meant for the modern world? One has to decide for himself or lose all self-respect. There is no law fixed from above. It's all relative. What's right for some is wrong for others and vice versa. The trouble is—" she paused and it was as if she had recited some known and familiar formula but now came to its application—"the trouble is, you don't find out till you . . . get the effects. And then it is too late. Oh well—" she gave a little helpless shrug—"it's just one of those things."

Tammy could make little of all this, save that she was in need of comfort. "It sounds kind of mixed up to me." They had come now to the building with the post office in it and Tammy said, "I reckon I'll go in here." Then she added, "If there's anything I've got that you want, I'd be proud to give it to you, if I could."

"Come on then," Rita said fiercely, seizing Tammy by the wrist and as quickly releasing her. Then as they went down the walk together, she added in a light crisp tone, "It's just a phone call I have to make. Have to tell my family I'm pregnant."

Tammy rubbed her wrist, saying "Oh, I didn't know you was married!"

"What's marriage got to do with it? Come on." She turned in at a drugstore with glass walls. Many students were there, some standing, some sitting at small tables, eating and drinking. "Well, come on. You said you would do something for me if you could and all I want is somebody standing by. That's not too much to ask, is it?" Her tone was sharp now with a desperate note in it.

"No," Tammy said quietly, "that is not too much," and followed her in.

"Hey, Rita, have a soda," one of the boys called, and as they passed one of the tables, a girl said, "Come sit with us, Rita. What's the rush?"

Rita only smiled and shook her head and went on to the back of the store. There was a man in a white coat standing behind a counter with bottles of medicine. She handed him a greenback from her purse, saying "Keep the change, Mike. I want to make a phone call from your office. Too much noise in here. Long distance."

He nodded and they went on through a swinging door and down a short hallway and into a small room where there was a telephone on a desk. Tammy stood silent, not knowing what to do or say, or what might be expected of her. She listened while Rita named a city in New York and gave a number. Holding the phone to her ear she perched on a corner of the desk, swinging one leg back and forth. Then she said without so much as a glance in Tammy's direction, "Kay'll give me hell."

"Who is Kay?"

"My mother. That's why I need a little human company

173

while I——" She broke off to speak into the phone, "Wilkins? Miss Rita. Get my mother, will you? . . . Well, I don't care who she's talking to, just get her. . . ."

There was a long wait. Tammy stood motionless, trying to reconcile this girl's outward assurance with her inward uncertainty, her don't-care manner with her hidden anguish.

"Hi, Kay, this is your darling daughter. What? . . . Well, I'm not being very considerate of anybody right now. It's morning sickness. . . . Oh, Kay, don't be stupid, I *was* careful. . . . It's just one of those things. . . . Well, I thought you might like to know, so if you don't hear from me for a bit. . . . No, I spent it all on a week end in New Orleans, couple of thousand, maybe, and put some more to my account, will you? . . . Of course not. The last thing I want is you doing the mother act, it wouldn't become you. Besides, I've been on my own too long. . . . Yes, yes, of course I know all that. 'By."

She slapped the receiver down, missed the rack and then rattled it into place. She looked down at her own hand, held it out, staring at her trembling fingers as if they did not belong to her. Then she said, "Always get the jitters when I have to talk to my mother. Thanks for standing by." She crossed the room, her heels making defiant small clicks. She turned with her hand on the doorknob. "Coming?"

"I was just thinking," Tammy said slowly. "It is a grievous thing to be with child by whoredom. Likely his teeth will be set on edge."

"God, but you do call a spade a spade." Then with a short laugh, she added, "Well, don't worry, I won't let things get that far. You can do anything if you have the money to pay for it."

"Have you got money?" Tammy asked, following her down the hall.

"That's what I called up for, money. That's all I ever call up for." Then at the swinging door, she said without turning her head. "Thanks. And forget it, will you?"

In the big room she saw Rita join a group at one of the tables, her manner as gay and sure as ever. Tammy passed through and went on to the street. Rita, who had so much, had not known right from wrong. She had nothing to go by. That was why she was lost, and now so lonely and frightened she had to ask a stranger for help. "And I envied her!" Tammy said to herself, and went on down toward the post office.

She was coming down the steps from the post office, again empty-handed, when she bumped into one of the girls from the class in public speaking, one who often smiled and said "Hey, there" in friendly fashion. "Oh hello, I'm sorry—" Tammy swooped down and picked up the notebook the girl had let fall, for she had an armful of books.

For a moment she stared at Tammy as if she might be dirt. Then she took the notebook from her with a little shrug of the shoulder and went on without a word.

Then it came over Tammy all of a heap. It might be that Rita was not mad with her, but all the rest were. What a mess she had made of everything! How would she ever face that class again? And Mr. Freeman. He would be feeling the same way about her. He wouldn't ever in this world come to the *Ellen B.* now.

She felt bowed down with grief and shame, and once in the safety of the swamp, she let the tears come. One thing she was certain of, she was not going back to that class any more, and if she saw Mr. Freeman here or yonder, she would dodge and cut and run.

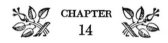

CHAPTER
14

THE NIGHTS were cool now and every day the deck of the *Ellen B.* was strewn with leaves that fell from the cotton-woods and willows round about. Mrs. Call, who had been knitting a sweater for Tammy, finished it just in time, for Grandma's coat was too heavy for these in-between days and Tammy's old jacket was out at the elbows.

These were busy days for Tammy. She had several baby-sitting jobs, one after another, and everywhere she went she was wanted back again. She was glad, not only for the needed money but for the chance it gave her to see how people lived and how their houses were arranged. She had little time for love-pining or moping over the lack of any word from Pete. She thought that surely by now he must have received her long letter telling him about the college and her coming. But there was no answer. She had time enough, however, to mull over the hurt and the humiliation of her speech-making effort and all week she held to her resolution not to go back to that class. She slipped in and out of her other classes, speaking to no one lest she blunder again.

Today there was no letter in her box at the post office, only another call to go baby sitting that afternoon. The note told her to stop by the employment office before going to the address given.

"Oh yes," Miss Jenks said when Tammy came in. She took off her glasses, leaned back in her chair that turned and squeaked as she moved. "It is not an easy job that I am giving you today and ît is only fair to tell you that several of the girls have refused to go back after one try."

"What makes it so hard?"

"There are three boys, aged five to ten or eleven or thereabouts. I suppose they will turn out all right in the end—their father is one of our most brilliant young instructors in psychology and the mother is a Ph.D. in child training. They should know what they are doing. But you must understand that the children are being brought up under the permissive system, with certain modifications of their parents' own devising."

"What does that mean?"

"You will soon see. I suppose there is more to it, but for all practical purposes, it is a sort of learn-by-experience method. They have been permitted all their lives to do exactly what they wanted to do, they have never heard the word no and indeed you are forbidden to use it."

"No wonder their pa and ma have to get away for a little spell now and then," Tammy said. "But what is the idea back of it? What makes them think that's the best way to bring up children?"

"Don't ask me. I have none of my own and know nothing about it." There was a little twitch of her thin cheek, then she went on briskly, "But as I understand it, the general idea is that children raised in this fashion are never troubled with complexes and in afterlife they are not sexually inhibited."

"If that means what I think it does, a little holding back might be something to be desired. That is, unless they are going to just run wild like so many beasts of the field."

"Well, after all, that is not your problem. It is just up to you to see that they do not involve themselves in any actually fatal activities. Aside from that, give them a free hand. No

178

doubt the parents will give you any further instructions they think necessary. Good luck."

"I'll do my best, and thank you for the warning."

Then, having received directions as to how to get there, she set out, puzzled by what she had heard and interested to see what the children would be like. She wanted to learn all the ways of the upbringing of children because likely she and Pete would have a whole passel of them and now was a good time to get all the modern methods.

The house was somewhat like the one in which she had first seen TV, being in a row with others all alike except for the colors. Only here the lawns and bushes and little trees had been longer planted. Tammy wondered how people could tell tother from which in the night time when the colors did not show and she thought it would be a shameful thing to have to know your own house by a number and nothing else, though it was pretty convenient for a stranger like herself to walk along the walk counting till she came to the right one.

As she mounted the steps, she heard a child's high voice raised in a continuous ear-splitting shriek. Something awful must have happened to him and Tammy was glad the parents were there to see to it. From another part of the house there came a great banging noise as if carpenters were driving nails. The front door was open and before she could knock, the parents appeared, coats and hats on, all ready to leave.

"Come right in," the lady said, paying no heed to the yells that continued to come from somewhere upstairs. "We will be back about eleven. The boys are: Harold—he is on the back steps right now; Julien, who is quite absorbed in a project in the dining room; and Neal, the youngest. He thought he would have a nap but I believe he has changed his mind. Just see that they don't harm themselves. But Miss Jenks has probably told you something of our system."

"We must go, dear," the professor said. "We are already late. Ah, there is Neal now. Good-by, Neal."

Tammy looked to the head of the stairs. The little boy standing there had so sweet a round fair face that he might have been an angel that had forgotten to put on his wings. The odd thing was that while he was smiling and waving good-by and looking down at Tammy with an expression of interest, he kept right on screaming. "Does he make that noise all the time?" Tammy had to shout above it.

"Yes, yes, when he wants to. Food is in the refrigerator. They will tell you what they want. Now we must run."

On the steps the man turned. "You might just bring in those matches when Harold has finished with them. He is satisfying an admirable curiosity about smoking."

"A little boy smoking?"

"He will discover the ill effects for himself."

From the room across the hall there came the sound of a great crash and Tammy made a start in that direction, only to have the boy's mother call her back. "Best not to interrupt. Julien is making a little experiment in aerodynamics." With a nod and a smile, they went on their way.

Tammy stood in the hall, looking around, listening, considering. Just don't let them harm themselves, Miss Jenks had said. But how could she be sure unless she knew what they were up to? She peered into a large dining room and saw young Julien standing on a chair which he had placed on top of the table. In one hand he held a number of strings to which balloons were attached. In the other he held a small kitten with a ribbon around its neck. Tammy went to look through the glass of the back door and there she saw Harold sitting on the top step with a cigar in his mouth, striking match after match in a vain effort to light it. There were two boxes of matches on the floor beside him and when he reached for another match he saw Tammy. "Hi, broad," he called to her.

Tammy opened the door and said, "I'm not broad, not fat either. I'm the baby sitter."

"Then why don't you sit?"

"I reckon I will," and she went back to the living room and

sat down. Little Neal had come downstairs now and he followed her, coming to stand at her knee and look up at her with his sweet smile, all the while filling the room with his piercing scream. How he got the breath to keep it up so was more than Tammy could understand. Maybe if she paid him no mind he would get tired of it after awhile.

She took up a magazine from the table beside her, and sure enough, little Neal left her, though he did not leave off screaming. This was not a story magazine, it seemed to have nothing in it but short articles about new books along with many advertisements of them. It was enough to discourage a body from ever trying to catch up, there were so many. Maybe people had given up trying to keep up with them and just read about them, then maybe chose one or two that pleased the fancy.

But what strange books these were, and what sort of people would want to read them? They were mostly about sin and there seemed to be more kinds of sin than you could shake a stick at. The most puzzling thing of all, however, was that these books were praised and lauded to the skies as if sin was the most interesting thing in the world. Here was one about an unregenerate woman, full of lusty passions. Another was admired for being a lively, shocking tale, of intimate revelations. A swift, juicy murder, a tale of horror, the thrilling story of assassins and their killings and beatings-up, two men and a woman lost in the jungle, stripped of the inhibitions of civilization. The secret soul of a nymphomaniac, franker than the Harlot of Harlem or Vice in Vermont, this is a story not to be missed, this will startle and amaze, never before has ALL been told. Strong, primitive emotions of an uninhibited he-man.

Hell's bells, Tammy thought, here were these children being brought up to be uninhibited, and see into what that would get them. Trouble, trouble and nothing else, for sure. She had been trying to put the thought of Rita from her mind, but now in a flash she saw that Rita must have been brought up in some such manner as this, so she had to find out for herself what was right and what was wrong, and now what a mess she was in!

A sudden silence brought her sharply to attention. She laid aside her magazine and went down the hall to the kitchen. Little Neal was seated on the high counter beside the sink, a round tin box open in front of him and he was just reaching in for another fistful of chocolate cake. "Want some?" he asked with a smile that might have been winsome but for the dribbles of chocolate on chin and cheek. Tammy found a knife and cut a generous slice for herself, she closed the box then and set it high on a shelf, for this did not seem a sensible supper for a five-year-old. She opened the refrigerator door to see what else was there for him. There was a platter of fried chicken covered with paper you could see through, there were tomatoes, apple sauce—enough to feed a regiment.

"Cheese, cheese," Neal said, holding out his hand. "I want cheese."

Tammy unwrapped a package and gave him a slice. "Bread?" He shook his head. "More cheese." After that he demanded pickles. When he had eaten all the cheese and six pickles, he climbed down from his perch and went into the living room. Tammy ate a chicken leg before she followed to see what he was doing. To her surprise, she found he had stretched out on the sofa and fallen asleep. Well, if he wanted to sleep there, she must let him. If the pickles made him sick maybe he would know not to eat so many next time. He was learning by experience, no doubt.

A loud caterwauling came from the dining room and Tammy crossed the hall to investigate. Julien had tied the balloon strings together and fastened them to the kitten's ribbon. As Tammy entered the meowing grew weaker, the string tightening. She could not say no, but no one had told her not to act. She snatched the kitten from his hands and loosened the ribbon. "Are you trying to hang this kitten?"

"No."

"Then what——"

182

"I'm going to set it in orbit."

"Whatever is that? And do you want to kill it?"

"Not necessarily. I would rather bring it back alive. It would be a far greater achievement. Now give it back to me." He scowled at Tammy, a fierce-looking little boy with a thick tangle of reddish hair falling across his forehead.

"But what's it for, all this?" Tammy asked.

"Simple. I am studying the air currents right now, and trying to get the right amount of upward pull—not for outer space, though I call it orbiting. When I have solved this problem, I shall go outside and release balloons and cat. Now, will you kindly return the animal?"

Silently, Tammy did so, turned and left the room. This way of raising children was certainly hard on furniture and cats, and baby sitters too. Crossing the hall, her eye was caught by a cloud of smoke blowing past the door. Another experiment, no doubt, but rather too much smoke to be coming from a cigar. She flung the door wide and found Harold humped over on the steps puking for all he was worth. Behind him two boxes of matches were afire, sputtering and sending out smoke and sparks, the flames licking at the steps. Tammy ran back to the kitchen, filled a stewpan with water, dashed it over the flames and ran back for more. Another splashing and the fire was out, though the wood still smoked and smouldered. "How did you ever do this?" she demanded.

"Quite unavoidable," he said between gasps. "Don't excite yourself."

"Don't excite myself! Did you want the house to burn down?" Then she saw that sparks had landed on his cotton shirttail and a small flame was curling upward. She poured the rest of her pan of water over him.

"I say, was that necessary?" he asked, rather plaintively.

"Yes. Now come in the house and change your clothes."

He stood up, reached out to steady himself, clinging to the rail. "It is a rather curious effect I get from smoking. The

183

cigarettes gave me only a slight reaction, but the cigar seems to interfere with my vision. All is quite black. Is this the usual thing or just a personal idiosyncracy?"

In spite of his grown-up manner of speaking, Tammy thought him a rather sad sight, for he was white around the gills and wavering where he stood. "I reckon you'll get over it in a little bit. Here." She led him into the house and helped him into a chair in the kitchen where he leaned over and rested his head on the table. She went with more water to make sure the fire was out, then came back to him. "You might have set fire to the house and burned it down, and burned up yourself to boot," she said with severity.

"But it is to prevent such contingencies that you are here. Is that not true?"

"I daresay it is," Tammy admitted. "You still feeling pukish?"

"The nausea has not entirely passed but I believe the active stage is over."

Tammy went to the cupboard and searched till she found baking soda. She put some in a glass, filled it with water and took it to him. "Drink this."

"What is it?"

"Soda. It will settle your stomach."

He took one sip and set it aside. "I don't like it."

"I don't care whether you like it or not. Drink."

"And if I won't?"

"I'll skin you alive and hang you up by the ears and pour it down you," Tammy said fiercely.

"I doubt if I would be in any condition to benefit by it after such treatment. However, I will drink the nauseous potion, not because you tell me to but because I find your language picturesque." He drank it then and after a moment said, "I begin to be able to see again. Curious that the optic nerve should have been affected. I shall have to investigate that. Meanwhile, will you please sit down and talk some more? Your speech and accent are new to me. Of course, physiology

184

is my main interest but speech is my hobby. From what part of the country do you come?"

Tammy, sitting across the table from him, studied him with the same puzzled interest he was giving to her. "I come off the river," she said, and told him about the *Ellen B.* and her coming here to get some learning and polishment.

"Very interesting. You have the characteristic expressions not so much of another region as of another age, as if you had come out of time. I am interested in the time-machine, but that's another matter."

"Funny, here you tell me just what I heard in my speech class. How can a young one like you know what a professor knows?"

"Oh, I suppose it is the System. My parents are psychologists, you know, and they try out their theories on us. We are therefore quite precocious in certain ways."

"Well," said Tammy after a moment, "if my talk sounds funny to you, it ain't a circumstance to the way your talk sounds to me."

A loud explosion came from the dining room and Tammy dashed to see what was going on there. Julien was standing on the table, one of the balloons hung limp and the entire contraption was drifting slowly downward while he tried to keep it aloft by leaping up and giving it little pushes. The kitten lay limp and seemingly lifeless in its network of string.

Tammy mounted the table, caught the kitten and began to unwind the cord from its neck, the balloons bouncing around her head as she struggled with it. She freed the kitten and it began to cough and sputter. "You like to have kilt it! Haven't you any feelings? Why can't you use something that ain't alive? How would you like to be hung up in the air like that?"

"I wouldn't mind, if it was in the cause of scientific advancement," he said with maddening coolness, taking the kitten from her and reaching up to catch his balloons which were again floating against the ceiling.

"I'll show you what it's like," Tammy cried fiercely. And

with that she seized him by his thick mop of hair and swung him round and round till she herself began to get dizzy and he let the kitten slide to the floor. Then with a small bang, she dropped him down too. "Now march out to the kitchen and eat your supper and don't——" She caught herself up just in time—if "no" was forbidden, doubtless "don't" was too. So as she jumped to the floor she said, "Next time pick on somebody your own size."

He stood for a moment, looking at her as if she were something new in his experience. "Is this some new method of child training you have invented?"

"I reckon it's been right much used," Tammy said, watching the kitten and relieved to see it was sitting on the rug licking its rumpled fur. "Come on and eat your supper."

He followed her out, saying, "Then it could not have been very successful."

"Why not?"

"Otherwise the world would not be left in such a state as it is now."

"I've been hearing about that in my current events class, and it is in a sorry state, for a fact. But I reckon you've got to give the devil some credit for that."

Harold who had come from the kitchen, perhaps to see what was going on, said, "Oh, but we don't believe in the devil. Or in sin."

"Well, maybe you don't believe in the sun, the moon and the stars, but they're up there just the same. Now come eat your supper and stop looking at me as if I was something that come out of the Ark."

They came in and sat down at the table in the kitchen, Julien asking, "What is the Ark?"

"Hell's bells," cried Tammy. "Are you heathens as well as savages?" She went to the refrigerator and got out chicken and everything else in sight, for their ma had said let them decide what they wanted.

186

"But wait," said Harold, "what is wrong with savages and heathens? Are they not both well adapted to their environment?"

"I never met up with any before," Tammy said.

The boys ate heartily, Tammy thought, as she sat perched on a tall stool watching. But what manners! They chewed with their mouths open, they kept their elbows on the table and grabbed for what they wanted and gulped their milk in noisy swallows. "I never seen such gobble-guts in all my born days," she said at last. "Looks like somebody might have taught you some table manners and behavior."

Harold wiped his mouth on the sleeve of his shirt, a nice clean one, too, for he had changed his clothes after the dousing. "But don't you understand? Nobody teaches us anything. We are allowed to learn as the occasion arises and our interest becomes engaged."

"It don't seem right," Tammy said, shaking her head. "It don't seem right, asking you to learn everything and settle everything for yourselves. Like as if you was newborn into a world where no human had ever been before, or left any understanding or knowing for you to go by."

"On the contrary," Harold said, "we are saved from having to unlearn what is unsuitable or antiquated or irrelevant to the age in which we live."

"How do you get such words as all that?"

Julien answered this time. "We absorb things from our parents who treat us as equals." He gathered up the chicken bones from his plate and dropped them into the milk pitcher.

"What for is that?"

"I want to see if they will float."

"You fish them out of there."

"When I finish my observations."

"Do you want me to whop the living daylights out of you?"

"Daylights?" Harold asked with interest. "I don't know of any such organ in the functioning human body." Then, turn-

187

ing to Julien, he said, "Rather fascinating, isn't it? This direct approach."

"Yes," Julien agreed, removing the bones from the pitcher with a thoughtful air. "Fewer words that we are accustomed to and leaving us in no doubt as to the meaning. And rather interesting, historically."

Tammy began clearing the table. "I'm plumb discombobbled. I'm just about ready to give up."

"Don't do that," Harold cried.

Tammy made no answer and washed the dishes in silence, hearing the boys whispering together as she worked. When she had finished, she found them standing waiting for her attention. They had doubtless plotted some new devilment, she thought.

Harold had put on dark-rimmed glasses and he stood there looking like a small-sized professor. "Don't give up. We think you are the most interesting baby sitter we have ever had."

"You aren't terrified at all. Most of them are," Julien said.

"Please come in the living room and talk some more."

"Well," Tammy said, "I ain't one bit taken in by your sugar-talking, but I'll come."

Harold went at once to a table on the far side of the room and began working with some machinery there. "I'd like to make a tape, if you don't mind."

"A tape? Only tape I know about is a tape worm and I ain't got nary one of them far as I know."

"It's a recorder, takes down what you say, music or anything," Julien explained, seating himself at the end of the sofa, pushing his little brother round to make room. "You play it back and hear it over again."

"Oh. Then that's what Mr. Freeman meant we all had to come talk into. But what are we going to talk about?"

"Can't you tell us a story or sing a song? Don't you know one out of ancient times? Not Biblical, that's taboo. Until we are older."

"Lordamussy, now that beats all. Too young for the Bible but old enough for all this! Well, I know a sight of stories, mostly the Bible ones. Know songs, too. Reckon I'll sing you one about the old woman that sewed on Sunday."

The machine began to buzz and Tammy sang:

"Was a old woman sewed on Sunday,
Sewed on the Lord's day—
Folks kept a-telling her, 'Better look out,'
Trouble coming your way.

She kept right on, sewing on Sunday,
Setting and sewing and rocking,
And one day she's a-setting there,
Come a mighty knocking.

Old woman get up, got to the door
A-wondering in her head;
Open the door, nothing there—
Excepting of a spade.

She kept right on, sewing on Sunday,
Knocking come once more;
When she got there and look around—
A pick-ax by the door.

She kept right on sewing on Sunday,
Knocking come like hail;
Open the door and there he be—
Devil with a forked tail.

And in the morning folks come down,
For to see what they'd behold,
And there by the door was a new-made grave—
And the fire in the ashes was cold."

"Thank you very much, that was beautiful," Harold said, turning off his machine. "Though the subject matter is rather curious. I mean that suggestion that Sunday is different from other days."

"And the devil," Julien put in. "But I liked it. I'd really like to know more of those religious myths." He lowered his voice and added with a certain amount of embarrassment, "Maybe

189

you'll give us the low-down on all that sort of thing some time."

"Lordamussy, you'd think it was something nasty so's we had to seek out a by-corner or a creep-hole afore we dast speak of it!"

"We are not supposed to hear too much of all that till we are older," Harold said with rather a smug reproving look at his brother. "But I admit it is a bit fascinating. Can't you give us another song? I've more room on the tape."

"How about Annie Christmas?"

"Good! I want to know about her."

So Tammy sang the ballad again as she had sung it under the live oak tree for Mr. Freeman, and when she had finished, the boys clapped so loud that little Neal woke and sat up rubbing his eyes and said, "I heard something."

"One thing I don't understand," said Harold. "Why are those twelve sons not born till a year or so went by? The normal period of gestation in the human being is only nine months."

"It might have taken longer for so many as twelve," Julien suggested.

"Yes, or, with that mustache of hers, it could be that certain male characteristics were predominant and had to be overcome. Shall I play it back?"

"You mean, make it sound back the way I sang it?" Tammy cried. "Oh, please do. I ain't never heard myself. It'll be like looking in a life-size looking glass, only sound instead of sight."

Tammy sat on the edge of her chair listening with as much interest as the boys had shown when she was singing, for this surely was one of the wonders of the world. When the recording came to an end, the two boys whispered together for a moment, then came to her.

Harold said, "Do you know what is in the Bible?"

Tammy nodded. "That's one thing I know for sure, and about nothing else but."

Julien lowered his voice. "Tell us. Tell us a Bible story."

190

"You don't know any of it?"

They shook their heads, Neal shouting, "A story, a story!"

"Then I better begin at the beginning with Adam and Eve and the garden of Eden."

They sat in a row on the rug before her and listened with their mouths open, for all the world like birds in a nest, waiting for worms. Tammy talked on and on, telling about the garden and how the devil came in the form of a serpent and tempted Eve so they ate of the fruit of the forbidden tree. "And that's how come the angel with a flaming sword had to throw them out of Eden and that's how come ever after people have had their knowledge of good and evil." She paused at last, looking down at their bright, innocent-seeming faces. "I reckon everybody comes into the world free of troubles and wickedness and the knowledge of such. Of course, there's some that believes in infant damnation, but Grandpa never did hold with that."

"Infant damnation!" Harold repeated. "It has a lovely, gruesome sound. Like a horror picture. Is it in the movies?"

"Not as I know of."

"Get on with the story," Julien said.

"There ain't much of any more of that one. Excepting the moral, maybe."

"What's that?" Neal asked.

"Well, near as I can make out," Tammy said slowly, thinking of her own life and all she had seen since she first left the *Ellen B.*—and she reckoned maybe the *Ellen B.* had been a kind of garden of Eden, in a way—"near as I can tell, it's like this. You know about evil in one kind of way when you are young, by hearsay and reading mostly, but it don't rightly touch you nor seem real till you grow up and get out amongst people. That's what eating of the fruit of the tree of knowledge is. It's the dream running full tilt into reality."

"As if you had the theory but not the practice?" Harold asked.

191

Tammy nodded. It sure was a funny way to bring up children, but somehow it seemed to make them able to get right at the root of things. "Likely that's it," she agreed.

Then, hearing the front door open, she said. "Here comes your ma and pa, so I've got to go. Next time I'll tell you about sin and Sodom and Gomorrah. You'll believe in sin when I get through with that." She looked round quickly at the sound of an exclamation from the doorway.

"There'll be no next time, I think." That was the boy's ma, speaking quietly, but she looked fit to be tied.

The professor said, "Take it easy, Pat. I'll handle this. Boys, don't you want to go to bed now? Say good night."

They mumbled their good nights and went away with only a troubled glance toward Tammy who stood looking blankly from one to the other, not knowing what to do or say.

"Let me explain," the professor began.

"Such people never understand. Pay her and let her go." Her voice was low, but Tammy heard.

"For a fact," she said, "I don't understand. But I know I don't want to come where I ain't wanted." She started for the door, paused to receive the money that was held out to her and said, "Leastways, I told them a thing or two." Then she went on out, stumbling a little in the dark and hearing the mother begin, "Such language—I'll phone Miss Jenks——"

Oh, Tammy thought as she hurried on toward the swamp and the *Ellen B.*, how was a body to know? Seemed like everything she did was wrong one way or another.

192

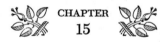 CHAPTER
15

Now it came on to rain. For several days Tammy was able to go back and forth between showers. But on this Saturday morning the clouds came darkly rolling up from the Gulf of Mexico and rain fell in sheets. At breakfast, Mrs. Call said, "Why do you go out today? It's Saturday and you have no classes."

"I'm bound to go," Tammy said, pushing aside her coffee cup and reaching for the fig-tree toothbrush she kept in an empty glass in the middle of table. "I might have another baby-sitting job if those boys' pa and ma haven't pizened the world against me. And I've got to take that bug-man-artist, Mr. Woodly, his handkerchief or he'll be thinking I'm a thief, for sure. I keep forgetting it day after day and week after week."

Mrs. Call shook her head. "All good reasons but not one of them the real reason. You are going looking for that letter that never comes."

"It will, and before long now. I've been counting up the days." Yet she delayed her leaving, making the rain an excuse. Maybe she had been too eager for a letter. Pretend she didn't care and there might be one come. So she let most of the morning pass, along with the rain, while she read one of the books that her professor in modern literature had said everyone in the class must read.

"I'm going by skiff this morning," she told Mrs. Call as she left. "There's water a plenty all through the swamp now."

Mrs. Call waited in the doorway to see her haul the skiff close and step in. "Anything you want? The boatman comes by this morning."

"Nothing I want but a letter." Tammy pushed off and took up the oars. It felt good to be pulling on them once more.

Mrs. Call stuck her head out beyond the shelter of the doorway to say, "If you see anybody to ask, you might inquire if the burglar at my house got caught."

Tammy laughed. "Likely I won't see a soul, and I don't reckon Mr. Freeman is coming, after all. This was the day, but——"

Her voice broke and she put her strength to the oars, shooting cross current, sending the skiff in among the tree trunks. It was a real treat to travel so over the swift-moving water, golden with mud and adance with raindrops, the bushes round about her trembling with the river's motion. She passed easily along under the canopy of leaves that still held on in spite of wind and weather and the fall of the year. She tried to put the thought of Mr. Freeman from her. No use crying over spilt milk or of worrying about there maybe being no more baby-sitting. Wait and see.

Crossing the campus, her thoughts turned to Pete. Was he like the three little boys, was he one of those who had to find out for himself? He was a rover, no doubt about that. He went from one thing to another without staying long enough to find out what was in this before he went on to that. Like his ma, always flitting. His pa, now, he had greater steadfastness, being anchored perhaps by his learning in the way of physics. Was Pete a flitter and a rover in love as well as in his work in life? Was he gone now from her forever?

Thinking such thoughts as these, she came into the post office

194

and looked through the small glass window into her box. There was nothing there. So now a greater uneasiness possessed her. He might be sick and ailing, far off there alone. He might be dead, and how would she ever know? Such sadness came upon her then that all her thought was beclouded as the day, and walking along she sang a snatch of the old song:

"Where is my dear one,
I ask of a star.
Do you see him coming afar, afar?
Does he come sailing from over the sea,
Or does he lie ailing in a far countree?"

She was almost to the rise below which she had tied the skiff when she remembered the handkerchief she had to return.

She knew the building the artist man had told her was his, an old-seeming building with many large glass windows on the top floor. She went in, mounting up and up so it was like climbing the golden stairs to heaven. Only these steps were gray and dingy and there was no living soul about. Saturday, that was why. No students marching back and forth in the halls, no classes meeting in the rooms that stood empty with the doors wide. Only at one of them she saw a solitary student at a book-strewn table. Perhaps the artist would not be there when she found the room with his name on the door—Buford Woodly. Well, she could leave the handkerchief and be rid of it anyway.

The door was closed. She put one hand on the knob to turn it, then knocked, thinking it more mannerly if he should chance to be there. After a long moment, a voice called, "Come in." She opened the door on a large room with glass all across one side so a cold north light came in on this gray day. All around against the wall and resting on racks such as Miss Renie had, were paintings done in strange colors, showing mostly trees and mountains aflame in purple and magenta, orange and red. They were trees such as grew on no earthly land, such as never the true sun shone on.

"Well, if it isn't the little wild river nymph! Come in, come in." He came from behind his easel, a palette of paints in one hand and brush in the other.

"Good day, sir," Tammy said, still looking round and round again in wonder.

"What do you think of my studio?"

"It ain't like anything I ever seen before in all my born days. Nor you neither, the way you're got up." For his trim, slim body was nearly covered over by a tight-tied apron streaked with paint. He was like some manner of eel that had got itself wrapped round in Joseph's coat of many colors. "I've brung you back your kerchief. I reckon you thought I'd forgot the loan of it." She brought it forth from her pocket and held it out to him, adding, "I'm much obliged, I'm sure."

"Just drop it on the table, will you?" He stood there with his head cocked to one side, never taking his eyes from her face, the tip of his red tongue flicking in and out of the corner of his mouth for all the world like a lizard's.

"You're nothing less than an answer to prayer. Do give me just a few minutes' time. I've lost my model in the middle of a picture and I need one desperately. It will be a great help. Will you just sit for me a little while?"

"Sit?"

"Pose. Please. It won't take long." He was so eager seeming that Tammy thought that if she didn't say yes soon he would fair be down upon his knees before her.

"You mean you want to make me into a picture?"

"Just your face. You don't need to undress."

"I got no notion of undressing," Tammy said, drawing back a little.

"But you will sit?"

"It ain't much to ask and I'd be proud to have my face painted into a picture. And even if I didn't want to, it would be hard to say no to a body as stirred up about it as you be." For his great dark eyes were fastened on her so intently that she felt as if he might be weaving a spell about her.

He brought a high stool from beside the table and set it in position. "Just perch here for a bit. There, that's wonderful. Look off. At that spider web, the middle window. That's it. Now hold it." With that, he took up his palette and brush and got to work on his canvas, giving Tammy quick sharp glances now and then.

A few minutes, he had asked for. It seemed more like hours to Tammy before he released her, and then he only said, "Good. That will do for the present. Thanks a lot." He stood before the canvas, not even looking round as she rose and stretched her aching muscles and moved silently toward the door. If he was like Miss Renie, he wouldn't want anyone breaking into his composition frenzy.

Once outside his door, Tammy ran down the steps and out into the misty cool day. It was nigh on to the time Mr. Freeman would be on the rise, if he was coming, and she was all of a tremble, first wishing he would and then that he wouldn't be there. The clock chimed the hour and she saw him crossing the green. Could it be that he didn't hold anything against her? She ran to overtake him, arriving breathless at his side. "I was afeard. Afeard the rain might scare you off."

"It would take more than rain to make me break a date with you—with you and the *Ellen B.* Though you've been breaking dates with me. I've missed you at class."

"Oh. Yes." She stood silent for a moment, eyes on the ground. Then she faced him saying, "I didn't go to make a figger of fun out of her. I was just trying to be like her, to speak after her manner . . . and . . ."

"I should have known, and I did have an idea that might be at the root of it. I've tried to find you. But see, Tammy, my dear, don't you know I've been preaching all year that the first and most important thing is to be yourself?"

197

"That's a fact," Tammy said with humility. "I just . . . I reckon I just got carried away, admiring her so and all. But the class——"

"I'll make that clear next meeting. Will you be there?"

"Yes, oh yes," Tammy cried. She drew a long breath. "Seems like a heavy burden rolled away."

He smiled. "Then let's go."

"I've got the skiff tied up just below the levee, all ready and waiting, and it's going to clear. Yonder's enough blue sky to patch a Dutchman's trousies."

"You're all out of breath," he said, swinging his cane and falling in beside her with his halting step, one long, one short.

"It's having you here so big and fine and smiling and not angry or scornful. It makes me feel important and excited, so I reckon that kind of took my breath." Then she ran ahead to untie the rope that held the skiff and draw it close ashore so he might climb in with ease. He knew just where to step, never tipping the boat as land folk were apt to do, yet taking his place in the wrong seat. "I reckon you'll have to move so I can row."

He said, taking up the oars, "There's nothing wrong with my arms." Then when she was seated he sent the skiff out into the muddy, swirling water.

"Looks like you've been in a boat before."

He nodded. "Fishing in the north woods, and then I was on the college crew one year."

"Well, it will purely pleasure me to sit back like a lady and let you do all the work. Only you're going the wrong way to get to the *Ellen B.*" For he was making off upstream against the dark current, weaving in and out amongst the tree trunks.

"I like to row upstream and then float back with the current."

"That's right. That's what Grandpa says. Matter of fact, you kind of favor Grandpa in some ways."

He gave her a quick, wry smile. "Not in age, I hope."

"Hell's bells," Tammy cried, "that ain't a bit what I had in mind. It's how you know so much and speak so kind and encouraging. Heartening, that's what you are. Grandpa's old as God, nigh abouts. He's got a voice too, not like yours, but a good bellowing one for preaching in the open air. It don't dulcify the words the way yours does. Was you born so, or did it come with public speaking?"

"A little of both perhaps. I set out to be a singer."

"Oh. Then sing. I'd mighty like to hear."

So, keeping time with the sweep of oars and with an occasional glance over his shoulder to make sure he was headed right, he began: "*Comme je t'aime, mon petit chou chou . . .*"

Tammy listened, entranced, the song falling on her ears as smooth and sweet as the night ripple of water alongside the *Ellen B.* and it held her as a cradle, rocking a babe to sleep. A little wind was blowing, enough to play a soft accompaniment amongst the leaves overhead. As he finished, he sent the skiff more swiftly through an open space and out into the main stream of the river.

Tammy clapped her hands, crying "That's mighty fine. I never heard a sweeter. But I wonder what for it calls the one it loves a cabbage-cabbage."

He gave her a startled glance from under his bushy dark brows. "You know French?"

"Not rightly to say I know it, but I picked up some from living alongside some Cajuns down in the bayou country. They was tied up nearby us when I was little, French talking, and there was two little twins used to sing a song so old it was handed down from way back. It was a monstrous funny thing, about a bridge they planted cabbages on with their noses. Seems they're mighty fond of cabbages."

"Ah, yes. *Sur le pont d'Avignon.* Very interesting, that such old songs should have been handed down through the years. Just as many of your expressions that go back to the time of Chaucer."

Tammy shook her head. "I don't like being so old-timey as

that, talking talk that's not good talk for now." And a sadness came over her, thinking that.

"But often it is historically correct, even to the double negatives and the *ain't*."

"I been trying to break myself of that *ain't* but it keeps popping out when I ain't noticing. Like now."

He dodged a log that came shooting at them. "You must know a lot more songs. Could you sing me one now?" He rested his oars, floating with the current.

"I reckon I might. There's one Grandma used to sing, old a-plenty, going back to the time of some war out of olden days." She drew a deep breath and thought of Pete for whom she had sung it last. "It's so old it's been a long time sweetening. It's a man come home, weary, weary from wars in a far country and this is the manner in which he sings when he meets his true love once more. Supposed to be a man speaking." She looked up at him to make sure he understood.

"I understand," he said with gravity.

So, her eyes on the brown water than ran with them, carrying them along, she sang:

> "Come my love, let down your hair
> And kindly comfort me,
> For I have come a powerful way,
> I've come a far journee
> And I'm bone, bone tired."

She sang on till she came to the verse that said:

> "I do not ask for linen sheet
> Nor silken cover now,
> I'd lay my head upon your breast,
> Your hand to smooth my brow,
> For I'm bone, bone, tired."

There, thinking of Pete, her voice faltered. But she swallowed her grief and went on to the end.

"Lovely," he said. "But it makes you too sad."

She looked up at him her eyes bright with tears. "It puts me in mind of . . . of . . . someone that wanted more, I reckon. For I'm no linen sheet nor silken cover. I'm a patchwork quilt, more like, made of odds and ends, and there be some that find me powerful odd."

Then, seeing how far down river they had drifted, she pointed, saying, "Yonder sits the *Ellen B.*," and hoped Mrs. Call was safely in her room, hoped she was abed and quiet even if not truly sleeping.

Mr. Freeman guided the skiff shoreward, brought it alongside so Tammy could leap aboard. Then she held the boat close while he climbed out awkwardly, handing her his walking stick that he might rest his hands on the deck and let his arms do most of the work of lifting. It was a sad thing, Tammy thought, to see a man so mighty in other ways, not free and easy in the use of his legs. But she said no word of that, just busied herself, placing the loop of the rope over its iron hook, then giving him welcome. "Likely you'd take a cup of coffee after all that rowing. The pot is on the stove," she said and led him into the kitchen. She saw in her first quick glance that Mrs. Call's door was fast shut—must have heard them coming—so now she had naught to worry about and could give herself over to the pleasure of company and relish the words of admiration about the neatness and charm of such a place as the *Ellen B.*

Mrs. Call had left two cups in place on the table, and on a plate there were some of her most elegant teacakes, the nutty kind, full of scaly-bark nuts she had gathered from a tree on the edge of the swamp and dug out herself, cracking them between two flat stones and taking pleasures in the task because, she said, it reminded her of other times. Her son that was dead had often gathered such nuts and these teacakes were his favorite of all the kinds she could make.

Tammy poked up the fire in the stove and put in some pine knots to make sure the coffee was hot, and while she busied herself at this she answered Mr. Freeman's questions about Grandpa and Grandma and the life they had lived. She brought down from the window ledge the jar of cream set there for safe keeping and for coolness, for cream was one of the fine things Mrs. Call insisted on having brought twice a week by the boatman.

"I wisht I had my nanny goat," she said, sitting down to pour the coffee. "Goat's milk is a sight tastier than this. It's got a flavor to it. And Nanny was my best friend, till I met you. I had her trained to follow like a dog. She was a sight of company for me."

So the talk flowed freely between them, for this was a man easy to talk with. It was only when he asked about the old lady who was living with her that Tammy found herself hesitant and halting. "She's asleeping in yonder," she said, lowering her voice and giving a nod in the direction of the closed door behind her. "She's a great one for long naps. Do have one of these teacakes. I reckon she takes such a sleep every day because she is so busy the rest of the time, cleaning and cooking. I never seen such a workbrickle woman."

"Did she make these cookies?" He took another bite and munched away with a thoughtful air.

"Y-yes. I . . . I reckon lots of people know about scaly-bark nut cakes and things," Tammy said hurriedly. "They grow wild in the woods, free for the taking. It's a rough-barked tree——"

But Mr. Freeman was not to be distracted from his thoughts. "They remind me of some I used to have, but as you say, doubtless it is a well-known recipe." He leaned back in his chair, biting into another of the teacakes. "By the way, I was really disappointed when Mrs. Call wouldn't have you as her companion. But I must admit you have a more interesting setup here. And it is perhaps just as well you did not get in there, for it seems that Mrs. Call has taken off for parts unknown without a word to anyone. No one has seen her since the president's tea. Her niece is quite upset about it."

"Well, I vum," Tammy said, shifting uneasily, moving her chair to make a bit of noise, hoping it would cover the sound of the creak of the bed that now came from Mrs. Call's room. Like as not she had heard her own name and was creeping toward the door for better hearing.

"To tell the truth, I'm a bit worried about her, myself," he added.

"But why should you——" Tammy began.

"Because, in spite of her coolness toward me these last few years, I am very fond of her, and grateful, too. She was like a mother to me when I first came here, and her son was my best friend in college, and after."

"Whereabouts did you come from?" Tammy hoped to turn the topic of conversation.

"New York State, and I came here largely because the tuition was low. Then I went back north for public speaking courses, and when I came down here again, to teach, Mrs. Call let me room at her house till after the plane crash. After that she couldn't bear the sight of me. But nothing can change my feeling for her. That's why I worry a bit about her now."

"But she left word she was going on a boat or something—or so I heard tell," she added quickly.

"I know. But it does seem rather mysterious, not letting her niece know in advance and simply walking out."

"Maybe she thought her niece would not like it."

"She was right about that. Now Bill, her son, would have understood. He was a prince of a fellow, generous and understanding in every way. But Sandra, she is just the opposite, and she wouldn't want Mrs. Call spending money on a cruise. She's scared to death the old lady'll leave everything to some institution and cut her out."

"That don't seem human." Tammy rattled the coffeepot to cover the sound of a snort from the other room.

"Well, that's how it is."

"I heard tell she had a thief come in the night not long ago. Did they catch him?"

"Probably just imagination on Sandra's part. She's full of

alarms, always was. Nothing was missing. The silver was all untouched, though I believe she did find some brooches in the hall, or out of place somewhere. The police would have paid scant attention if she had not suggested that this might be connected with Mrs. Call's vanishing so mysteriously."

"You mean . . . you mean the police are out looking for her?"

"I believe some inquiry has been made."

"Hell's bells! Looks like a body might be allowed to do as she pleases when she's got the money to pay for it and knows what she's doing."

'That's just the point. Sandra claims she is *non compos*——"

"Insane in the head?" Tammy broke in. "Why, I never heard anything so silly. She's no more so than most old folks. I mean—" her hand flew to her lips—"I mean, just notional, and really more sensible than most."

Mr. Freeman was leaning forward, looking at her with some curiosity. "You seem to have been very observant in your brief encounter with her. Do you always see right through people like that?"

"I don't see through people, no sir. There's some I just can't figger out for the life of me. Now you, take you for an example." Tammy smiled, happy that she could turn the talk from Mrs. Call.

"Yes, take me by all means," he said, leaning back in his chair and smiling at her across the table.

"Well, I took you for one who knows what he is doing and not always changing from one thing to another like some folks I know. I thought I had you figgered for a kind that didn't go flitting here and yonder. But a while back you said you started out to be a singer and then changed over to be a speaker."

"That's true. But if a man finds he has made a mistake—I really did not have quite the voice for the concert stage—then he must change. Otherwise all his life will be a frustration.

204

Sometimes it takes real courage to change, especially if a man has dependents. Luckily I was free."

"Would somebody a man was about to marry be a dependent?"

"Of course, to a man of honor."

"Courage. You said it would take courage to change. I hadn't thought about that. I reckon it did take courage." She was silent a long moment, thinking. Then she added, "I wouldn't want to be a hinderation and a hold-back kind of dependent. If just loving anybody makes you a dependent." She gave him an enquiring glance.

"Being loved by you would be a delightful responsibility."

"You reckon?" Tammy said with wistfulness in her tone.

"I not only reckon, I know."

"I wisht I could be sure of that."

"Maybe you chose the wrong man to love."

Tammy shook her head. "What a man does or how he alterations, that's got naught to do with the loving of him onct you give him a lavish of loving and not just a stingy smidgeon of it."

Mr. Freeman drew a long sigh. "Lucky devil. I envy him." He stood up, taking his cane in hand. "Thank you for a delightful afternoon. Now if you will take me back——"

"Wait, I plumb forgot—" Tammy sprang up. "I promised you some muscadine jelly and it's right here all wropped up and tied round so Mrs. C—— I mean so's nobody wouldn't eat it by mistake." She brought the jar from the shelf and gave it to him. "You'd ought to have reminded me."

His gray eyes under their heavy brows laughed at her. "I remembered it all right. But I thought if I didn't mention it, I might have an excuse to come again."

"You've seen the *Ellen B.* now."

"It's you I came to see. I'd like to come again."

There was a small silence while Tammy considered that. The warmship of the kitchen came round about them as they stood there and that, or something, seemed to bring them of a sudden closer than the real distance between. "I am proud to have you want to come," Tammy said slowly, moving a little from him. "I count you my friend. I make you welcome to come again."

"Thank you," he said with a slight bow, giving her back her own grave look, his eyes holding hers. Then, limping through the door, he added, "I want to hear more of your songs, you know. Perhaps you will teach them to me."

"I'd like that mightily," Tammy cried, happy that the small puzzlingly awkward moment had passed. So with a light heart, she followed him to the deck, drew the skiff near, and this time it was she who rowed him back through the swamp, glad of the exercise, for the clearing of the skies while they talked had brought a real fall coolness to the air.

Coming back, she rejoiced in the change in the weather. That meant that time was passing, that summer was gone. Now there was only winter and spring to be lived through till Pete should come home. And if someone like Mr. Freeman could change from one work to another, maybe Pete had but done right to do so. Of course, one small corner of her mind reflected, Pete had changed three times to her own knowledge. But she would not heed that reminder. Some took longer than others to find their whereabouts in this world. So, having settled this to her satisfaction, she let herself remember with pleasure the visit just ended.

It was good to have a friend. She came singing under the trees, across the swiftly flowing brown water, singing again, "Come my love, let down your hair." This time it had no sadness for her and she found herself thinking of Mr. Freeman instead of Pete. It must be, she thought, that singing it for him had taken away the sadness from it.

Mrs. Call was on deck waiting for her, walking up and down, laughing to herself. "What's hit you, Mrs. Call?" Tammy asked as she drew alongside and leaped aboard.

206

"I've got the best of them for once. Oh, but that does me good! They don't know where I've gone, and they won't find out if I can help it."

"But she's worried, Mr. Freeman said. Didn't you hear?"

"Not worried about me. It's the money she's thinking about. Tom Freeman has her sized up all right. I've a good mind to . . ." She sat down on Grandpa's bench, silent now, drawing closer around her the red knitted shawl that kept sliding off her shoulders.

Tammy perched on the rail in the sun that felt pleasantly warm on her back. The clouds were gone, the air was clear and cool, washed and refreshed by the rain. Now and then one of the last golden willow leaves drifted down to lie on the deck.

"Seems to me," Tammy said at last, "it would be sight easier for all concerned if you just told your niece you were here and going to stay here and no two ways about it."

"Never!" Mrs. Call looked fair dumb-struck with horror. "You know what would happen if she found me here?"

"I ain't got a notion. But it couldn't be much."

"She'd clap me into an institution, put me away so fast I wouldn't know what was happening till it was over and me in a strait jacket."

"Institution? Like a college or——"

Mrs. Call tapped her forehead. "Then she would have herself appointed conservator of my estate. Nothing she would like better than that."

"But how can anybody do that to another human? Ain't there a law——"

"There are ways," Mrs. Call said darkly. "She'd get the matter brought up in court, have witnesses, everybody who ever saw or heard tell of my doing or saying a thing out of the ordinary would come blabbering about it. Oh, I know how it would go. I wouldn't have a chance. It would be the end of me."

"But it don't make sense. Why, just look at you now, how

you get around without your cane and you don't have too much meat to your height any more and you look ten years younger. Besides, you're enjoying yourself and not just setting there in your house like a bump on a log feeling lost and lonesome. Coming here is the out-and-out sensiblest thing you ever did. Mr. Freeman would understand. I reckon you heard what we said."

Mrs. Call brightened at that. "I did so, and I haven't had such a good time in a coon's age. He's got Sandra sized up just right. And you, too."

"Me?"

"He sees you for what you are, and likes what he sees."

"I reckon he must kind of like me, he is so kind and encouraging to me."

Mrs. Call gave a snort. "Kind and encouraging, is he? Why, can't you see the man is in love with you? I must say I'm glad I've lived to see him in love. When he was staying with me years ago, I used to invite the prettiest, brightest, most charming girls in college and the town as well, and once I had the queen of the Mardi Gras come for a visit. I was a great matchmaker in those days. But he was my worst failure, never took the least notice. And now, here you come along in a shanty boat and he gives up without a struggle."

"But that ain't true!" Tammy cried. "Why, he's a professor. And me, I don't know nothing compared to him."

"You know enough." She leaned forward, hands on her knees, her black eyes shining with earnestness. "And my advice is, snap him right up. He's a fine man, you won't find a better. What's more, he appreciates you and that's more than that Pete of yours does."

Tammy slid down from the rail. She wasn't going to have Pete maligned and scandalized by anybody, but all she said was, "Pete suits me. If he would just write me a letter now and then. And now I got to work out what they call a review of that book I been trying to read for my class in modern lit. It sure is a puzzler."

"Bring it out here where it's nice and bright and I'll see if I can help you with it."

Mrs. Call was good about helping with such things. She had read most of the books on Tammy's list and knew how to put the gist of them into understandable words. Then it was not so hard to read through for herself, the meaning coming clear by way of the key so given. This time, however, Tammy had tackled the book herself, reading by the kitchen lantern till late in the night. So when she came back with it now, she handed it to Mrs. Call, saying, "I'm getting better at making out things, but there's some in here I can't make head nor tail of and I've got to write out what I think before Thanksgiving holidays. It's going to be mighty hard work for me."

Mrs. Call gave a sniff at the picture on the cover of the paper-backed book. "These cheap editions. They pick out the most lurid scene to illustrate. Hoping to catch the eye of those that like such things, I suppose. Low, I call it."

"That there picture, I read about it. The man seen her first through the window, and tail-nekkid she was. It put me in mind of David walking on the roof and seeing Bathsheba washing herself. But look what this man in the story does, comes round every night, goes creeping and crawling up to her room and there he squats on the floor like in the picture, with her sleeping all loose and unconfined in the bed. Hell's bells, why don't he get in and have it over with? David sent right out and got Bathsheba and she come and lay with him and I reckon it pleasured him and her both, though not pleasing to the Lord. But leastways, he wasn't just squatting on the floor like this picture. Don't seem natural, taking on like that."

Mrs. Call, who had been listening with her mouth open, burst into laughter. When she could speak, she said, "Tammy, I declare you'll be the death of me yet. Talk about the out-

209

spokenness of modern novels, you have them all beat. Of course, you are quite right. Such things as this are not natural."

"I'm mighty glad to hear it. I'd hate to think every man was like this one. And then riding round nekkid as a jay bird on top of a horse. That was his way of enjoying himself and a mighty selfish way, too, if you ask me, and not one likely to be favored by any woman, her being left out of it all."

Mrs. Call was turning the pages at the front of the book. "Have you read this introduction? It might help you in writing your review."

"I worked at it all one evening, but all I got out of it was that this book was writ out of somebody's feeling dreadful over the awfulness that there is in living nowadays—or in living modern like the TV calls it."

Mrs. Call was skimming the printed pages. "It is something they call the 'mystery of it all' which fills such writers with dread and——"

"Mystery?" Tammy broke in. "I wonder, could it be the same mystery as was writ on her forehead? I never quite understood, except it was something mighty bad."

"Whose forehead? Or are you out of your head?"

"No, ma'm. You know, in Revelation some place. She sat on a scarlet-colored beast having seven heads and ten horns and she was arrayed in purple and scarlet for all the world like those trees in the bug man painter's painting."

"What on earth are you talking about?"

"It was the whore of Babylon, and writ on her forehead was 'MYSTERY BABYLON THE GREAT THE MOTHER OF HARLOTS AND ABOMINATIONS OF THE EARTH.' I reckon this book comes under the head of abominations."

"Well, I have not read this book. But remember that Revelation is said to be symbolic, and so is this. Or so it says here."

"What is symbolic?"

"Oh, something that stands for something else, a kind of short-cut way of saying one thing by way of another, maybe.

Here, do what you can with it and if you can write the way you talk, it will be a treat to the professor to read your review."

Tammy took the book from her and stood puzzling over all they had said. "It tells you here in the front that the thing this stands for is something too awful to talk about. But how can anything that *is* be too awful to mention? Or to say straight out plain? Well, it beats me." With that she went to the kitchen and sat down at the table to try to write out all she was thinking. Maybe it would teach her to write what she felt and thought when she wrote letters to Pete. That was what she needed most to learn.

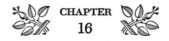

THE DAYS went by so quickly now that there was scarce time for love-pining. Tammy had written to Pete, telling him the names of her courses and how she was earning her way, but there came never a word in answer. It was casting a hook into water where no fish swam, it was calling into the deep of the night and hearing not even so much as an echo in return, the sound going forth to be lost in the darkness. Not having the gift of writing nor the power of acceptable words, she could not tell him all she felt and thought. She wrote of baby sitting but she did not know how to make known to him the feeling she had when the wee one woke and cried and had to be cradled in her arms and walked to sleep again. That was a lovely feeling, and as she moved with rhythmic step to and fro across the night-lighted room, humming a sleepy tune out of olden times, "Go Tell Aunt Nancy" or "Swing Low, Sweet Chariot," her thoughts ran ahead to the time when it might be her babe and Pete's that she was lulling to sleep with her song.

Such things did not go easily into written words, they were meant to be whispered in broken phrases in the dark of night when two, a man and a woman, lay side by side, four walls making private their own small place in the world. Caring for

213

a little one left in her charge, one who was so loved and cherished by his young mother and father, Tammy's thoughts went often to Rita's child that was not wanted, that might never be given a chance to breathe and eat and cry or laugh. Just a would-be, it was. Just a wee one wanting to be. It seemed she could almost hear him speaking, this one who had no voice nor ever would have one, speaking and begging to be born because life was something worth having whether it be good or ill that befell. Small hands of one who had no hands reached out to her, the fingers seeming to close fast on her, soft and warm, helpless, yet insistent, not to be denied.

Her only baby-sitting jobs were with babes in arms now. For Miss Jenks had called her in and told her how upset the boys' parents were, how they thought she should not be allowed to go about to care for older children, corrupting the morals of the young, they called it. "Of course," Miss Jenks had said, studying Tammy all the while with her dark, penetrating gaze, "of course I realize they have rather unique ideas about child care and training and so I give you the benefit of the doubt." She went on and on using words like environment and disadvantages.

At last Tammy could stand it no longer. She broke in, saying "But all I did was keep them alive, like you told me. They might hold it against me that I poured water over Harold when he took fire, and I swung Julien around by the hair of his head so he wouldn't kill the kitten and I did threaten to skin one of them alive and whop the living daylights out of another one, and I told them they et like gobble-guts, and for a fact, they did. But that's all I done, excepting to sing songs and tell them a story. They liked me, I know they did," Tammy insisted, nigh to tears now, "and they wanted me to come back. I was going to tell them about sin and Sodom and Gomorrah, things they'd ought to know about——"

"Ah, I fancy that was where you got into trouble. But no matter now, I'll get you what work I can, with little ones, so there'll be no further complaint." There was a twitch of a smile at the corner of her lips as she dismissed Tammy, yet she still held to her faintly puzzled look.

A kind of suspicious-seeming woman, Tammy thought as she mulled it over later, something pinched and hurt-looking about her thin lips. But what with Miss Sandra scandalizing her name and then all this talk about corrupting morals and such, maybe Miss Jenks couldn't help taking her with a grain of salt. She reckoned not everyone could be as kind and understanding as Mr. Freeman.

The day of his class came and Tammy went to it with eagerness, hoping he would make all plain so that they would not be misliking her, so she could hold up her head again before them all. She took her place in the back of the room and as soon as he began to talk, she felt an easement spread through her. Out of all the words he knew, he chose the right ones, and by the time he was through, more than one of the class turned and gave her a kindly glance or a small smile.

Then Mr. Freeman went on to draw a kind of moral from it all, the moral being that everyone must keep to his own true self and cherish his own personal flavor. Such things as mistakes in grammar were small matters, easily corrected. Then he said, "Miss Tyree's speech is of particular interest to the student of language because, due to the isolation of her early life and the manner of her upbringing, she has been quite out of touch with the modern world. Her vocabulary, therefore, has a flavor of the Elizabethan, as is true of some of the mountain folk of Kentucky and Tennessee. Now we will hear from Miss Tyree."

Standing as she had stood before beside his desk, all thoughts seemed to flee from her head. She turned to Mr. Freeman. "Nothing comes to my mind to be said."

He gave her an encouraging glance. "I think you might give us your impression of the college, or of any new experience you have had since coming here."

Tammy bowed her head, remembering that Grandpa had said sometimes when he stood up to preach he hadn't a notion what he was going to say till he listened. Then the Lord gave him the words he had need of. So she listened, making a great stillness round about herself and out of the stillness she began to speak.

"It comes to me that I should tell of one of the wonders of the world, something never before seen by me in all my enduring life. It was in the evening that it came to pass. I crossed the green-cut grass feeling blithesome in the thought that I was to care for a wee suckling babe for the first time his pa and his ma were away, that I was to change his hippen and walk him up and down and quieten him if he would be dauncy or crying. This is called baby sitting, and there is much cash money paid for it. I come to the house that had the right number and the parents greeted me and gave me welcome and went their way, the babe asleeping all the while. Yet in the house there was the sound of great palavering and music that beat on the ears and gave me no peace. So I went into the parlor and there were no humans there, only a box that was like to a window one could look through and see all manner of images of people speaking and moving about. All very small but really a kind of movie such as I once saw in a theayter. This is called TV."

There was a little stirring in the room, a faint ripple of laughter. Mr. Freeman lifted his hand and all was silent again save for Tammy's voice telling of all she had seen and heard on TV. Now and then she was conscious of laughter, even Mr. Freeman joining in, and again she was aware that all were watching her with wide startled eyes but she remembered in the midst of her speaking that Grandpa always said the way into hearts was twofold, one way being by laughter and the other by tears, so she felt no dismay but went on, thankful for the gift of gab that had likely come straight down to her from

Grandpa with a little help from the Lord in this unexpected emergency.

So thinking of Grandpa and his sermons, she finished telling how she washed her hair and did not gain in glamour or enticement, and went on to point a moral. "Here I been going on like a sermon, only without a text such as should rightly be set forth at the beginning. So I will speak it now and the verse that comes to me is 'Vanity, vanity, all is vanity.' For after my time of wonder at such an invention had passed, wonder at such a contraption which is a window to look through and be instructed, then I began to consider it. So now the thought stands in my mind that such as this should be concerned with words of wisdom and noble sights and sounds and not be given over to unseemly noises, to murder, adultery and suchlike sins of the flesh, not to new ways to wash a woman's hair or oil a man's to make it more alluresome. The same being false, and a snare set to catch the unwary, as a wayfaring man though a stranger may see by looking at mine which is no more than decent and clean, and the moral is you might better wash with soft soap made from drippings and save your money and that's all I got to say on this subject."

With that she went to her seat, rather overwhelmed by having spoken at such length, yet feeling all eyes upon her with a new look, one that was full of warmth and interest.

The bell rang and the class was over before they had finished speaking of certain words that had fallen strange upon their ears. They were just common words such as anyone might use, Tammy thought, and it amazed her that they were not known and familiar to all. As she left the room, several who had taken no notice of her before, nodded and spoke and one asked where she had been living all her life; another wanted to know from whom she had learned her speech. It was pleasant to be noticed, yet Tammy felt a vague sense of uneasiness. She had not come to be studied herself, she had come to study others and their speech. How was she going to learn if all they did was examine her words?

She was thinking of these things as she crossed the campus and saw Rita just ahead, for once alone. She had seen Rita in class this morning, on the far side of the room, and she had glimpsed her here and there in the preceding days, laughing and talking with other students, too busy to speak or more than look and glance quickly away as if reminded of something she wished to forget. It must be, Tammy had thought, that she was waiting for the needed money to come. Then she could go and do what she felt she must do. You could do anything with money, she had said, even evil coming easy.

Tammy saw now that she had a going-away, citified air this morning, for she wore a dark blue suit with hat to match, with white gloves on her hands and a big blue pocketbook that might have held a thousand dollars without bursting its clasp. At sound of Tammy's step behind her, she made reluctant pause.

"Thanks for helping me out that day," she said and started on as if to take another path, and paused again as if held by something in Tammy's face. "I'm off at noon today." She put a finish to her words. No more to be said, her tone said.

"Where to?"

"Paris." She gave a little toss of the head. "I'll be there by tomorrow night."

"Paris that is across the ocean?"

"Right. They'll fix me up there." She nodded another good-by, but still stood, her mouth giving up its crispness, growing wistful and down drooping.

"I wish——" Tammy began.

"What do you wish, you funny little one?" There was a kind of condescension in her tone, a quick twist of amusement at the corner of her lips.

Tammy did not like that, her eyes flashed. "I ain't half as funny as you, you that never thinks it is part of you that you

218

throw away, nor that it might favor you, never taking thought of how even a beginning human has got some rights, once begun."

Rita's face darkened. "I'd go mad if I thought all that and I don't thank you for reminding me. I've got to think of myself. What could I do with a child? My God, my life would be ruined, don't you know that, you poor little ignorant shantyboat girl? Who are you to be telling me what should be done? I've got to think of myself, I tell you. I'm young. All my life is ahead of me and if you think for one silly minute that I'm going to mess things up, you with your crazy, out-of-date notions——" Her breath gave out.

"They was your notions before I spoke them into words," Tammy said with quietness.

All the life, the defiance, seemed to go out of Rita then. "What could I do with it?" she asked in a whisper.

"You could give it to someone that wanted it."

"Humph. You don't know how complicated . . . and who would that be? You?" she ended fiercely.

"Yes, me," Tammy cried. "Me, if there wasn't any other. Lordy, when Pete comes home and we get married, we're going to have all manner of children, a whole passel of them. One more wouldn't make a mite of difference one way or the other. The more the better."

"You're crazy."

"It ain't me, it's you."

Rita stood motionless, her face that had been so cold and proud and angry, growing all at once to be a troubled child's. "I just don't know what to think." Then with a quick turn and a change of tone she said, "Come, walk beside me. People are staring at us, damn them. Let me think."

They left the walk and went together across the green-cut grass. Hell's bells, Tammy thought, I'm the one that ought to be thinking. What would Pete say? Well, she couldn't help it, she had to do what she had to do, no matter what.

219

When Rita spoke at last, her tone was brisk and businesslike. "March is the time. Would you come?"

"Come where?"

"Paris, of course," she answered with impatience.

Tammy let out a gasp. "I didn't mean——" Then she shook her head with a rueful smile. "I couldn't no more pay for such a far journey than I could swim acrost the sea, and besides——"

"Nonsense. Don't be stupid. I'd pay your expenses, and something extra besides." Then she added with a twisted little laugh, "At that, it might be fun, showing you the world. God knows I need a little fun."

"Lordy," Tammy breathed, "what a happening that would be!" For a wild moment she saw herself flying in planes and sailing on big boats and stepping on and off trains in strange places. Then common sense got the better of such notions. "I may be crazy, but I'm not plumb loco. Looks like it would be more sensible if you'd come and just stay on the *Ellen B.* with me. I holped born a babe onct and I reckon I could do it again."

For a moment Rita stared at her as if wonder had got her tongue. Then with that same little laugh that was no laugh, she said, "You do go back a hundred years and over. No, none of that primitive stuff for me. I want the latest, no matter what I do. It's hellish enough either way." Suddenly she turned on Tammy with fierceness. "But tell me, why would you take the child of a stranger like me? Is it some damn church nonsense?"

"I ain't never been in a proper church in all my enduring life. But that ain't saying——"

"Then why? *Why?*"

Tammy considered that for a long moment. "First time I laid eyes on you, first day I come, I thought you was the prettiest—no, not prettiest—the noblest-looking one I ever seen in all my born days. Thought that's what I'd like to be, so finished and fine cut like something made of precious metal and polished to a fare you well."

"Then when you found out what I really was, you changed your mind, I suppose," Rita said with bitterness, her head bowed.

"Yes."

"Then why all this?" She made a helpless small gesture of one white-gloved hand.

"I reckon it's because you're human, like me, and so, pitiful. And maybe it is partly because when I was baby sitting and walking a little one that was living and breathing and being loved and cherished, I got to thinking about yours that wasn't even so much as wanted in the first place, and I felt sad for it."

Rita walked on, her eyes on the ground, her face turned away. Then all at once she said hesitantly, "I suppose I could try it. But if I get in a jam, would you . . . I'd send ticket and everything, money for clothes or whatever you needed and I'd meet you at the Paris airport."

"Well," Tammy said, considering. "I reckon I'd do it if I had to, but see here, you won't get into any jam. You can do anything you want to, especially if it is right, the way this is right. Then you can just bring me the babe and that's that. Of course, I would have to tell Grandpa and Pete so's they wouldn't——"

"Good Lord, complications! I might have known. I thought you were an orphan. Who in hell is Pete?"

"I told you. I'm going to marry him. I think."

Rita's laugh was bitter. "Hell, what's the use? I wouldn't do this to anyone. Of course he would think it was yours and if he's already uncertain . . . no, I'm low-down and no good, but not that low."

"If Pete don't know me better than that, well, I'll just give up!"

"You would chance it?" She put the question warily.

"Y-yes, I would do that." Even as she spoke, one corner of her mind reminded her. If Pete had cast her off just for coming here to college, what would he do about this? Could she really count on Pete? Then she straightened her shoulders and stiffened her spine. "Even if Pete . . . well, I'd have the little one, anyway," she finished with sadness. "And Grandpa would stand by me. He would say I done right. A body has to do what's right, no matter what comes of it. That's what I been preaching to you, and I'd be poor shucks if I didn't practice what I preach, regardless."

"Okay. It's a bargain, if I go through with it." Rita looked at her wrist watch. "I've got to go. The taxi will be waiting." Then for one brief moment, the tense control of her lips wavered and she spoke without the mask of hardness, her words coming bare and unguarded. "It's because you are so sure, that's why I trusted you that first day when I had to phone. It's why I dare trust you now. You are sure of what is right."

Tammy looked back at her steadily. "I am true. I won't fail you."

"It's funny, but I believe you. I never believed anybody before in all my life. Good-by." She turned on her heel and went quickly away, not looking back once, though Tammy stood watching till she had disappeared around the corner of a far building.

"Lordy-Lord," Tammy said. "I sure got myself into something this time."

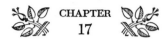 CHAPTER
17

As THE days passed, Tammy's encounter with Rita began to seem more and more unreal. Had she truly been so rash as to promise to take over a suckling babe? Being out in the world surely caused some mighty funny things to come to pass, she thought, as she tied the skiff to a small tree at the foot of the levee. Yet, was there any commonsense reason why she shouldn't do this? She could think of none. At least, she hadn't promised to go flying across the sea.

When she got to the post office, there was a letter, but not from Pete. It had no stamp and the writing was strange to her. She stood over against the wall of the room that served as post office and tore the envelope open. It was not another baby-sitting call, as she had expected, it was from Mr. Woodly, the painter, the bug-man, as she had called him first. He said a very important exhibition of his work was to be hung in a few days and that he must finish the painting for which she had posed because it was one of his best. His masterpiece, he called it, and he must have it in the exhibition. "Please, please, I beg you, come at noon today. I will not keep you long." Then he signed himself "Forever gratefully."

It was nothing to be forever grateful for, but he was a man given to extravagant sayings. Tammy slipped the note into the pocket of her sweater and went on to her class in current events. But she had a hard time keeping her mind on the situation in the Middle East. It was too exciting to know that her face was to be in a picture that was to be shown to all the world at an exhibition. She wished Pete could see it. She wished Grandpa might come and look upon it and be proud. She herself longed for a sight of it. Maybe he would allow her to look today. For this would be better by far than seeing herself as she had for so many years in the wavy, cracked looking glass in her room on the *Ellen B.* or in the spring-water barrel, or even in Miss Renie's long mirror at Brenton Hall where she had first seen herself whole. In the painting she would be seeing herself fixed forever, not fleetingly, and she would see too, how she seemed in the eyes of an artist—those large heavy-lidded dark eyes that had the power to hold one against her will.

As soon as class was over, she hurried across the campus to the old building that stood at the far end of the green and mounted the steps to his studio. She was glad to get in out of the chilly wind that was blowing dark clouds across the sky. No matter if she missed her noon dinner, for Mrs. Call never bothered to wait for her, just set something aside and she could eat when she pleased.

In answer to her knock there came a shout, "Come in!" and as she entered Mr. Woodly came quickly across the studio with his easy-flowing stride, both hands outstretched. "Splendid! Oh, I need you so!" He held her hands, looking at her with his blazing eyes. "I was so afraid you would not come."

Tammy knew it was the making of the picture that he was thinking of, yet his words and his manner were enough to make a body feel welcomed in her own right, to make her feel necessary, important. It was pleasant, it was good to be wanted. "I'm proud to be in your picture," she said, withdrawing her hands.

"You haven't had lunch?"

"No, but——"

"Never mind. I was just about to have mine, and there's plenty for both. I can't eat when I have important work on hand, just live on coffee. Come along, let's get this over with and then to work, to work. Come."

He led her to a chair beside a table where there was a basket sitting amid bottles and brushes and tubes of paint. He pushed them aside and from the basket took several sandwiches which he laid on a paper napkin before her. "Take your choice. Here, give me your sweater. . . . There now." He perched on a high stool beside her, twisting one leg twice around the other so he was for all the world like a limber merman with naught but a tail, just swum up from the deep sea depths.

The sandwiches were of boughten bread with beef slices laid between and hanging over the edges. "It looks powerful good," Tammy said. "My mouth fair waters at the sight. But what I really hanker for, more than food, is a look at the picture you are making of me."

He shook his head. "Not finished. Wait and come to my exhibition. You'll see it there with the rest of these." He made a sweeping gesture of one hand toward the paintings that were banked against the wall. He took one bite then and chewed and chewed on it as if he had forgotten how to swallow, all the while looking at her, cocking his head this way and that as if he might see better slanchways than straight ahead. When he spoke, it was as if his mind was so fixed on other things that he spoke from but one small corner of it. "I was afraid you might be tied up in classes today, and I wanted you while the light was the same as the other time. Luckily it is cloudy again."

"I hadn't anything but current events class this morning. It's about all the trouble in the world today, and there's more of it than I ever had a notion. Even to the ends of the earth, there is trouble."

"I have enough troubles of my own without going into the

woes of the world. Never read a paper. Say, have you had enough for the moment? We'll have coffee later. It'll keep hot."

Tammy licked the butter from her fingers. "I've et hearty. But how can it stay hot when there's no stove?"

"Thermos bottle," he said with impatience, picking up the stool and waiting for her to rise.

"A thermos. I've seen suchlike in the catalogue." She wondered if Grandpa had ever considered a thermos bottle. He was always trying to reconcile science and inventions with the Bible and like as not he would figure out some way for a big thermos contraption to keep hell hot without the Lord or the devil either one having to have his mind on it all the time. Rising, she said, "You ain't had but one bite yourself."

"Oh well, anything to keep you satisfied." He snatched up his sandwich from where it lay on top of a tube of yellow paint, took one big bite and gulped it whole, so he might have been a snake swallowing a frog. Then he carried the stool across the room, set it down with a bang. "There. Now sit. And keep on talking about the woes of the world. I like the expression you got on your face when you were talking about all that. What else do you know about the world situation?" He took his place behind the easel, snatching up palette and brushes as he went.

"Well," said Tammy, settling herself on the high stool and trying to keep her head motionless while her tongue wagged, "it's enough to scare the living daylights out of you, the state the world is in nowadays. And it is a fearsome thing to think the time might be now, the time that was prophesied about in the Bible."

"What does it say? Hell and brimstone?"

"There's more to it than that. Hail and fire mingled with blood falling down from somewheres, and a great mountain burning with fire and cast into the sea, just like bombs blowing up. Like as if the prophets had that very thing in mind when they was prophesying. A great star falling from heaven, burning as it were a lamp. What could that be but a missile? And a third part of the sun smitten and a third part of the moon and the stars, and a third part of the sea all blood—that's another bomb for sure—and all habitations swallowed up and children and sucklings swooning in the streets and the land desolate with a noise even to the ends of the earth and men dying grievous deaths and some so scorched by fire they seek death and cannot find it." Tammy paused, overwhelmed by such horrors. Besides, what was the sense of talking to the back of an easel with him just popping out now and then to look at her?

But he must have been listening enough to know when she was silent, for he said, "Go on, tell me what else is happening in the world."

Hell's bells, Tammy thought, did he believe all this was going on in the world right now and they two alone escaping to tell the tale, like Chicken Little when the sky was falling? Likely he would go right on painting till the fire got him and the paints blazed up. "It ain't here yet," she said, "but looks like it's mighty near. Looks like the world's got one foot on the brink of war and destruction and the other galloping off trying to hop on the moon. Ain't no sense to it."

"Turn a little," was all he said to that. Then after a long silence he asked, "What brings on all this trouble?"

"Mankind's what's at the root of it. Humans with their strife and contention, their murders and fornications. I declare I get the all-overs when I think that now might be the Day. You ought to hear Grandpa preach his sermon on the end of the world, from the text, 'Woe, woe, woe.' He's got another one, mighty powerful, on Sodom and Gomorrah and the atom bomb."

Mr. Woodly leaned way back on his legs like a long-stemmed weed blown by a winter wind, his half-closed eyes on the painting before him. Then he nodded. "We'll have a coffee break now," he said and laid down his paints and brushes.

They went back to the table by the window and Tammy said, "Can I have that other sandwich? Seems a shame to waste it, and sitting so still makes me hongry."

"Help yourself." He set out two cups and reached in the basket for the thermos. He fumbled around, mumbling to himself. Then he snatched up the basket and flung it across the room. "Damn that woman, she forgot it again! Oh, there are times when I could wring her neck."

"Whose neck?"

He gave her a sulky, smouldering glance. "My wife's, of course. She knows perfectly well I have to have my coffee and——"

"It don't seem fitting to talk so about the . . . the wife of your bosom."

"Wife of my bosom!" He gave a kind of snort and then stood still glowering at the overturned basket on the floor.

Tammy went on eating her sandwich. She thought that if Mr. Woodly ate more sensibly, he might not be so tetchy. Then, thinking to distract him from his anger, she turned to study the paintings standing round about. No doubt about it, he was plumb crazy about trees, trees that looked like people and people like to trees. Men like trees walking, that would be his text if he had one, it was real Biblical. Only some of them were up to some mighty unholy things. "This picture you are doing of me—are you putting me in the midst of such-like trees?"

His face brightened and his wrath slid from him like an old skin. "Yes. How did you guess? It depicts the story of Daphne and Apollo. You know it?"

Tammy shook her head. "Never heard tell of them."

"Apollo was the sun god and he fell in love with Daphne. She was a wood nymph. Like you. Remember that first morning I met you? He chased her through the forest and the streams and just as he overtook her, she cried out to her father to save her. He was a river god. He changed her into a laurel

228

tree. All Apollo got was a handful of laurel leaves, and he wore them as a crown for his head."

"Served him right," Tammy said with satisfaction. "Only it wasn't fair that Daphne had to be turned into a tree. I wouldn't like that if I was her."

He laughed. "She had no business leading him on like that. My sympathies are all with Apollo." He perched on the edge of the table, leaning toward her. "You wouldn't have treated me so if I'd chased you through the swamp, now would you?"

Tammy, with the sandwich half way to her mouth, sat motionless, looking back at him, puzzled. Was he of a sudden seeing her, not just as a model for his picture, but as someone he would like to chase through the woods? "I reckon I could have got away, me being more knowing about swamps than you're like to be," she said and took another bite of sandwich.

"For Godsake, do you have to eat all the time?"

"You said I could have it."

He laughed. "Tantalizing little thing, do you know it?" He leaned nearer, dark eyes holding hers. "Stop chewing, will you? I want to get the feel of that jaw line."

Obediently Tammy clamped her lips tight and sat still while his fingertips moved down her cheeks, her jaw, her throat. Anything to get the picture right, she thought. His fingers brushed behind her ears, the nape of her neck, his warm breath was on her cheek as he bent closer, murmuring, "Lovely soft skin, charming. What's the matter?"

"Sorry," Tammy said through her bite of sandwich, "I just got to swallow or drool over." She gulped twice as his hands fell to his sides, adding, "But at that, I reckon you got the feel of the shape of my bones."

He studied her for a moment with the oddest expression, half angry, half puzzled. Then with a quick change of manner, he said, "Let your hair down, will you? A wood nymph should not have a pony tail, or whatever you call that."

Tammy unloosed her hair, letting it fall free down over her

shoulders, shaking it back to lie loose and easy. She was glad he was going to paint her hair hanging down. Pete liked it that way.

"Come along now," he said with impatience, "if you've finished that damn sandwich. Never met up with one like this before in all my days," he muttered, going back to his easel, while Tammy returned to the high stool, her head in the now familiar position.

It was hard to sit like one frozen into stone, or wood. Was this how Daphne felt when she began to know that she was fixed and rooted in the earth, her rosy flesh grown rigid to the roughness of bark and only her leaves, new sprouted, dancing freely at the touch of wind or the fall of rain? Tammy was glad she could still move her eyes when Mr. Woodly was busy laying on the paint and not noticing. She took quick little looks around the room. She saw his coat and necktie hanging on a hook on the far wall. And fallen to the floor below them, was a scarf of strange, metallic, unreal colors that matched some of the purple and magenta trees in the paintings round about. There was something familiar about that scarf and Tammy kept looking back at it again and again. Where had she seen it before? Perhaps he had been wearing it that first morning when she met him chasing butterflies. No, not then, for she could remember the way his shirt was open at the throat and how its thinness showed his naked hide.

As she puzzled over this, it came to her. That night, passing the old cabin, a scarf flung across the window sill. She stiffened, drew back from the implication of this.

"Hold it. Don't move. Keep that look on your face. No, keep your lips parted. That's right." He talked on and on as if his short, sharp words were links of a chain to hold her fast.

But why should she obey him? Tammy thought. He was not a man one should find pleasure in helping, either in the painting of a picture, or in aught else, for that matter. Yet she was held by his words, his high excitement, she was caught in

230

a spell from which she could not break free. He was like some charmer out of old tales, one who could hold the beasties still against their will and his words came to her like some incantation out of ancient times.

Had it been so with Rita? Had he bewitched her? Not like this, but with a stronger power, the man-and-woman kind of spell. She had known it, with Pete. In her mind she went back to Brenton Hall. They were sitting on the steps of the ell looking out over the moonlit courtyard, the sweet olive filling the air with a sweetness that was like to the very smell of heaven. There Pete had first touched her hand and held it in his, lightly, yet all her body and soul had flowed into his and she was bound fast. The house could have burned down round about her, the skies could have fallen, the earth could have opened up to show the burning brimstone and the fires of hell and she would not have paid it any mind, for this was a glory like to heaven, it was a holy thing. There was an old love song Grandma used to sing:

> True love's got a holy feeling
> Like the early morning dew,
> Like the sound of church bells pealing,
> Like the sight of folks a-kneeling
> In their Sunday hat and shoe.
> True love's got a holy feeling
> Like the early morning dew.

But it had not been so with Rita and this man who was some manner of wizard. He had taken one part of true love and not the other. He had made her his mommet to dance to his tune and so had brought her to shame. He had looked on her nakedness, and then he had laughed her to scorn, tossing her aside like the butterfly he had crushed that first morning, wanting only the bright color of it. This was the power a man had over a woman, and a woman over a man.

The slow moments passed as Tammy sat perched on the stool, thinking these things and Mr. Woodly's voice came to

231

her as from a great distance when he said, "There. Now I have you fast for now and forever."

He had drawn back from his canvas, eyeing it this way and that, his face alight, a slow smile touching his lips while the red tip of his tongue flicked at the corner of his mouth.

At sight of him, thus, absorbed in his own work, the spell that had held her was broken. Tammy slid from the stool, snatched up her sweater and like a flash was across the room and out the door. She closed it softly behind her. Likely he had not so much as noticed her going, so wrapped up he was in his triumph. Down one flight of stairs and then another, she ran, her feet scarce touching the steps. She thrust one arm into a sweater sleeve as she went, and almost collided with someone who had stopped on the first landing and was standing there, one hand on the rail, the other holding a red fat bottle.

"Oh, Miss Jenks! I'm sorry." Under Miss Jenks' shocked, angry gaze, she was all at once conscious of her tousled hair, of the sweater, half on, half off. "I-I was just——" she began and could go no further. What was Miss Jenks thinking?

Miss Jenks shook her head, a strange look of sadness coming over her pale thin face. "You!" she said and went on up the stairs, her lips clamped tight shut and her heels clicking hard and sharp as daggers on each step.

Tammy stood there, stricken. A mumble of voices followed the opening of a door. Then Mr. Woodly's rose, sharp and angry: "No, no, you can't come in. I'm busy."

The door slammed and slow steps began descending. Tammy waited no longer but fled out into the clean fresh air. It was coming on to rain. She held her sweater close around her and lifted her face to the fine mist that was falling and only then could she begin to put one thought together with another. Miss Jenks was bringing his coffee. Was she his wife? And going by the name of Miss? Stranger things than that were to be met with out in the world. He had said he had a wife and she had had the look of one, there on the stair, one outraged by his falseness. "Lawsymussy, likely she took me for a strange woman or something," Tammy said and went on toward the great oak tree, her head bowed in shame. "All I give him was my face and I wouldn't have give him that if I'd knowed."

A voice stopped her. "What are you doing, wandering around in this drizzle mumbling to yourself?"

"Oh, Mr. Freeman." Tammy stopped short, she drew a long breath. "I'm so glad to see you. I'm so glad to see somebody that's a true human and not a snake in the grass."

"And I was wishing I would meet you. Come under the tree. It's like a big umbrella." Then, looking down at her, he said, "My dear, what is it? You have been crying."

His voice was sweet with concern, it came round her as gently as the gathering round about of angel wings. "It's mostly rain," Tammy said, wiping it away with the sleeve of her sweater. "I was letting it wash the slime from off my face. I been looking into a regular sinkhole." She let him lead her to the seat that went round the tree trunk and there they sat down side by side.

"Do you want to tell me?"

She shook her head. "I'd mightily like to, but it ain't really my business. Excepting what's coming of it, and that ain't till the spring of the year. So I'll just try to put it out of my mind." She leaned back, resting her head against the tree, looking up into the great gray twisted branches and feeling easement spread through her. Along with it came a strange lonesomeness. She felt lost in a world and a time that were alien to her.

Mr. Freeman said, on a long breath that might have been a sigh, "Yes, some things we have to keep to ourselves, and forget when we can."

He was lonely too, Tammy thought. Were all humans so?

Grandpa said every living mortal had a little mite of immortal in him and that made him sometimes feel a stranger to the world, like a dove that was strange to his own kind. For she had heard tell that every dove had one drop of human blood in him, and that was why a dove's call had such a mournful sound, and it went by the name of mourning dove.

Thinking so, sitting motionless and silent beside Mr. Freeman, she felt his eyes upon her and it was as if his loneliness reached out to hers, two pieces of the same thing, akin and so drawing them close, joining them as if there might have been all of a sudden a bridge set up between them, delicate as a spider web but strong. Across the bridge something passed, she knew not what, only felt his warmship flowing toward her and through her. For a little she was held so, she savored it, refreshing herself, coming alive by way of it. She gave herself up to it as a fish in the water might leave off swimming to bask in quietness while a swift, warm current weaving deeper and deeper under the surface, bore him where it would.

Such feelings should be for Pete. But it could be that there was more than one manner of loving. One was like this, having naught to do with one's will or wish or with foreverness, being mostly just a kind of comforting, one of another. It was of the body as well as of the spirit. She thought then of Rita and the painter she had just left. She stirred and moved a little away from the man beside her.

"Why? Why do you draw away from me?" His voice was deep and gentle and slow, as if she might be some small beastie he held out a morsel to, making the motion smooth and easy lest it take fright, and all the while wondering that so shy and wild a living thing should dare to come so near.

She turned then and met his eyes. There was a brightness in them, a summoning, a kind of hurt, too, such as she had seen once in the eyes of a catamount wounded beyond flight and driven by his need to ask for help from an alien kind. As if life in its going from man or beast, and life in its need to come again through the meeting of two mortals, were close kin, two ends that came round as in a circle. Tammy looked away from him, holding such thoughts in her mind and pondering them. She sat for a long moment with bowed head, her loose hair shielding her from his eyes.

"Why?" he asked again.

"I reckon it's because you give me a . . . a womanish feeling. Like as if you were a man and me a woman."

"Aren't we?" There was the twitch of a smile in his voice.

Now she was able to come out of the current into which he had been drawing her, to move without moving, and after a little she nodded and rose, buttoning her sweater against the chill in the wind. "That's why I must go now."

He stood, leaning on his cane, looking down at her. "Because of . . . someone?"

Again she nodded. "But I am proud you find me a woman growed. There's some—some that think me still a child in need of time to grow up in." She was silent, filling up with sadness, thinking of Pete. Then she gave him a quick, grateful glance and would have gone but he held her with a word.

"Wait. I have something for you." He reached in his raincoat pocket and brought out a shiny, metal tube with glass at one end.

"Whatever is it?" Tammy turned it round and round in her hands.

"It is for you, when you go back and forth through the swamp in the dark. A flashlight, see? You push the button here on the side and——"

Tammy pressed upon it and nothing happened. He put his hand over hers and showed her the right sliding motion. At once the glass end grew bright. "Now ain't that a wonder," Tammy breathed. "A miracle. Like when the Lord said let there be light and there was light."

He smiled down at her, his hand still covering hers. "It is a wonder and a miracle," he said, and somehow he did not seem to mean the light, for his eyes were on her.

"How do you turn it off?"

He showed her, saying, "It turns off easily. Not like some things that arrive and stay forever." Then he took away his hands and let her turn it off and on without his help.

"It's mighty pretty, and handy, too. Only you hadn't ought to have. It must have cost a sight of money."

"It gave me pleasure to buy it for you."

"Then it is acceptable and I thank you." She would have gone but again he stopped her. "Wait. It will be raining before you can get back to the *Ellen B.*, and your hands are cold." He slipped out of his raincoat and laid it round her shoulders, his hands withdrawing reluctantly. She felt his warmth in the garment.

"I'm obliged. But you——"

"I've only a little way to go. To the Faculty Club over there."

So they parted, and as she rowed back through the swamp, feeling his coat around her, the flashlight's weight in her pocket, she thought, "That is one monstrous kind man, a good one. He come this day to me like a sweetly ripe persimmon after one so green and sour it purely puckered my mouth."

Drawing near the *Ellen B.* she saw Mrs. Call hanging out her wash on the long cane pole set from window ledge to rail. Like as not it would get rained on, though the rain was holding off and way in the west there was a patch of blue showing.

She made the skiff fast and as she stepped aboard, Mrs. Call said, "Had your lunch?" For out of long habit she would call dinner lunch every time.

"Some, and I ain't hungering after more. Excepting maybe a cup of coffee." She went on into the kitchen and found a good fire going, the coffeepot steaming on the back of the stove.

236

She poured a cup and sat down at the table, resting her head on her hand. What a full day it had been! Her thoughts went back to Mr. Woodly and Miss Jenks. So when Mrs. Call joined her, sitting down at the table and rolling down her shirt sleeves, she said, "Is it possible for a woman to be married and still go by the entitlement of Miss?"

Mrs. Call looked at her rather quizzically. "I've known some that did."

"Well, you know lots of people at the college, living so near and all. Tell me about Miss Jenks. Is she really married?"

"Yes, more's the pity. Woodly, rather a horrid chap but with a streak of genius in his painting. He never would be on the faculty but for her. She keeps her maiden name because when she can't take his philandering any more she has to get out and support herself. Not that she didn't do that, and take care of him as well, in all those years he was an art student in Rome."

"I should think it would be kind of hard on any children they might have."

"Luckily they have none, though I believe that is a great grief to her. Why she doesn't get rid of him once and for all is more than I can see."

"Could be she loves him."

"Love!" Mrs. Call snorted. "It makes a fool of a woman every time if she doesn't watch out. Stella Jenks takes him back every time he comes crawling. By the way, where did you get that coat that fairly swallows you up?"

"Mr. Freeman. He thought it was going to rain some more. I'd better hang it up so it won't get wrinkled." She slid out of it as she rose.

Mrs. Call got up too and started toward her little room back of the kitchen, but she paused to say, "What did I tell you? Looking after you, that's what he is doing, and that's a sure sign."

"I don't know." Somehow she did not want to talk to Mrs. Call about him, and she was glad when the door closed behind her without any more being said. She was in no mood for teasing. Then, remembering the present he had given her, she reached in the coat pocket, pulled out the flashlight, and something more. She stood staring down with unbelieving eyes at a scarf that was exactly like the one she had seen in the studio and in the window of the cabin.

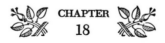

CHAPTER
18

THAT NIGHT, lying sleepless on her narrow cot bed in the kitchen, Tammy's thoughts went round and round, searching out the truth. They see-sawed back and forth between the two men. Grieved and hurt, she told herself with bitterness that there was no putting trust in any man, not even Pete who left her still without any word. Every man living was a snare set to catch the unwary. Yet how could one know, when what he did and what he was did not resemble his manner of speech or the way he seemed? She had counted Mr. Freeman as a prince among men, he had been so kind, so understanding. Put not your trust in princes, the Bible said. How right that was! She could see how one like Rita who had not the habit of being cherished, might have been overwhelmed by those very qualities.

As for Mr. Woodly, he was married, he had little care for aught but his painting. Or was that quite true? For now of a sudden, safe on the *Ellen B.* and at so great a distance from him, it was as if she felt again the touch of his fingertips moving across her cheekbones and the line of her jaw, searching out the ways of her hair, playing lightly round her throat and stroking the nape of her neck, and all the while his great dark eyes, half hidden by drooping lids had held something more than mere observation in them, they had been prowling, seeking, as a wild beast stalking prey. She could understand it now as she had not understood then.

And strangely, now she was stirred as she had not been at the moment of its happening. She was moved by the memory of his hands, his eyes. It was as if lightning had struck afar, afar, so that only now, long after, there came the shattering, shuddering roll of thunder. Only now her body responded. In the darkness, she covered her face with her hands and thrust from her this strange delayed response. For it was the flesh alone that answered him. Carnal desire, the Bible called it. And for a fact there was naught that has holy about it.

Oh, she knew now that Mr. Woodly had not been thinking of his painting then. It was she who had had her mind on it, and on that mouthful of bread and meat she had not dared swallow lest the movement of swallowing disturb his study of her. He had been piping unto her and she would not dance. She had not even heard the playing of the pipes. No wonder he had been bewildered and had turned away muttering crossly to himself. He had been used to a more wonted response. Perhaps from Rita? Yet how could such a man charm one so proud and beautiful that all the students flocked around her wherever she went? By way of the flesh, yes, that was how it could have been.

She wanted to believe this. Yet she knew well what sweet words Mr. Freeman could speak, how he could make the giving of a present a rare and wonderful happening. And there had been something about him which called to her, even to her who would never love any man but Pete. Surely it would have been only to such a man that Rita could have responded.

In the morning, waking, she felt sure of this, and she resolved to have naught more to do with Mr. Freeman. First thing, when she went to the campus, she took his coat to the Faculty Club Building he had pointed out to her as the place where he lived. She left it there without a message, left it with a white-coated man who came to the door. When she saw Mr. Freeman in the distance next day, she turned aside and took another path to her destination. Another time when she almost came upon him unexpectedly, and when he called to her to wait, she ran swiftly across the green-cut grass, not stopping till she had reached the levee and dropped out of his sight behind it.

The day of his class came, she slipped in, taking her seat at the back of the room, and she was the first out the door afterward. The next meeting of the class came and he said before taking up the work of the day, "I would like to speak to Miss Tyree after class, please." But again she slipped away and would not see him, again she ran across the green, not even stopping to go by the post office, but rowing back through the swamp to the *Ellen B.* where she knew he could not reach her.

Later, when it was getting on toward sunset, she went back to pay her daily visit to the post office. This time there was a letter. With fingers a-tremble, she snatched it from the box and held it tight against her breast. She wanted to be alone to read it, and here, students were coming and going after their last classes of the day. But she could not wait. She moved across the small room to lean against the wall beside a shelf where pen and ink were kept. There she tore open the envelope and unfolded the single page it contained. She read:

> Dear Tammy, I have waited so long to write because I did not want to be hasty in my judgment, and then too, I thought you'd probably be tired of all this nonsense after a few more weeks. Now I have made up my mind. You must go back to Brenton Hall at once. I have written Aunt Renie to expect you. I have asked your grandfather to see to it. This is for your own good, Tammy. You must trust me in this.
>
> Yours, Pete.

Tammy stood for a time, staring down at the letter, her eyes wide and incredulous. Then such a rush, such a flame of anger swept over her that for a little while she could not see the room around her. She crumpled the letter, thrust it deep in her pocket, and took it out again at once. She tore off the blank half of the paper on which he had written and snatching up the pen from the shelf beside her she wrote, this time with none of her usual fumbling for words:

Dear Pete, I ain't agoing.

Yours, Tammy.

Then, folding the paper, she rummaged in her pocket for money, ran to the small window where stamps were sold and got there just as the wooden shutter was half-way down toward night closing. "Please, an envelope with the fastest stamp you've got."

The student who served as clerk laughed and reopened the window. "No rocket service yet, but here's an airmail one ready to go."

She slipped the letter in, sealed and addressed the envelope, slid it through the slot, then blindly turned and ran from the room, heedless of the curious glances that followed her. She wanted to get away, to be alone in her hurt and her anger. Mrs. Call would be on the *Ellen B.*, and she would be curious and questioning.

So without noting where her steps took her, Tammy walked through the swarm of students released from their last class of the day. She went on out by the east gate and up and down streets without knowing where she went or when her footsteps brought her back again to the dark deserted campus. She saw and heard naught but the clamor of her own thoughts and did not know that she spoke them aloud. "I ain't agoing. He's got no right, ordering a body round like this. He went off and he's changed. Reckon I can, too. Can't nobody hold still. What's right for him is right for me. Now he would send me home like a misbehaving child. I ain't a child and I ain't agoing. Him sicking Grandpa onto me like a hound dog after a rabbit. Upsetting Miss Renie. I ain't agoing."

A dark shape loomed up before her, someone stopped her and spoke. Mr. Freeman's voice seemed to have been going on for a long time before she could comprehend what was being said. "Tammy, Tammy, what are you doing here in the cold and the dark? What is the matter, my poor child?"

"I . . . I didn't know . . . I didn't notice where I was." She blinked and looked around and saw that she was near the steps that led to the building where his class was held. "I didn't know. It is so cold. I didn't notice it was dark. I am so mad I could claw the bark off a hickory tree. . . . I'm clean forspent with grief and pain."

"Come," he said, taking her hand. "Come with me." He led her up the steps, through the building, past his classroom to the next door. There he put a key to the lock, flung the door wide and turned on a light, never letting go Tammy's hand till he had closed the door behind them. Tammy stood blinking at the light while he crossed to the fireplace, struck a match and lighted the fire that was ready-laid there. The flames crackled and leaped high and sent forth a quick welcoming warmth.

Why had she come here? Tammy thought now. Why was she here with this man she had wished never to speak to again? The reasons for this seemed at the moment far away and vague, of no importance. A greater hurt had wiped out this smaller one, or had at least set it at a distance for the time being.

"Sit here," Mr. Freeman said, pulling a big easy chair close to the fire. "You are half frozen." Then when she tried to speak, he stopped her. "Not a word till you are warm."

She leaned back in the chair, drew a long shivering breath and saw now that this room was like a small library with easy chairs, books on three walls and only the desk by the window to make it into an office. It was a comforting room. She rested in it and felt an easement in all her limbs. When he bought her a small glass of wine and told her to drink, she drank without a word. The wine was sweet and warming and it did not take the skin off her teeth the way Grandpa's corn likker did. She held the glass out so the dancing firelight shone through it, making it the color of rubies and she said, "Look not upon the wine when it is red in the cup."

"Ah," he said, sitting down across the hearth from her, "now you sound more like yourself. But this wine is in a glass, not a cup."

"And somewhere else, it says give wine unto those that be of heavy heart. And I be one of them tonight."

"Can you tell me what the trouble is?" His voice was gentle and it fell sweetly on her ears.

For answer she took the crumpled and torn letter from her pocket and handed it to him. "That's what has undone me. It just come. Afore sundown."

He held it to the light of the fire, read it through twice and kept it in his hand. "So, now what?"

"I ain't agoing, I ain't agoing."

He was silent, studying her as she sat with her eyes on the fire. After a while he said, "Then now, now you are free of him." Yet there was something of a question in his tone.

Tammy sighed. "When you love anybody, you ain't never free of him, no matter what."

The fire crackled, a stick burned through and sparks flew up the black chimney. He laid the letter in her lap and said, "But this has just come, today."

"Yes, today."

"There has been something else, then, that has kept you from me all these days."

"Yes." Tammy did not want to think about it. She wanted to rest in this warmth of wine and fire, in this quietness.

"I think I have the right to ask why? Why?"

There was no avoiding it. She straightened up in her chair and said without looking at him. "It ain't a fitting thing to

244

speak of, between a man and a woman." Then because she could feel his eyes upon her in puzzlement, she thought to give him a grain of comfort—if that was what he was wanting—by adding, "I will just say that if I have to care for him according to my given word, I reckon I'd rather it might be yourn than that other one's. At least you ain't so dauncy-looking and the child will likely be healthy."

"What on earth are you talking about?"

"It was the scarf that told me. I seen it in the cabin window one night as I passed by," she went on, indignation getting the better of her reticence. "I wasn't going to say a word, I was just going to let you go, and be a friend no more. But I will say there is one thing I can't understand. How a man can act so careless of his seed whether there be marriage or giving in marriage or no. That has naught to do with it. Because it is part of him all the time and forever, going down through all generations. Why, it's like as if when your leg got hurt and no more was perfect as the other. Like as if you had said, 'Cut it off, throw it away, cast it into outer darkness,' disowning your own flesh. It ain't right. It is a sin, that's what it is and——"

"Tammy, Tammy, please. Wait. I don't see——"

But she was launched on her own flow of words and could not stop, she had to pour forth all the thoughts that had been running through her mind these last days. "Why, way back in the Garden of Eden good and evil came to be known. But nowadays, out in the world, looks like folks have lost the power of telling t'other from which, and some there be that say there is no such thing as sin. But I don't hold with that. I——"

"Tammy, wait a minute. Look at me." Then when she reluctantly met his gaze, he said in a voice so real, so true that it brought her up sharp, "Tammy, I give you my word that all this makes no sense to me."

Seek as she would, Tammy could find naught but honest

bewilderment in his face. For a long moment she sat, leaning forward, staring at him. Then she covered her face with her hands and turned away her head. When she could speak, the words came brokenly, "I . . . I do believe you. It's me that's done wrong. I've made a most grievous error. I been thinking evil in my heart. I'm ashamed, I am humbled and brought low."

It was a long time before he spoke. Then he said, "Tammy, I don't know what you have done, or rather, perhaps I do. In any case you must let me help you. Tell me true—are you in trouble?"

"Ah, I'm in trouble all right, I'm sorely troubled." She brushed away a tear.

"God, anyone who would take advantage——" Anger choked him.

"I thought you were my best friend . . . and so . . . so good. I couldn't bear to see you any more, or tell you what I thought I had found out."

"Of course I am your friend."

She gave him a quick, imploring glance. "You won't hold it against me?"

"I couldn't hold anything against you, poor child." He rose and limped back and forth on the rug before the fire, his face troubled.

"Then everything is all right," Tammy cried, springing to her feet and facing him.

"Everything? I don't understand."

She nodded, smiling. "Everything, that is, but the babe——" She was silent. If he knew naught about it, then she could not speak, she had given her word to hold it in secret.

"Tammy!" His voice and look were stern. "Tell me frankly, are you or are you not going to have a child?"

Tammy hesitated only a moment. She could not tell a lie, and already he knew so much, there was no hiding from him.

She nodded. "In March. That's when I'll get it. If I do——"

He turned from her and rested his head on the high mantelpiece, looking down into the fire. "And yet you think it is all right, if I just don't hold it against you. That's not your problem, don't you see?"

"No, my real problem is Pete, of course. I don't know what he will say when I turn up with a suckling babe."

He whirled on her, his tone angry. "He'd better think well of it. His own child. That's why he orders you back to Brenton Hall."

"Hell's bells! It ain't his'n any more than it's mine. Pete ain't like that nor me neither. Lordy, did you think . . . ? And I thought you——" She stared at him for a moment, then her laughter rang out. "Praise be! Now we're even. We both been thinking evil of each other."

Relief spread over his face and puzzlement took its place. "But I don't——"

Then Tammy told him, naming no names and telling how she had seen the scarf in the cabin window, had thought it was his.

"There are any number of those scarves," he told her. "One of the shops in town gave a lot of them to a benefit sale one of the clubs had, the glee club, I think. So——" he shrugged, then added—"you have really undertaken quite a lot."

"Somebody has to do it and maybe it will all work out. Only now Pete——" She was silent, the weight returning, the ache coming again. "I wrote back to him in anger. I reckon I hadn't ought to have done that. But I was plumb mad, and I reckon I still am." She laid her hand on his arm. "You been kind and patient this night, and I thank you. And now I'd better be going."

"I'll come with you."

So they crossed the campus together and came to the levee and the skiff. "I won't ever think evil of you again," Tammy said, pulling the boat close.

"Nor I of you, my dear," he said softly.

She stepped down into the skiff, put on the flashlight that was stuck between two planks in the prow and pushed off, feeling his eyes upon her in kindness and concern. The dip of her oars was loud above the soft murmur of the river and the yellow light gave her a trembling path of gold among the tree trunks and their blacker shadows that stirred with the flow of the water and yet remained.

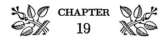

CHAPTER
19

No MATTER what happened, a body had to keep on coming and going and living and doing this and that, Tammy discovered. One great comfort to her was the knowledge that Mr. Freeman was still her good friend with naught in the way of misunderstandings between them and no wickedness to be laid at his door. As for the whole question of who was the father of Rita's child, that was a small matter and no concern of hers, she told herself. The innocent babe himself was important, nothing else, and she thought of him more and more tenderly. She even began to be glad that she had something to look forward to, now that it seemed as if Pete had been set at a yet greater distance by reason of their letters. She did not regret her decision to stay on here. After all, one had to maintain his ways, his own ways, at all costs. But there was a deep ache within her, underlying all her surface activities.

Only a few days had passed when, returning to the *Ellen B.* from her morning class in modern lit, she was startled by the sound of a motorboat and voices coming from the river. Who could it be? Had Mrs. Call been discovered? She made the skiff fast and did not go at once aboard, just sat there, listening.

Mrs. Call was speaking, but not with her usual manner of words. She spoke after the fashion of river folk. "Haven't seen hair nor hide of any such a thing, and I been tied up here for some time now. Why, the *Ellen B.*'s been right here since afore she disappeared."

Someone asked her name, a man with a voice of authority, speaking like those who had come and taken Grandpa for the making of corn likker in the swamp.

"They call me Shanty-boat Annie," Mrs. Call said. "That's the name I go by all up and down this here neck of the woods. Ask anybody hereabouts and they'll tell you quick enough. Oh yes, I'm an old-timer round here."

Another man spoke, "Well, let us know if you see anything looks like a body. She was wearing a black silk dress and lots of jewelry and such when she disappeared. Her niece has got people out combing the countryside and we have orders to search the river because she was last seen crossing the ferry."

"I'll sure let you know if I see anything suspicious. A mighty sad case. Her kinfolks must be nigh on plumb distracted. Yes, I feel for them mightily." Mrs. Call had a tremor in her voice, but Tammy well knew it was but her unholy glee that she was covering up with pretended sympathy and fellow feeling.

The motor roared, then quietened as one of the men shouted. "And much obliged to you, sir, for your expert advice as to where a floater is most apt to be. We'll stop by for you on our way back, take you to the city if you've finished your visit by then."

"Much obliged to you."

Tammy listened no more. She leaped aboard shouting, "Grandpa, Grandpa!" and dashed round to the other side of the deck. Oh, but it was good to be once again in the safety of his arms.

"There, there, honey." He patted her on the back, he smoothed her hair from her face, then held her at arms length saying, "Now, now, let me look at my girl," just as he used to do when she was small and came running to him for comfort after some small hurt. "See here, it ain't as bad as all that.

250

Nothing's as bad as it looks to be first off. Tell your old Grandpa about it, honey."

Tammy gulped back her sobs. "It's just that I am so all-fired glad to see you, Grandpa. I . . . I been needing you."

"Ah, but you've had Miss Annie here. And I'm mightily pleased to make the acquaintance of this good lady that's staying with you. It's the Lord's hand that led her here, no doubt about it."

"Miss Annie?" Tammy looked around Grandpa's shoulder, staring at Mrs. Call.

She was choking back her laughter and at the same time making desperate signals, one finger to her lips and her head shaking a no, no. She was wearing an old pair of Grandpa's pants, a faded, torn shirtwaist of her own, shirttail out, and the whole was topped by Grandpa's lopsided broad-brimmed felt hat pulled down over her eyes. No wonder the men out looking had not known her for the elegant lady in silks and satins and beads who had poured tea at the president's on the day of her vanishing.

"Yes," Tammy said in response to Mrs. Call's gestures. "Miss . . . Miss Annie. Yessir, Grandpa, she's been powerful good to me. Don't leave so much as feeding the chickens for me to do, and she knows to help me with my lessons, too, sometimes."

"I appreciate that, ma'm," Grandpa said, turning and giving her a bow like as if she might be the queen of Sheba. "I am eternally grateful to you for looking after my little girl in a strange land."

"And vicy versy, Mr. Dinwoodie. I hadn't had a job in a long time till she give me a roof over my head. So now, I will go and get you some dinner ready. I reckon you'll be wanting a little private talk with Tammy here." And off she went to the kitchen.

Grandpa drew Tammy down beside him on the bench by the rail. "Now tell me all about it, honey."

251

"Didn't Pete write you?"

"Yes. And he's about worried to pieces, he's nigh on to being plumb distracted in the head. Or so I gather from his manner of writing."

"His letter to me sounded like some high and mighty king giving orders to a slave. Grandpa, I was fit to be tied when I read it and right there on the spot I fired back a letter saying nothing but that I ain't agoing back to Brenton Hall and what's more, I ain't." Then with a sigh she added, "I reckon I let the sun go down on my wrath because I ain't cooled down yet."

Grandpa shook his head sorrowfully. "If Pete wrote in anger, it was account of his being so worried. And you forgot that a soft answer turneth away wrath, child. When a man is as concerned as Pete is, he is apt to speak more sharply than he means, the words coming forth at variance with the manner in which they seem to him in his heart."

"Oh, Grandpa, you are so good. You can see naught but good. Me, I have looked on evil out in the world and it has warped my seeing. I see meanness in people even when it is not there. Yes, it might be that Pete was just worried. Oh, what shall I do? Do I have to go back to Brenton Hall and never get any learning so as to make Pete be unashamed of me in the world? Tell me, Grandpa, what shall I do?"

"Now that is something no one but the Lord can tell you, child. All I can say is, do not act in haste. Wait and turn it over in your mind. Be still and the Lord will speak into the stillness. Then you will know."

Tammy leaned her head against his shoulder. "I'll try," she said at last in a small voice. "I'll try."

There was more to tell, to talk over with him, yet no words came. She would have told him of Rita, naming no names, and she wanted to tell of others, but somehow, all that was set at a distance and made unimportant by her renewed hope of

252

Pete and Grandpa's notion that his anger was out of concern for her, and not out of his wishing either to rule like a king or to find some excuse to be done with her. Just because some man, not known to her, had tossed Rita aside when he had finished with her, that was no sign that Pete was like that.

"Seems good to be back on the old *Ellen B.*" Grandpa said, a wistful note in his voice.

Tammy turned with quick compunction. "Oh, Grandpa, here I been talking about just nothing but me, me, me. Are you all right? Do you want to come back to the *Ellen B.?*"

"I go where duty calls, honey, though I ain't saying I don't get a longing from time to time and now and again. But the Lord's work comes first. I'm apreaching the Word and I'm bound to keep on as long as the Spirit moves me." He paused as there came a great rattling of pots and pans from the kitchen and the sound of smothered laughter. "Seems like it's kind of a gay little lady you've got here with you, honey. And a fine figger of a woman, to boot," he added with a chuckle. "Especially in my old pants."

"Well, you wasn't using of them, Grandpa," Tammy cried, "and I didn't think you'd mind. She didn't have a thing that was fitting."

"These here are fitting, all right," Grandpa laughed with a roguish look.

Tammy had to laugh too, though she knew very well that Mrs. Call was wearing those old things of Grandpa's not out of need but so as not to be seen and known by any comers. And of course it was downright wicked of her to be taking such delight in all the worry and trouble she was giving to her niece, not to mention the police. But she only said, "For a fact, she does keep a cheerful countenance. She's been on land for a long time and it pleasures her to be living on the *Ellen B.* It agrees with her." That was the truth anyway.

"Dinner, dinner! Come and get it," Mrs. Call shouted from

the kitchen. So they went in. "I'll have mine later. I know you'll want to keep right on visiting and palavering whilst you eat."

But Grandpa would not hear to such as that. "It's most kind and considerate of you, ma'm, to suggest such, but half the pleasure of the meal would go with you." She must sit with them, he went on. He had been looking forward for a mighty long time to making her acquaintance, he said, and he wasn't going to be cheated of it now.

So she sat down in high good humor. And truly, Tammy thought, she had sure enough outdone herself on the dinner, so it wasn't right for her not to be present to see it enjoyed. As for Grandpa, he kind of sparked up under her good cooking and her cheer, telling tales of how he got the *Ellen B.* real cheap during the depression and talking on and on as if he might have been long hungering for some listening ears. He even went back for stories out of his growing-up days. Why, Tammy thought as she listened, there were things coming out such as she had never heard tell of in all her enduring life.

Mrs. Call listened as if she had never heard the like either. Then it was her turn and she told about living on a shanty boat when she was young, only she skipped the parts that would give him the notion it was a journey made in ease and luxury with horses and servants and all that, a pleasuring trip, and she beamed all over when Grandpa praised her cooking. Hell's bells, Tammy thought, if they wasn't the both of them so old, she'd say they was making up to each other for all they was worth. She was beginning to feel quite out of it, as if she might not so much as be present, though she knew she was because the box she was sitting on so they could have the comfort of the two chairs, was beginning to ache her behind.

When there came the sound of the motorboat, Grandpa gave her one quick kiss, patted her on the head and said, "Trust in the Lord, honey. He will find a way. I leave you in His hands, and in Miss Annie's." Then he made his farewells to Mrs. Call

254

and promised to come again soon, and he ended up with such a flourishing bow that he put Tammy in mind of one of the knights out of olden days come to life again.

On deck Mrs. Call shouted down to the men to know if they had had any luck in their search and when they said no, it was hard for her to contain her delight over the situation. Grandpa went aboard the motorboat, he took off his hat and waved good-by and Tammy and Mrs. Call stood by the rail waving till boat and men were out of sight around the curve and the sound of the motor had died away.

"You never told me what a fascinating man your Grandpa is," Mrs. Call said.

"Fascinating?"

"Oh, children never see their parents or grandparents as human beings. They are just relatives to them, nothing more." She took off her hat and tousled her short hair, adding, "But see here, isn't this the afternoon of the exhibition, the time when you are to see yourself as others see you?"

"Lordy, I plumb forgot," Tammy cried, and ran to smooth her hair and put on her best Miss-Renie dress, for likely people would be looking at her to see if the portrait favored her or no.

When she came out on deck again, she found Mrs. Call still sitting on the bench, her eyes with a faraway look in them, so she said she wished she could be coming along too, and did she look all right to go to an exhibition?

"You look fine, child. But me, I wouldn't go for love or money. I'm just going to sit here in the sunshine for a bit gloating over the way I've got them all in a stew over me, searching the river and all. Heavens, I haven't had such a good time in a coon's age." She burst into gales of laughter.

So Tammy left her and pushed off in the skiff, making for shore. She didn't want to miss a minute of the exhibition and she hoped to get there early so she could see herself without others roundabout seeing her see herself.

255

When she came to the steps of the building where the exhibition was to be, she began to wonder if she could have made a mistake in the day, or was she just a long time too early? For in her haste she had not stopped to look at any clock. She mounted the steps, read the sign that said the hour and the opening date. An arrow pointed the way. Then, through open double doors to the large hall where she had come that first day for registering, she saw all arranged as for a party, a table down the center laden with all manner of goodies. The walls were hung with paintings, those strange trees she had seen in the studio and others equally strange. One caught her eye because it was so different, being of a girl standing with her head turned away and hair covering her face so it remained unseen. Only one knowing well the line of neck, the slope of shoulder could guess that it was Rita and no other.

Her body was beautiful. She might be a queen, by the beauty of it. Such a man as this painter could not look on her nakedness and not be moved. It was Rita standing there in a gold frame, stark nekkid. Tammy turned her eyes away, not wanting to see, wishing there might no one come to see, and that the hall remain empty as now.

A murmuring came from somewhere out of sight, a man's voice rising in anger, and now Tammy knew for sure that it was the same voice she had heard that night as she passed the cabin, high-pitched with a high whiny note that was strange coming from a man growed. He was saying, "You have no right. It is my best, my masterpiece. Who cares about such a——"

A woman broke in on his hot words, her voice low and tense. "I care. Do you want to lose everything, be dropped from the college in disgrace? I won't have it, I tell you. Take that down or I will."

Tammy shrank back out of sight, but not before she saw Miss Jenks dash across the room, snatch a knife from the long

256

table and run to the wall that was hidden from her view by the turn of the room.

"You wouldn't!"

There was no answer, only a whacking and slashing around. Lordamighty, Tammy thought, she's killing him! She ran into the room, stopped short at what met her eyes. Mr. Woodly stood apart from his wife, for all the world like a whipped dog. Before him on the wall was an empty picture frame, the canvas falling face down toward the floor, and Miss Jenks was even then slashing the last corner loose. There was no blood, there was no murder being done. Tammy began to back away, hoping she had not been noticed.

But Miss Jenks, rolling up the canvas as she turned, had seen, and by the look of her she could have been made of fire and hell. "You poor little fool! I could have you expelled for this!"

"Me?" Tammy looked from one to the other and then at the empty picture frame. There was a placard down below with the name "Daphne" on it. Her picture. "You don't like my face?"

"Your face! Here, take this and get out of here with it. Show it and I'll have you thrown out of this college so fast——" She thrust the tightly rolled canvas into Tammy's hands as she spoke.

Tammy turned to Mr. Woodly, but he had slunk away with a tail-between-the-legs air and now stood with his back turned and his head tucked low. "But . . . but . . ."

"Go, go," Miss Jenks whispered fiercely. "And be in my office tomorrow at nine." Then with a fearful contortion of her white face, she shook the fury from it and managed to set her muscles into some sort of smile as she said, "Come, dear, our guests are arriving," and she advanced to meet the group who were just then entering the hall.

Tammy slipped past them and out toward the main door, meeting others entering. One or two students, classmates, called, "Hi, Tammy, what's your hurry?" but she went on faster and faster, out to the walk, across the campus and over the rise to the skiff. She did not know what to think. Was her face so terrible-looking as all that? What had Mr. Woodly made of it? He must have made it big, big, for the frame had been at least six feet tall. Lordy, Lordy, he'd likely made her into some manner of monster. She started to unroll the canvas—but no, she would wait till she was safe on the *Ellen B.* Some one might come along and see it, or think that she had stolen something. Luckily Mrs. Call would be asleep, for Grandpa's visit had delayed her usual nap.

But what a disappointment! She had been imagining herself made beautiful, made worthy of being in a picture that might last a thousand years. She had been thinking it would be something to point to pridefully, maybe taking Pete to see it in some great art gallery of the world, saying, "Behold, that's me, me up there in the picture. That's how I look to a sure-enough artist." Hot tears stung her eyes and she nearly rowed smack into a tree trunk, being so blinded.

At the *Ellen B.*, she made the skiff fast and stepped softly aboard, though when Mrs. Call slept, she slept, and was not like to wake. Then standing there by the woodpile in the late afternoon sunlight, she searched out a smooth stick of wood, and laying the edge of the canvas on the window box of geraniums, she placed the stick as a weight to hold it there. The painting unrolled to the deck and Tammy stepped back to view it, seeing the whole of it at once.

"Lord-mighty," she breathed. It was more than a face. It was her own face set atop Rita's body, and that nekkid as a jay bird. A strange rigidity held Rita there, the rosy, smooth, warm flesh already suffering an alteration of hip and shank, the fair skin changing to rough bark. Blue-green mosses crept up the calves of her legs and he had had the decency to let it outspread across one hip so as to cover her private parts. Erect as the tree trunk it was fast becoming, there was that lovely young body, arms outstretched as branches and every finger already hung with leaves, the delicate, pale, scare-opened leaves of spring.

All this Tammy saw in one swift glance. But it was the face that held her transfixed—her own face, wrenched to fear and dismay, her own face distorted with horror, lifted in agony of realization, the body stiffening into wood, the mind comprehending and shrinking from the fearful change. Her hair, blown back by some ghostly wind of the shadowy forest depths behind her was already touched with an unholy green where soft tendrils curled.

At a sound behind her, Tammy turned. There stood Mrs. Call. "So! So this is what you have been up to," she cried.

"No, no, it ain't me. It ain't me. See, my neck ain't that long and my tits ain't that big. All I give him was my face, and I didn't know. Please, believe me."

Mrs. Call looked from the painting to Tammy and back again. "I believe you, but who else will? No wonder you cut it out."

"Nobody else is going to see it. And I didn't cut it out. Miss Jenks did." Then she told Mrs. Call how it had happened, ending, "I didn't mean for you or anybody to see this. But now, well, we both have a secret. I'll keep yours. You keep mine."

"Yes. But it's a pity."

"What is a pity?"

"This is a superb piece of work. No wonder he said it was his masterpiece. Too bad it can't be shown. The man—I have no use for him as a human being, but he does have a streak of genius, and this proves it. It will be valuable some day, mark my words. I know something about such things."

"I wouldn't show it to a dog," Tammy cried, and tossing aside the stick of wood that held it in place, she began to roll the canvas up. "It would shame me to have it be seen. I've a mind to throw it overboard."

"You have no right to do that. It is a work of art and you——"

"Well, I'll stow it away in the closet for the moment, but I just get mad all over when I think it might be mistook for me. And supposing people had come before Miss Jenks took it down. Oh!" And with that she went into the kitchen and thrust the painting deep into the closet. She never wanted to look upon it again.

TAMMY had a restless night, dream ridden. Once she cried out and Mrs. Call came hurrying to see what might be the matter. "I was turning into a tree," Tammy said and shivered, the horror still upon her. Mrs. Call's laughter was reassuring.

At breakfast she was jumpy and uneasy. "I don't know what Miss Jenks is going to do to me," she said. "Thinking what she thinks about me, she's liable to skin me alive."

"Tell her the truth. That's your only hope. She is a fine woman. Indeed, she is a noble woman, worth ten of him and no fool either. She will recognize the truth when she hears it."

But hell's bells, Tammy thought as she set out to meet her nine o'clock appointment, how ever in this world was she going to tell the truth without at least partly betraying Rita's confidence? Oh, what a fearful mess it was! She could do nothing but try, and then hope that things would work out somehow.

At the door of Miss Jenks' office, she paused with bowed head. Be still, Grandpa said, and into the stillness the Lord would speak. She waited, but never a word could she hear. So there was naught to do but go ahead alone. She gave a small weak-hearted rap on the door and Miss Jenks' crisp cool voice said, "Come in."

Miss Jenks was seated behind her desk, writing, and she did not look up, only said in a cold tone that sent chills through Tammy, "Be seated, please." It was a tone to put one at a distance, to cast one into outer darkness.

Tammy sat on the edge of the chair, the desk between them. She reckoned if it came to blows she might could outrun Miss Jenks, who was thin chested and looked to have no more breath in her body than she needed for talking. Besides, this morning she was more bloodless-seeming than usual, her cheeks pale as paper and the movement of her hand in writing was jerky and uncertain. When she laid down the pen and lifted dark, blazing eyes, Tammy said, "It wa'nt me, ma'm. Not me."

Miss Jenks broke in, "No denials, please. I could have you dropped from the college and sent away for this."

"It was just my face," Tammy began again. "That's all."

"However," Miss Jenks went on as if she might have learned her speech by heart and would hear nothing, would make no alteration in it till she had said all the planned words, "however, since this unfortunately would involve my husband, I shall do no such thing in a public way. But I advise you to leave. These . . . sittings . . . must stop. These meetings——"

"There ain't been any sitting nor lying either, and as for meetings——"

"Don't bother to lie. A wife knows." There was a small bitter twist to her thin lips. "I have known of this ever since the opening of college. Don't imagine you are the first, or that you will be the last. Just be thankful, poor little fool, that you have got out of it so easily. That is all." Then as Tammy made no move to go, she added, "You may go now."

Tammy stiffened, she lifted her chin, drew a deep breath. "I ain't agoing. You've had your say. Now I'll have mine."

She described her first meeting with Mr. Woodly and her returning of the handkerchief he loaned her, and she told how he asked her to sit on a stool and let him draw her face. Then she told of the note that asked her to come again so he could

262

finish what he had begun. "That's all there was to it, and he didn't so much as ask me to take off my clothes. I didn't neither sit nor lie in any manner whatsoever that I shouldn't. What's more, I didn't have the least notion what he was doing with my face. I thought maybe it was going to be a pretty picture I could take pride in and show off to folks. I never knowed it would be something to shame me before the world. That's all there is to tell. Excepting that I'm obliged to you for cutting it down afore folks come to lay eyes on such. And nobody ever will, if I have my way about it. So there. That's all I got to say."

After a pause, Miss Jenks said, "I have no proof of the truth of this. And after those other reports, from Sandra Rook, from the psychology professor——" Now there was a small note of uncertainty in her voice.

"You can come to the *Ellen B.* and stand me up tail nekkid alongside the picture and you will see. I ain't near that tall and skinny and . . . and . . . there's other ways of telling."

Miss Jenks' eyes went over her from head to foot, a look of dismay, of bewilderment spreading over her thin face. She leaned forward, resting her arms on the desk as if of a sudden she could no longer sit upright. "It's true. You're not like that, and you're not at all his type. Could I . . . could I be mistaken?" Her voice was just a whisper on the last words she spoke.

"You could that. And that's what you be."

"Then, if not you, someone . . ." Her face crumpled, as if the hard bone beneath the flesh had all at once given way. She bent over till her head rested in her arms.

Tammy sat motionless, not knowing what to do or say or whether to steal quietly out. Yet she could not do that. It seemed heartless, somehow, to leave another human being so humbled and bowed as this. At last she said, "I reckon it ain't easy, loving a man like that."

Miss Jenks flung up her head and her words came tumbling

over each other. "Yes, yes, go ahead, ask what everyone asks. Ask why I stick by him. Ask why I keep on and on beyond human endurance. I'll tell you why. It's because I love him, damn his eyes." Then after a moment she went on more quietly, almost as if speaking to herself, "He is a child and I must take care of him. I have no other. He has to be looked after and saved from himself. If I had had a child of my own, and of his—" she choked, then went on after a moment, her words scarcely audible—"it might have been different."

She sat with bowed head till she had regained a measure of her usual composure. "I'm sorry. I don't know why I am telling you such things. It is no affair of yours. Maybe I am jealous of you, of your youth and your beauty. I was never pretty. It seemed the most wonderful thing in the world for him to even look at me and to then want to marry me, plain me! I thought I could hold him by leaving him free. But——" She broke off abruptly, gave herself a little shake and spoke again. "I'm sorry. I'm not myself and you—" she paused, her face softening as she gazed earnestly, almost imploringly at Tammy— "there is something about you, something real and true and honest." She turned away to hide the sudden moisture in her fine dark eyes.

"Miss Jenks, ma'm," Tammy said, speaking right out as the notion came to her smack out of nowhere, as if indeed the Lord had spoken at last, "Miss Jenks, would you like a child of his? Not yourn?"

Miss Jenks flung around as if she had been struck. "What do you mean?"

"I think you might want such a one, if you knowed about it. There was a girl—I promised not to tell who—but——"

"Ah, I knew it. He can keep nothing from me. Yes, yes, go on."

"It was a mighty strange thing, ma'm, how it come to pass. I knowed her no more than by sight, and that because she was beautiful and it looked like she had all of what I wanted for

264

myself, what I was come to try to learn, polishment and ease of manners and speech and such. I don't know how it come about. She never took the least notice of me, except that first day she give me a scrap of pencil to write with, me not knowing what to write at the time of registrating. But this day, I talked with her face to face on the walk and it was as if she reached out, unseeing, blind in her despairing, reached out and caught me by the wrist." She went on to tell of the telephoning and the cold, strange way the mother took the news, just promising money. She told of their second meeting, naming no names.

Miss Jenks sat all the while, dumb struck, her eyes wide and wondering and holding a wounded look. But as Tammy talked on, there came a change, a softening. Was it pity growing there, pity for the girl?

"So," Tammy concluded at last, "the long and short of it was she come to see that the babe was blameless, so she could not go on as she had planned and as she had had a mind to do. There was maybe something about speaking of him that made him real to her—human. Like as if he turned into a him instead of a it. So it come about that she is going to let him be born. And me—" she gave a little helpless laugh—"me, I said I'd take him and keep him, if none else should want him."

"You?" Miss Jenks cried. "But what an incredible . . . what a——"

"Yes, ma'm, I reckon it be that and more so. But you know, if you have a lot of children like I mean to, well, it's the more the merrier. And it was like as if the Lord told me then and there what to do. I was as took by surprise as she was. Anyway, I'm agoing to do it. I give my word and there's no going back on that."

"But what on earth will you do with a child? How can you? . . ."

"It could make a ruction in my life, maybe, but I reckon I'll have to leave the straightening out of it to the Lord. It was

His notion in the first place and I'm just going along with it best I can. Of course," she added uncertainly, giving Miss Jenks a questioning look, "of course it might be that all this—and us talking together one with the other, is the Lord's way of making a kind of suggestion—if you was so minded. Grandpa says He moves in mysterious ways His wonders to perform and most of the time we can't more than begin to seek them out and understand. So, if you should . . ." She paused, not knowing how or quite daring to go on with so bold a thought.

Miss Jenks sprang up and began walking back and forth between the window and the desk. Tammy leaned back in her chair, relaxing a little now for the first time. It was out of her hands.

At last Miss Jenks stopped and faced Tammy, resolution in her face, and a light that had not been there before. "I'll do it." She was breathless, as if she might have been running a far piece. "As you say, the child is blameless, and it is his. Maybe it will make a difference. . . ." Her voice trailed away into silence. "Anyway," she added with defiance in her tone, "anyway, I would always have something."

Tammy drew a long breath and rose. "Mrs. Call was right. She said you were a noble lady and I know it is true."

"Mrs. Call?"

Tammy bit her lip. But it was too late, the name was out. She gulped, she pretended to choke, and after a moment, said, "You remember, you sent me there the first day, thinking she would have me come to live with her. We talked some. I told you, she would not have me in her house." That was the truth. But a long way from being all of it.

"Sit down a minute more," Miss Jenks said, going back to her chair and putting on her dean-of-women manner. "I'd forgotten about that. You must have been one of the last people to see her."

"No, ma'm. I seen her again with lots of people round about, thick as molasses. It was the tea party the president had."

"She did not speak to you there?"

266

"No, ma'm, she was too high and mighty to so much as look down her nose at me, not even so much as to give me good day."

Miss Jenks thought a moment, then she asked, "When you went to her house that day, was she packing or making ready to leave? Did you see any indication of such a thing?"

Tammy studied that over in her mind before replying. Miss Jenks had not asked about the next morning, she had said "that day," the day she had come first. "The niece, by name of Miss Sandra, she was just about to leave. She told me, no, go away. But I went back, thinking I should see Mrs. Call, her being the one most concerned. It was then she too said no, don't come. She was just asetting there in the garden looking half mad, half downhearted all at one and the same time. I felt for her."

Miss Jenks nodded. "She never got along with her niece. But I must say she is doing everything possible now, trying to find Mrs. Call, offering a thousand dollars reward for news of her and sending out search parties on land and river. She is afraid there has been foul play. Mrs. Call cashed a large check that last day, the day of the tea. Of course, if she is alive, it is possible that she is wandering about quite helpless. She's been getting more and more queer, or so Sandra says."

"She ain't any queerer than you or me," Tammy cried.

"You seem to have formed quite a positive opinion in such a brief interview."

Hell's bells, Tammy thought, rising, why can't I learn to hold my tongue? "It was my grandma and grandpa raised me, so I reckon maybe I'm just used to old folks."

"Well, it is a most mysterious case. Sad, too." Then with a quick change of manner, she rose and came to stand before Tammy. "Forgive me, child, for thinking——"

"Ma'm, it's me that's obliged to you. And I'm mightily relieved that the young one will have someone ready-made for loving him when he comes. Or maybe even loving him a little right now, sight unseen."

Miss Jenks' eyes filled with tears. "We'll talk again, of how

267

and when." She gave Tammy's arm a quick pat, then turned and went back to her desk.

Once outside, Tammy felt like running and jumping and shouting and singing. She felt free of a great load. She sang to herself as she crossed the green-cut grass, a line from an old hymn, "And the burden of my heart rolled away, rolled away." Only it would not be rolled clean out of sight till she knew that Grandpa was right and she was still loved by Pete in spite of everything. To be loved—that was what everyone wanted.

A voice stopped her. "Hey, there! What are you so cheerful about?" It was Mr. Freeman, rising from the bench that ran around the live oak tree where it might be he had been lying in wait for her.

"Well," said Tammy with a smile for his eagerness, "to tell the truth, I was thinking about love."

"That sounds interesting. Come. Come and tell me." He led her to the seat and she sat down beside him, swinging her legs back and forth.

"I was thinking it was something wanted by every human. And how it comes to each in a manner that is different from all others. Love, I mean." She turned to him to make sure he understood what she was talking about.

He gave her his grave, sweet smile. "I understand. Tell me."

"Well," she began again, thinking of Miss Jenks, "there is one way that it comes—by way of the wish to care for and cherish a body regardless of what sort he might be or what pain might be given. There's another way. It comes by some manner of dream that all at once is true. Or you think it is true." She paused to consider. "I reckon that is how I come by my love for Pete." Then, thinking of the man beside her, whom she might have loved but for Pete, she added, "And I reckon it can come creeping in upon one unawares, by way of another's kindness, such as you have shown to me. If there was none other there to stop it."

268

"Thank you, Tammy." The glance he turned on her was both tender and sad. Then he shook his head while a small smile touched the corner of his lips. "There's no one like you in this world."

Others had said that—Pete, as she well remembered. "That's what some have said. And mostly when they said it they seemed to like me."

"More than like, my dear," he said softly. "I only wish I had got here first."

Tammy said, "I'm sorry, and it might be mean and selfish of me to think and to say so, but truly it pleasures me to hear you speak in such fashion. I treasure it in my heart." She rose. "Now I must go. There are things I have to do."

He stood and watched her hurrying off toward the river, and when she reached the rise and turned to look back, he waved good-by. She waved and then put the thought of him from her. She had to hurry back to the *Ellen B.* to tell Mrs. Call there was a big reward of money being offered for news of her. More people might be coming to look and to search out the secret paths of the swamp. What a mix-up it was! Seemed like she was always getting herself into such. If it wasn't one thing it was another. But maybe that was what made living out in the world amongst folks so exciting. She was learning a lot, for sure, and most of what she learned did not come out of books.

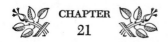

Mrs. Call was not amused by the tidings Tammy brought. "For money," she said, "people will do anything."

Several days passed, days of warm sunshine such as often came in November, the high water went down and it was possible for Tammy to go back and forth on comparatively dry ground. So now seekers could come by land as well as by water, and this added to Mrs. Call's uneasiness. At breakfast on this morning she told Tammy, "The one who might betray me for a reward of a thousand dollars is the boatman who brought me and comes with the groceries every week. But Saturday when he comes, I will give him enough money to keep his mouth shut, top the reward if need be. Though that might make him suspicious."

Tammy set down her coffee cup quickly so she would not drop it. "A thousand dollars?"

"Of course, child. That should seal his lips. Especially if I promise more later."

"You've got so much money as all that?"

"Don't look so wide-eyed! Money isn't that important, though there are times when it is convenient to have it."

"B-but, does it mean as much as all that to you? Is it worth all that to be here on the *Ellen B.?*"

Mrs. Call leaned her arms on the table and looked Tammy firmly in the eye, her own dark eyes fiercely bright. "My dear, for me it is the difference between life and death." She rose and began to clear the table.

Tammy finished her coffee in silence. There was no doubting Mrs. Call's feeling. And for a fact, she was truly a new woman since coming here. She had lost untold pounds. Actually she was, as Grandpa had said, a fine figger of a woman, and just see with what ease she now moved and how much work she did each day. Why, she looked ten or more years younger than that fat hopeless critter Tammy had first seen sitting in the garden of her house. Yes, this alteration was really worth something. But over a thousand dollars? "I reckon I ain't never given a proper evaluation to the old *Ellen B.*," she said, rising and setting her empty cup in the sink. "But hark, what's that?"

They both stood motionless, listening. The *chug-chug* they heard was not just a tugboat pushing a line of barges upriver, it was a motorboat coming nearer with every chug. Tammy went to the window. "It is a government boat."

"Where's that hat?" Mrs. Call cried and snatched it down from a nail on the wall. She clapped it on her head and picked up the bucket of clothes she had put to soak on the back of the stove. "I'll be at my washing when they come. Leave everything to me." She rushed out on deck, set the bucket on the bench by the rail and began sousing the garments up and down, not even looking round as the boat came closer.

Tammy watched through the window, keeping out of sight, hidden by the geraniums, waiting for the boat to come within her view. Then above the sound of the motor, she heard a known voice and rushed to the deck, calling, "It's Grandpa, it's Grandpa. It's all right."

Mrs. Call went right on washing the clothes while Grandpa thanked the men who had brought him, and said he would be ready any time they came back by for him. It was not till he was aboard with Tammy in his arms and the boat heading out toward midstream that Mrs. Call turned, wiped her hands on the seat of her blue jeans and gave Grandpa proper welcome.

"How did you ever come to pick up such a fine ride?" Tammy demanded.

"Well, child, I got to talking with these here government surveyors and when they heard I was of a mind to come down to see my little granddaughter, and Miss Annie, here—" he made a bow to Mrs. Call—"they offered me a lift. I'll always take to the river any time I am free of my duties. And by the way, she's arising again. They've had heavy rains up north of here."

"Splendid," Mrs. Call cried with enthusiasm that made her forget for the moment to speak after the manner of one who had lived always on the river. "And now I'm sure you would like some coffee and battercakes. I can whip them up in a jiffy." She was all agog at the prospect of cooking for a hearty-eating man, Tammy thought.

"Battercakes, ma'm?" Grandpa said. "They would be most acceptable. These cool fall days give me a real appetite." He went with Mrs. Call to the kitchen, Tammy following on behind the two of them.

She perched on the edge of her cot bed on the far side of the stove while Grandpa took his old chair with the goatskin seat and tilted it way back like he always did. He asked how her schooling was coming along and when she said everything was fine except that she had not heard again from Pete, he said, "You will, honey, you will," and then gave all his mind to Mrs. Call who was bustling about, stirring and mixing at a great rate.

"Bread crumbs, buttermilk and sody? That's the only way to make a proper battercake," he said with approval. "I mind the time I had my first that come out of a box. Ready-made, they call it. What's this, says I. It's a pancake they tell me.

Rightly named, I says when I had a bite. Tastes more like a pan than anything else in the world." He went on talking with relish and enjoyment. He could live mighty plain when the occasion required, he said, and he knew full well the truth of the saying, "Better is a little with the fear of the Lord than great treasure and trouble therewith." But he did treasure a tasty morsel now and then, for the stomach's sake. Then he said, "Tammy child, speaking of the stomach's sake, didn't I leave a mite of what's-good-for-us somewhere roundabout?"

So Tammy fetched forth the jug and he and Mrs. Call had a swig each that seemed to put them in even better spirits than before. She was glad Mrs. Call could ease off from her worrying about that reward money. Great treasure and trouble therewith was what she had. Likely if she was bone poor that niece of hers wouldn't be seeking her out or trying to manage her but would let her go her own way in peace. It was downright wicked, the way a body's own kin could be so mean and grasping. No wonder Mrs. Call had about given up, settling down to get fatter and fatter and older and older.

She didn't look the least bit old right now. She was blossoming out under Grandpa's praise, listening to his talk and putting in some of her own now and then in a hungry kind of way, like as if she had been hungering and thirsting for converse with one of her own age. Tammy sat silent, feeling as if she were not even so much as present, and when she chanced to glance at Mrs. Call's little clock on the shelf, she saw that she shouldn't be. "I plumb forgot about my class," she cried, "and now looks like it's coming on to rain."

"Wait, take my raincoat," Mrs. Call said. "I won't be wanting it." She went to her room and returned with a flimsy shiny garment no size at all. "Hat's in the pocket."

"That won't more than keep the rain off the end of my nose."

Mrs. Call laughed. "Wait till you shake it out. You'll see."

Grandpa gave her a big hug in farewell, saying he was sorry she must go, but that Miss Annie would entertain him. "I'll likely be gone afore you get back, honey, but it does this old heart good to see you, even for so short a while."

As she went along the riverbank toward the old roadbed, Tammy could hear their voices going on and on as if they might be old-time friends met after long parting. It could be that old folk, just by dint of being old, had a kind of common meeting ground where they could disport themselves with ease, and of course, Grandpa was always pleasured to hold converse with one who had never heard his best stories that he had gathered together through all the years of his life. All these things she kept in her mind as she went along and she tried not to be thinking anything more, especially what might be counted disrespectful. But it kept coming to her that if they just wasn't the both of them so old, she'd think they was sparking for sure. She wondered at what age a body got over such notions. It was something one could not ask any grownup, so she reckoned she would just have to wait and see for herself.

As she crossed the campus, big drops began to fall. Tammy shook open Mrs. Call's raincoat and slipped it on over her dress. She could see right through, yet it kept the rain off. A wonder for sure. It was just like walking about in a glass house. She reached in a pocket for the hat that was like a handkerchief with strings, and something shiny and heavy fell to the grass. She picked it up and studied it with wonder. It was a flat round thing no bigger than a silver dollar but set with shiny bits of glass, a big green piece of glass in the middle. It was real pretty and it had a chain to hang round the neck. Tammy put it back in the pocket and tied the rain hat under her chin. Then she thought the necklace might fall out, so she hooked it round her neck for safe keeping.

There was time to go by the post office before class—time a plenty, but no letter. She had almost stopped expecting one. So why, she wondered as she went on to her current events, why on earth did she keep on agoing and alooking? Was it just habit, and Pete become a habit and naught more? Was this how married folk, like Pete's pa and ma, for instance, kept on tarrifying, the one with the other, wound up and can't stop, just on account of because they'd got into some manner of rut and couldn't get out and surprise themselves anew? Love was a mighty strange thing, she thought, strange in its ramifications. Downright ramblesome, that's what it was, and taking on odd shapes with time. Some of the shapes were wearable and fine to behold, and some didn't fit any more than some old garment worn just because it was handy to put on. It ought not to be like that. Love ought to be refreshed each morning and rise up as on wings of a dove.

At class even the state of the world could not turn her thoughts from their puzzling, and when class was over, she hurried across the green, hoping to find Grandpa still aboard so she could ask him what was what. He was a believer in love. Mrs. Call, now, she had a kind of blight on her mind where love was concerned—true love, though she was really long on loving-kindness.

She was passing the old professor emeritus when he stopped her with a wave of the hand, and out of kindness and respect, she fell in beside him for a little way. He was wearing a long dark coat against the rain and he looked as droopy and as solemn as one of the priests in Miss Renie's drawing. "It does me good to see such youth and life," he said, "for my heart is heavy today."

"What might the matter be?" Tammy asked.

"I have an old friend who must be in a sad way, if indeed she still lives. You have perhaps read about her. It is on the air, in all the papers. A great mystery and a tragedy to those who remember her when she was young."

"You mean . . ." Tammy hesitated, not wanting to put the name to him lest it be another that he was thinking of.

"Mrs. Call. Or Miss Annie, as she was when first I knew her. And what a lovely dainty little slip of a thing she was in those days! It is strange," he went on after a moment in which

Tammy did not dare venture a word of sympathy lest she let out something that should be hid, "strange indeed, how death alters the perspective, for I feel sure she must be dead. I see her now, not as she became in these last troubled years of her life, but as she was long ago—as rosy cheeked, gay and light-hearted as you are today, my dear." He shook his head and sighed a long sigh.

Tammy wished she could tell him that Mrs. Call was well and at this very moment, no doubt, laughing and talking and being quite as gay as she ever had been. Oh, the bread of deceit might be sweet to Mrs. Call, but it sure filled a friend's mouth with gravel.

After a moment, Tammy said, answering his last words, "I reckon age is a kind of cloak that wraps the body roundabout and gives it some manner of disguise. Or it might be like a jail that you get in and can't get out of no matter how you wriggle and twist and kick against the pricks."

He nodded. "True, true."

He seemed so downhearted over everything that Tammy did not turn off at the fork in the path but walked on with him as he headed toward the east gate of the campus. She hoped to think up some way to let him know that Mrs. Call was flourishing like the green bay tree. But she could think of naught to say save that maybe she was just off on a trip having a good time right this minute. Then she added, "Well, sir, I reckon I'll say good-by."

He touched his floppy, rain-dripping hat and bowed and said, "Good-by, my dear."

Tammy stood looking after him for a moment, then she sighed and moved with downcast eyes along another path that led back across the campus. What with her thoughts and the rain, she bumped right into a lady who was carrying a red umbrella low down over her head. "Oh, excuse me. I'm sorry. I——" Then words stuck in her throat.

Miss Sandra gave a little grunt. "You!" She was starting on

when all at once she stopped, her big blue eyes growing wide. "Wh-where did you get that?"

"Get what?"

"So it was you. Oh, I see it all now. Thief, thief! Stop, thief! Police——"

For Tammy had taken off as fast as she could run, heading for the swamp. Must be the raincoat. Oh, what could she do? For if the police came—and they would, because it was down in the college books that she lived on the *Ellen B.*—then they would find Mrs. Call. Maybe she ought to have stripped off the raincoat and given it to Miss Sandra instead of taking to her heels like a scared rabbit. Atop the levee, she paused, panting, and looked back. The red umbrella was bobbing up and down as Miss Sandra went running toward the drugstore, and a telephone, no doubt. No help for it now. She just had to hurry and warn Mrs. Call. Maybe she would think of something to do. Oh, if she could only get there in time to catch Grandpa. He would know how to help.

It seemed as if everything was against her. The rain had stopped but there must have been a cloudburst somewhere up river because already the swamp was filling up. She had to wade knee deep through the swift-flowing water before she could reach the *Ellen B.*, and when she got there at last and leaped aboard, all was still. Grandpa had gone. She ran to the kitchen. Mrs. Call's door was closed. She was likely having her nap. Well, let her be happy and peaceful a little longer. Trouble would come soon enough, though the rising river might make them safe on the land side for a little.

Tammy flung off the raincoat, built up the fire, set her shoes to dry, then dropped down in a chair close by the stove, bent over, head in hands. The necklace dangled under her chin and she looked down at it, knowing all in a lantern puff that that was what Miss Sandra had seen, taking her for a jewel thief. She unfastened it, tossed it over on the table. She must think, think fast what would be best to do. Untie the *Ellen B.*

278

and let her drift down river? No. No, they would find her. For Miss Sandra would have called the police before now and would have found out from the college records or maybe even from Miss Jenks that this was her place of abode. There was no hope. They would come and arrest her. All this when she was getting straightened out with Pete! For he would hear, Mrs. Brent would have a conniption and——

"Tammy! What on earth is the matter with you?" It was Mrs. Call, and when Tammy had told her, she sat staring at her, blinking a little. Then she rose, laid one hand for a moment on Tammy's shoulder, thrust the necklace into the pocket of Grandpa's pants she was wearing and said, "I suggest you go about your studying as usual, my dear. If you are hungry, there are some leftovers in the skillet on the back of the stove. As for me, it's a bit stuffy in here. I'll go on deck for a bit." With that she took her coat from a nail on the door and with it on her arm, she went out, closing the door softly behind her.

"Well, I vum," Tammy said. "Who would have thought she would take it like this, so calm and cool and resigned-like." Maybe that was best, however, Tammy thought after a moment. Might as well go on as usual till what had to happen, happened. You just had to leave things to the Lord when you reached your own wit's end, and that was where she was. She ate a bit of leftovers, though she had small appetite for even Mrs. Call's best company cooking. Then she stretched out on her cot bed and tried, and at last succeeded, in putting her mind on the book she had to read for her class in modern lit.

It was a book to make one wonder, being mostly concerned throughout all its pages with an old man catching a fish. It took him all the book to catch it and bring it ashore, and when he got there, the sharks had et it clean to the bone. The professor said it was symbolic. That was what Miss Renie said her pictures were; she said it was all the fashion nowadays to be symbolic. That meant it was a real trick to figger out the meaning, and what did this story mean? That a body worked and struggled to get something, then when he got it, found it wasn't worth a picayune? Unless maybe he had got something you couldn't put a finger on or sell in any market, something not seen by the naked eye. Now take me, for instance, she told herself, come here to get learning and polishment. And I sure been through a time, what with Pete's raising a ruction and me getting mixed up with unborn babes and nekkid pictures and stolen jewels. Maybe the p'int of the whole matter was that you had to keep on struggling and trying your best, come good or come bad, and the best of all would sneak in unbeknownst to you. With that she laid the book aside and closed her eyes and slept.

The sound of wood chopping awoke her. She went on deck and there was Mrs. Call splitting kindling with the hatchet. "What are you up to, Mrs. Call? That's my job."

"Your grandpa very kindly did the most of it before the boat came by for him. What an obliging man! You never told me, nor what a fine storyteller he is. I could listen to him by the hour. A real original and most appreciative of the little cooking I did for him. I don't know when I have had a more delightful day." She sounded as if she had completely forgotten what might happen at any moment.

A delightful day, she called it, did she, Tammy thought with indignation; and me about to be taken up and off to jail! Here I'd got the notion she was real fond of me, not gauby about me, but with a true, true liking. With that a sadness came over her. There was just no counting on any human being, and as for the Lord, He seemed far off from her at the moment, removed beyond reach of her need. She looked down at the flowing brown river, then up at the uncertain clouds. They were caught by contrary-minded winds, some blowing one way, some the other. Nothing to pin to.

She leaned against the rail watching the vigor of Mrs. Call's movements, the spring of her muscles and the ease with which she wielded the hatchet, and wished the old professor emeritus could see her now. "There be them that truly mourn you for dead," she said at last, and told about meeting him and what he had said.

"Ah yes. Caleb has always kept a tender spot in his heart for me. A great scholar and philosopher. Personally, I like a man with more vigor and individuality, not so bookish. Here— I'll let you finish." She gave the hatchet to Tammy.

Like Grandpa? Tammy wondered, but before she could frame a question, there came the *chug-chug* of a powerful boat moving fast down river in their direction. The sound beat on the air, as if it would set the world atremble. The boat had the look of the one Grandpa had come on, but it was different, and these were other men. Police in uniform, and they sprang aboard, all three of them as soon as they swung alongside, leaving another who sat in a little pilot house.

"Tammy Tyree?"

"Me," Tammy said and then, because it had come out as no more than a whisper, she said again, "It's me."

"I have a warrant for your arrest." This seemed to be the chief, for he turned to the man beside him, saying, "Get that hatchet from her."

Tammy released her grip on its handle. She had not realized she was still holding it. "I . . . I reckon I'd better get my coat."

"Follow her," said the chief.

"It ain't any distance," Tammy reached inside the door and took down her sweater from the nail where it hung.

"Search the place."

"Just a minute, if you please." Mrs. Call's voice rang out so clear and authoritative they all turned and stared at her.

"Who are you?"

"I'll tell you who," Tammy cried. "It's Shanty-boat Annie, that's who."

"Thank you, but never mind that now, Tammy." She turned

281

to the men. "No need to search. I have what you want." She reached in the pocket of Grandpa's old pants and brought forth the necklace.

"Okay. Hand it over. Take it from her, will you?" he said to one of his men.

"Oh, no you don't." She drew herself up so high and mighty that in spite of the look of her clothes she might have been a queen on a throne. "This happens to belong to me and you have no right to it. Furthermore, I ask you all to bear witness to what I now do." She crossed to Tammy, hung it round her neck saying, "I give you this freely for now and forever."

"The old woman's batty," one of the men said in a low voice.

"But you mustn't," Tammy cried when she got back her breath. "You . . . they . . ."

Mrs. Call paid her no mind. "I do now publicly state that I am Mrs. Annie Rook Call, the object, I understand, of a recent search."

"Oh—" Tammy gasped—"but you shouldn't, just to save me! And I'd been thinking you didn't care."

Mrs. Call gave her a small nod, looked at the necklace and added, "It becomes you, my dear. Rather nice stones. And of course the emerald in the center is quite valuable." Then turning to the men who were all in a little whispering huddle, she said, "If you have any doubt of my identity, I will accompany you to town, call my lawyer and prove it."

The chief officer said, "Well ma'm, no matter who you are, you are coming along with us."

"It was my suggestion, remember," she said with dignity, and moving to the bench by the door, she picked up the coat and handbag that were lying there ready and waiting.

"You knew!" Tammy cried. "You had it all planned, you——"

"Of course, child. Come along, only don't tell them a thing till I get my lawyer."

"Separate them," the chief said.

So they were taken from the *Ellen B.* to the police boat, Mrs.

282

Call being led aft and Tammy taken to the forward deck. She stood there with her eyes on the *Ellen B.* till they had rounded a curve of the river. Then she became aware of a voice coming to her from the pilot house behind her, the chief policeman speaking as if into a phone.

"Yessir, we're bringing her in. And listen to this. We've got Mrs. Call. The one they had the reward out for. . . . Sure, she's alive. . . . Yessir, I understand. I'll wait orders. . . . Oh no, sir, she is not violent. Came of her own accord. . . . Yessir!" There was a click, then he said, "Take it easy, Captain. We must receive further orders before we dock."

The engine slowed at once and the boat moved lazily against the current while the sun sank lower and the air grew chill. Tammy pulled her sweater close and sat down on the bench. Poor Mrs. Call! She shouldn't have done this. But since she had, there would be no more talk of stealing, once it was explained to all ashore. She looked down at the pretty Mrs. Call had hung round her neck and wished she had never laid eyes on it, even if it might be valuable as Mrs. Call had said. It was the cause of all their trouble.

After a while, a buzzing from the pilot house caught her attention and she heard the officer again. "Yessir, right here. . . . What? Did you say kidnaping? . . . Oh, I see. That's her niece, is it? . . . I understand. . . . Yessir, straight to the hospital. . . . I'll keep her under close guard. You bet it's serious. . . . Right."

There was a murmur of talk, quick footsteps and the other two men came to stand, one on each side of Tammy. "I ain't fixing to run away," Tammy said.

"We take no chances with kidnapers," one of them told her grimly.

Tammy's lips parted, she started to speak, then clapped one hand over her mouth. Mrs. Call had said don't talk.

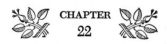
WHEN SHE AWOKE next morning, Tammy did not know
for a little while where she could be. Her cot bed on the *Ellen
B.* scooped down in the middle. This narrow bed was flat, hard
and unwelcoming and did not curve cosily around her. She
opened her eyes on bare gray walls that were all unknown to
her. She blinked at sunlight that fell on the wall beside her,
stripes of sunlight. Then, looking up at the high window, she
saw the iron bars, and everything came back to her.

A pretty state of affairs! Trouble, born to trouble as the sparks
that fly upward, was that how things always had to be with
her? But it was just crazy, this kidnaping idea, it made no
sense and there was no figgering out how it came to pass or
what to do about it.

The lawmen had not let her speak to Mrs. Call on the boat.
They had been kept apart, Mrs. Call having a chance to shout
nothing more than, "Don't talk till I get my lawyer." So she
had held her tongue when the men taking pictures had plied
her with questions, she had choked back the things she longed
to ask them.

Why would they want all those pictures, anyway? Mrs. Call
was not ready to be pictured, she was wearing Grandpa's old
pants with her shirttail out and they gave her no time to pret-

tify herself. Then at the landing they followed along and got more pictures when she was having such a time with the men in white coats. Oh, but that was a sorry sight, for Mrs. Call was fit to be tied when she found they were going to put her in that big white closed-in car. You wouldn't think a woman that little could put up such a fight. And it was most pitiful when she just sort of caved in and let them haul her off.

There was no use fighting the law. So Tammy had gone where she was told and made no resistance. And now all she could think of was what was Pete going to say? And Pete's ma, anybody that took on as she did over Grandpa's being in jail and who shivered every time she heard a *ain't* or a *hells bells* or mention of corn likker, anybody like that wouldn't stop to ask why or wherefore. Just being in jail even by mistake and wrongfully was enough for her. Now Grandpa, he would understand, he had been preaching up yonder at the state jailhouse and he would know what to do to get her out.

She rose and smoothed her dress as well as she could. It had not seemed fitting to take it off last night with jailers and such roaming up and down the halls. Then she bosomed the necklace, thinking it too fine to be seen in such a place as this. She washed her face in the little tin bowl that sat with a pitcher of water on the table in one corner of the room. There was no sign of a towel, but there was a roll of rough paper and she dried her face on some of that and wondered if she could write a letter to Grandpa on it and get it to him some way.

There came a rattle at the door and the same jailer-woman who had gone through her pockets the night before set a dish of bread and mush on the floor along with a cup of coffee. She slammed the door then and locked it behind her without so much as a good day to you. Mighty unsociable, Tammy thought, and not much on manners either. She ate what she could, sitting on the edge of her bed. Then she waited for something to happen.

Grandpa said a body learned from every experience of life,

that was the way to wisdom, he said. Well, now she was learning what it was like to be in jail. Jail had a funny smell, like as if the air come out of a bottle of bad medicine. Sounds came through the wall, muffled and choked by the thickness of the wall. A drunk yelling, "Let me out, let me out!" had a far-off, unreal sound. There were car noises that came in by way of the window, cars going by and never stopping to say a word to them held here against their will. Worst of all, there came a queer, shut-in feeling, desperate-like, as if the walls might be moving in closer all the time. And even that stingy small splash of sunlight now seemed naked and lost, being deprived of green fields and trees to dance amongst. It was still as death. If it moved at all across the floor it was by so stealthy and slow a motion that it seemed to mark not time but eternity, minutes stretching out to hours because they were empty. Was that how eternity got to be so long you couldn't even think of it? Because there was nothing in it but space and emptiness?

The phrase came to her—a thousand years as a watch in the night. Maybe it was like that when one was free, but in jail the watch would not go, it had stopped and so held time forever fixed. As she sat bowed over, thinking these things, there came a rattle of keys and the sound of voices outside the door. Could it be Grandpa, come to save her? She sprang up and stood facing the heavy door as it swung open. But here was only the lawman bringing in another. This other one wore a proper suit, a boiled shirt and a tie and he carried a flat leather case in his hand. He was a ruddy-faced man with gray hair and a well-washed look to him. Not at all the kind one would think to meet up with in a jail. He said some word to the lawman who went straight away, locking the door behind him.

"Good morning, Miss Tyree," the man said.

It was good to meet a mannerly man, and Tammy gave him a hearty "Good day, sir," and while he was looking around for some place to set himself on, she added, "What are they jailing you up for? If it be polite to so inquire."

He gave her a startled glance, such a glance as she had often received since being out in the world, but one she had not yet grown accustomed to. It made her feel queer and shy. "I am Joshua Welling, Mrs. Call's lawyer and at your service, if you so desire." He spoke with the manner of a man who spoke much in the world, but his eyes had a kindly mite of laughter in them, and this gave Tammy ease.

"That's mighty kind of you, sir, and I'm sure glad to be able to talk again. Mrs. Call told me not to say a word till you come, and I tell you it's been hard to keep a bridle on my tongue all this while. Won't you set?" she added, with a gesture toward the narrow hard bed. "It's all I've got to offer."

He looked at the bed as if it might be already occupied and Tammy hastened to reassure him. "There ain't a bedbug in it, or I'd be well bit, after the night in it." Then, thinking he might be shy of sitting alongside of a jailed-up body, she sat on the floor over against the wall, leaning against it, hands clasped around her knees.

"Ah, thank you," he said, seating himself on the edge of the bed. "And I may say that it was very wise of Mrs. Call to warn you against talking. There has already been an unfortunate amount of publicity. She, alas, has talked too much for her own good. But let us think of you now. Please tell me just how it all came about." He gave her a kindly look and leaned forward, resting arms on his knees, studying her earnestly as she spoke.

Now her tongue was loosened and she told him all, from the first day of being sent to Mrs. Call's house from the employment office, right down to finding the necklace, so before she had finished she had just about told him the story of her life. "Most interesting, and if I may say so, unusual. The charge of kidnaping was ridiculous from the first, of course. But Mrs. Call's niece rather lost her head when she heard that Mrs. Call was with you, and since she is a young woman of . . . er . . . persuasive power, she was able to stir up some excitement. I would have had you out last night but it was too late before I could collect the information."

"You mean I will go free? The law? The judge——"

"The kidnaping charge was dropped after I got a statement from the boatman. He has made an affidavit to the effect that Mrs. Call went to you of her own volition. So this part of an unfortunate incident is closed as far as you are concerned."

"And Mrs. Call?"

"Ah, there is another matter. And your clearance of any guilt in the matter automatically puts her in a yet more difficult position." He was silent, his face clouding over with worry.

"How can that be? It is the truth, and the truth should make her free."

He hesitated for a moment, then with a slight gesture of apology, "Well, the fact is that most people, including the judge who will preside over the hearing, will conclude that no one of sane mind would leave a comfortable home to go and live on a shanty boat. If you will pardon me for saying so."

"I will pardon you," Tammy said gravely. "But she has been so happy there. It's a pity to have all this come of it. I can't understand. Why should she have to stand for judgment before a judge?"

"Her niece is going to try to prove that she is of unsound mind, incapable of managing her affairs. I am much afraid that she will succeed in having her committed, or at least, confined to her home with an attendant."

"Hell's bells," Tammy cried. "I never heard tell of such a piece of trumped-up nonsense! Though it's what Mrs. Call was scared of all along, and that's why she sneaked off and kept it all a secret."

"Quite understandable, though in the eyes of the world rather eccentric, to say the least. Now will you be willing to appear in her behalf and testify as to her sanity?"

"I certainly will. Can I get out now?"

He shook his head. "I believe bail is being arranged."

"Bail? I thought you meant I was plumb free."

"No, no, Miss Tammy. The charge of theft still remains."

"But Mrs. Call said . . . and she give it to me in the presence of officers of the law . . . this here thing round my neck . . . so——"

"You do not understand. There must be a hearing to rule on Mrs. Call's sanity. If she is proved to be in her right mind and so pronounced by the judge, and if she then declares under oath that the piece of jewelry was a present from her to you, all charges against you will be dismissed. If, however, she is declared *non compos mentis*, her word is of no standing in a court of law."

"Hell's bells, looks like Miss Sandra is trying to come out topside up in two ways—putting Mrs. Call away and getting me into trouble at the same time."

Mr. Welling nodded. "You put it very clearly."

"But surely the judge, if he's got a grain of sense in his head, will see Mrs. Call is sound as anybody out in the world and sounder than most. I'll tell him, I'll——"

"You may give evidence in her favor," Mr. Welling interrupted, "and I hope you will. Yet you must remember that it is possible Miss Sandra's council may be able to discredit your testimony on the grounds that it is much to your advantage to prove Mrs. Call sane, and therefore competent and able to have given you a present if she so wished."

"Well, I vum. I see it ain't so simple. But Mrs. Call, where is she now?"

"She is in the hospital. For observation."

"Who would be observing her?"

"The doctors. So they can testify as to her mental state. I will notify you when and where the hearing will be held. In a few days, I hope. And since this is Thanksgiving week, you probably won't even miss any classes because of it." He bowed and shook her hand, for the lawman had come and opened the door for him.

Tammy had had but a few minutes to think over all she had heard, when the officer opened the door. He was mighty nice and polite this time. He said the papers had come through, the charge of kidnaping had been withdrawn and she was free to go on bail. But when she started down the hall toward the street, eager to sniff the clean morning air and see the sky once more above her, he stopped her. "There are some friends waiting to see you. This way, please." And he led her down another corridor.

It was Grandpa. Tammy ran into his arms and held tight to him. When she could speak, she asked, "How did you ever get here so fast?" Then she saw Mr. Freeman standing there. "Oh, I might have known you would come to help me." She gave him her hand. "This is my best friend, Grandpa," she added.

"We have already discovered each other, to my great pleasure," Mr. Freeman said. "And now, I have my car here and at your disposal."

"All I want to do is get back to the *Ellen B.* I won't feel truly free till I get there. But you, Grandpa?"

"I have asked for leave so I can stay with you, child, till Miss Annie can come back."

"You reckon they'll let her?"

"It's in the Lord's hands, honey, but we'll do all we can to help."

"I wisht we could see her," Tammy said as they went down the hall and out by the big double doors.

"I've made inquiry," Mr. Freeman said. "She is at St. Luke's, and if you like, we can go by to see her now. Visiting hours are ten to noon."

Even in the city it was good to be free, Tammy thought, as they drove through crowded streets. A body didn't know how good it was to be free till after a spell in jail, nor how good it was to talk till after holding tongue for a while. But now she had to find out about how Grandpa had got here, and she began to ply him with questions. He had seen the news in the morning papers, he said, had heard it on the radio as well, and he had come straightaway, as had Mr. Freeman, the two of them waiting since early morning to see her.

"Were you surprised when you found out Miss Annie was Mrs. Call?" Tammy demanded.

"Well, honey, to tell the truth—" Grandpa chuckled—"I knowed right off she wasn't just what she wanted folks to believe. Then when we got to talking and reminiscing, she forgot to talk like Shanty-boat Annie. So I had my suspicions. Not that I could name any names."

"I didn't like it one bit, being deceiving about it," Tammy said. "But I give my word and I couldn't break it. Now I reckon everybody knows if it was in the papers. I wisht I could see how they put it."

Mr. Freeman, driving the car with great skill in and out among others, said, "Feel in my pocket here and you will find one of the papers. Rather a charming picture of you, so I won't give it to you for keeps."

When Tammy had the paper open before her, she could scarcely believe what she saw. "Student booked on kidnaping charge," the headline ran. "Sensational discovery of missing woman." Not only was it written out to be read by all that could read, but there were pictures for them that couldn't. There they were, she and Mrs. Call standing on the deck of the *Ellen B.*, then there was Mrs. Call being put into the big white car they called an ambulance. "That was a mean, low-down trick," Tammy said, "catching her when she was plumb distracted and trying to get away. Oh, what a sorry sight to lay before the world."

It was a yet sorrier sight when they had arrived at the hospital and had been led by a crackling, starched nurse to the room where Mrs. Call was. She sat by the window wearing her blue dressing gown that was now so much too big for her. She was looking out the window at a single bare, sad tree and she had such a lost look that Tammy, with a small cry, ran across the room to drop on her knees before her. "Don't, don't repine, dear Mrs. Call. It will be all right. It's bound to be. Look at me, I'm out, I'm free and so will you be, and back on the *Ellen B.* before you know what's happening."

Mrs. Call looked down at Tammy and laid one hand on top of her head like a blessing and said never a word.

Then Grandpa came forward. "Miss Annie," he said, taking her hand in both of his, "Miss Annie, I declare, it does me good to see you. And how that blue does become you!"

It was a miracle, the change that came over her. It was like as if his good, strong hands holding hers made a passageway from him to her, so that he was pouring life and hope into her. Eyes grew bright, a delicate color came into her cheeks, she straightened up till she was sitting in her chair like a queen on a throne with Tammy a slave at her feet and Grandpa some knight out of olden days. She fair blossomed forth, like Aaron's rod.

"Mr. Dinwoodie! A pleasure to see you, no matter what the circumstances." Then, seeing Mr. Freeman standing hesitant by the door, she called him over and gave him her hand and said, "Tom, I've done wrong to hold against you all this time some things you could not help and that you have suffered for. It was Tammy here who brought me to see this. Forgive me."

Oh, it was a fine little time they had there together, Tammy thought, and never a word said as to whether Mrs. Call was in her right mind or no. For it was plain to see she had all her senses alive and in use.

As they drove back to the campus, Grandpa said with satisfaction, "It was a regular little love feast."

Mr. Freeman left them as close to the swamp as he could drive. He had work to do and could not accept their invitation to come along and have dinner on the *Ellen B.*, but he hoped to see them soon. Tammy thanked him and said, "I was mighty downhearted and disgraced feeling over being hauled off to jail like that, but now it is all over, you and Grandpa standing by me and all—well, I see it was a right eddifying experience. What's more, they ain't ever going to make me out to be a thief."

So they made their farewells to Mr. Freeman and hand in hand Tammy and Grandpa took the path to the river, dodging the sinkholes as best they could.

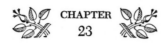

CHAPTER
23

ALL THIS WEEK was to be holiday time because it was Thanksgiving. Grandpa said at morning prayers that there was more than a little bit to be thankful for, mostly that the boatman had made a true statement telling how Mrs. Call had come of her own free will to the *Ellen B.*, so the charge of kidnaping had been withdrawn. Then he said they should be mighty thankful to Mr. Freeman for arranging bail even before Mrs. Call got round to remembering anything about it. A good friend, Grandpa called him and he gave Tammy a quick keen glance as he said it.

There was still the charge of theft to be met. Tammy did not speak of that when Grandpa was listing over their blessings, but it was constantly in her mind like a buzzing bee fixing to sting at any moment. It was bad enough to have spent a night in jail and had it all in the papers and on the radio and maybe even TV too, for all she knew. But if she was found guilty of thieving and got sent to prison, it would surely be the end of everything. Pete's ma would never get over such as that, or Pete either, maybe.

She tried to write him all that had happened, putting it first this way and then that, but all her efforts just piled up in the wood box to start the fire with. Once more, after dinner this day, she began again, "Dear Pete, I been in jail. I might get put back——"

Grandpa came in from the deck where he had been sitting in the mild November sunshine smoking his after-dinner pipe, and found her chewing on the end of her pencil and looking fair distracted. "What's the matter, child?"

"Grandpa, I been trying and trying to tell Pete about everything and I just can't seem to do it. It's the funniest thing."

"Why, honey, if Pete's the man I think he is, he'll understand, won't think any manner of evil of you, no matter what the law says."

"That's just the trouble, Grandpa. I don't know, don't truly know what Pete is any more, or where. I been losing him for a long time, off and on. It's like as if he had melted and run off into nothing but a kind of notion I had, a dream."

"What in the world do you mean?" Grandpa sat down across the table from Tammy and studied her with troubled eyes.

"Well, I go to write him a letter, like right now, and it is like as if I'm hollering into a deep hollow place, like a well, or a cave maybe, and all I get back is an echo. It's like being lost in the dark and reaching out and finding naught there. Like having a dream and waking in the morning. Grandpa, he has withdrawn his face from me and I . . . I can't so much as remember what he looks like. I feel so ashamed." She let the pencil drop from her fingers and covered her face with her hands.

"Now, now, child. No need to get all upset about it. Pete's been away too long and too far. Why, if he was to walk in that door right now, I bet you——"

Tammy looked up. "If he was to walk in that door this minute, it would be like some stranger come to call. So much has happened, so many people I've come to know—all that has set him at a great distance. Half the time I go through the whole day and never even so much as think about him." She touched her breast with her fingertips. "Just empty, empty."

"But, my child, if you love him——"

"I don't believe any more that there is any such of a thing as love," she broke in fiercely. "If all I felt for Pete can just melt away into nothing, then there ain't any such thing as true love, and I can't put dependence on any feeling. It plumb scares me. Oh, Grandpa, I'm sorely troubled, I'm fair distraught."

"I can see that, child, and there ain't much I can do to help you beyond telling you that truly there be such as love and there be times when there is naught to do but trust in the Lord." He rose, went to the closet and got out the jug of corn liquor and took a swig, then sat down again, his breath coming fast and one hand to his side.

"Wh-what's the matter, Grandpa?" Tammy cried in quick alarm.

"Nothing, nothing, honey. Just a twinge I get sometimes. The old rheumatiz in a new place, I reckon." His color was coming back now but his face still had a queer, strained look.

"Grandpa, I been laying my troubles on you and it's about got you bowed down. I hadn't ought to have done it. Why don't you lie down and have your nap now and rest yourself and forget about me? I'll make out."

"Sure you will, child, and don't worry about me." But all the same he lay down and let her cover him over with a blanket.

"I'll go see if there's any mail," Tammy said. "Then I'll come back and cook you a good supper."

The campus was deserted of students on this November day. Off in the distance Tammy saw the professor emeritus taking his daily walk, but she scooted round the corner of a building without stopping to pass the time of day with him. Likely he would want to talk and talk about Mrs. Call, plying her with questions. Another day she would linger and hold converse with him.

There was no letter from Pete—she hadn't really expected one—but there were other letters, one for her and one for

297

Grandpa, both from the same, for in each corner was printed Mr. Welling's name, att'y. at law and where he might be found. Inside Tammy's letter was word of the hearing. The judge would hold a sanity hearing the next day at ten o'clock in the morning and she must be there to make a statement. The letter had a stately, lawlike sound in its manner of expression, a solemn turn to its words, far removed from common speech. It fair gave Tammy the shivers to read it. But Grandpa, when she got back to the *Ellen B.* and gave it to him to read along with his own, said all legal talk was in suchlike fashion, being full of wherebys and inasmuchases. It was naught to be afeard of, he said, this being a lawyer's natural speech, just as a frog has a croak and a bird a tweet. Grandpa was a great comfort. More than once she almost told him about Rita and the babe. But each time something held her back. Sufficient unto the day was the evil thereof and March was a long time off. So she gave herself up to the pleasure of having Grandpa back on the *Ellen B.* It was like old times, only the high bluff was not there above the river, nor the little graveyard atop it where Grandma lay sleeping under the cedar trees.

Next morning she dressed with care in her clean best cotton dress and she brushed Grandma's old brown coat, for this was a clear cold day and at dawn there had been a heavy frost. Grandpa got himself up in his good preaching suit of clothes and even put on a necktie, though his gray whiskers covered where a tie went. At the edge of the swamp Mr. Freeman, true to his promise and prompt as always, was waiting to drive them into town. He and Grandpa had taken to each other at first meeting and today, rolling along the paved highway, they spoke of politics and preaching and the state of the world—a sorry one, they both agreed. Tammy sat listening, saying little, feeling puffed up with pride that Grandpa could talk with the best, and feeling, for the moment at least, eased of her worries, and distracted from her nervousness about the hearing.

"You know, sir," Grandpa said, leaning back as if savoring

the luxury and elegance of Mr. Freeman's car, "you know, I wonder sometimes if it would not give easement to the international situation if we just started being mannerly, one to another. To all nations no matter who, but especially to them that might be enemies. Not out of fear but on the known proven principle that a soft answer turneth away wrath. I think the Rooshians would be more upsot by that than by any manner of threats and suchlike ways known and familiar to them. More dignified, somehow, too."

Mr. Freeman seemed pleased with the idea and he went on to make inquiry into Grandpa's opinion of other matters, the atom bomb tests and what he called the fallout.

Grandpa had plenty of thoughts on every subject named and he never was one to hold back when there was a chance to hold forth. Tammy thought that if the journey were a thousand miles, he still would be talking away at the end of it. "Trouble with these tests," he said, "is that they pollute the air for all breathing human beings the world over, not just them that makes and shoots or gives the orders, but for every innocent unborn babe to the third and fourth generation. No sir, I don't hold with any of it."

"But we have to be able to defend ourselves, don't we?" Mr. Freeman put the question not so much as if disagreeing, but rather as if he might be trying to squeeze more juice out of fruit while he held it in his hand.

"Sir, I am just a plain country preacher, but at the same time I am a kind of prophet in a way, a voice come out of the swamp and wilderness. I tell you the military is behindhand in its thinking, backwards in its going. The military don't seem to know this here is a new time and a new state of affairs in the history of the world. Wars don't win, neither for this side nor the other, and one more will be the end of us and our habitations. Like the prophet says, instead of man, wild beasts of the desert shall be there and their houses shall be full of doleful creatures and owls shall dwell therein and satyrs shall dance there. Wild beasts of the islands shall cry in their desolate houses and dragons in their pleasant places. That's what will come to man and his towns and cities and all his dwelling places, if one more war comes."

"Some say it is bound to be," Mr. Freeman said.

"I don't believe it. But if we got to get kilt and wiped off the face of the earth, here's how to meet it. Let's keep just enough bombs to hit back onct, and let all the world know this. Then let us take a stand for peace and nothing but. Put all this military money into helping them that have need, the world over, regardless of race or space, of creed or greed, regardless of color and outward appearance. Then if we get kilt it will be dying in a noble manner, worthy of humankind at its best. Noble and right." He was silent at last and Tammy thought likely this was part of a new sermon he'd got up for the state prison folk. She thought it good enough for saints as well as sinners and breakers of the law.

Mr. Freeman had listened with respect and interest plain to see, and Grandpa was still holding forth when he drove the car slantwise into an open space in front of a big brick building and said, "Well, here we are."

On the steps and inside the entrance a lot of men were standing around with cameras pointed, and others came pushing forward with questions on their lips. Grandpa seemed to take it for a good moment to preach a sermon on the rights of private citizens to keep their privacy when they were just attending to their own business, but Mr. Freeman took him by the arm and took Tammy by the hand and hustled them quickly up to an officer of the law in a uniform. The crowd fell back a bit, afeard of the law, no doubt. Then Mr. Freeman said good luck and good-by and he would be waiting outside when they were through because the public was not admitted to the hearing. But before he left them, he gave Tammy an encouraging pat on the shoulder. "You just speak out. You'll say the right thing.

After all, you have been studying public speaking with me, haven't you?" He smiled down at her as he spoke.

"I'll do my best," Tammy said right gratefully, and followed Grandpa where they were led.

It was not a big room such as one might expect for a big trial of murder or some such thing, but it was plenty spacious and ample for chairs and benches set in a kind of half-circle, with a raised platform at the far side in the center, a desk and chair waiting there. It was not a regular courtroom, Tammy thought, for surly that would be stripped bare of all but justice, that being something that took no decoration. Here were pictures on the wall, important-seeming figures out of olden times, and there were yellow chrysanthemums in a vase on the desk where likely the judge would be, commanding the whole. Altogether it was an elegant room and full of dignity.

Some people were already seated roundabout, all quiet as if awed by the nature and ornamentation of the room. Mr. Welling that was Mrs. Call's lawyer came quickly up to meet them and said where they were to sit. Miss Jenks was there. She gave Tammy a slow bow of the head in greeting and took one quick wondering look at Grandpa. There was a strange man beyond her, one unknown to Tammy but of pleasing aspect. That was all she saw at first glance.

Seated, she was able to look around and take it all in. Across the open center space sat Mrs. Call's niece, Miss Sandra Rook, dressed in black as if she might be already gone into mourning for her aunt that was lost. It became her, and likely that, rather than grief, had decided her on it. She spoke to no one and just fidgeted in her chair, taking sideways glances this way and that. The boatman was right behind her alongside a man in a white coat. There was a lady unknown to Tammy and wearing a hat too brightly pink for her hide and her years, and behind her was Della, the cook Tammy had seen the first day she went to Mrs. Call's house. They all had a waiting air, and

301

the room was filled with a scary, waiting silence that was louder than noise.

It was Grandpa who spotted Mrs. Call. She was sitting off to the side, almost hidden by her lawyer, Mr. Welling. She was so little and scared seeming and squunched down in her chair that it was as if she was trying not to be there at all. Grandpa, having the habit of gatherings of people and the custom of preaching to multitudes, was not put down or awed by the solemn air of the room. Soon as ever he laid eyes on Mrs. Call, he was up and over to where she sat, without so much as a by-your-leave to anybody. He bowed himself over and took her hand. He spoke too low for Tammy to know what he was saying, but it must have been words fit to hearten the dead, for directly Mrs. Call began to perk up and kind of prune herself.

A little sound of whispering ran round the room, a rustle of words like leaves in a small wind. It died down when a door opened at the side of the room and in came a tall thin man with a face as lined as a hound-dog's and nary a hair on his head when seen frontways. This gave him the look of having a pure brain, Tammy thought, and a plenty. He went straightway to the chair behind the table, he gave a small nod that took in all present, lifted a kind of hammer and let it fall just once. He set some dark-rimmed spectacles on his nose, giving himself a learned air, then took up a paper from the table and part reading, part talking, began to speak in a deep rolling voice that might have got him the calling of being a preacher if he had not come to be a judge.

"This is an informal hearing to inquire into the sanity of one Mrs. Annie Rook Call of this city and county, called at the request of her niece, Miss Sandra Rook of New Orleans in the State of Louisiana, who believing her aunt to be of unsound mind due to age and general debility, prays that said aunt be committed to a suitable institution or confined in her own home in the care of proper attendants. Furthermore, she prays that

302

she, the said Miss Sandra Rook, be appointed administrator and conservator of the said Annie Rook Call's real and personal property together with all rights and remunerations pertaining thereto. Being mindful that all are presumed sane until proved otherwise, I now ask if you have witnesses to prove the validity of your claim." He looked to the niece and her lawyer over the rim of his spectacles.

The lawyer sitting beside Miss Sandra rose, saying "Yes, your honor, I do." Then he beckoned to the man in a white coat. Dr. Stach was his entitlement and it seemed that he was a medical doctor by calling. He stood up, swore to tell the truth, not just a little of it but all of it. He said he was the one in charge of getting Mrs. Call to the hospital. He named a long list of diseases she had along with symptoms of violence. "When I met her at the dock, I took her arm to guide her to the waiting ambulance. She had refused to use the stretcher and I humored her in this regard. But when she came up to the ambulance, she became violent. It was necessary to administer a hypodermic before she could be subdued and brought to the hospital. Since then I have observed her daily in the hospital where she alternates between high excitement and fits of depression in which she refuses to speak to anyone. Such behavior is typical. I submit herewith a detailed, more technical report of her condition, your honor." He laid a folded paper on the judge's table and continued, "In my opinion she is *non compos mentis* and should be institutionalized under competent medical care. The prognosis at her age is not favorable."

The judge nodded to Mr. Welling and he got up, saying, "Just one question, your honor." He walked over to stand in front of the doctor. "Sir, let us take a hypothetical case. If you were off on a fishing trip, were forcibly brought back and thrust into an ambulance, would you not make some objection thereto? Would you not——"

Miss Sandra's lawyer bounced up and objected and the two

303

of them came nigh to having a real fraction then and there. But the judge calmed them down and the next witness was the lady in the pink hat and falsely pink lips that stayed in a straight line no matter what. She lived neighbor to Mrs. Call, right in back. They hadn't been speaking since Mrs. Call's pet turtle trespassed over into her garden and got chewed up by her chow dog. But she had seen plenty from her back windows that overlooked Mrs. Call's garden.

"Tell us some of the things you have observed, please, ma'm," the lawyer said.

"Well, I've seen her walking up and down the garden walk whacking at the hedge with her cane. Violent, she was and none there to stay her from it. That was after the turtle. She used to talk to him, gave him the name of Wirt."

"Did you hear what she was saying at any time?"

"Couldn't help it after she got so mad at my dog. She would come to the back fence and shout, called him a bastard cur, said he was a purple-tongued turtle-eater and she would shoot him if he ever came her way. Anyone that would take on like that over a turtle—well, I don't feel safe in my bed."

"Do you recall any other incidents?"

"There was the business of the ball of yarn."

"Describe it, please."

"Well, I looked out one day and there she was throwing the ball of yarn up into the sweet olive tree. Then she would pick it up and throw it back and she kept right on till the whole thing was unwound and draped over the tree like a big red spider web. I declare, it was downright scary, seeing her carry on so."

Now it was Mr. Welling's turn to put a question. He said, "You are fond of your fine chow dog, are you not, ma'm?"

"Oh, yes, he's a thoroughbred and so smart he's about human. Why, sometimes——"

"Sometimes it seems as if he understands every word you say?"

"You took the words right out of my mouth. One time——"

"Your honor, I object." That was Miss Sandra's lawyer bouncing up like a frog onto a log. He used a lot of words like irrelevant and immaterial but the point was that he didn't like it. The judge made a rule in his favor and Tammy's heart sank. Things looked mighty black for Mrs. Call, and for me too, she thought.

Mr. Welling looked very well pleased, however, and sat down and said no more, likely thinking he had proved his point already. So another came forward to testify, and this was the boatman. He told how this lady in silks and satins and strung with beads had come off the ferry just as he was tying up his boat for the night and she asked him to take her downstream a ways. "I thought it was mighty queer at the time but she paid me to do it, and to come by every week to where she was and bring her supplies. So I done it, thinking it wasn't none of my business. But if I had of heard in time about there being this lady missing and her folks all upset and worrying, I natchully, knowing my duty as a public citizen, I would have come in and give information, and got the reward ahead of them officers of the law." He cast a sour glance around the room, adding, "Wouldn't nobody but a crazy woman ever go to such a place to live."

The cook came next. "Yessir, I been cooking for Miz Call six year come Christmas. Notional, and getting more so every day. If it hadn't been for Miss Sandra here begging me not to, I'd have quit long ago. So when Miz Call give me the bus fare to go visit my daughter in Chicago, and said clear out, well, I wasn't going to do nothing else but. She said she was going on a trip and don't go blabbing. So I didn't, just lit out for Chicago and I'd be there yet if Miss Sandra hadn't got me back so's I could swear she's crazy in the head. I testifies to that."

Mr. Welling put a question to her. "You have cooked for other white ladies?"

"Yessir."

"Did you find any of them notional, as you call it?"

"They all is." A small titter of laughter ran round the room, the judge rapped on his table and she added quickly, "But this here was the most."

Miss Sandra herself was the next, and she had a plenty to say. Making herself out to be the lovingest relative in the world. Being the only living relative, she felt a responsibility, she said, and as often as her affairs permitted, came up from New Orleans to look after her aunt. She was thunderstruck when she got the note saying Mrs. Call was off on a boat for—she didn't say where. Nobody could tell Mrs. Call a thing. "So I did what I thought was right, your honor, I reported her disappearance to the police and even, poor as I am, offered a reward for information about her. Foul play was what I was afraid of, especially as she had drawn out a large sum of money from the bank the day of her disappearance. I thought someone might have murdered her for the money." She paused to wipe her cheek with a small lacy handkerchief as if there might be a tear there. "Also, I thought someone might have taken advantage of her mental condition to keep her a prisoner, as indeed is exactly what happened. I don't care what anybody says." She gave Tammy a mean look and went on, "There's more to it than that. I was staying at my aunt's house, worried sick about her, and one night this girl came sneaking in and stole my aunt's jewelry, dropping a diamond brooch on the floor as she escaped, and what's more——"

Tammy was on her feet. "I never stole nothing! I——"

Then Mr. Welling broke in, objecting so loud he drowned them both out, along with the judge's hammering, and he said this was a sanity hearing and not a trial for theft. The judge agreed with him and told Miss Sandra to stick to the case now before the court.

She did so by the hardest gulping-back of her words and then went on to say, "When they called me from police headquarters and told me they had a report from the officers who had gone to arrest this . . . this girl for thieving, because I saw her with my own eyes wearing a diamond pendant——" Mr. Welling didn't have to object this time because the judge did it and told Miss Sandra she must watch her words or he would hear no more.

"Yes, your honor," she said, meek and sniffling a little. "I'm sorry but I am so upset. Well, anyway, when I got this report on my aunt, that she was living in squalor and discomfort on a shanty boat, I just knew this girl was at the bottom of it and if she wasn't—which you will never make me believe, no matter what this man here says about her asking him to take her there in his boat—then I knew her mind had failed completely. My aunt's mind, I mean. For surely, your honor, no one in her right mind would slip off or allow herself to be taken off to live on a shanty boat with a girl nobody had ever heard any good about, a river girl with no culture or background, not to mention morals, who has been taking advantage of a poor old irresponsible woman, bleeding her of money and though she has managed to get out of it somehow, holding her a prisoner on that dreadful shanty boat." She went on and on about this in spite of Mr. Welling's saying it had naught to do with the case, and the judge's pounding on his desk. Tammy, hearing her name thus scandalized, had difficulty holding her tongue, and Grandpa was all swole up like a turkey gobbler.

"I just want to do my duty in this painful matter, your honor," Miss Sandra said, winding up, "and so I ask that my aunt be declared *non compos mentis*." Then she put her handkerchief to her eyes and shook her shiny gold hair down across her cheek and seemed overcome.

Now it was Mr. Welling's time to question her, and he did. She did not want to answer, that was plain to see. And the p'int of all he was getting at was that she'd up and started buying a big house down in New Orleans and she couldn't keep on paying for it, so she was needing money the worst way. Her lawyer kept bobbing up and objecting but he could not keep it from being made plain for the judge and all to understand that she was hoping to get her hands on Mrs. Call's money. When Mr. Welling was through with her and she nigh on to tears—true tears this time—her lawyer tried to make things all smooth and fine again. That seemed to be the manner of the law, Tammy thought, see-sawing back and forth with the judge saying naught, just setting there taking it all in and making up his mind.

Mrs. Call had sort of slumped down in her chair with her hand over her eyes. And for a fact things did look pretty black for her. But now the judge creaked his chair around, it being one of those that turned on a kind of screw, and said, "I believe we have some witnesses to the contrary?"

The first one was the stranger sitting right behind Mrs. Call and he turned out to be her doctor, a slow-speaking man, making every word count. He didn't like to disagree with his colleague, he said, but he had attended Mrs. Call for the past twenty years. He had now examined her mentally and physically and found nothing abnormal, in fact her condition had greatly improved during the recent months since he had last seen her.

Then it was Miss Jenks's turn. She was quick and to the point and no nonsense. She had seen Mrs. Call on the day of her disappearance. At the president's tea Mrs. Call had poured and had been spoken to by many old friends. "We were delighted to have her once more taking some interest in the affairs of the college." Yes, it was true, she had sent Miss Tyree to be interviewed, this in answer to Miss Rook's request for a student. "Neither she nor Mrs. Call liked the choice and simply sent her away. That is all I know," she said. "Except that later Miss Tyree reported to me as dean of women that she needed no such position as an elderly lady was staying with her."

"Just a minute," Miss Sandra's lawyer began when it was his turn, "was Miss Tyree the first you had sent there?"

"No."

308

"Why did not the others stay?"

"They . . . they found it difficult."

"Ah, now we are getting down to the facts of the case." And with that he went on at a great rate about how difficult Mrs. Call was, wasn't she? Miss Jenks rather sadly said yes.

Grandpa was called up next, Mr. Welling asking if he had visited the shanty boat while Mrs. Call was there. "Yessir, to my great pleasure," he said. "A very suitable arrangement, the two of them living there in harmony." Then he likely forgot he was not preaching a sermon, for he had a plenty to say about liberty and what a crime it was to deprive a human of his God-given freedom. "On more than one occasion I have returned to visit my granddaughter and while she was at the college attending her classes, I have spent many happy and edifying hours holding converse with Miss Annie—that is to say, Mrs. Call. If she be of unsound mind, your honor, then I say let us have more such who will give up the gewgaws and fine fixings of civilization and return to the age-old simplicities, the fundamentals of life." He might have gone on longer but for Miss Sandra's lawyer objecting and the ruction of the two lawyers got into over it.

"Miss Tammy Tyree," Mr. Welling said, and then when she was settled in the proper place, he asked her to explain to the judge how she came to be involved in this affair. "I'll be glad to," she said, "for there's been some mighty mean low-down things spoken here this morning, spoken with forked tongues and what's true has been twisted till it's hindside to and wrong meaning. Me, I been held up to scorn. A shanty-boat girl off the river, has been said. Well, that is what I be and nothing to be ashamed of if a body be honest and decent and God-fearing.

"I come here to get some learning, seeking out the ways of people, because it is true there's been no trimmings to my life. Lacking money, I looked for a way to earn my keep, and so came to Mrs. Call that would have none of me, like Miss Jenks

309

here has said. But we got to talking, Mrs. Call and me. Next morning I brought her a catfish, fresh caught, and cooked it for her. She was took with the idea of me living on a shanty boat. So it came to pass, out of no wicked design on my part, that I said folks wouldn't let me live alone on the river, no more than they wanted her to be living alone there, so I said wouldn't it be sensible if she come to stay with me. It was my idea. This much of what has been said is true.

"So she come by stealth, because this lady, her niece, might do what she has just done, for a fact, and Mrs. Call well knowed it. It was all considered and reasonable. Living alone in her fine house she was lost and lonesome. Only pleasure she had was eating. I never was acquaint with the turtle she made a pet of in her lonesomeness, giving it a name. But ain't nothing crazy about loving a turtle. Balaam had him a ass that saw more than he did and a poor man told of in the Bible had one little ewe lamb that was as a daughter unto him and lay in his bosom and et of his food."

"Amen!" Grandpa cried, like as if it was a sermon she was preaching.

The judge rapped and said, "Continue, please."

"Living on the river has done her a world of good." Tammy went on. "She's trimmed down till she's a fine-looking figger of a woman, like Grandpa says. What you can't see is how she's changed inside. She don't hold grudges any more, she's of a loving spirit because she's got plenty to do. She rejoices all day long for the rustling of the trees and the running of the river and the birdcalls and frog croaks, she pleasures in the casting forth of a line for fish and the cooking of it. She come to life again, and she got back her soul that was shriveled up to nothing in her elegant house alone.

"Talk about her being crazy in the head for doing so—well, I never heard tell of such a trumped-up piece of foolishness in all my born days. Ain't nobody living more sane and sensible than Mrs. Call, and that's all I got to say on the subject." She drew a long breath and looked around, expecting to be asked questions. But nobody said a word, and the lawyer Welling beckoned her back to her place. Grandpa gave her a pat on the knee so she knew she'd done right.

There was a long silence. The judge polished off his spectacles on a big white linen handkerchief. Then he said, "Any further witnesses?"

"Just one, your honor," Mr. Welling said. "Mrs. Call?"

She shook her head. "Enough has been said."

He bent over her, whispering, and after a moment she nodded reluctantly. Then when she was settled—and a small shrunken, sad figure she seemed—Mr. Welling said, "Will you please explain to us in your own words just why you went to live on the river?"

"I went seeking something I had lost, the zest and wonder I had as a child when I once came down the river on a flatboat." She spoke slowly, her eyes on the floor. But now, turning to the judge, she continued with greater confidence, "At the end of my life I wanted to step away from it and see it whole. When I had done this, I began to live again and I was happy. This I cannot explain."

That was all anybody had to say, except the two lawyers who acted as if nobody had been listening so that now they had to repeat all, each one twisting it and turning it to suit his own ends. According to Miss Sandra's lawyer, Mrs. Call's few words were the senseless meanderings of a maudlin mind. By Mr. Welling's account they were of deep philosophic import.

How could a judge know, when they had finished, what was true and what was false? But he was likely a man used to deciding, Tammy thought, used to weighing and considering and separating the wheat from the chaff. By the time he had polished his glasses once more and banged on the table, his mind was made up. "The court has heard the evidence and finds the plaintiff of sound mind." With that he rose and went out with no further word or look to anyone.

Tammy sat dumfounded. All that gibble and gabble and then the whole business settled in so few words. There was something to be said for the law! And she, she too, was free!

"A good man," Grandpa said and went to shake hands with Mrs. Call, and everyone began to talk all at once, Mr. Welling coming up to say he would see to the ending of all charges against her.

Tammy thanked him, then took a quick look around. Miss Sandra looked as if she might be a doll all the sawdust had just run out of. Pitiful, she looked, for a fact, walking slow with her hair hanging close around her face and her head down. In the jostle of the two groups leaving all by the same door, she came right alongside to Mrs. Call, Tammy right behind.

"Well, Sandra, that's that," Mrs. Call said in a crisp, finishing tone.

"But, Aunt Annie, it's true. I was worried about you," she gulped and met her aunt's eyes briefly.

"You put me through the wringer all right. But I reckon I was a mite thoughtless, myself." Then she added in a low tone, "Why didn't you tell me your allowance was not enough?"

"I . . . I . . ."

"Oh, well, blood is thicker than water. Come along back to the house and I'll see what I can do about it. Only leave me alone hereafter, to live as I please."

"Yes, yes, Aunt Annie."

Tammy moved alongside Mrs. Call as they went through the door. "Aren't you coming back to the *Ellen B?*"

"Ah, Tammy, you really saved the day for me. But come now and stay at my house for a bit. Then maybe in the spring I'll come back with you to the *Ellen B.* Will you?"

"Yessum, I'd like that mightily."

312

Grandpa was suddenly beside them, hearing her last words. "That's kind of you, ma'm. I'll feel easy about my little girl if she's with you, no matter where. And I hope to drop in on you from time to time, but now, things being cleared up and Tammy settled, I reckon I'll just go board up the *Ellen B.* for the time being and then take my leave and get on back to preaching the Word."

The first to leave the hearing room had spread the news and those waiting to hear could now rejoice with Mrs. Call and question and take pictures as they pleased. They all looked astonished to see her leaving with Miss Sandra. It was a kind of miracle, Tammy thought, and as for herself, looked as if the least she could do was to forget all those mean things said. She'd try, anyway. Then at sight of Mr. Freeman at the top of the steps, smiling and nodding his pleasure, she slipped through the crowd, eager to tell him his words had given her courage to talk free and say all that was true and needed.

All at once her way was blocked. She looked up at a tall man standing before her, not letting her pass. She blinked and gulped and looked again. "Pete, Pete! How did you ever——"

"Hitchhiked day and night. Started as soon as I heard. I stopped by Brenton Hall to pick up the old car—and here I am. Oh, Tammy, let me look at you. I've been so worried. Are you all right? Without me to look after you?"

"I'm all right. Even without you," she added slowly, knowing it now to be true, and with the knowledge feeling an emptiness and a stab of pain, as if a wang tooth had just got yanked out by the roots, the deep, deep roots.

Standing there at the top of the long flight of steps with people passing, turning to look, moving on, he studied her, one brow up, one brow down. It was his puzzled look she knew so well. "You've changed."

Tammy nodded. "Yes, Pete, I reckon I have." In the pause that followed, it was as if all her knowing of him passed before her the way a drowning man's life was said to flash by in his last moment. "It's strange, and sad, too. There's something gone from me, and not without pain—a kind of dream maybe. But now I've been out in the world, Pete. I've et of the fruit of the tree of knowledge and now I can see you and me clear, not through a glass darkly."

"You're growing up, honey, that's what it is. But you're still mighty cute, do you know it?" His dark eyes laughed down at her, telling her yes, you may have grown up, but to me you'll always be that cute little girl off the river.

"Cute?" Tammy repeated. "That's what you've always thought, isn't it? And it's not enough."

"Then—" he moved back a little from her—"then it's all right like this and——"

"It's all right, Pete. I never thought I'd be the one to say it but we've come to the parting of the ways. I'll always be beholden to you for taking me in at Brenton Hall, and now for coming down here to help me in time of trouble."

"I'll always help you any way I can, Tammy darling. You can count on it. And as for this trip, I had to come anyway. Aunt Renie's got some wild idea of selling off the slash pine on the lower forty and I couldn't let her do that. Got to rush back now and finish convincing her it'll be worth more later. So come on."

"Come on?"

"To Brenton Hall, of course. Oh, just for the holiday," he laughed. "I'll never try to boss you again." Then sobering, he added, "But I'll always feel—well, responsible for you."

Tammy hesitated, she looked up at the sky now wearing its deeper November blue and of a sudden she was aware of the free morning air on her cheek and the sweetness of her own new liberty. Not just liberty from jail, but from the kind of spell Pete had laid about her since the first moment of their meeting, a one-sided spell as she saw so clearly now. Her glance went roundabout, seeking. Grandpa and Mr. Freeman had fallen into converse with a few people who lingered on the

314

sidewalk and thereabouts. She turned back to Pete. "Thank you, Pete. But no."

He drew a long breath and said never a word, just looked down at her with something—was it easement spreading over his face? "Maybe you're right, you usually are, you wise little woods owl, you." He took both her hands in his, bent and put a kiss on her cheek. "Don't forget Brenton Hall is your home any time you need it." It was what he had said when he left the river, just recovered from his near drowning.

"I won't forget. Give my love to Miss Renie and Osia—and Nanny goat."

Then with a wave of the hand, Pete was gone, running lightly down the steps toward his car. Tammy looked around. The last of the crowd had drifted away. There was only Grandpa there with Mr. Freeman who had turned his back—as if he didn't want to see her with Pete. Slowly she went down the steps and across a strip of green-cut grass to where they stood.

"Where's Pete?" Grandpa said. "He said you were going back with him."

Tammy was looking at Mr. Freeman. A man growed, she thought, not one still fumbling and uncertain. Here was one to put dependence on, and maybe more.

He said, "I saw you meet him, Tammy, and I wish you every happiness, my dear."

"Hell's bells," Tammy cried, "you sound like a funeral sermon."

"Ain't you going to Brenton Hall with Pete?" Grandpa asked as the sound of Pete's engine roared down the street somewhere. He went by with a wave of the hand and never slowing his speed.

"I ain't agoing," Tammy said, a new manner of shyness coming over her as she felt Mr. Freeman's eyes upon her and sensed without seeing the sudden change that had come over him. Like as if he'd been struck by lightning, she thought, or maybe it was more like the sudden coming of the sun from out

315

behind a dark cloud, and the warmship of the sun spread from him to her.

With nary a word spoken, he hung his cane over the crook of his arm and took her hand between the two of his, and he kept on looking down at her in a manner that was both solemn and blithesome, and so a kind of glory encompassed them round about.

Grandpa chuckled to himself. "I reckon I'll sit on the hind seat going back to the *Ellen B.*," he said.

14590

W9-BZH-783

When Children Kill

when children kill

A social-psychological study of youth homicide

Katharine Kelly and Mark Totten

broadview press

©2002 Katherine Kelly and Mark Totten
All rights reserved. The use of any part of this publication reproduced, transmitted in any form or by any means, electronic, mechanical, photocopying, recording, or otherwise, or stored in a retrieval system, without prior written consent of the publisher – or in the case of photocopying, a licence from CANCOPY (Canadian Copyright Licensing Agency), One Yonge Street, Suite 201, Toronto, ON M5E 1E5 – is an infringement of the copyright law.

National Library of Canada Cataloguing in Publication Data
Kelly, Katharine D. (Katharine Doreen)
    When children kill : a social psychological study of youth homicide
Includes bibliographical references and index.
ISBN1-55111-417-8
1. Juvenile homicide—Canada—Case studies. 2. Juvenile homicide—Psychological aspects. I. Totten, Mark Douglas, 1962- II. Title.
HV9067.H6K45 2002   364.15'23'0830971   C2002-900699-6

Broadview Press Ltd., is an independent, international publishing house, incorporated in 1985.

North America:
P.O. Box 1243, Peterborough, Ontario, Canada K9J 7H5
3576 California Road, Orchard Park, NY 14127
TEL: (705) 743-8990; FAX: (705) 743-8353;
E-MAIL: customerservice@broadviewpress.com

United Kingdom:
Thomas Lyster Ltd.
Unit 3&4a, Ormskirk Industrial Park
Old Boundary Way, Burscough Road
Ormskirk, Lancashire L39 2YW
TEL: (01695) 575112; FAX: (01695) 570120; E-mail: books@tlyster.co.uk

Australia:
St. Clair Press, P.O. Box 287, Rozelle, NSW 2039
TEL: (02) 818-1942; FAX: (02) 418-1923

www.broadviewpress.com

Broadview Press gratefully acknowledges the financial support of the Book Publishing Industry Development Program, Ministry of Canadian Heritage, Government of Canada.

Design and composition by George Kirkpatrick
Cover Photo by Wayne Eardly

PRINTED IN CANADA

For
Peter, Valerie, Alison, and Kenny

and

Sharon, Daniel, Kaila, and Leah

Our study could not have been possible without your unwavering commitment, patience, understanding, and support.

This book is just as much yours as ours.
We love you dearly.

KK and MT

contents

acknowledgements

This book would not have been possible without the help and support of many people. We wish to express our sincere gratitude to the Youth Services Bureau of Ottawa for their financial and staffing support. We thank, in particular, Dan Paré, Executive Director; the Board of Directors; and the management team—Gordon Boyd, Mary Conroy, Francine Gravelle, Judy Perley, Wes Richardson, Yvan Roy, Michael Tross, and Denise Vallely. Special thanks are extended to those who helped us with invaluable word processing, transcribing, research, technical support, and supplies—Audra Bennett, Michael Blench, Claudette Contant, Sandie Cybulski, Joanne Moore, Sabra Ripley, Sarah Villani, and Mary Wehrle. Members of the Research Committee—Drs. Tullio Caputo, Robert Flynn, Robert Glossup, Don Loree, and Paul Reed—provided us with a critical reading of our work and many helpful suggestions. Finally, Bob Bennett, Linda Byron, Gordon MacDonald, and Terri Thorhauge gave us invaluable assistance.

Thanks also to Carleton University and its support of the work through its GR-6 grant program and to our colleagues there: Dennis Forcese, Karen March, Flo Kellner, and Zhique Lin.

We extend special thanks to Catherine Latimer and Eileen Hornby, Department of Justice Canada, for their financial support which made this study possible. Their insights into the issue of youth homicide helped us in the presentation and analysis of our data.

Shaila Beaudry, Gerry Bezanson, Roger Boe, Melanie Ferdinand, Skip Graham, Kathleen Hunter, Stephanie MacLeod, Larry Motiuk, Michelle Motiuk, Alyson Muzzerall, John Rives, Rick Sauve, Joe Chmiel, Derra Thibodeau, John Watters, and Francine Wilks assisted us in identifying participants, guided us through the paperwork of getting access to those in custody, or helped with additional administrative tasks. We thank them for their valuable time and insights.

This book would not have been possible without Michael Harrison, Vice-President, Broadview Press; Barbara Conolly and Betsy Struthers, our wonderful Broadview editors. We hope we have lived up to their faith in our work. They have provided us with support and have been tireless in making sure it was known in the academic and publishing world.

Finally, we are grateful to the 19 young people who shared their stories with us. The opportunity to discuss with them some of the most intimate aspects of their lives is one we will always remember. For us this was, at times, a difficult sharing. For them it was even more demanding as they relived horrible events and terrible moments in their lives. We wish them well.

The opinions expressed in this book are ours alone, and may not necessarily reflect those of the Youth Services Bureau of Ottawa, Carleton University or the Department of Justice Canada. Any errors are, of course, our own.

preface

This book is entitled "When Children Kill." We do not attempt to explain *why* children kill, but to explore the conditions leading to and occurring at the time of the murder. We purposely included the term "children" in the title, despite the fact that our participants were *adolescents* when they committed homicide. We did this to emphasize our belief that these youth had suffered so much emotional damage during their lives that they were essentially functioning as *children* when they killed.

What drew us to study the lives of these adolescents? We wanted to provide a more textured understanding of both youth homicide and the young people involved, an understanding that challenges stereotypic notions of youth convicted of homicide as "monsters." We found that our participants were neither simply victims, nor solely villains. They were young people who, in response to emotional, physical, and sexual harm, adopted behavioural patterns that put them at risk to commit murder.

Most children who are harmed as they grow up do not kill. They deal with their harm in other ways, some constructive and some destructive. What led our participants to kill were the choices they made, choices constrained by their abilities (biological, physiological, psychological) and their social circumstances. Our participants chose to respond to their harm and to deal with negative emotions and circumstances through violence. Some were actively violent towards others, some became involved in risk-taking that included aggression towards others, and some kept their commitment to violence hidden in a fantasy world. The choice to use violence led them to hurt others.

Our research has caused us to reflect on some broad philosophical questions about children and youth in Canada. How do young people come to be involved in homicides? Is there a single pathway or are their multiple routes to committing a homicide? What is the nature of responsibility of young people who commit violent crimes? What should be the legal response to young people who kill? Where should these young people be incarcerated—in youth facilities or in adult facilities? Is there anything that can be done to reduce the risk of young people using violence? We address some of these issues in our book.

Our study is exploratory and interpretative. This type of research on a sample of young people charged with homicide has never been done before in Canada. Given the small number of youth who have killed in Canada (an average of 52 young people are charged with homicide offences each year), and in the absence of any available lists of homicide perpetrators, we did not have the luxury of being able to randomly select participants. These factors resulted in important constraints on the generalizability, in the statistical sense of the word, of the results. However, we have discovered patterns and insights that are worth exploring and testing in future research.

Conducting the in-depth interviews and combing through the nearly 1000 pages of interview transcripts and 3000 pages of related documentation was an exhausting and sometimes terrifying process. At times, we were exhilarated, buoyed by the fact that we were breaking new ground in a much talked-about but poorly-understood phenomenon. However, we also found that researching violent and often brutal murders took its toll. We both suffered from symptoms of what has been referred to as vicarious (or secondary) trauma.[1] These included nightmares and anxiety; obsessive thoughts about the offenders, their horrifying actions, and the brutal deaths of the victims; and feelings of hopelessness, sorrow, and anger. How did we cope? We both drew heavily upon our respective external support networks—family, friends, and colleagues. The fact that we both are parents of young children and have understanding partners who have not only tolerated but embraced our passion for this work, helped a great deal. However, some of our children were the same age as the participants were when they killed their victims. This made us vulnerable. We could not help but look at our own kids, thinking "what if?" Arriving home after interviews was always a rush; a rush to embrace our loved ones, a rush to regain some sense of normalcy. Debriefing immediately after interviews was extremely helpful. Journal writing and long-distance running were useful coping mechanisms.

In the end, we hope that we have produced a book that will engage others in a discourse about young people who commit extreme acts of violence. Our wish is that, instead of viewing these adolescents as monsters, the reader will join us in contextualizing their monstrous actions within the bio-psychosocial framework of their life courses.

Note

1 Figley, 1995; Ruzek, 1993; McCann and Pearlman, 1990.

Theories of Youth Homicide

It goes to that no-emotion thing where you can just do anything. That's why I say rage really had nothing to do with it, because it wasn't because I blew up and flew off the handle, when I heard this and went out and killed him. It was like a blankness of no emotion. So anyway, it was somewhere from the game to becoming a reality. I struck him with a baseball bat, and then from the first blow that I hit him, it sort of snapped me into reality of what was happening. I just struck this guy, and it was a pretty bad blow to start with. I went into a panic from there, where I was hitting him more. Then what evolved from there, is that I felt he was going to die from the injuries he had sustained, and there was nothing I could do, couldn't call an ambulance or something like that 'cause he was already basically going to die, but that he was suffering on the way to there. At that point, I got a knife and cut his throat. That was, the purpose of that was, because I felt he was going to die, but I couldn't handle watching him suffer while he was going there. So that was really the essence of the plan. After that was the panic, now this is done, and I don't want to be around here, and clean the place up and things like that. I was picked up the next day.

This is Phillip's[1] account of the homicide he committed. Phillip had been a troubled young man before the murder, with significant psychiatric problems and a history of violent outbursts. As this study demonstrates, he and the others we interviewed are not simply "monsters" who murder. Rather, they are troubled young people whose childhood and adolescent histories contributed to their killings and involvement with the criminal justice system. While adolescent homicides have garnered much attention and outrage over the past number of years, the problems these young people experienced prior to these acts have remained virtually invisible. Instead, public

I

concern has centred on their criminal histories, their "depravity," and their lack of values. This is likely due to a perception that "[j]uveniles who kill challenge long-standing and widely held conceptions of childhood and adolescence."[2] The emotional, social, and economic context of their lives is often forgotten during this public discourse.

We use a life-course approach, through in-depth interviews, to understand how the histories of the 19 adolescents in our study contributed to their extreme acts of violence. When we quote these young people, we attempt to provide the proper context; the quotes are verbatim, and the language is often raw.

Defining Homicide

Homicide is a general term for the culpable killing of one human being by another. In legal terms, homicide includes murder, infanticide, and manslaughter (Criminal Code of Canada [CCC] s. 222). In this study we examine only murder and manslaughter.

According to the Criminal Code of Canada, homicide is defined as a murder:

a) when a person who causes the death of another means to cause that death, or means to cause harm, knowing (or ought to know) that causing death is a likely consequence of that harm and is reckless.

b) when death occurs by accident or mistake when the perpetrator means to cause death or means to inflict bodily harm that she or he knows (or ought to know) is likely to cause death.

c) when, during the commission of an unlawful act, a person does something that he or she knows or ought to know is likely to cause death, notwithstanding that there is no desire to cause death and/or bodily harm. A wide variety of acts are considered: high treason, treason, sabotage, piratical acts, hijacking an aircraft, escape from prison or lawful custody, assaulting a peace officer, sexual assault (levels 1, 2, and 3),[3] kidnapping and forcible confinement, hostage taking, robbery, break and entering, and arson. The perpetrator is held to be guilty of murder whether or not she or he intended to cause the death.

Murder is classified as first or second degree. First-degree murder is generally regarded as a murder that is planned and deliberate. However, the CCC statutes on first-degree murder include acts where the death is both intended and unintended and where the accused both commits the offence and does not. With respect to the latter, "murder for hire," or contracting a murder, is considered first-degree murder, even though the person charged did not commit the actual offence. First-degree murder also includes deaths whether planned or not when the victim is a peace officer,[4] or when the death is caused while the offender is committing or attempting to commit hijacking, sexual assault, kidnapping or forcible confinement, or hostage-taking. The CCC also includes as first-degree murder deaths that occur when committing criminal harassment and when an associate of a criminal organization uses explosives.

Second-degree murder is a residual category; it includes all murders that are not first-degree murder. Manslaughter is commonly understood as a reduced, or less serious, charge than murder, and its general definition is a culpable homicide that is not murder or infanticide. The CCC does allow for an act that would otherwise be defined as murder to be reduced to manslaughter when the act is committed in the "heat of passion" caused by provocation.

Another charge related to homicide is death caused by criminal negligence (CCC s. 220). In this case the accused can be convicted of either murder or manslaughter; the issue is whether the offender showed a wanton or reckless disregard for the lives or safety of others. For the conviction to be a murder conviction, the perpetrator must have intended to cause death or bodily harm. For a negligent homicide to be considered manslaughter, the issue of intent to cause death and/or bodily harm becomes critical. Criminal negligence charges that could result in a manslaughter charge include deaths resulting from drunk or reckless driving.

The CCC also stipulates that a person can be guilty of a homicide both when they commit an act and when they fail to act. Thus, a parent may be culpable in the death of their child not because they directly caused that death, but because they failed to protect their child from violence by another that they foresaw or ought to have foreseen. Similarly, one can be charged with homicide when one participates in a crime that results in a death at the hands of a co-criminal.

Our case studies include young people who were convicted of first-degree murder, second-degree murder, and manslaughter. Some of them committed the actual murders. Others were charged and convicted when

3

they were involved indirectly in events that resulted in deaths. For some, simply being present in a location where a homicide occurred and not acting to stop it was enough to result in conviction. In some of these situations, participants reported that they felt unable to stop the events. In most, they didn't try. Finally, some of these offenders were convicted of murder because of criminal negligence—for example, drunk driving causing deaths.

Theoretical Understandings of Youth Homicide

While youth homicide is rare in Canada, it is an event that raises substantial concern, anger, and fear. Why do "kids" kill? In answering this question, it is important to recognize that youth homicides are not homogenous events—there are different types of homicides.[5] Homicides vary according to the type of victim. Some victims are family members (parents, siblings, grandparents, etc.), some are strangers, and many are acquaintances (friends, schoolmates, and casual acquaintances). Homicides also vary in the context in which they occur: during the commission of a crime,[6] motivated by hate or bias, revenge killings, and senseless killings for "thrills."[7]

Despite this diversity, Marvin Wolfgang and Franco Ferracuti remind us that what unites homicides is that they are all acts of violence.[8] While this is helpful in framing a study of homicide, it begs the question: why are human beings violent? Wolfgang and Ferracuti argue that the extent to which any individual is violent (either lethally or sub-lethally) is learned (that is, we are socialized to use or not use violence).[9] What factors impact on an individual's socialization to use violence? Traditional approaches focus on the ability of social institutions (the family, school, neighbourhood, community, peers) to provide individuals with non-violent means to resolve conflicts, with vocabularies of motives to support non-violence, and with the means to meet their needs without violence. While we recognize the importance of institutional factors in violence, we argue that socialization to violence begins with macro-social factors and is mediated through individual capabilities. Macro-social factors—such as the organization of production, social definitions of youth, and state policies—contribute indirectly to the likelihood of any member of society committing violence through their impact on the social institutions (the family, schools, peers, religious institutions, communities, and neighbourhoods) that provide people with the knowledge, skills, norms, and abilities they require. Finally, socialization depends upon the individuals' capabilities (their biological and psychological make-up). These factors combine (interact) to increase the risk of young people becoming involved in crime. Eron *et al.* sum up this position as follows:

> As the individual child develops and matures, he or she learns how to interpret the surrounding world as hostile or benevolent, how to solve interpersonal problems in pro-social or in anti-social and violent ways, how to manage or mismanage frustration, and how to meet emotional, social, and physical needs through either legal or illegal means. This learning takes place in multiple contexts: in the family, school, peer group, neighbourhood, and larger community, each of which are affected by social and cultural forces in society at large.[10]

Socialization contributes to the development of particular attitudes towards violence in certain children. However, it also impacts on the kinds of situations that these children find themselves in and hence indirectly on their risk of both using violence and becoming its victim.[11] As we shall see, situations are often a key factor in the culmination of violence in a death.

While our integrated approach argues that homicide and violent behaviour are the outcome of individual, social, and situational factors, most existing theories, primarily from Britain and the US, tend to focus exclusively on biological/physiological, psychological, *or* social factors as leading to violent and deadly outcomes, but fail to integrate these important areas. However, individuals are born with certain bio-social psychological features and exist within socio-cultural locations. These locations impact profoundly on how any particular child "turns out." A bio-social psychological approach integrates all significant factors related to child and adolescent development and contextualizes violent behaviour within life experiences. Figure 1.1 summarizes these factors.

We argue in this book that young people are not born killers. Rather, over their life course, their experiences, their emotional responses to them, and their behavioural choices come together to place them in situations where homicides are likely to occur. While the choices made are important, it is critical to note that these are *constrained* choices: constrained by life experiences and by each person's unique abilities. It is critical to recognize that there are multiple pathways to involvement in homicide. Children have different biological make-ups. Some face biologically based problems, such as Fetal Alcohol Syndrome (FAS); others have brain injuries that limit their ability to cope. They also experience different kinds of negative social events—poverty, neglect, abuse, family violence, bullying, and teasing—and they struggle to deal with them in a variety of ways. They have differential access to positive social support. Families, communities, school, health, and social services supports vary from young person to young person. All too often these institutions fail to identify the problems facing young children or they are unable or unwilling to respond to them. Children themselves have different skills and abilities that influence their ability to respond to adversity. Some are very resilient and survive well despite serious trouble; others are unable to cope in pro-social ways with their pain and trauma.

Generally, children learn a variety of ways for dealing with the pain, frustration, isolation, and other negative feelings they experience. These patterns of behaviour lead some to engage in behaviours that put them "at risk" to harm themselves and others. Most do not set out to kill.

None of these factors alone will cause a youth to use serious violence; instead, the presence of many of these factors *in interaction* can dramatically increase this likelihood.[12] In addition, wider social features (macro-sociological features of a society) and the immediate situations impact on homicide events.

Macro-level Factors: The Role of Poverty, Gender, and Race

How do macro-sociological factors impact on the ability of institutions to socialize children into positive (non-violent, non-deviant) roles? How do they impact on the failure of these institutions to meet these goals? There is considerable evidence that violence, including homicide, is a consequence of socio-economic factors, particularly economic inequality[13] and labour markets.[14] The social definition of youth is an important macro-level factor in shaping youth violence.[15] Gender also plays a pivotal role, as males are more likely than females to use violence generally and lethal violence in particular. Although race has been a critical concern, many researchers argue that it is a "mask" for broader social factors related to poverty, as well as to community and familial disruption, which are more common in some minority communities. Finally, government policies also impact on the ability of institutions to socialize children away from violence.

Poverty
Poverty can aggravate any number of the social psychological factors discussed in this chapter, creating conditions conducive to extreme youth

Individual Factors	► Pregnancy and delivery complications; low birth weight; FAS/FAE; developmental delays.
	► Girls: internalizing disorders (nervousness/withdrawal, anxiety, eating disorders, suicidal behaviour, self-mutilation).
	► Boys: externalizing disorders (hyperactivity, concentration problems, restlessness, risk taking, aggression).
	► Early initiation of violent behaviour.
	► Involvement in other forms of antisocial behaviour.
	► Beliefs and attitudes favourable to deviant or antisocial behaviour.
Family Factors	► Parental criminality.
	► Child maltreatment.
	► Poor family management practices (neglect, poor supervision, severe and inconsistent discipline, unclear expectations).
	► Low levels of parental involvement.
	► Poor family bonding and conflict.
	► Parental attitudes favourable to substance abuse and violence.
	► Residential mobility (frequent moves).
	► Stress (unemployment, social isolation, lack of resources).
	► Parent-child separation, leaving home at early age.
School Factors	► Academic failure.
	► Low bonding at school (low commitment and educational aspirations).
	► Truancy and dropping out of school.
	► Frequent school transitions.
	► High delinquency rate of students at school.
Peer-related Factors	► Delinquent siblings.
	► Delinquent peers.
	► Gang membership.
Community and Neighbourhood Factors	► Poverty.
	► Community disorganization (presence of crime, drug-selling, gangs, poor housing).
	► Availability of drugs and guns.
	► Exposure to violence (home, elsewhere) and racial discrimination.

Figure 1.1: Summary of Youth Violence Risk Factors[16]

violence. Many studies have suggested the link between low socio-economic status and physical violence. Findings are generally attributed to the higher levels of stress and the lack of access to relevant resources to remedy prevalent problems associated with living in poverty (for example, physical and mental illness, unemployment, substance abuse, parenting difficulties, crime, etc.). It must be noted that poverty alone does not cause violence; the vast majority of low-income individuals are peaceful citizens. However, it is one important mediating factor.

At the macro-level, inequality and poverty combine to lessen the ability of institutions, such as the family, to meet the needs of young people. Macro-level changes in the economy are associated with the availability of entry-level, low-skill jobs and the potential for social mobility. The loss of entry-level jobs tends to raise unemployment:[17] one consequence of limited employment opportunities is poverty. Poverty denies people access to traditional sources of status and respect. This may have a number of profound impacts not only on individuals, but also on their ability to parent children. Poor parents are at greater risk for feelings of shame, humiliation, and disrespect—all antecedents to violence.[18] These feelings affect their parenting skills.

It is important to recognize that families across the socio-economic spectrum may be unable to meet the needs of their children—child abuse and neglect may also result when parents are stressed, addicts, alcoholic, mentally ill, or emotionally disturbed. It is the combination of both family breakdown and poverty that contributes to the risk that young people will become involved in violence. Research indicates that in poor households parents are often less able to monitor children and to provide them with positive role models,[19] due, in part, to the overwhelming number of single-parent households living in poverty. It is simply more difficult for a single parent than for two-parent households to adequately supervise children. Such families are also less able to provide their children with the skills, capabilities, and knowledge they need.[20] This often leads to conflict with the educational system, as children not only lack basic skills and knowledge, but things such as homework, permission slips, or information packages are not completed. Poor families may also have problems providing their children with adequate nutrition. Poor nutrition contributes to disruptive behaviour and poor performance in schools. The result is that children lack the social capital (skills, knowledge, and capabilities) they require to succeed in mainstream society. This lack of social capital has been linked to involvement in crime, violence, and homicide.[21]

Changes in economic opportunities impact directly on youth violence and homicide, although the specific patterns vary from urban centre to urban centre.[22] Two of the three cities in Crutchfield et al.'s study had a persistent underclass, which resulted in higher homicide rates. In the third city changes in the structure of the job market negatively impacted on employment opportunities and increased homicide. The declining availability of low-skill, entry-level jobs has resulted, internationally, in higher rates of unemployment and indirectly on higher crime and homicide rates,[23] suggesting that a decline in access to low-skill jobs affects violence indirectly through increasing economic deprivation.[24] Lack of entry-level employment opportunities are particularly important for youth violence and homicide because high-risk youth are most likely, given their lack of social capital, to be looking for such low-skill, entry-level jobs.

Gender

Gender role socialization—that is, the development of socially appropriate gender (masculine and feminine) behaviour—has an impact on violence. In general hegemonic masculinity is associated with many of the following characteristics: power, independence, aggression, dominance, heterosexuality, and violence. Femininity is portrayed as related to dependence, nurturing, passivity, serving others, and maintenance of social relationships. Although these are gross overgeneralizations, the common themes are undeniable. What does this have to do with violence and murder? Gender role socialization theory offers important insights into gendered differences in violent behaviour by explaining why it is that males commit by far the majority of physical and sexual violence, particularly the most serious forms of violence. It indicates that there are significant differences in the causes, forms, and consequences of violent behaviour by male and female youth.

Gender role socialization supports young men's utilitarian approach to violence and their use of violence, including the initiation of unprovoked attacks. In contrast, young women are discouraged from using violence. As a consequence, young men are more likely to be charged with violent crimes in Canada and are more likely to engage in unprovoked violence. Further, the injuries sustained by the victims of male violence tend to be more serious than those sustained by victims of female violence. Clearly, some young women do kill, and some engage in unprovoked violence. However, their numbers pale in comparison to their male counterparts. This research suggests that it is how we socialize boys to be male that leads to their increased risk of engaging in violent behaviour.

Generally, young people who engage in this behaviour hold rigid, traditional gender beliefs. It must be stressed that many people who hold these beliefs are not violent and that only a handful of those who are actually commit murder. Again it is a combination of factors that increases the risk of violence. When a young person adheres to rigid gender roles and also has exposure to a variety of the other risk factors discussed here, the likelihood of serious violence dramatically escalates. Male youth who perceive that they are unable to achieve the traditional entitlements of power and privilege associated with masculinity (for example, a high paying job, material possessions, sexual relations with desirable females, success in academic/social/athletic pursuits, respect, and status) are at particular risk.[25] Many boys who kill adhere to traditional roles and are "caught" in situations in which they are unable to achieve the entitlements of those roles. These young men often report feelings of being "disrespected," shamed, and humiliated by others and by their circumstances. They may act violently to give themselves the power they lack in their personal lives and have been socialized to expect.

Race

While most research on race, violence, and homicide is American, there is concern about race and crime in Canada. We share with our American neighbour an overrepresentation of visible minorities in our jails and prisons. Aboriginal peoples are particularly at risk for involvement with the criminal justice system.[26] How does race factor into involvement in violence and homicide? Parker and Pruitt claim that apparent racial differences in homicide in the western and southern US are accounted for not by race but by differences in structural and cultural forces. However, in a second study they note that poverty and growing up in areas of high poverty (poverty concentration) do vary by race,[27] suggesting that the impact of social conditions varies by racial group. Lee argues that racial differences in homicide reflect the measures used, *not* real differences.[28] Thus, blacks and whites growing up in similarly poor conditions are both at greater risk for involvement in homicides. The effects may be stronger for blacks, which is not surprising, given that these individuals are also dealing with problems related to racism. In the Canadian context race issues are similarly compounded by experiences of poverty, family disruption, and drug and alcohol abuse.[29] There are no Canadian homicide statistics by racial group, so it remains unclear if Aboriginal Canadians or other visible minorities are more likely to be charged and/or convicted of homicide in Canada.

Policy

Perhaps one of the most important areas of the macro-sociological structure affecting crime is how state policies, such as cuts to spending on education and social services or new policies on who is eligible or ineligible for aid, impact on social institutions. These, in turn, can affect factors like unemployment, lack of employment skills, poverty, and family break-up.

For example, it has been reported that the restructuring of the Canadian welfare system resulted in increased unemployment, poverty, and community instability in Atlantic Canada.[30] Changes in social welfare policy have led to increased homelessness among the young;[31] homelessness is highly correlated to substance abuse and involvement in violence and other illegal activities.[32] Social welfare policy in the US has had unintended, negative consequences. For example, the failure to extend social welfare support to family members other than parents caring for minor children too often results in putting families at financial risk.[33] On the positive side, programs such as "I Have A Dream" (IHAD), which offers long-term financial, academic, and social support to youth in grade six, has been enormously successful in keeping young people in school.[34] The negative effects of economic marginalization and higher youth crime rates in the post-Fordist global economy on low-income groups can be mitigated by political policies.[35]

While we do not examine policy initiatives in depth here, it is important to note that policy decisions play an important role in shaping the life-situations of young people and hence on their risk of involvement in high-risk behaviour. The examination of changing Canadian policy and the loss of the social safety net is a study in itself.

Social Institutions: Neighbourhoods, Families, Schools, Peers, and Media

Neighbourhoods
Research has shown that neighbourhoods are important in meeting citizens' social needs.[36] Crime, a mirror of the quality of the social environment in which people live, is increased in poor neighbourhoods.[37] How do neighbourhoods impact on crime? One key feature of the social environment is the kind of institutions they attract. Poorer neighbourhoods have difficulty attracting conventional institutions, such as recreational facilities,[38] which provide young people with positive sites not only for recreational activities but also for socialization and the development of positive social skills. Communities can reduce violence by developing a larger base of certain types of institutions (such as recreation centres) and preventing the encroachment of negative institutions (such as bars or strip clubs). However, attracting positive institutions and preventing the encroachment of others requires support, including municipal government support through by-laws prohibiting certain institutions in residential neighbourhoods and through funds for recreational and other facilities.[39]

There are other features of neighbourhoods that impact negatively on youth crime. Neighbourhoods with low population stability, inadequate housing, and high population density are more likely to be violent and to have more homicides,[40] perhaps because they contain sites that are more or less conducive to violence.[41] Such neighbourhoods lack social cohesion; their citizens have few ties to one another and lack a sense of responsibility for what occurs around them, resulting in an increased vulnerability to violent crime.[42] The lack of social trust has been linked to homicide, suggesting that in these neighbourhoods mobility, poverty, and high population density may impact on social trust.[43]

Families

Families are affected by the socio-economic conditions in society and communities. In turn, family dynamics impact on the development of young people. Exposure to family violence, child abuse, and neglect are all correlated with an individual's use of violence as a teenager and as an adult.[44] Neglect, deprivation, and witnessing violence (both in person and through the media) all contribute to the risk that young people will become involved in murder.[45]

Social learning theory provides important insights into violent behaviour, by suggesting that violence is not an innate characteristic; instead, it is learned through interpersonal modelling (both inside and outside the family) and exposure to violent imagery in other sectors of society. Victimization by serious and prolonged physical, sexual, and emotional abuse in childhood can result in many mental health and behavioural problems, including depression, low self-esteem, self-destructive and criminal behaviour, aggression, and violence. Witnessing chronic and severely abusive behaviour between caregivers has similar results on many children. Boys who experience these forms of abuse have a significantly higher likelihood of becoming violent themselves, whereas girls tend to experience ongoing victimization by suffering abuse in their later interpersonal relationships.[46]

However, experiencing serious violence in the home, on its own, does not cause one to engage in serious violence. In fact, most children who grow up in families like these are not violent, and some individuals who do not experience abuse at home become violent. The impact of dysfunctional families on violence can be mitigated by other institutional supports young people can turn to—recreational opportunities, supportive schools, and peers with intact and supportive families. In sum, the surrounding institutions and young people's relationship to them can combine with

12

negative family experiences to increase the risk of violent and other risky behaviours, or can help to lessen them.

Schools

School problems and early school leaving (dropping out) are linked to youth involvement in crime. For example, it has been found that among skinheads, use of violence is exacerbated by negative school experiences.[47] Education has a direct influence on criminal involvement; early school leaving contributes to the risk of young people being involved in crime.[48] Most juvenile homicide offenders do not do well in school.[49]

Schools are supposed to provide young people with the social capital (skills, knowledge, and capabilities) necessary for competing in the wider social world. These include reading, writing, and communication skills, base knowledge, and assessments of ability. When young people fail at school or drop out, they do not gain the necessary certifications and skills to work at many jobs. As a result, they are closed out of (legitimate) well-paying jobs and future education and training programs. These youth depend on low-skilled, entry-level jobs. One alternative is jobs in high risk, criminal enterprises, such as dealing drugs, breaking and entering, car thefts, and robbery. What moves young people to choose these occupations is a complex combination of factors, but it is the combination of the youths' immediate circumstance with their past socialization in the family and community that makes them more or less susceptible to taking a criminal pathway in adolescence and early adulthood.

Most youth involved in violent crime have experienced failure at school, because of learning difficulties, bullying or being victimized by bullies, attention-deficit and conduct disorders, and other such reasons. The result is often a pattern of grade failure, frequent suspensions, absenteeism, and dropping out altogether. Again, the problems in school by themselves may not lead young people to become involved in crime. In some cases they reflect abuse, neglect, and violence at home, while in other cases the cause is a failure to identify the problem early and/or a failure to respond effectively to these problems.

School completion supports a healthy socialization process and development of academic and vocational interests and credentials. School also provides structured daytime activities. The absence of this structure increases the risk that young people will become involved in crime and violence.

Peers

Our social definition of youth impacts on the kinds of activities in which youth engage and the individuals with whom they come into contact. These social definitions are reflected both in the laws that make education compulsory and in the criminal justice system response to young people through a separate court system. We have increasingly segregated young people into same-age peer-groups, initially within the school setting. The result of this has been the growing importance of the peer group as a location for youth socialization.[50] These peer groups contribute to the kinds of choices young people make and the risk that a young person may become involved in crime.[51] Most youth in Canada belong to *groups* of friends, which are a positive, healthy influence upon their social and emotional development. Groups can provide acceptance, identity, self-affirmation, and support young people in their transition from dependent childhood, through the difficult stage of adolescence, into independent adulthood.[52]

However, on a negative side, some peer groups can and do provide other youth with information on how to commit crimes (contacts, tools, skills "training"), with a vocabulary of motive and with a set of normative values that support their activities. Involvement in peer group activities, particularly the use and abuse of alcohol and other drugs, contributes to youth involvement in criminal activities. Youth who use and abuse drugs and alcohol are more likely to carry weapons and to engage in violent behaviour.[53] Association with delinquent peers can place youth at risk for criminal involvement, while association with positive peers can assist in protecting youth from involvement in crime.[54]

Gender is an important factor in determining which peers young people associate with, and the resulting risk of their engaging in violent behaviour. For male youth, associations with violent male peers can lead to serious violence, often collective in nature. The collective provides youth with "techniques of neutralization,"[55] which allow them to carry on with their lives while engaging in deviant activity. Males who engage in serious violence do not identify their behaviour as wrong; instead, they argue that their values and actions are guided by a superior morality and are the *only* course of action given their situation. Their description of violence has been termed a "vocabulary of adjustment,"[56] in which the social unacceptability of their behaviour is denied through the sophisticated use of justifications.

Often when people hear about groups of delinquent youth they assume these are youth gangs. This is not the reality. Very few adolescents in

Canada belong to hard-core criminal youth gangs. The key difference between a group and a gang is the gang's high degree of organization for violent, criminal objectives. A youth gang is a group of three or more youth whose members routinely commit serious crimes and regularly engage in serious acts of violence. Hard-core gangs are highly organized, have some degree of permanence, and usually protect an identified "turf" (related to crime, the drug trade, and/or a geographic area). Members must demonstrate allegiance to the gang, abide by its code of honour, and use common hand signals, clothing, graffiti, and vocabulary.[57] Visible and ethnic minority youth, who face blocked opportunities in school and employment, are at an increased likelihood of joining such hard-core criminal gangs.[58]

Again, it is important to note that association with violent peers is only one factor in explaining youth violence. Many of these youth are economically and socially marginal and find excitement and adventure through extreme violence, which allows them to express their anger and frustration. They view their environment as intolerable and hostile and see themselves as having no value. They have no anchor to their family and community and no sense of broader social purpose in their lives. Internalized norms regarding the impact of harming others are lacking. The varied societal agents of socialization have collectively failed these young people. [59]

The Media
The modelling of violent behaviour also occurs through the media. Certain elements of television, music videos, video games, movies, pornography, sports, and the military glorify violence and contribute to a desensitization among viewers. Frequent exposure to these images can result in violent and aggressive behaviour by viewers who closely identify with the situations and/or central figures. The negative effects of repeated exposure to these forms of violence can be mediated by the stable presence of an adult mentor, who provides an alternative, healthy role model throughout a young person's life. As with the other factors discussed above, however, exposure to these images on their own is not enough to cause a young person to engage in serious violence.

Individual Factors

It is not simply the impact of macro-sociological factors on various social institutions that results in homicides; there are other important factors.

Individual agency plays a critical role. Often when we speak of the role of the individual in criminal behaviour, we imagine an individual who is "genetically" driven to commit crime. It is true that there are physiological theories on extreme violence that focus on genetic factors, including brain structure and hormones, as causes of crime.[60] However, more common are intrapsychic theories that explore the attributes of individual personality features—including personality disorders, addiction, fear of intimacy or abandonment, depression, other psychiatric illnesses, and learning disabilities—on criminal behaviour. However, once again, these individual problems do not exist in isolation. Learning disabilities can be problematic when the school system is unable to identify and/or respond to them. Thus, it is the combination of learning disabilities with the response to them that places children at risk for school failure, dropping out, and problems gaining access to legitimate occupations. As well, individuals vary in their susceptibility to drugs and alcohol. These variations can have profound consequences for the risk of addictions and the subsequent likelihood of young people becoming involved in both crime and dangerous situations.

Most youth with significant psychological or psychiatric problems are not violent. It is only a minority of seriously violent youth who have a diagnosed mental illness, although many youth who commit homicides have experienced psychological problems. These include periods of emotional distress, feelings of low self-worth, or chronic, low-grade depression (mostly undiagnosed). In addition, many engage in self-destructive behaviours including suicide attempts, slashing and cutting with knives and razors, and substance abuse.[61] These factors, combined with feelings of shame, humiliation, and disrespect, are related to their use of violence. Further, many of these problems originate from having suffered or witnessed abuse and/or neglect as a child and become aggravated in the absence of appropriate supports to address them. But, even factoring in all these dimensions, not all youth with such problems nor those who have been exposed to maltreatment become involved in violence. This is because young people vary in their resilience.

Resilience is the ability of individuals living in adverse conditions to achieve positive outcomes.[62] It is through resilience that the combination of societal level, institutional, and individual factors[63] to which young people are exposed result in positive and negative outcomes. It is important to recognize that diverse outcomes are possible for young people living in similar negative life situations. The key is the ability of individual, family, schools, and community to mitigate the risk factors. For example, young people who live in abusive families but have positive community supports (e.g., access to recreational activities), and/or positive support within the school setting (e.g., high achievement and/or supportive teachers), and/or particular individual attributes (e.g., perseverance, determination, intellectual ability, athletic ability) create some protection against the risks of experiencing family violence (i.e., risk of using violence themselves or of delinquency). But what can we expect from a typical young person, with average skills and abilities? When these young people live in situations where the community, schools, and family are all unable to provide needed support and guidance, they are likely to remain at high risk, a risk that can be exacerbated by contact with delinquent peers and engagement in activities such as drug and alcohol use. This can begin a pathway to involvement in violent activities and to an individual's involvement in a homicide.

The Homicide Context: The Micro-Environment of Homicide

Thus far we have focussed on perpetrators of homicide. It is important to note that almost all young people who experience the personal and social disruptions discussed above do not commit homicides. Linking these factors with actual offending requires us to consider the context in which the homicide occurs. Every crime has a history of events that precede it, a place where it occurs, and a socio-cultural context that defines it.[64] Youth homicides are more likely to occur when there is a weapon present, during the commission of another crime, and when the perpetrator and/or the victim(s) are intoxicated.[65] Victims are at risk for a variety of reasons: because of where they are (e.g., in locations where drugs and alcohol are consumed), or who they are ("attractive" targets who offer valuable possessions, or who are unable to defend themselves, or who are alone with no one to defend them).[66]

To the extent that conflict results in homicide, the management of conflict can be critical to determining whether or not a homicide occurs. Consuming drugs and alcohol can contribute to the escalation of conflict.[67] The presence of a third person can lead to the escalation of conflict or it can contribute to reducing it,[68] hence decreasing the risk for homicide.

The relationship between the victim and the perpetrator also impacts on homicides.[69] Girls are more likely than boys to kill a family member. However, most youth homicides are committed against strangers, often during the commission of another crime.[70] Youth are more likely to kill other youth.[71]

Lifestyle-exposure theory suggests that the more time an individual spends in risky situations the greater their risk of victimization. Lifestyle choices can increase risk—this includes decisions on alcohol/drug consumption, peers, and choice of recreational activities. It is important to note that a homicide may be a culmination of poor choices but not necessarily of lethal intent—although it may also be the result of lethal intent. Distinguishing these features is important for responding to the young person and to the crime, and for prevention.

Notes

1 Pseudonyms are used with all participants to maintain anonymity. For a discussion of other measures taken to ensure anonymity, see p. 31.

2 Ewing, 1990, 13.

3 Under the CCC, there are three categories of sexual assault: level 1 sexual assault (incidents which include the least bodily harm to the victim), level 2 (with a weapon, threatening to use a weapon, or inflicting bodily harm), and level 3 (aggravated sexual assault, resulting in injury, mutilation and disfigurement or endangering the life of a victim).

4 The term "peace officer" includes police officers, police constables, constables, sheriffs, deputy sheriffs, wardens, deputy wardens, jailers, guards, and a permanent employee of a prison acting in the course of his/her duties.

5 Avakame, 1998; Ewing, 1990; Myers, 1994.

6 Cheatwood and Block, 1990; Ewing, 1990; Heide, 1999.

7 Heide, 1999; Ewing, 1990.

8 Wolfgang and Ferracuti, 1976.

9 ibid.

10 Eron *et al.*, 1994, 25.

11 Hindelang, Gottfredson, and Garofalo, 1978; Cohen and Felson, 1979; Miethe and Meier, 1994.

12 Totten, 2000a.

13 Hagan, 1994; Kennedy *et al.*, 1998; Lee and Bankston, 1999; Lourie *et al.*, 1995; Parker and Pruitt, 2000.

14 Crutchfield et al., 1999; Lee and Shihadeh, 1998; Shihadeh and Ousey, 1998.

15 Tanner, 1996; Acland, 1995; Smandych, 1995; Minor, 1993.

16 Based upon Hawkins *et al.*, 1998; and Totten, 2001c.

17 Lee and Shihadeh, 1998.

18 Wilkinson, Kawachi, and Kennedy, 1998.

19 Lipman, Offord, and Dooley, 1996.

20 Rosenberg, 1995.

21 Hagan, 1994; Kennedy *et al.*, 1998; Putnam, 2000.

22 Crutchfield *et al.*, 1999.

23 Lee and Shihadeh, 1998.

24 Shihadeh and Ousey, 1998.

25 Totten, 2000a.

26 Engler and Crowe, 2000; Moldon and Kukec, 2000.

27 Parker and Pruitt, 2000.

28 Lee, 2000.

29 Engler and Crowe, 2000.

30 MacDonald, 1998.

31 Berger and Tremblay, 1999.

32 Caputo and Kelly, 1998.

33 Hegar and Scannapieco, 2000.

34 Kahne and Bailey, 1999.

35 Pitts and Hope, 1997.

36 Kawachi, 1999; Krivo and Peterson, 1996; Peterson *et al.*, 2000.

37 Kawachi, 1999.

38 Peterson *et al.*, 2000.

39 Peterson *et al.*, 2000.

40 Lee, 2000; Parker and Pruitt, 2000.

41 Peterson, 2000.

42 Kawachi, 1999.

43 Kennedy *et al.*, 1998.

44 Totten, 2001c; Statistics Canada, CCJS, 1999b, 2000b; Athens, 1992.

45 Hardwick, 1996.

46 Totten, 2001c.

47 Baron, 1997.

48 Crutchfield *et al.*, 1999.

49 Heide, 1999.

50 Minor, 1993.

51 Hindelang, Gottfredson, and Garofalo, 1978.

52 Totten, 2000a.

53 Dukarm *et al.*, 1996.

54 Dekovic, 1999.

55 Sykes and Matza, 1957.

56 Kanin, 1967.

57 Totten, 2000a.

58 Totten, 2001b.

59 Totten, 2001b.
60 For example, Niehoff, 1999.
61 Totten, 2000a, 2001a; Lundy and Totten, 1997.
62 Howard *et al.*, 1999; Luthar *et al.*, 2000; Smokowski *et al.*, 1999.
63 Dekovic, 1999; Gutman and Midgley, 2000; Smokowski *et al.*, 1999; Voydanoff and Donnelly, 1999.
64 Miethe and Meier, 1994; Sacco and Kennedy, 1994.
65 Heide, 1999; Parker and Rebhun, 1995.
66 Miethe and Meier, 1994.
67 Meithe and Meier, 1994.
68 Silverman and Kennedy, 1993.
69 Meithe and Meier, 1994.
70 Crepi and Rigazio-DiGilio, 1996.
71 Cheatwood and Block, 1990.

Studying Youth Homicide

Introduction

In this chapter we introduce the study of youth homicide in Canada: its extent or number, the issue of youth homicide rates, and the Canadian statistics on youth homicides. Although crime data (even homicide statistics) have been collected in a variety of ways over the past century, the information recorded has changed; age is not always recorded, and the definition of "youth" has varied. Sometimes convictions are recorded, other times, only charges (and not all youth that are charged are convicted). This makes comparisons of trends difficult. Finally, we will discuss our study: its methodology and ethics, the questionnaire design and interviews, the truth status of accounts, coding and data analysis, the life-course approach, the participants, and its limitations.

Youth Homicide in Canada

Youth homicide is not common in Canada. From 1990 to 1999 an average of 52 young people were charged each year with homicide, most of them—87 per cent—males. About one-fifth are accused of killing other youth, and the same percentage are accused of killing elderly people. About 46 per cent know their victim. Most homicides (95 per cent) in Canada involve a single victim, while about 5 per cent involve multiple victims. Five in ten people accused and four in ten victims were drunk and/or high at the time of the offence. Approximately 60 per cent of homicides take place in private residences—40 per cent in the victim's residence, 13 per cent in the accused's residence, and 8 per cent in other residences. The rest take place elsewhere—26 per cent in an open area, 7 per cent in a commercial area (including places of business), 4 per cent in a private vehicle, and 2 per cent in public institutions (prison, schools, etc.).[1]

The number of homicides committed by young people has changed over the years. In the beginning, only one or two homicides a year were committed by youth, but, by the mid-1970s, both the number of murders and the murder rate had increased considerably. When considering numeric data it is important to compare not only the "raw" numbers but also the rates of occurrence: the number of youth homicides may increase (or decrease) with the number of youth in the population in general, *not* because there are a greater proportion of young people committing homicides. In our data we use the number of homicide events or charges per 100,000 youth. This allows easier comparisons per year, since changes in the homicide rates cannot be attributed to changes in the number of young people. In addition, as we shall see, the inclusion of youth 16 and 17 years of age in youth court statistics had an impact on the youth homicide rate, as this is the group most likely to be accused of killing.

Reporting Homicide Statistics

There is virtually no Canadian literature on long-term trends in murder rates among young or juvenile offenders. This reflects the problems associated with comparing rates. Comparisons are limited by changes in the legislation, which impact on what statistics are collected and who is defined as a juvenile or young offender, and the time period during which the data are collected.

What Is Reported?

Canadian statistics on young offender or juvenile crime have been published since 1886. Prior to that, criminal statistics were recorded in the Parliamentary Sessional Papers,[2] which recorded crimes for which people were charged and convicted by province, gender, and age. For youth, age was recorded as under 16 years only; there was a 16- to 21-year-old category, which included some youth now covered under the Young Offenders Act (YOA). There were few murders recorded in the collected statistics, suggesting that the youth homicide rate was quite low.

Recording practices were changed in 1908 with the introduction of the Juvenile Delinquents Act (JDA). The JDA allowed for the establishment of juvenile courts; however, this took considerable time. Thus, until 1922, juvenile statistics continued to be recorded with adult statistics, and some areas in Canada that had not established juvenile courts did not report at all. By 1922, "... a sufficient number of juvenile courts had been established to warrant Statistics Canada commencing the separate statistical handling of juvenile delinquency cases."[3] From 1922 to 1926 the data reported the number of juvenile offences, but not the number of juvenile offenders charged in the incident. This diminished delinquency rates, since a single offence would be recorded even when more than one offender was charged and/or convicted. From 1927 to 1969, court appearances were used as the basis of counting. On the one hand, this meant undercounting some delinquency, because only the most serious offence was recorded when an offender was charged with multiple offences in a single court appearance. On the other hand, it tended to overcount the number of delinquent youth, because it recorded each new court appearance as an additional delinquent charge. In 1970, the recording procedures were revised again. From 1970 to 1983, the courts began recording two statistics: the most serious offence for which a juvenile appeared before the court, and a count of all delinquencies, excluding the most serious.

The figures therefore do not provide an unduplicated count of the number of children brought before the court, for a child referred to a court two or more times during the year is counted as a separate case each time. Neither do they represent the number of offences committed by the boys and girls brought before a court for more than one offence because, for a juvenile charged with two or more offences at the same hearing, only the most serious offence would be recorded.[4]

Since homicide was the most serious offence for which an offender could be charged, this counting method was not likely to undercount the number of youth charged with homicide as juveniles. However, charges are not equivalent to a finding of guilt.[5] Further, data on the number of young people who were transferred to adult court and tried as adults are not available. Under the current YOA legislation, charges are also recorded, with the result that the number of youth who are convicted of homicides is over-counted, because not all young people charged are convicted.

Who Is Counted as a Juvenile or Young Offender
Each new piece of legislation changed the definition of who is a juvenile or young offender and on the ease of transfers to adult court. Prior to the passage of the JDA, statistics on crime recorded the age of the offender in broad categories: under 16 years, 16 to 21 years, 21 to 40 years, and 40 years

and over. Under the JDA, juvenile offenders were defined as children over the age of six and under the age of 16. However, only juvenile offenders over the age of 14 and under the age of 16, who had committed indictable offences and were not transferred to adult court, were included in the juvenile statistics. Variations in provincial upper-age limits further muddied the count. These differences meant that who was included in the category of juveniles varied between and within provinces and by gender.[6] With the passage of the YOA the age range for youth included in "juvenile" statistics changed dramatically. It excluded children under the age of 12 and increased the upper age to 17. It also restricted the transfer of juvenile offenders to adult court. Over time, revisions in the YOA also changed the transfer process and whether young people over the age of 16 were charged as adults or as youth.

These variations in age cut-offs and in how the statistics were recorded make comparisons difficult. Changes in rates may reflect how delinquency is counted, not that substantive changes in the actual delinquency rates have occurred. The rates since 1970 are generally comparable in terms of *what* was recorded, but not in terms of *who* was defined as a juvenile or young offender.

Recording Practices
Estimating juvenile crime rates generally and juvenile homicide rates in particular is also affected by the recording of delinquent acts. Though the early records indicate that murder was very uncommon for young offenders, a closer examination of the raw data (contained in Parliamentary Sessional Papers) shows that the age of the offender(s) was *not* actually recorded for most homicide events. For example, in 1877, 62 people were charged with manslaughter or murder in Canada, 23 were convicted, and of these, ages were recorded for only two individuals. In 1878, 56 people were charged, 32 were convicted, and ages are provided for only 11. Thus, these early data are not a reliable estimate of juvenile homicide rates.

Further, recording practices were often implemented at different times in different provinces and municipalities. The JDA, with its reliance on both legal and status offences, was vulnerable to shifts in norms of behaviour and morality. This impacted on who was or was not adjudicated as delinquent.

Provinces varied in how they recorded statistics and how they enforced the legislation. Leacy notes that:

... a number of provinces since 1970 have reorganized their systems of statistical reporting of juveniles; these reorganizations resulted in very marked increases in the number of forms submitted from certain provinces in some years, indicating a significant rate of non-reporting in earlier years... There is and has been extensive variation among the provinces in judicial policy regarding procedures for juvenile cases. At one extreme, a formal charge is laid in every instance where a delinquent act is alleged to have occurred; at the other extreme cases which are not deemed serious by law enforcement and court officials may be dealt with informally without any charge being laid or formal charges may be withdrawn if it is thought that no benefit would accrue or where the appearance of the juvenile in court might prove damaging to him [sic] or his [sic] family.[7]

In addition, the differences in the court's findings between the JDA and the YOA are problematic. A child might not be "guilty" of the crime that brought him or her to the attention of the juvenile court authorities, but still would be adjudicated as a delinquent. Under the YOA, the young offender must be found guilty of a crime.

As a result, under the YOA there was an increase in the number of homicide charges made against young people, because most young people charged with murder are 16 or 17 years of age.[8] Thus, their inclusion under the YOA had the effect of inflating the youth murder rates. Further, the changes made to the YOA with respect to transfer to adult court also impacted on juvenile crime rates.[9]

Youth Homicide Rates, 1974 to 2000

Table 2.1 reports youth homicide rates (number of youth charged per 100,000 youth) from 1974 to 2000. Comparisons of the rates are problematic due to changes in reporting practices and the definition of youth. This makes it difficult to assess whether the homicide rate is increasing, decreasing, or stable.

In 1984 with the introduction of the YOA, there were dramatic changes in who was counted as a youthful offender. In particular, it included 16- and 17-year-olds, the age group within the young offender population that is most likely to commit homicides. This contributed to an increase in the number of recorded youth homicides. The data presented in Table 2.1 have been adjusted to make comparisons before and after 1984 easier. The mean

	Females Charged	Males Charged	Total Charged	Charge Rate per 100,000	Total Youth as % of Total Charged
1974	3	53	56	1.98	10.2
1975	13	55	68	2.38	10.8
1976	8	41	49	1.71	7.9
1977	8	55	63	2.20	9.4
1978	10	48	58	2.07	8.4
1979	11	44	55	2.02	8.9
1980	7	39	46	1.74	8.7
1981	13	47	60	2.36	9.5
1982	9	42	51	2.07	8.0
1983[10]	10	31	41	1.72	6.7
1984	11	25	36	7.54	6.5
1985	5	52	57	2.48	8.9
1986	11	31	42	1.85	7.6
1987	8	58	36	1.59	6.1
1988	3	44	47	2.09	8.9
1989	5	42	47	2.09	8.4
1990	12	35	47	2.08	8.5
1991	7	41	48	2.11	7.5
1992	5	53	58	2.52	8.8
1993	3	33	36	1.54	6.5
1994	6	52	58	2.46	10.1
1995	15	53	68	2.85	11.8
1996	3	47	50	2.07	9.1
1997	11	44	55	2.25	10.7
1998	3	54	57	2.33	10.8
1999	9	36	45	1.84	9.2
2000	5	36	41	1.67	8.9

Source: Adapted from Fedorowycz, 2001

Table 2.1: Youth Homicide Charges, 1974-2000

number of homicide charges for 1974 to 1983 inclusive was 54.7 and for 1984 to 2000 (inclusive) it was 49.3. The mean homicide rate for 1984 to 2000 (inclusive) is 2.08, slightly higher than the mean for 1974-1983 (2.03).

Other Violent Youth Crime

Youth violence has been the focus of growing concern in Canada over the past decade.[11] While violence and victims of violence are serious concerns, the extent of youth violence is often over-estimated. Indeed, there is a wide gap between the general public's perception of youth crime as violent and escalating out of control and reality,[12] which is that youth crime generally, and the most serious forms of violent youth crime in particular, are decreasing. In 1999, fewer than 100,000 youth 12 to 17 were charged with crime, a decline of 7.2 per cent from 1998 and the seventh consecutive year of decline. The violent crime rate declined by 5 per cent between 1998 and 1999, the fifth year of decline. The decline was 4.6 per cent for males and 6.5 per cent for females.

Further, few youth are actually involved in crime. Less than 5 per cent of Canadian youth between 12 and 17 years of age (inclusive) are charged with any crime. Violent crime makes up only about 20 per cent of all youth crime, and most of these charges are for relatively minor offences. The female youth violent crime rate is one-third the rate of male youths (47 charges per 10,000 females compared to 131 charges per 10,000 male youths).[13] Of those youth charged with violent crime in 1998, most were charged with common assault. Males were much more likely to be charged with the most serious types of violent crime compared to females (approximately 4 per 10,000 female youth and 16 per 10,000 male youth). This rate has been in decline since 1996. In this same year, 1,438 young people were charged with sexual assault, 97 per cent of them male. In almost all of these cases, the charge was for the least serious form of sexual assault. The youth charge rate for sexual assault has dropped every year since 1993.[14]

There were major differences in the violent crime rate by province and territory in 1998, some of which can be explained by differences in charging patterns. The highest rates were found in the Northwest Territories (191 youths per 10,000), Manitoba (153 per 10,000), Yukon (143 per 10,000), and Saskatchewan (134 per 10,000); the lowest rates were in Prince Edward Island (50 per 10,000) and Quebec (54 per 10,000).[15] Boys who engage in criminal violence tend to be older than girls. Whereas charge rates peak at age 17 for males, they are at their highest point at age 14 and 15 for females. Despite the comparatively lower rates of violent incidents involving young females, violent crime by young women (primarily minor assaults) has risen twice as fast as that of young men (mainly major assaults and robberies) over the past decade (plus 127 per cent compared to plus 65 per cent).[16] In reality, not much has changed regarding girls' use of violence. Ten years ago, the police, media, and general public did not place much emphasis on reporting these incidents. Physical fights and threats by girls were dealt with outside the formal justice system. Today, there is a heightened sensitivity.[17]

Overview of This Study

The killing of even a single person does and should raise concerns; these concerns are exacerbated when the killer is a "child." Statistics leave us with no sense of "who" these young people are. We do not know how it is they came to be involved in a homicide, what they did, nor how they see these events. Putting a human face on youth who commit homicides can provide us with valuable insights not only into the factors that may lead them to kill, but into how we can assist young people at risk.

The purpose of this study is to explore how youth charged with homicide (murder and manslaughter) make sense of their behaviour and how we can understand their behaviour within their life courses. We do this through the exploration of the intentions, meanings, and motives associated with their actions, along with recounting their negative and positive life experiences. We argue that we can better comprehend adolescent homicide if we understand the bio-social psychological context of these offenders' lives.

Our theoretical position is based on a life history approach, which suggests that youth involvement with the criminal justice system and in high-risk activities is the result of a lifetime of events and that this involvement, in turn, contributes to the risk of participation in a homicide. Thus, we need to know about the life histories of offenders: their experiences in childhood and adolescence; and in communities, schools, peer groups, families, the criminal justice system, and the social welfare system. In addition, our approach also indicates that contextual factors (factors more immediate to the homicide event) also contribute to the commission of the murder. Thus, we need to detail the actual homicide event. Finally, we are concerned with how the youth and adult criminal justice systems responded to these young people and their actions and how our participants have fared since their convictions.

Research Design and Methodology

Researching youth homicide places a number of constraints on research design. First, there is no easily accessible list from which to select young people for interviews. This is a serious concern for researchers, because it means we must develop other means for contacting participants, and the resulting sample is not necessarily representative of youth convicted of homicide. To identify subjects we employed a number of techniques. We contacted young offender facilities in a number of sites in Canada, asking if there were any youth convicted of homicide currently in custody or recently discharged, and if the institutions could explain the study to these young people and ask them if they would be willing to participate. We used a similar process with parole and probation officers, again in selected sites. For legal and ethical reasons we could not have access to names of potential participants prior to them agreeing with the institution/probation/parole officer to take part in our study. We also asked participants if they knew any other suitable youth that would be interested in participating. The resulting sample of young people is not representative of youth convicted of homicide in Canada.

To ensure that similar information was obtained from all participants, we developed an interview questionnaire, with questions that our theoretical perspective indicated were essential for assessing youth involvement in homicides (see Appendix A). We conducted face-to-face, semi-structured interviews with 19 young people convicted of homicides committed when they were 17 years of age or younger. This method provided these young people with a space to explore the meaning of their behaviour. The interviews and supporting documentation—parole, probation, psychiatric, and psychological assessments, and reports of subjects at time of charge, sentencing, and release from custody—provided the base data for the analysis. Like any series of conversations, the interviews were unique. They provided us with insights into the lives of our participants, their crimes, and how they viewed their world.

In this book we examine a wide range of factors in the lives of our participants. We asked young people personal questions about their family lives, the homicide itself, their experiences with the criminal justice system, and their engagement in violent, illegal activities. Some of these questions were potentially embarrassing, some were upsetting, and others brought back difficult and painful memories. Some of the participants were engaging in dangerous activities at the time of the interview. In addition, some of the information provided to us referred to criminal activities unrelated to the homicide and implicated other people. We needed, therefore, to be very careful to ensure that our research conduct was ethical.

Conducting Ethical Research
Ethical considerations are a critical part of any research involving people. For this study we went through ethical reviews from a variety of organizations, including a Tri-Council University ethics committee, a community agency ethics committee, the ethics committees within various govern-

ment ministries, and those of some institutions. A Youth Court Judge's Order was obtained, pursuant to the requirements of the YOA. Each of these reviews required us to establish a number of protections for the people we interviewed, which ensured voluntary participation, informed consent, no harm to participants, and anonymity and confidentiality.

Voluntary participation means that the individuals who participate in a study do so voluntarily without any pressure to participate and with the freedom to leave at any time. For example, in the course of our research we approached ten young people about interviews, all of whom declined. They reported prior problems with the press and were unwilling to risk telling their stories again. Further, all said that they had started new lives in the community and did not want to revisit their past.

Informed consent is a critical part of voluntary participation. Each person who participated in our study was provided with an informed consent form (see Appendix B). The form was reviewed before each interview. We read it out loud and discussed all points at length. After confirming that the offenders understood what they were being asked to do, the forms were signed and placed on file.

Another ethical concern was ensuring that we did no harm. In most social research this is usually interpreted as harm to subjects or participants. For our research, we included not only concerns about harm to participants, but also the potential for harm to others by participants and harm to the families of the homicide victims. Each of these concerns required us to develop a research methodology that was responsive to these issues. To prevent harm to our subjects, we were careful in our selection process. Offenders who were initially assessed by referral sources (or following referral by parole, probation, or institutional staff) to be emotionally or mentally unstable were not interviewed. We worked with local agencies and institutions to provide all participants with follow-up support, including counselling and life skills (such as job skills, resume writing, and assistance in finding housing on release).

Interviews were transcribed with some changes. First, all names were removed from the interview transcripts to protect others who were identified by participants. One of the main components of our informed consent was a promise that none of our participants would be identified. We used pseudonyms for each subject and used these in the interview transcripts. We selected these pseudonyms randomly from a list of 200 names, excluding any actual first names of participants. Next, we encrypted the interview transcripts to protect them from access by others, and we destroyed the audio tapes six months after the interviews. We also sought to protect our subjects and the victims' families in our presentation of the case information. To this end, we excluded particular details that would identify cases (geographic, family, ethno-racial, and other information).

We had to do a number of things to ensure confidentiality; for example, it was necessary to keep the signed consent form separate from any other material that could identify the participants. We informed participants that some information could not remain confidential. We were required to report certain admissions to the authorities, including any involvement in life-threatening criminal activity, and cautioned participants not to reveal any information they did not want reported in these areas. Apart from disclosure of life-threatening harm, two other issues limited the confidentiality of the interviews: disclosures of child abuse and/or neglect and suicidal behaviour. Provincial and territorial child welfare legislation in Canada requires that any professional having suspicion of child abuse or neglect of a young person under the age of 16 years must report these suspicions immediately to the local child welfare agency. As well, we expected that some of the participants would have significant mental health issues. For these reasons, the informed consent form clearly indicated that confidentiality would be breached should any of these issues arise during the interview. All participants told us that they understood these measures had to be taken to ensure the safety of all parties involved.

Questionnaire Design

The interview questionnaire (sometimes called an interview schedule) for our study is in Appendix A. This schedule was developed specifically for this study. It consists of a series of questions that begin with the participants' current profiles and then explores over the life course their experiences with the major social institutions we identified in the literature review: family, school, peer group, recreation, religion, health, social and child welfare organizations, and the criminal justice system. Each interview was tape-recorded, and hand-written notes were kept as a backup to the tapes. Some questions provide answer categories, and others are open-ended. Though the schedule originally had a fixed format, we quickly found that questions had to be modified to ensure that participants understood what we were asking. These offenders had a variety of learning styles and different levels of literacy and verbal skills. Many were learning disabled. So, for example, question 2.7 asks: "Were you ever involved with the child welfare system?," and question 2.8 asks "Were you ever taken into care?" We supplemented these questions by asking if there had ever been child welfare investigations in their homes and if their parent(s) were being supported by social welfare. We also asked about why they were involved with child or social welfare agencies, the reason they were taken into care, how long they were in these facilities, and how they felt about these experiences. In the course of these discussions participants provided us with additional information about their placements and experiences, and we followed up with appropriate questions. For example, one participant indicated that his foster family had been racist and abusive. We asked what he meant by abusive and for specific instances of maltreatment. We asked how he knew his foster parents were racist and what actions suggested that they were racist.

We allowed participants to tell us their accounts as they emerged and to guide the sequencing of issues if they so chose. For example, in the section on school experiences, we made sure we had all the necessary data, but allowed other information to emerge in the course of the dialogue. If required information was not provided, we asked specifically about it. Here again, participants provided details that were important to them. We wanted to uncover the participant's world, from their own viewpoint. So, while we asked about attendance, participants also explained why they did not attend and what happened when they did go to school. Bullying emerged as a key issue after the first few interviews. Another prominent issue was the feeling of being stigmatized as a result of placement in special education and learning disabled classes. Masculinity emerged as an important factor when discussing violence. We were aware that research suggested this as an important factor in male violence; however, we wanted to see if participants would implicate the issue of masculinity themselves, instead of forcing the topic upon them.

Some questions did not work well. For example, not all participants knew their parents' salaries or their sources of financial support. Others inflated the status and incomes of father-figures. Again, this has been found previously in the literature.[18] We were able to get at this issue in a roundabout way in other questions about living arrangements (1.12) and family background (2.1).

In-depth Interviews
The interviews do not follow either the pre-determined order of the schedule nor are they a simple life-course description. Dialogue on new

issues provoked participants to return to items already discussed. In addition, events would be reported at one point in the interview and then contextualized later on in talking about other incidents. Thus, when we asked about their own use of violence, often they would bring the discussion back to their family, adding new details (e.g., being taught to box by a father at a very young age) or back to school experiences (e.g., violence initiated in response to bullying). A few wanted to discuss the homicide early on, whereas most would not have discussed it if we had not brought the matter up. Most easily discussed all the good things about their families, yet avoided talking about child abuse, neglect, abandonment, and witnessing violence at home. Many who had suffered serious maltreatment presented idyllic pictures of their home lives or minimized the severity of these incidents. It is not uncommon for youth who have engaged in severe violence to do this.[19] Probing at different points in the interviews was necessary on these latter issues.

In most cases, the dialogue was "all over the map," bouncing from one issue to another. This reflected the various behavioural and emotional difficulties of many offenders, as well as the setting of the interview. For example, two offenders (George and Walter) had difficulty sitting still and constantly fidgeted. They were both illiterate and had serious learning disabilities. Both were visual learners and responded to questions best when imagery and drawings were used to illustrate concepts. It was difficult to get complete information on an issue at one time, because their concentration span was minimal. In one case, the interview was split into three sections and took place over a seven-day period. George had serious, unresolved issues related to childhood trauma, and the tape recorder was turned off many times to provide him with emotional support. At the age of 23, he still sucked his thumb.

Walter had a serious stutter, which became evident when he talked about his painful early childhood experiences and his role in the murder. He was covered in tattoos and took pride in his artistic work (he had done most of his tattoos and had a portfolio of his art). About one hour into the interview, he asked if he could go to his cell and get his art folder. The guards reluctantly agreed to this. We then spent some time viewing his work, which was truly remarkable. Following this, he was much more engaged in the interview and more forthcoming about events in his troubled young life.

Susan, on the other hand, was very bright and articulate. She had no difficulty talking at length about her experiences, emotions, and the homicide. Her interview was free-flowing, and little prompting was required in her accounting of events. However, the truth-status (see below) of her accounts was low. The interview took place in the community.

One key factor in our interview conversations with participants was the rapport we established. When rapport was good, we found that participants were willing to share openly about their experiences, emotions, and behaviours. They provided a wealth of unsolicited details and were willing to entertain critical questions (in these cases, we could confront offenders on inconsistencies and obvious inaccuracies in their accounts). In other interviews, rapport was low. While participants agreed to answer questions on the schedule, they were not always forthcoming with information and rarely provided accounts on unsolicited issues. When we probed for details, they refused to provide them, changed the subject, or simply shrugged and waited for the next question. For example, Mitch painted an idyllic portrait of his father and had little that was positive to say about his mother. He blamed his co-accused for the murder and told us that he was well on his way to rehabilitation in penitentiary (the interview occurred in a maximum-security wing). However, there were numerous inconsistencies in his account, and his clothing and tattoos suggested gang involvement. This was later confirmed by the institution.

These interviews were structured conversations on intimate issues, where there was little intimacy and often minimal trust. As interviewers, we had to work hard to develop rapport; we sought to be non-judgmental of behaviours and experiences and to develop a sympathetic identification with participants as they told their stories. We tried to encourage openness. This meant that the interview process was volatile. For some participants, recalling memories opened a floodgate of difficult emotions. At times we had to turn off the tape recorder to deal with these feelings. On occasion, these offenders and ourselves were reduced to tears during accounts of abuse, abandonment, racism, and the homicide. At times, the dialogue resonated with anger and bitterness about these experiences. But in some interviews we were unable to elicit any affect at all. Participants recounted events, but would provide only the briefest details.

Nigel, for example, explained repeatedly that he was "not too good with words" and that he had difficulty talking about his emotions. He answered questions, after long periods of silence, with "ummm, yeah," "ahhh, no," or "I dunno." When he elaborated after probing, often his response was a couple of sentences only, following very long pauses. During these periods of silence, he made no eye contact. What seemed to gain his trust was permitting him to talk at length about the apparent injuries he had sustained in his murder of a middle-aged woman. He used a hunting knife; she, waking up with this offender on top of her, grabbed a small pair of sewing scissors to defend herself. After spending about 45 minutes on the homicide, we were able to guide him back to other issues on which his accounts were incomplete.

Another key factor which influenced accounts was the location of the interview. Interviews in young offender facilities took place typically over an eight-hour period, with breaks for meals and stretching. Staff were flexible about the length of time required. Interviews in medium- and maximum-security penitentiaries, however, were interrupted by inmate "counts" and had to be fit around mealtimes and guard shift changes. These interviews were more controlled and closely supervised. Interviews in minimum-security prisons were more relaxed. Finally, interviews in the community were the most open and flexible. There were not the same constraints around time, nor did they take place in a coercive setting.

Truth Status [20] *of Accounts*

The in-depth interviews provided a chance for participants to talk about their lives from childhood through adolescence, to provide details of the homicide event, and to discuss what had happened since that fatal day. This retrospective view of their lives was likely to be affected by a number of factors. Events may have been forgotten or distorted over time, or the participants themselves may have intentionally distorted them for reasons of social desirability bias and "faking bad." Social desirability bias is the tendency of people to present themselves in the best possible light, which often means pretending to conform to cultural ideals — their versions of events are meant to make them appear to be socially desirable; thus, they do not tell the truth. This common response may lead participants to deny both negative things they have done and negative experiences they have had. This has also been referred to as using "socially approved vocabularies"[21] to justify socially unacceptable behaviours.

The second type of response bias, "faking bad,"[22] means that participants attempt to appear markedly deviant because they perceive some advantage in doing so. In our study, some participants sought to present themselves as "bad"; hence, we were concerned about the presence of bias due to "faking bad." We sought to deal with the incorrect information (resulting from bias in responses and memory) through triangulation, the use of additional data sources in all cases.

How truthful were the accounts? In considering truth status we looked for accounts that were characterized by elements of boasting, bragging, internal inconsistencies, and significant discrepancies with official documentation. Inconsistencies might reflect purposed attempts to distort the truth, the vagaries of memory, or the inability of participants to deal with memories. Finally, we looked for inconsistencies between the reports that young people provided of exposure to trauma and their behaviour. When there were claims that there was no abuse but behaviour suggested trauma, we probed further to ascertain the factors that contributed to that behaviour. Other studies have used this kind of detailed analysis of the accounting of violent youth for their actions.[23]

There were four areas of our study where we felt that participants were most likely to distort the truth: victimization by serious child maltreatment (including sexual abuse), perpetration of extreme violence towards females and children (especially sexual violence), their involvement in the homicide, and their negative behaviours in custody or in the community while on probation or parole. These were serious issues for us, and we dealt with this through data triangulation. Data triangulation involves "... the explicit search for as many different data sources as possible that bear on the events under analysis."[24] We asked participants for written access to confidential documentation from relevant social or child welfare files, case management files generated in the correctional system, pre-disposition reports, psychological and psychiatric assessments, and documents from their trials. We also conducted a comprehensive search for newspaper accounts of the homicides.

Many participants found it difficult to tell us about their engagement in extreme violence, the homicide, and being victimized by serious child maltreatment. It took a great deal of reassurance and hard work on our part to get these offenders to open up their lives to us. In some cases they feared negative consequences related to their disclosures. Although we assured them that their responses would be confidential (i.e., not be shared with any authorities) and that they themselves would remain anonymous in all publications (their names would not be published and neither would any details that might allow them to be identified), trust remained an issue. We were honest with these offenders about the limits to confidentiality.

Because it was not possible to gain any information related to participants without their expressed written consent on official forms, some of the participants attempted to "manage" the interview situation. Norman Denzin notes that interview situations are not unlike conversations between strangers. Because it is difficult, if not impossible, to tell if a person is lying, there is a tendency to fabricate. In addition, respondents "… may selectively distort, mask, or lie about their attitudes on [answers to] any given questions"[25] in order to present themselves in a positive light.

One young man clearly tried to control the interview. Scott, a sadistic psychopath who said he modelled himself after Jesus and Charles Manson, came to the interview with binders full of his artwork, newspaper clippings detailing the murder and other violent assaults, and poetry. As with all the others, we had no information about this young man nor the homicide prior to the interview. He had been approached to participate in the study by a worker from a non-profit organization. He consented, allowing the worker to forward his name and institution to us, and the worker arranged for the interview, following institutional approval. This offender obviously enjoyed accounting the minute details of his sadistic torture of the homicide victim and two other victims (who had survived vicious attacks by him). After allowing him to talk about this for some time, we redirected him to other issues. The truth status of his accounts was very low, as he attempted to present himself in the best possible light. For example, he painted himself as a protector of women and children. We later found out through official documents that he had beaten his fiancée, his mother, and sisters. He had also sexually assaulted a six-year-old girl when he was 12 and had been convicted when he was 15 of stealing Halloween candy from another small child.

David, one of the youngest participants, was not willing to allow us access to his records; we had to rely on newspaper and witness accounts.[26] Nancy only consented to partial release of records. However, the others provided their correctional case management files, psychological reports, and psychiatric assessments. Therefore, we had excellent documentation on family histories, drug and alcohol abuse, criminal histories, infractions in custody, risk assessments, and detailed descriptions of the homicides. Newspaper files provided another source of data on the homicides and victims. Records from social welfare agencies provided us with information on child maltreatment, education, therapeutic interventions, and social histories. We used these various data sources to cross-reference the data provided by participants during the interviews.

Ultimately, we cannot know for certain how accurate the accounts were. We note where we have evidence that suggests inaccuracies. When we do not have direct contradictory evidence but there are indicators of inconsistencies, we accept the account with critical skepticism. The transcriptions are mirrors of the interview conversations. Our hand-written notes also provide important details regarding body language, voice cue messages, and physical and mental health issues. We focussed on how these offenders explained their actions, from their own perspective. Although we attempted to gain as much information as possible about the participants, our data set of both the encounters and the lives of our participants is surely incomplete. As a result, our interpretations of these encounters and related documentation remains open-ended and open to question. In the end, it does not matter how accurate the accounts are; the words of these 19 offenders *are* the data.

Data Coding and Analysis
Transcriptions from the interview audio-tapes provided rich accounts detailing offenders' perspectives on their behaviour, giving them—and us—the opportunity to explore the meaning of their behaviour. The method used for analyzing this data is based on the techniques of ethnographic data analysis.[27] It examines how these offenders made sense of their homicides and life courses and situates their behaviour in a broader social context. The result is 19 individual interviews, yielding nearly 1000 pages of transcripts and an additional 3000 pages of related documentation. For all, we have a core set of data on standard questions, plus a great deal of information specific to each case.

The development of coding categories involves the interaction of our theoretical concerns with the empirical observations contained in the data. The vast amount of data collected in the interviews was organized into analytical categories, which focussed on similarities and differences among participants and attempted to understand what would account for these. There were a number of different ways of organizing the data; our decisions allowed us to highlight particular features of some over others. We began with a number of areas of interest, including the supports that young people had in the home, community, and school. During the course of the interviews we found that the participants' experiences with the criminal justice system varied depending on whether they had done their time in young offender facilities, adult facilities, or both. This became an important coding category. We also found that the offenders had been convicted of different kinds of homicide (murder, manslaughter, criminal negligence causing death) and sought to see if that made any difference to their experiences.

Our coding technique followed a well-established method of analyzing qualitative data.[28] Our questionnaire was loosely based on relevant concepts previously identified in the literature on youth violence and homicide. Following data collection, we developed a preliminary model, based upon this same literature (the final version of this model is Figure 2.1). Based on the life-course approach, we then attempted to identify all negative and positive experiences for three age groupings: birth to age 11; age 12 to immediately prior to the homicide; and, finally, from the homicide to the time of the interview.

We grouped the offenders' biological, psychological and social attributes and experiences into categories, such as bio-physiological attributes, family-based experiences (e.g. parenting), school-based experiences, peer group interactions, contact with the criminal justice system, contact with child welfare and mental health organizations, evidence of emotional harm, behavioural responses to experiences (coping), socio-economic factors, race and ethnicity, gender, type of homicide, and culpability. We then coded one interview (coding for each case took on average 15 hours in total) to see if it fit our conceptual model. We made revisions, after consulting the literature. The model fit reasonably well. Next, we each took nine cases and proceeded to code each interview (along with the other supporting documentation). After completing this, we exchanged our cases and reviewed the other's work. This process ensured the use of consistent criteria for classification and the reliability of coding.

Often, we went back and investigated literature when data emerged that did not fit our conceptual model. For example, our original model did not account for the significant roles for participants of brain injuries and bullying. As well, the literature highlighted the role of negative factors and downplayed resiliency and protective factors. In many cases, this did not fit with the experiences of our offenders. Although all of our participants had negative social experiences, the number and degree of severity varied, as did the degree of harm suffered. Their resiliency and protective factors likewise varied. We anticipated that we would find multiple pathways to homicide.

A Life-Course Approach

Our study takes a life-course approach to understanding youth homicide. We argue that events that took place over the life courses of the participants contributed to their involvement in murder. This approach is premised on the existence of *multiple pathways* to homicide and through the correctional system after conviction. These young people were victims of harm. However, it is important to understand that what is experienced as seriously harmful varies. Some young people can survive severe trauma with only minimal disruption. Others may be exposed to what appears to be relatively minor trauma and "spin" out of control. This is related to resilience—the ability of individuals to deal positively with negative life events and experiences. Trauma can occur early in young peoples' lives or it may occur quite late. There are also many different types of trauma.

Here, we trace the experiences over the life courses of 19 young people who committed homicide before they reached age 18. We begin with the endowment they received at birth. All children are born with a variety of strengths, weaknesses, and intellectual abilities, the result of the complex interaction between their biological make-up and their prenatal experiences. Conditions such as Fetal Alcohol Syndrome and pre-natal drug addiction impacts on intellectual ability. Children are born into a variety of social circumstances: into single-parent families living in poverty, to abusive or neglectful parents, or into stable homes. Physical features have an effect as well: some children are overweight, some are underweight, and some are seen (according to cultural preferences) as physically attractive, while others are held to be unattractive. Thus, some children are privileged at birth whereas others are disadvantaged. The extent of disadvantage varies, and the importance of these disadvantages will depend upon the experiences they have as they grow towards adulthood.

We begin our analysis by identifying the positive and negative features (social, bio-physiological, and individual) that our participants had at birth. These features were what they carried into the social world. We then examine the interactions they had within their families, with peers, in school, the social and child welfare systems, the criminal justice system, and the health care system. Some of these were sites where they engaged in important positive and negative interactions with others, and these young people responded in a variety of ways. When experiences were negative, many struggled with feelings of shame, humiliation, fear, and anger. These feelings were linked to their behaviours; they struggled to deal with their negative, and at times destructive, feelings about themselves. These experiences and related emotional and behavioural problems did not always come to the attention of the criminal justice system, health care professionals, or the social and child welfare systems. These institutions are part of a social safety net in Canada that assists many children and families facing negative experiences. In some cases, the participants' problems never came to light, and they received little assistance. In other cases, problems did come to light, but there was little or nothing anyone could do to deal with them, because of their families' resistance to intervention. Finally, sometimes the safety net responded in ways that exacerbated problems and further harmed these young people.

Our life-course approach to youth homicide, summarized in Figure 2.1, led us to ask about positive and negative experiences from birth to age 12.[29] We then examined their experiences, feelings, and behaviours from age 12 to the homicide. We found that events over the life course contributed to the homicides, but were not, in and of themselves, determinant of them. Rather, negative experiences, feelings, and behaviours placed these young people into situations where they were at risk of committing homicides.

The immediate context of the homicide also contributed to the killings. Since events directly leading up to the deaths were often critical, we examined what happened during the homicide and how past experiences influenced behaviour at the time of the killing. We combined these proximate events with histories of negative experiences, feelings, and behaviours, to identify different pathways to homicide. We suggest that it may be possible to compare young people who end up committing homicide with those who engage in dangerous or high risk behaviours and yet do not kill.

We explored with our participants how they viewed the homicide. Did they accept responsibility for killing their victim(s) or not? We also explored their sense of why they did what they did and what they believe contributed to their involvement in killing. These young people had, not surprisingly, complex understandings of both the homicide and their involvement. Finally, we examined their lives since the homicide to the time of the interview. We asked them what had happened since their convictions, about their time in custody, the types of support they received and/or sought, and (where appropriate) how being tried as an adult impacted on their experiences.

Introducing the Participants

Before we begin to explore the lives of our participants, we want to introduce them to you. What follows is a brief biography of each of the 19 people we interviewed for this book. Because our snapshots of the participants at the time of the interview are impressions, some information is similar; in all cases, we avoid physical descriptions and have omitted some

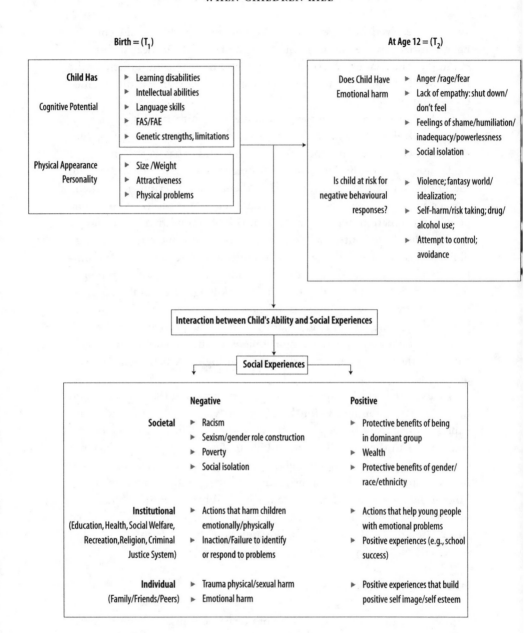

Figure 2.1: A Life-course Approach to Youth Homicide

Just Prior to Homicide = (T_3)

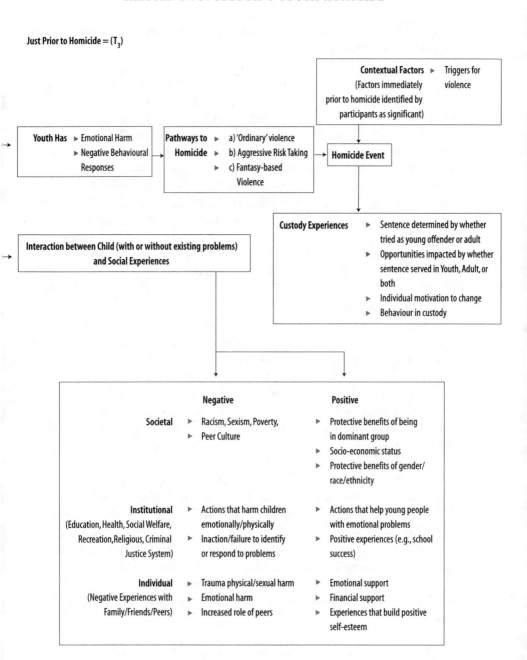

details to ensure anonymity. The participants are introduced in the order in which they were interviewed.

1. *George.* At the time of the interview, George was 24 years old and awaiting trial on a theft offence. He had completed his sentence for the homicide, committed when he was 17, but had since been returned to custody on two separate occasions for other crimes. George came from a poor, single-parent family and had had only sporadic contact with his biological father throughout his life. His mother was an addict, and her numerous partners were emotionally and physically abusive to both her and George. George identified as part-Aboriginal. He had severe learning difficulties and school-based problems; as a result, he was illiterate. A gang member, he was involved in crime at an early age and had a history of violence towards others. George became addicted to drugs as a young adolescent and identified as being still addicted at the time of the interview.

2. *Phillip.* Twenty-two-year-old Phillip was in a minimum security federal correctional facility, having served six years of a seven-year sentence for manslaughter. He had been institutionalized as a child, beginning at age seven, in "too many psychiatric facilities to count." His parents were loving and supportive, but clearly overwhelmed and limited in their abilities to deal with him. There was no abuse at home, but Phillip had significant problems coping with school and serious substance abuse issues. He described himself as a "loner" and "social outcast." He was 17 at the time of the homicide.

3. *Susan.* Since her release on probation 18 months previously, Susan had been living at home, successfully working full-time hours and taking university courses. A visible minority, she had been involved in serious drug trafficking and gang violence for two years prior to her arrest for the homicide. She was convicted of manslaughter when she was 17 years old. She came from a relatively affluent background. Her parents' divorce when she was 12 or 13 years old caused her extreme emotional distress, though even prior to this upset she indicated that her parents had difficulty controlling her.

4. *David.* David was interviewed while in custody for another offence committed subsequent to his release for manslaughter. He had had little criminal involvement prior to the homicide, but had been incarcerated for

a serious crime of violence immediately following his initial release into the community. He was 15 at the time of the murder and involved in gang activity. David was angry about his incarceration, reporting that he had had no direct involvement in the homicide and that he had been punished by a racist justice system—he was a visible minority. He was raised by his mother and had lived in poverty since his arrival in Canada at a young age. He was 21 years old at the time of the interview.

5. *Kyle*. Kyle had a history of both being a victim of child abuse and perpetrating sexual abuse on children. He had been convicted of child sexual abuse at age 12 and of manslaughter by age 17. He had lived in social housing projects prior to coming into institutional care. At the time of the homicide, he was a ward of the state and living independently in the community. A gang member, he was supporting himself through welfare and criminal activity. At the time of the interview, he was 22 years old, had served his time for the homicide and been released, but was back in custody for the second time since his original release.

6. *Steven*. Steven was in a federal halfway house at the time the interview, after having served ten years of a life-ten sentence[30] in federal prison for first-degree murder. At the time of the interview, he was 27, married with children, on a work program, and a full-time third-year student in university. He was one of the few offenders in our study who had a clear and realistic plan for the future and had encountered considerable success following his release into the community. He had survived poverty, neglect, abandonment, and physical abuse as a child and had been involved in gangs during his adolescence. He was 17 when he committed the homicide.

7. *Bruce*. Bruce, 32 at the time of the interview, was the only participant who denied guilt for the homicide, a drug-related killing for which he had served 14 years in prison. He was 17 at the time of the murder and was convicted as an adult under the JDA. Bruce had a serious learning disability, many problems at school, and was illiterate. He had been told throughout childhood that he was "stupid" because of his learning problems, and this created a life-long frustration for him. He was addicted to drugs by age 11, although he maintained that he had been clean for a number of years. At the time of the interview he was working towards release on parole.

8. *Johnny*. Johnny, 24, had been out of custody for three years at the time of

our interview. He had suffered years of verbal and occasional physical abuse by his father, an alcoholic; he, himself, had become an alcoholic. He had a history of risk-taking behaviour, which involved aggression towards others. Johnny had made a successful transition to the community when he told us his story. He was working, had attended post-secondary school, and was adhering to a ten-year driving ban. He was, however, still drinking to excess, and his abuse of alcohol, at times, interfered with his work. Johnny had been charged with homicide at age 17.

9. *Connor*. Connor was on full parole and had been living successfully in the community for ten years when we interviewed him. He was 37, married, the father of one child, and had been working full-time at a variety of jobs since his release. At age 17, he was convicted of first-degree murder as an adult under the JDA and had served ten years in federal penitentiaries. He did not remember any details of the murder, which occurred when he was drunk and high on drugs. He had been involved in serious, escalating substance abuse and other self-destructive behaviours for five years prior to the murder.

10. *Allan*. Allan was 26 at the time of the interview and in a federal minimum-security facility. He had served ten years of a life-8, first-degree murder conviction. He had been physically and emotionally abused at home. In addition to his murder conviction he had been convicted of attempting to kill a family member. He described himself as a loner and an outcast, who never had any friends. He had been bullied at school and was depressed throughout adolescence. Allan was a ringleader in a school-based, anti-social peer group. He was 16 years old when he developed a scheme with peers to murder a friend.

11. *Ian*. Ian was convicted of manslaughter for his involvement in a beating death. He claimed that the intent of the assault, by a group of teens, was not to kill the victim, but to "teach him a lesson." Sixteen years old at the time, he was tried as a young offender and was serving a sentence of just over three years in custody, to be followed by two years probation. Ian was a victim of bullying while growing up and increasingly used violence to protect himself and to gain status. He had been involved in a gang and began abusing drugs at age 13. He was 18 when he told his story to us.

12. *Mitch*. Mitch was in a maximum-security penitentiary at the time of

the interview, having just begun serving a life sentence (with full parole eligibility in seven years) for second-degree murder. Although he denied it, penitentiary staff revealed that he was involved in serious gang violence in the prison. He was 17 at the time of the murder, had a history of engaging in serious violence, and had been dealing drugs and leading a transient lifestyle for the two years leading up to the murder. His father, a violent alcoholic who also had been convicted of some serious crimes, trained Mitch to be a boxer. Mitch reported that he had been abandoned by his mother following his parent's divorce and that he was suffering from the emotional trauma of those events. He grew up in poverty and was 20 when we interviewed him.

13. *Leo.* Leo was 18 years old at the time of the interview and had already served four years in custody — two in a young offender facility and two in a federal maximum-security penitentiary. He was sentenced to life with eligibility for parole after seven years for a double homicide. Leo was a survivor of severe physical and sexual abuse, which began at a very young age. He had coped by escaping into a violent fantasy world. He was socially isolated and had trouble expressing his feelings. He was in school at the time of the homicide and had no prior contacts with the criminal justice system. He was shocked, not so much by the murders, but by the fact that the killings had not given him the satisfaction he thought they would. He expressed no remorse.

14. *Paul.* Paul was an extremely gullible, naïve 17-year-old with low self-esteem when he committed murder. He had poor interpersonal skills and adhered to a rigid, traditional moral code. He was convinced that the murder victim was a rapist and a wife-beater and saw the homicide as a way to define his identity and prove to the world that he could "do good." He had been bullied at school and teased at home because of his serious learning problems. His parents divorced shortly after he was charged. Paul told us that while growing up, his family communicated by screaming and fighting. His family was middle class, and he had no prior criminal history. He was released on day parole shortly after giving us his life story and has been living and working successfully in the community since. He was 26 years old at the time of the interview.

15. *Scott.* At the time of the interview in a medium-security federal correctional facility, Scott was 27 years old and had already spent ten years in fed-

eral prisons. Diagnosed as a sadistic psychopath, he had been convicted of first-degree murder and was serving a concurrent sentence for the homicide and two brutal torture-beatings. At the time of the killing, he was 17 and on probation for assaulting his girlfriend. Scott was a victim of extreme abuse as a child and had experienced severe head trauma at age two. He reported that he learned his violence from his father, an abusive alcoholic. Scott lived on the street after being kicked out of home at age 14 for ongoing violence against his mother and sisters. He was illiterate and severely learning disabled. He had been addicted to crack cocaine and alcohol since age 14, though he claimed to have been clean since his incarceration.

16. *Frank*. Frank, a 41-year-old drug addict, was in a minimum-security federal facility when he told us his story. He had spent the past 24 years in at least ten different penitentiaries. At age 16, he shot and killed a criminal associate, was convicted under the JDA, and received a life-25 sentence. His sentence was later reviewed, and his parole eligibility was reduced to 16 years. While in prison, his addiction worsened, and he developed serious health problems from intravenous drug use. He had never been granted escorted or unescorted day-passes due to his numerous drug-related infractions. He is Aboriginal and had been adopted into a white family after being abandoned on the street by his mother. He reported that his adoptive parents used emotional and physical abuse to "strip" him of his culture.

17. *Nancy*. Nancy, 21 years old, was in a multi-level security facility at the time of the interview. She had a history of disruptive behaviour and began running away from home when she was 11. Around the age of 12, she was committed to a hospital psychiatric ward for one year. Though she denied being a victim of child abuse, she reported that "there was lots of conflict with my father" and that he had punched her in the head on one occasion, possibly causing brain damage. She vilified her mother and deified her father. Nancy was hostile to authority and had attempted to escape when first arrested. She expressed no remorse for her role in murdering a close friend at age 16. Her co-accused (and boyfriend at the time), whom she blamed, was described in court records as a "psychopath with no chance of rehabilitation."

18. *Walter*. Walter was 17 when he shot and killed his victim. He had a history of abuse, neglect, and institutionalization in the child welfare system. Aboriginal, Walter had many school-based problems, which may have been

the result of Fetal Alcohol Syndrome. He grew up on reserves, where he reported that crime, violence, alcoholism, and racism were commonplace. He found safety from racist attacks through gang involvement. He had a history of violence and aggression towards others beginning at age six. He began carrying a gun at age ten and was addicted to drugs by age 11. He was 23 years old and in a maximum-security prison when he told us his story, having already served almost seven years of a life-ten sentence.

19. *Nigel.* Nigel killed his victim at age 16 and had served five years in a maximum-security prison at the time of the interview. He was convicted of second-degree murder and was sentenced to life imprisonment with parole eligibility after seven years. Nigel had been a victim of bullying throughout his childhood and had coped with his feelings by withdrawing into a fantasy world of comics and baseball cards. He began carrying a hunting knife and reported gaining some status from this. He blamed his victim, a mother who was asleep at the time of his assault, for the murder. He claimed his actions were in self-defence.

Notes

1. Fedorowycz, 2001, 2000; Statistics Canada, CCJS, 1999a.
2. Leacy, 1983.
3. Leacy, 1983, n.p.
4. Leacy 1983.
5. Under the JDA youth were found delinquent rather than guilty or innocent. Thus, children charged may still be adjudicated as delinquent even when they have not committed the offence.
6. In Alberta, the age limit was higher for girls (18 years) than for boys (16 years) for a lengthy period of time.
7. Leacy, 1983, n.p.
8. Statistics Canada, CCJS, 1999a.
9. There has also been a change to the definition of the end of the "statistical year" to which the data refer. Currently the statistics cover the calendar year. Previously it defined the year as ending on September 30.
10. Beginning in 1984 the YOA is in effect, and youth are considered to be between the ages of 12 and 17; prior to 1983, juveniles were defined as 7-15 years old.
11. Totten, 2001c.
12. Bessere, 1997; Roberts, 1992; Sprott and Doob, 1997.

13 Savoie, 1999.

14 Statistics Canada, CCJS, 2000c.

15 Savoie, 1999.

16 Savoie, 1999.

17 Doob et al., 1998.

18 Totten, 2000a.

19 Totten, 2000a, 2001b.

20 Silverman, 1993.

21 Scott and Lyman, 1968, 46, 52.

22 Denzin, 1989.

23 Totten, 2000a, 2001a, b.

24 Denzin, 1989, 237.

25 Denzin, 1989, 108.

26 The witness accounts were provided in the court records of one of his co-accused, who also participated in our study. This participant gave us transcripts from her court proceedings and witness statements. We discovered that sections of these documents focussed on David's role in the homicide.

27 Glaser and Straus, 1967.

28 For example, see Glaser and Straus, 1967; Gubrium and Holstein, 1997.

29 We use the age of 12 as a cut-off to fit into the current legislative definition of a young offender.

30 Life sentences are described by the term of potential incarceration and then the number of years that must be served before being eligible for parole. A life-ten sentence means that the person is sentenced to life in prison and must serve at least ten years before applying for parole. If paroled, the person is placed under supervision in the community for the rest of their lives. If they violate parole, they are returned to prison to serve out the rest of their life sentence with the right to apply to be paroled again.

The Role of Early Childhood Experiences

Introduction

In this chapter, we study the life courses of our participants, beginning with their endowment at birth and continuing with their experiences to age 12 in their families, communities, schools, and other institutional settings. We conclude this chapter with a discussion of the positive (protective) and negative features in their lives. From birth our participants had a range of abilities — some had problems such as Fetal Alcohol Syndrome and learning disabilities, and others were endowed with superior intelligence or athletic prowess. They also had diverse experiences during childhood. Some had primarily positive childhood experiences, while others had primarily negative experiences. It is this diversity of backgrounds that best illustrates the multiple pathways to involvement in homicide.

Birth

Everyone is born with a different set of abilities and potential. As well as having varying genetic, bio-physiological, and personality traits, children are born into a range of social circumstances — such as being born to teenaged mothers or into poverty — which can contribute to prenatal care and infant health at birth and how children are parented after birth. In our study, we consider three areas of ability at birth: cognitive, physical, and personality. Cognitive ability includes intelligence and factors limiting intellectual functioning. We were particularly interested in intellectual functioning because, as Table 3.1 indicates, school failure is a risk factor for involvement in violent behaviour. Negative factors which influence intel-

	Physically Abused	Witnessed Physical Abuse	Sexually Abused	Sexual Abuse in Family	Emotionally Abused	Witnessed Emotional Abuse	Neglect	Loss of or Abandonment by Parent(s)	Failure to Provide for Basic Needs
George	x	x				x	x	x	x
Phillip									
Susan									
David	x	x					x	x	
Kyle	x	x	x		x		x	x	
Steven	x	x		x	x	x	x	x	x
Bruce							x		
Johnny	x	x			x	x	x		
Connor							x	x	x
Allan	x	x			x	x	x	x	x
Ian									
Mitch					x	x			
Leo	x	x	x	x			x	x	
Paul					x	x			
Scott	x	x		x	x	x			
Frank	x	x			x	x	x	x	
Nancy					x	x			
Walter	x	x			x		x	x	
Nigel								x	

Table 3.1: Physical and Sexual Abuse, Neglect, Abandonment, and Emotional Abuse in Family (from birth to age 12)

lectual functioning include learning disabilities (e.g., dyslexia), Fetal Alcohol Syndrome (FAS) and Fetal Alcohol Effects (FAE), maternal drug abuse, and genetic circumstances. We also considered protective or positive cognitive factors including average or above-average intelligence.

Physical factors at birth may contribute to resiliency and risk. Children who do not meet normative standards for male and female body types — those who are socially defined as unattractive, too tall or too short, over- or underweight, or with a physical disability — may find themselves at risk for bullying, teasing, and other negative social interactions. On the other hand, children who are socially attractive may reap positive benefits. These features, like cognitive factors, do not exist in isolation. Cultural understanding of them is also important.

		Parent(s) Experienced Family Violence	Parent Incest Survivor	Parent Substance Abuser	Family Living in Poverty	Parent(s) Mentally Ill	Parent(s) had Criminal Convictions	Parent(s) Taken into Care by CW	No Risk Factors
Low Risk parents	Paul					X			
	Susan								X
	David				X				
	Phillip								X
	Connor								X
	Ian								X
Medium Risk parents	Bruce			X			X		
	Johnny	X		X		X			
	Nancy	X						X	
	Frank			X	X		X	X	
	Nigel			X	X				
High Risk parents	Kyle	X		X	X			X	
	Mitch	X		X	X		X		
	George	X		X	X		X	X	
	Leo	X		X	X		X		
	Walter	X	X	X	X		X	X	
	Steven	X		X	X	X	X	X	
	Scott	X	X	X	X		X		
	Allan	X	X	X			X		

Table 3.2: Parental Risk Factors

Personality is perhaps the most difficult feature to define at birth. Even as young infants, some children are placid and easy-going while others are fussy and difficult. These early personality traits have consequences for how children are parented and how they learn to deal with social interactions. It is, perhaps, the most difficult dimension to document. For most of our participants we did not find data in this area.

Detailing bio-physiological features at birth is not always easy. Our participants have no independent knowledge of their births. While some features, such as learning disabilities, are revealed through later testing—often as a result of behavioural problems—others are not. Thus, our knowledge of our participants' positive and negative features is likely incomplete.

	Few Negative Social Experiences	Many Negative Social Experiences
No Protective Factors		Highest Risk ► Scott ► Leo ► George
Few Protective Factors	Medium-Low Risk ► Paul ► David ► Kyle ► Nigel	Medium-High Risk ► Allan ► Bruce ► Johnny ► Nancy ► Walter ► Ian ► Phillip ► Mitch ► Steven ► Frank
Many Protective Factors	Lowest Risk ► Susan ► Connor	

Table 3.3: Summary of Participants' Risk and Protective Factors Prior to Age 12

Bio-Social Psychological Problems at Birth

Some of the participants in our study had serious bio-physiological problems at birth. These included FAS and FAE, brain injury resulting from trauma in the initial years of infancy, serious speech impediments, and a predisposition to a variety of serious mental health problems (related to a family history of mental illness). Genetics also played a role in the development of significant learning disabilities in over one-half of these youth. Nine participants faced significant social disadvantages at birth as well. Most were born to young teenaged mothers who had been living and would continue to live in poverty. There was indirect evidence that nutrition of the fetus and infant were problematic in these cases.

Three participants were born to addicted mothers. George's mother had abused cocaine for most of her teenage and adult life. The mothers of both Frank and Walter were alcoholics. These three young men were at risk for the behavioural and psychological problems typical of FAS/FAE children. FAS results in lifelong disability. Children exhibit a range of symptoms

54

including growth deficiencies; developmental delays; neurological, behavioural, and intellectual deficits; and skull or brain malformation.[1] FAE children exhibit some but not all of these features. In part, this may reflect the point in the pregnancy at which the substance abuse began as well as both the extent and type of substance(s) used. It may also be related to the ability of some children to overcome these effects. As a result, although some FAE children function quite poorly, others function surprisingly well while still having serious (less visible) FAE-related problems. It is difficult to assess the impact of FAS/FAE on our participants. However, George and Walter exhibited serious problems from an early age. Both had behavioural problems (fighting, aggression) prior to attending school, and Walter was extremely violent by age four. Frank appeared to function on an average level despite his mother's heavy drinking during pregnancy. Extensive testing is required to confirm the presence of FAS/FAE.

Learning disabilities were an important factor in our participants' lives. Research suggests that genetics play a major role in the development of these problems. Seven participants were diagnosed with serious learning disabilities and/or Attention Deficit Hyperactivity Disorder (ADHD) prior to age 12, and one participant seems to have had an undiagnosed learning disability. George, Phillip, Scott, and Walter had been diagnosed as learning disabled and were on medication for ADHD during their childhood. Kyle denied that he had any learning disabilities, but supporting documentation indicates that he had ADHD. Paul was diagnosed in grade seven with dyslexia and auditory processing problems. His problems with reading were not noticed by the school system until he was 12. Johnny had some difficulty with recognition and mathematics. He was tested for dyslexia; the results were negative, but the testing psychologist reported that it was likely he had some undiagnosed learning impairment. Bruce probably had serious learning disabilities and was illiterate. He attended school at a time when young people were not tested; he was regarded as "dumb" and later as defiant.

Genetics can play a role in the development of childhood psychiatric problems also. Five participants—Phillip, Allan, Leo, Paul, and Scott—suffered from depression and had serious personality disorders at the time of their arrest. Three of these—Allan, Scott, and Paul—came from families with documented histories of mental illness. Only one participant, Phillip, was diagnosed prior to age 12. There appears to be a genetic connection in his case. He was diagnosed with bi-polar disorder (commonly referred to as manic-depression), a condition believed to have a genetic cause. It is not clear whether Leo's problems were related to a hereditary mental health problem or to extreme child maltreatment.

A final area of bio-physiological interest for homicide research is brain injuries.[2] Recent research suggests that brain injury is linked to violent and criminal behaviour, which places people at risk for injuring and potentially killing others. Two of our young people report serious brain injury in childhood. Scott suffered a brain injury and other physical trauma due to a beating by his father at age two, and Nigel fell from a roof at age five and incurred serious injury to his jaw along with brain damage.

Another feature present at birth that became an issue for our young people later in life was their physical appearance. Two young men (Ian and Nigel) were obese, and, as we shall discuss later, this led to considerable problems.

Positive Features at Birth

A few of our participants had positive features at birth. Most were in good physical health. Steven and Susan were above average in intelligence. David had exceptional athletic ability, and Johnny was also a gifted athlete. The majority of our participants were simply average in their abilities. They were neither intellectually nor physically impaired, but they also were not gifted.

Bio-Social Psychological Problems and Criminal Behaviour

Linking bio-physiological problems to criminal behaviour is not a straight-forward process. The features that young people are born with and brain injury during childhood impact on experiences at home, in school, in the community, and in their interactions with others. Learning disabilities are linked to school failure, and this can be accompanied by feelings of low self-esteem, frustration, and anger. They may also lead to children being viewed and treated negatively by their peers and adults, leading to feelings of shame, humiliation, and anger, which put them at risk for aggressive and/or risk-taking behaviour. Mental health problems can impact on behaviour, marking children as different from others and, at times, making them dangerous to themselves and others. Depression can lead to drug and alcohol abuse as the individual attempts to struggle with negative and at times overwhelming feelings of pain. Brain injuries can impact on behaviour towards others and on risk-taking generally. Some brain-injured children lack impulse control, a behaviour pattern that can be viewed negatively by others, as expectations that they "control themselves" increase as they age. Thus, at an early age some children face deficits that may have long-term consequences. Many appear to have few deficits at birth in terms of their bio-physiology, but have social deficits that have negative consequences for them as they grow up.

Family-Based Experiences

The family is the primary agent of socialization for most children, including our participants. Families prepared them for later experiences in school, the community, and with peers. Some young people had extremely positive family experiences with supportive parents and a safe home environment; others had negative experiences in their families from birth onwards. The family units of 13 of our 19 participants broke down by the time they were teenagers. The nature of family breakdown varied. Some young people were born into single-parent families and never knew their biological fathers, some were born into two-parent families that broke down due to divorce, one family was shattered by death, and in others one or both parents deserted. Experiences with family breakdown took its toll; indeed, for one of our participants it was family breakdown due to divorce that began her involvement in criminal activity and ultimately the homicide.

A key issue for our participants was family violence, including experiencing child maltreatment and witnessing violence. The term "maltreatment" is used to capture all forms of child abuse and neglect. For this study we defined family violence as the physical or sexual assault of any family member by another, consistent with Criminal Code definitions of these offences, where a charge could have been laid. We deal with the issue of emotional or psychological abuse separately. Witnessing family violence can include both direct and indirect viewing—an example of the latter is seeing physical injuries on a family member the next day. Experiencing family violence means being the victim of direct physical or sexual assaults.[3]

Witnessing and experiencing family violence have been identified as a factor in youth violence, because maltreated children experience emotional harm and are at risk for developing behavioural responses such as aggression, drug and alcohol abuse, self-mutilation, and running away from home. These behaviours put them at risk of both being further victimized by violence and of using violence against others. Some may become numbed to violence directed against others and so do not react protectively when others are abused.[4]

Other negative dimensions of family life were neglect, abandonment, and emotional or psychological maltreatment. According to Latimer, neglect

> ... includes situations in which a child has suffered harm or their safety or development has been endangered as a result of the caregiver's failure to provide for or protect them. Unlike abuse, which is usually incident-specific, neglect often involves chronic situations that are not as easily identified as specific incidents.[5]

Neglect includes a failure to supervise or protect children from harm; failure to care for and to provide children with adequate food, clothing, and living conditions; and failure to provide adequate medical care to treat an existing physical or mental health problem or to prevent a future problem. Parents who permit children to engage in criminal or maladaptive behaviours and allow a child to be chronically truant from school are also neglectful. Finally, neglect may also be the result of a caregiver abandoning a child or refusing to exercise custodial rights.[6]

Emotional maltreatment is similar to neglect in that it typically does not involve a specific incident and because it leaves no visible injury. In addition, its effects tend to become apparent over time (e.g., impaired cognitive, social, and emotional development). Emotional maltreatment can include overtly hostile or punitive treatment or habitual or extreme verbal abuse (e.g., threats, belittling). It can also include a lack of nurturing and affection. Emotional maltreatment can lead to mental health, emotional, and development problems in children.

Any investigation of family-based experiences must consider parenting. While it might be tempting to blame parents for children's delinquency, the connection is neither so simple nor so direct. Not all young people who become involved with the criminal justice system are victims of abuse or neglect. Parents who have themselves been victims of family violence or child maltreatment are not as able to provide their children with good parenting. Further, parents may be dealing with problems of addiction to drugs and/or alcohol, further weakening their ability to provide children with the love and support they need.

Family Breakdown

Family breakdown increases the risk that young people will experience emotional and psychological problems. About one-third of our participants came from intact families, and about two-thirds came from families that were broken by death, divorce, or desertion. Family breakdown was often linked to other problems, the most common the loss of contact with biological fathers after divorce or separation. In some cases, such as for George, David, Kyle, and Steven, this parental neglect left them feeling hurt and angry. Connor's mother died suddenly when he was nine, leaving him and his family without anyone to care for them. An older brother who returned home to help committed suicide six months later; the family slowly fell apart. Some young people experienced more than one breakdown as mothers remarried or had a series of live-in boyfriends.

Ending marriages did not necessarily result in ending problems. Leo's parents had been divorced for years, but his father continued to abuse him physically. Divorce often exacerbated financial problems, leaving the family in poverty. George and Walter were left in the custody of addicted mothers after their parents separated. Allan's mother and father separated, and he was left with a mother who continually "bad-mouthed" her ex-husband to the children and who repeatedly told them that she hated men. She also began to work two and sometimes three jobs to maintain the family income and left the children alone for long periods of time.

While family breakdown had negative consequences for our participants, intact families were not necessarily a positive or protective factor. Living with emotionally or physically abusive parents, parents who were alcoholics, or parents struggling with mental illness took its toll as well. Some participants with intact families had positive experiences. Until her parent's marriage began to collapse when she was 12, Susan reported having a positive home life with no abuse or neglect. Phillip's family was supportive. His parents' marriage was strong, and his family life was free from neglect, abuse, or drug and alcohol use. Although Nancy reported a positive home life where conflict centred on her behaviour rather than any problems between the parents, her psychiatric reports indicate that there were some serious conflicts between her parents.

Witnessing and Experiencing Violence at Home

Witnessing and experiencing violence and abuse in the home is related to youth violence, putting young people at risk of becoming involved in homicides. We found that the participants who reported experiencing the most severe acts of violence in their family were the same young people who used the highest degree of brutality in their murders. However, there was tremendous variation. Some offenders in our study did not experience any physical or sexual child abuse.

How common was abuse in our participants' families? Ten of our 19 offenders reported experiencing or witnessing physical abuse in their families (George, David, Kyle, Steven, Johnny, Allan, Leo, Scott, Frank, and Walter). In addition, three of these reported sexual abuse in their families. Kyle was a victim of sexual abuse by a male cousin and, by age 12, had sexually abused his younger siblings. Steven reported that his sister was taken into care because of allegations of sexual abuse by his stepfather, and Leo's older brother sexually abused him. The extent of abuse varied, but all these young people reported negative feelings of anger, shame, fear, and humiliation as a result.

How extensive was the abuse? It varied considerably. We illustrate this with the cases of four participants. Scott, Steven, and Leo reported the most serious abuse. Scott had endured sadistic and cruel beatings and psychological terror at the hands of his alcoholic father until he left home for the streets at the age of 14. As noted above, one such beating at the age of two resulted in permanent brain and ear damage. Scott also witnessed the beatings and psychological abuse of his siblings and mother at home. His older autistic brother was made a Crown ward due to his father's violence. A younger sister was also made a ward of the state at the age of 15. Scott spoke about his father's extreme acts of violence:

> Scott: What kind of things did I go through, um, I got thrown down
> the stairs, I got kicked with steel toe boots, I got hit with what-
> ever object was in his hand, punches — closed fist punches, you
> name it... As long as I can remember, um, it was about three or
> four times a week. The worse beating I ever got at home. Ah,
> I'd say uh, kicked with steel toe boots, thrown down the stairs,
> ah, then my eye was black and blue and then the old man
> decided to get an onion, a half-cut onion, and put that on the
> eye... What happened was my sister turned around, she was
> outside playing — this is my younger sister — and she did
> something I really didn't like, being the younger sister and pes-
> tering, you know, so it ended up being an argument and that
> — between me and her — and she went into my bedroom

and started breaking things of mine. So I just went upstairs and started breaking things of hers. Brother and sister, typical stuff. And eventually she went to my dad and started saying that I was picking on her and everything. I was lying on my bed, and he just grabbed my hair, grabbed my pants, lifted me up, and just threw me against the wall — that was it, it started.

Scott was very forthcoming with his court records, psychiatric reports, and Correctional Services of Canada (CSC) parole and institutional records. Our analysis of this documentation revealed that he was quite accurate in his account of family members' victimization by his father. However, he was not quite so forthcoming about his own violent behaviour against his mother, sisters, and children in the community. Although he denied these assaults, records revealed that he regularly threatened his mother and sister with knives, physically assaulted them on numerous occasions, and had sexually assaulted a six-year-old girl before his twelfth birthday. Given his many serious behavioural and psychiatric problems, it is clear that he was severely traumatized by his home life. It is interesting, however, that he denied any violence against females. In fact, he went to great lengths in the interview to show us how he had protected women throughout his life.

Scott recounted the most serious assault against his mother by his father.

Scott: I was about seven years old, and I sat there in the back seat, my little sister was in front, and me and my older sister were in the back. We went to the doughnut shop, and we came out, and my mom wanted to leave because it was getting late, and we had Christmas gifts and that to give out and that stuff in the morning. He [father] didn't want to go — he wanted to have a few coffees and stuff like that, and he ended up getting a parking ticket... And we all got in the car, and he started blaming my mom. And, ah, he just started beating her, and she came out of it with a fractured arm — so this is like when I was like six or seven.

Int.: She went to the hospital?

Scott: Yeah, and she said she fell down the stairs.

61

What were the consequences of Scott's experiences with family violence? As discussed in Chapter 1, social learning plays a key role in the development of violent behaviour, and it appears that the model of sadistic and severe violence by Scott's father was an important risk factor. However, the exposure to violence alone did not lead Scott to act out violently. As we shall see later in this chapter, he also lacked resiliency and other protective factors that might have prevented him going down the pathway to violence and ultimately to murder.

Leo also experienced severe abuse. Throughout his childhood Leo's biological father beat him. Although his parents had separated before he was born, Leo's father continued to control most of the family's activities. He decided where and how they lived and ensured that they all followed his strict religious practices. He was a lay preacher in a fundamentalist church and justified the beatings with religious scriptures. Leo's brother, who was seven years older, lived with his father and was also subjected to these terrible beatings. Leo described the worst beating he remembered.

> Leo: The worst I have to say was with a two-by-four. Yeah, I think I was only nine. I skipped school for a day, and I guess they found out because I said I was running away because my mother would not let me go into an arcade. So I left and told my friends and guess they told everyone else, and the school found out, and they called home. I came back. I was going to really run away, but I got scared so I came home. He went in the basement, and I knew he was getting something. I started crying because I was so scared because of the spanking.

> Int.: How many times would he hit you with this?

> Leo: It's hard to say because he spanked so fast, like it wasn't just not smack, smack. It was over pretty quick, maybe ten times. That was easy compared to what my brother got. He lived with my father, and I lived with my mother and two sisters, so he was with my father, so he would spank him all the time.

Note that Leo described the beating with a piece of lumber as a spanking. His exposure to extreme violence distorted his sense of what is abusive behaviour and what is (perhaps) acceptable physical correction—a spanking. All too often, extreme abuse comes to be seen by survivors as a normal way of dealing with social events. In addition they blame themselves for the abuse — they were bad and deserved punishment. As these children grow into adults, they become the people offering "correction" for the behaviour of others. If they have continued to accept extreme violence as legitimate, they are potentially seriously dangerous to others.

Leo went on to describe the sexual abuse by his older brother.

> Leo: It was my brother actually. I'm not that sure, but I think it started when I was five or six. It ended when I was like nine or ten. He's seven years older than me, so if I was about five, he'd be whatever, 12. He was 12 or 13 when it started. Well he never forced himself on me. I knew it was bad, but it was kind of like I wasn't against it. I thought there was really something wrong with that. It was what do you call it? Mutual masturbation. It wasn't painful….
>
> For years whenever he'd do something wrong he'd say, "don't tell mom" or he'd say, "don't say anything or I'll tell them what we do and you'll get in trouble." I always thought I was really bad…. I've had psychiatrists or psychologists, I always told them about this. That's why the police came. I'm not angry at him for it. The way I see it, he was mostly a kid himself. I think I was shaped, because my life was full of violence and abuse, and I believe it was shaped. I'm not trying to put the blame off. I never lived with my brother, and when my father would come over, my brother would come over…. Yeah, and sometimes my brother would stay overnight, or sometimes I would stay overnight at my father's place.

Leo struggled with how to understand this sexual abuse, because it did not fit his stereotype: he said that "he [his brother] never forced himself," "it wasn't painful," and "I wasn't against it." For the longest time, Leo felt that he himself was bad and was the cause of the sexual abuse. It is common for sexually abused boys to minimize the abuse, blame themselves, and rationalize the actions of the abuser.[7] Leo explained later on in the interview that his brother had also been sexually abused.

Steven suffered less direct physical abuse than either Leo or Scott. He reported only one severe beating with a metal coat hanger at age two. This beating resulted in hospitalization and in his being taken into care for a one-year period. In Steven's case most of the family violence was directed towards his mother and his sister by his two stepfathers. He described the worst beating he witnessed as one in which his first stepfather beat his mother.

> Steven: By far the worst I ever witnessed was when my stepfather took a hammer to my mother—grabbing my mother by the hair and taking the hammer to her mouth. It was very traumatic, it sticks in my mind even today. He came home drunk. I think we had the stereo on loud or a little loud, and he came home and slapped me and my sister around a little bit, thinking it was us having it on, and my mom was like "no, no it was me that had it going." I think that's how it happened, and it went from there. We had to leave, the police came, and we had to stay at somebody else's home for the night.

Steven's account reminds us that these events which take place in childhood have long-lasting effects. Recalling the incident almost 20 years later, he noted that the events and the emotional trauma had stayed with him.

Exposure to violence had a variety of effects on our participants. For some, it rendered them emotionally numb. Scott noted that he learned to literally "feel nothing" as a result of his experiences of abuse. This included not only feeling nothing physically but also a general lack of concern for the harm done to others. He minimized his own pain and the pain he inflicted on others. Steven still recalled the abuse with horror. Leo struggled with thinking he was abused physically and sexually because he was bad. He also struggled with his anger at what was done to him, diverting his rage into violent fantasies.

Abuse was also tied in a variety of ways to attitudes that normalize the use of violence generally and corporal punishment of children more specifically. By all accounts, both Allan's parents were violent with him and his older sister. Allan described the abuse as "discipline," and it fit much more closely to this description than did the abuse of Leo, Steven, or Scott. Yet, as Allan acknowledged, this "punishment" was harmful emotionally.

> Allan: Both my parents have a ... strong belief in corporal punishment. In fact, for the first four years of both me and my sister's schooling, we were sent to a Catholic school, specifically because they still had the right at that time with parental consent to strap. Um, so on a pretty much regular basis both my

parents would take the strap to me and my sister. My mother had a lovely belt on her … it had, like it had holes all through it. You know, it was actually, had like two, I don't know what you call it, like prongs in the belt, actually two I think it was, and that was her favourite. Uh, it was … very ritualized, very specific. It was "Go get me the belt" …"Put your hands on the couch and put your hands on the table." Now we had this, like a dining room table, and so we would still go and put our hands on it. And so you know the position, like. I also remember a time when you put your hands on the couch, and that was like on the front part of the couch. We must have been pretty small, for that to have worked out, and then it was drop your pants, and there were times that uh, one or the other of us was forced to watch the other be disciplined, so to speak, either waiting our turn or just one was going to get it but the other was going to learn a lesson as well, so we had to stand and watch…. I think my earliest memory was of my father doing it the time that I was maybe pre-school…. I had nothing to do, and I figured, I know I'll go see my sister at school. So still wearing my pajamas, I must have looked so cute, I put on my sneakers, I put on my coat, and I locked the door behind me. All I knew was that my sister's school was down the end of the street and turn right…. I got about halfway there, and a friend of the family found me, brought me home, but had to wake up my father to get the front door open. He, he just snapped and he yelled "Hands against the couch," you know, went right back to get the belt. That was probably my earliest memory.

This "discipline" was highly ritualized and a regular part of growing up. Allan recalled that the last time his mother attempted corporal punishment, he was in tears from the first blow. Then it dawned on him that the belting no longer hurt—it was the humiliation that was upsetting him. He turned around and took the belt away from her. Dealing with unacceptable behaviour through physical abuse, especially (as in this instance) abuse designed to humiliate, is particularly problematic. While Allan's abuse seems minimal when compared to that of Leo, Scott, and Steven, it too left emotional harm. It also left Allan angry with his mother and feeling powerless.

Experiencing and witnessing physical and sexual abuse in their families had long-term consequences for our participants. These experiences and their emotional responses played a part in their involvement in the homicides. However, they were not determinative of that involvement; rather, they put our participants at greater risk for using violence and for acting out their strong negative feelings against others.

Neglect, Abandonment, and Emotional Abuse

Our participants were also vulnerable to psychological harm in their families as a result of neglect, abandonment, and emotional abuse. Feelings of low self-esteem, grief, anger, and frustration were reported as common. Neglect can also place young children at risk for physical harm and for future physical and mental health problems. Lack of supervision can result in children becoming involved in criminal and other anti-social activities. Parents who do not know whom their children are with and what they are doing run the risk of having their children become involved in drug and alcohol abuse, crime, gangs, and violence. Neglected children may also experience increasing difficulty with limits that authority figures — teachers, the criminal justice system, community members, etc. — place on their activities.

As with physical and sexual abuse, the extent of psychological harm suffered by the participants varied. Some of this variation reflected individual attributes; it was also associated with the nature and extent of the abuse. Table 3.1 summarizes our participants' experiences with emotional abuse, neglect, and abandonment. Fifteen offenders experienced one or more forms of this maltreatment. George, Steven, and Allan experienced all five forms of abuse — witnessing and experiencing emotional abuse, neglect, abandonment, and a failure to provide basic needs. Four of our participants (Susan, Phillip, Ian, and Mitch) reported no emotional abuse or neglect. One or both parents had abandoned 11 of our participants. Frank's mother literally abandoned him on the street to the child welfare system. He had no contact with his biological father. Leo and Nigel lost touch with their biological fathers when their families moved. Connor lost a parent through death, and George and Kyle never knew their biological fathers. Others were abandoned by non-custodial parents, who then had no or very irregular contacts with them. George was a case in point. His father kept limited contact with him, but these contacts were highly irregular; George could never count on his father being there.

It is important to note that the nature of the abuse and the extent of harm varied considerably. To illustrate this, we will look at the cases of Frank, Paul, and Connor. Their stories highlight how child maltreatment and psychological harm can be significant risk factors in pathways to homicide. All three of these young men were severely emotionally traumatized.

When he was six years old, Frank's mother abandoned him. She was an alcoholic and living with a violent partner who abused her and one of her three children. To avoid the beatings, Frank took his two brothers to live on the streets. Sometimes they would stay away for three or four nights at a time. They came home when they couldn't find food. Frank explained that his mother did not care where they were and made no effort to locate them when they ran away.

> Frank: Yeah. I was their guardian in a way because prior to going in the foster home we were living on the street and I had to look after them ... my mom took us out [of the reserve to a different province and city].... And then we were abandoned.... The man that my mom stayed with was Native in ethnic origin, he was a racist, and he was abusive to our mother, and he didn't look after us kids. He used to beat my mother when they were drinking. He used to beat my youngest brother because he had blue eyes and that's when I decided that me and my younger brothers, we weren't going to stay at this place.... So I used to take my brothers, and we used to trip around downtown, trip around the city during the day, we'd stay away for a few nights, and if I couldn't get any food for us or any water then we'd have to go back home....

Eventually, the police picked up the boys. The matter was brought to court, and the brothers were made Crown wards. They never saw their mother again. More than 30 years later, Frank still spoke with pain about being abandoned by his mother, not only because of the emotional harm it caused him, but because he believed that had he stayed on the reserve with his maternal grandparents, his life would have turned out quite differently. Frank and his brothers were fostered by a white family, where they were subjected to physical, sexual, and psychological abuse. In addition, they were soon stripped of their culture—yet another psychological blow.

> Frank: Um, and when the foster home father came home that day [the first day they were in the foster home] and the foster mother—they got together and they laid down the rules. And the rules that they laid down I didn't like at all and that was the

basis of my rebellion. First of all they said, "you're no longer an Indian. Your hair is coming off." Things along those lines that were just … blatant, but they cut right through you.… We couldn't have our friends, we couldn't associate with Indian people, we couldn't talk if you knew any Indian words — she said you couldn't talk that no more.

Frank wept a number of times when he was talking about the impact of his mother's abandonment and neglect and how his foster parents attempted to destroy his family's culture and identity. Clearly, these issues were deeply troubling for him, and he still had not been able to overcome the pain of these negative social experiences.

Paul attributed his low self-esteem to the extreme psychological abuse he had suffered at home. He had serious learning disabilities, and there was a history of mental illness in the family. Paul explained how the abuse started.

> Paul: Uh, I got called stupid a lot. But we know exactly, or yeah, I guess you could say we know exactly where that came from. That's an interesting story.… Uh, when I was about ten years old my father's mom, my grandma, committed suicide. And so we went to a family counsellor, and this family counsellor pulled me aside and stated that I was the cause of all the family's problems 'cause I was stupid. And then she went and told my family the same thing, and so for several years that stigma stuck with me and I was constantly referred to as "stupid" if anything happened.… It's funny how certain words stick with you.… That's when she [mother] started — I don't know actually why. I think it's 'cause my dad started withdrawing because of my grandma. After the suicide he just totally withdrew.

Paul's parents' marriage was in serious difficulty. Paul said that there was never any violence in the home, but the most common method of communication was screaming. This emotional conflict was stressful for the children and, coupled with Paul's sense that he was somehow responsible, was seriously harmful to his sense of self-worth.

Connor's case is again illustrative of our multiple pathways model. Until age ten, he had a positive life experience. The home was violence-free, and familial relations were positive. His mother stayed at home and was the primary care provider. His father worked full-time. Connor was in the kitchen with his mother when she died suddenly of what was probably a brain aneurism. Six months later his brother, who had come home to help out following the mother's death, hung himself in the house. Connor found the body. These deaths severely traumatized him.

Connor: Um, I had a great childhood, as far as I was concerned, up until I was ten, I guess. That's when my mother passed away and I guess things kinda went downhill from there.... I just lost it.... I don't know ... I had seven sisters and three brothers. They weren't all at home while I was.... Um, she had a brain tumour, they said. (Snaps his fingers) Just bang. No symptoms, no nothing. She ... I remember, she made me a sandwich and (snaps fingers) that was it.... She made me a sandwich and she was gone.... I ... I ... I just remember being very, ah, worried and scared, and the ambulance came, and, and, and, ah.... I remember my neighbours being there, and a friend, and I remember telling my friend, um, "She's not coming back. She, she died." He said, "No, no, it's okay." And I went on, "Oh, no, she" ... Um, my sisters were there. Two of my sisters. Um. My father was at work. And ah ... that was it.

Int.: Was there any counselling or support provided after this?

Connor: No. Nothing.... Well, there was a funeral and then ah ... after that, yeah, it was on with my life, and then six months later my brother actually came home. He was looking after us, and ah ... he ended up hanging himself (very long silence, crying). Excuse me.

Connor was very emotional throughout the interview, crying at numerous points. It was necessary to shut off the tape recorder and to provide him with support. We spent some time with him following the interview to ensure that he had the necessary help in place to deal with the painful memories we had uncovered. He assured us that his wife was extremely supportive and that he had a good psychologist whom he saw on a regular basis. It was clearly evident to us that he was still deeply traumatized by these events.

The psychological harm suffered by Connor was markedly different than that experienced by other participants. The trauma at age ten was the result of two sudden and unforeseen events, aggravated by a number of factors. First, these events were totally out of his control. There was absolutely nothing he could have done to prevent the deaths, yet it appears that he felt responsible in some way for causing them. Secondly, his father seemed unable to provide adequate supervision, support, and structure in his son's life following these deaths. According to Connor, after his brother died, his father continued to go to work, and no one else came to care for the children. They received little supervision and had no support to deal with the trauma. As a result, Connor went spiralling down a self-destructive pathway of serious substance abuse, overdoses, violence, and depression. He left school and moved out of home at the age of 12 into a transient lifestyle supported by drug dealing.

Positive Family Experiences

Not all of our participants had negative experiences in their family. Indeed, there were many positive experiences as well. Four participants—Phillip, Susan, Ian, and Mitch—reported happy family lives up to the age of 12. They did have negative experiences, some before age 12 and some after, but their family situations provided them with support and love. These features contributed to improving their self-esteem and their resilience in the face of other challenges.

Susan described the most positive family experiences. There was no physical, sexual, or psychological abuse in the home. She reached all developmental milestones without any difficulty, was bright, and did well at school. She was actively involved in community activities, including summer camps and a variety of sports. She was of mixed race. Because her birth parents were teenagers, we wondered if her mother received proper prenatal care, but could not confirm this as an issue. Prior to age 12, Susan was at lowest risk compared to all the other offenders in our sample. Her family situation was happy, and she reported that both her adoptive parents were loving and supportive. She also had few other negative experiences.

Even in families with problems, life was not uniformly grim. Johnny reported a strong positive relationship with his mother. Her love supported him as he grew up, although, to some extent, she indulged his risk-taking behaviour by doing nothing to check it. Instead, she warned him that sooner or later he would meet his match and get himself into real trouble. Kyle also reported a positive relationship with his mother and with his stepfather, whose marriage was good for a number of years. Leo had a positive relationship with his stepfather, who was kind and gentle, unlike his biological father. These positive supports helped our participants by giving them some feelings of being loved and respected.

Before we turn to the discussion of other sources of trauma, we need to consider the role of parenting in shaping the negative experiences and the emotional trauma that our participants endured. We put the parenting behaviours into context — a context that includes parents living in poverty, parents with mental health problems, parents who were addicted, and parents who themselves were poorly parented and unable to parent well.

Parenting in Context

Were the parents of our participants bad people? While this is an appealing explanation, it is too simplistic. Like the participants, these parents were exposed to risk factors and had both negative and positive social experiences in early childhood and adolescence. Some were more resilient; some had a variety of protective factors that mitigated these risks. All but three sets of parents had multiple risk factors. Sixteen offenders had guardians who had experienced serious emotional and/or behavioural difficulties growing up, difficulties directly related to their parenting skills and capacities. High-risk parents are likely to have high-risk children in the absence of significant protective factors.

There are a number of factors that contribute to high-risk parenting, including being a single parent, living in poverty, addiction, being abused and/or in care when children themselves, mental illness, and poor health. These features contribute to a number of negative behaviours related to poor parenting skills; neglect, abuse, and lack of supervision.[8] Using the literature and based on the accounts provided by our participants, we identified seven parental risk factors: parent was victim of familial physical violence as a child; parent was an incest/sexual abuse survivor; parent was a substance abuser; family lived in poverty; parent(s) were involved in criminal behaviour; and parent(s) grew up in the child welfare system. Using these factors, we classified parents into one of three risk categories: low risk (less than two risk factors), medium risk (two or three risk factors), and high risk (four or more risk factors).

Up to age 12, five offenders had parents with fewer than two risk factors (see Table 3.2). Phillip, Susan, Paul, Connor, and Ian's parents were employed full-time and lived in owned homes in working- and middle-class neighbourhoods. Four families (Susan, Phillip, Connor, and Ian) had no parental problems. Neither parent were substance abusers. They were not convicted of any criminal activity, had no mental health problems, and were not violent. Yet, these families were not problem free. Connor's family was shattered by the sudden death of his mother. Ian's mother was injured in a driving accident and could no longer work; she was in chronic pain and used a number of prescription drugs. Susan raised some concern about being adopted and noted that both her parents had been adopted as children. The other two low-risk families had a range of different problems. Paul's parents' marriage was extremely unhappy, and there was a great deal of arguing related in part to his father's mental-health problems.

The parenting contexts of the remaining offenders were more problematic. Six participants (David, Bruce, Johnny, Frank, Nancy, and Nigel) had parents with two or three risk factors and were classified as medium-risk parents. Table 3.2 summarizes the types of problems they brought to their families. Both of Bruce's parents were alcoholics, and his father had a criminal record. Moreover, Bruce reported, as did the media, that his father was a member of a motorcycle gang involved in criminal activity. Bruce said he witnessed no illegal activities and noted that his father worked in a local industry until he died. He also reported that the police were quite interested in trying to find out what the gang was involved in and pressured Bruce to give them information.

For part of his childhood before his mother remarried, Nigel's family lived on the edge of poverty. After the second marriage things were better. Both his mother and stepfather worked, although his stepfather was off work for a time due to injury. However, both were recovering alcoholics; they had stopped drinking prior to their marriage, about ten years before the homicide. Nancy's father had been taken into care as a child and had experienced family violence growing up. Frank's mother and father-figures were alcoholics and neglected the children. The family lived in poverty. While Frank knew nothing about his stepfather's upbringing, he reported that his mother grew up in the residential school system, an experience that shattered her life.

Eight participants had parents with four or more risk factors (high-risk parents), summarized in Table 3.2. All these parents had substance-abuse problems, and one or both parents were victims of physical abuse as children. In six of the households (Kyle's, Mitch's, George's, Walter's, Steven's, and Allan's), the mother had been battered as a child, and in five of these families their husbands and/or boyfriends also abused them as adults. Both of Scott's parents were battered as children, and Leo reported that his father was abused as a child. High-risk parents were more likely to have been taken into care as children. George's mother, Kyle's mother, both of Walter's parents, Steven's mother, and Allan's father had all been taken into care because of neglect, abuse, or abandonment as children. Except for Allan's family, all the high-risk families were living in poverty. High-risk parents also were more likely to have criminal convictions. While abuse victimization was more common among mothers, criminal records were more common among fathers. Mitch's father had a record for assault. Leo's father had a record for indecent assault—he had exposed himself to some school children. Scott's father had convictions for assault and for impaired driving. Allan's father was convicted of possession and of drug dealing. Two mothers (of George and Steven) had records for drug offences and shoplifting and had served time in jail. Steven's mother not only shoplifted herself, she also encouraged him to shoplift. During one arrest for shoplifting, all the children were taken into care, disrupting their chaotic lives even further.

Not surprisingly, the negative life histories of the parents were reflected in their problematic behaviours and emotional health problems. Kyle's stepfather was an alcoholic; Mitch's father was addicted to both alcohol and drugs, which led to serious financial problems. George's mother and most of her succession of live-in boyfriends were cocaine addicts. George noted that they used and dealt drugs while constantly warning him never to use them. Leo's father abused prescription drugs to function daily; he used uppers to wake himself and downers to put himself to sleep. Both of Walter's parents were alcoholics. Allan's father was an alcoholic and a drug addict. Scott's father was an alcoholic.

The following accounts by Johnny, Allan, and Mitch help illustrate how the social, economic, and psychological context of parents' lives can limit parenting skills and have negative consequences for their children. Johnny's home life was chaotic, dominated by his father's alcoholism, violence, and psychological abuse. His father was cruel, distant, and funnelled all his emotions into anger. Johnny located his father's behaviour in his own trauma.

Johnny: When he was younger, my father watched his father kill himself. My grandfather committed suicide because my grandmother was cheating on my grandfather with another man in the area. It was a small town. They had the family farm, and somebody told my grandfather this, and he had no inkling of it or whatever, and he lost his mind. In a jealous rage he went back because somebody told him he was at the farm now with my grandmother, which wasn't true. When he got back to the farm, he searched everywhere and couldn't find anyone, nor her, and when he walked into the barn there was someone there, and he had a shotgun with him. Instead of shooting the person, he went over to him and knocked him down, and in a rage he beat the man to death with the butt of the gun. When he finished beating him, he kind of come out it or whatever, and he realized he had killed his hired hand, which was his best friend at the time. Knowing he had did that, I guess he couldn't live with it, and he went out and just put the gun to himself and shot himself. He walked out like three fields from the house when he did it, but my father knew what he was going to do, and my father was running, trying to stop him, but never got there in time. My father and my uncles never got any help for it, which they should have had, because they were all young at the time, they were all kids.

Int.: How old would your dad have been?

Johnny: A teenager, 16, I think when it happened. To him, his father was the world, like his father could do no wrong, like he was the greatest man he ever knew, type of thing. He had no appreciation for his mother whatsoever after that. When she died, they called him at two in the morning or something, and if it wasn't for the phone waking him up or anything, he wouldn't have rolled out of bed. It would have never bothered him. I don't know if that's a bad thing or what, but I guess for the feelings he had for his dad, he was just never able to forgive her. He never tried, but he never stopped us from seeing her, like I knew my grandmother and stuff, but he never said anything about her in front of us, bad or good. We were just left to figure things out whatever way we wanted to.

The emotional trauma that Johnny's father experienced had a profound impact on his life. He channelled his grief, anger, and pain into negative behaviour patterns: drinking, withdrawing emotionally from others, and rage. He became involved in criminal activity related to aggression when drinking and drunk driving. The impact of his behaviour on his own children was complex. Johnny, too, became heavily involved in alcohol abuse and was violent towards others.

Allan suffered serious psychological harm from his mother. Official reports support his account of this dysfunctional relationship: his mother treated her son as a spouse and parent, requiring him to meet her emotional needs. At the same time, she had a very low level of involvement in his life, leaving him alone in the house with his sister most days. She was an incest survivor and repeatedly told Allan that she hated men. In expressing her anger towards men generally, she would say that Allan was not included, was not a man. He found this very painful. When she said "all men are pigs," Allan felt he had two bad choices "… so, either you're a pig or not a man." Her anger towards men included Allan's father. He recalled that when his father tried to commit suicide, his mother took him and his sister to see their father in intensive care. She reportedly said, "See what a stupid man your father is." Her actions seemed to be based in her relationship with Allan's grandparents.

> Allan: I've heard a number of things. I remember growing up hearing horror stories about her mother, about the horrible, horrible things her mother did to her as a child. Things like when she wanted to become a nurse, in [another country] there you had to go into residency and you actually lived at the hospital, and her mother called the hospital and told them that she didn't have permission to be there, and that she was a runaway, to try and get her kicked out. You know, another really abusive thing was like her, when her mother got pregnant with another child after my mother, uh, my mother had had some sort of child- hood disease that by her mother she had caught, and lost this baby because of it, and she was told right out to her face, "It's your fault that this baby died." You know, she was blamed for that, and that would have been very young, cuz she was like 14 or 15 when her sister was born, which was years later. And so I, you know, I always had this image of this horrible woman, but then it occurred to me, she always deified her father, and demonized her mother. And then I remember about how that sometimes when children are abused, sexually or physically, often they will deify the abuser and demonize the other parent. And so one time, in a family counselling session, I said to her,

75

you know, you do this. You deify your father and demonize your mother. You say he was so great, he could do no wrong. Didn't he ever do anything to stand up to your mother? To protect you? And then I just sort of sat back and she just started telling me really disturbing things about how the two of them used to compete for his attention, and how her father had a picture in his wallet of [his wife] at my mother's age, along with a picture of my mother. Right, so the two of them at the same age, and, and this drove her mother insane that he had these two pictures together in the wallet at the same age as each other, all looking a lot like each other, that sort of thing. And uh, it was just really bent, freaky stuff.... She'd say things like, she would be sitting with her father, listening to the radio, watching t.v. or something. Her mother would come in, in a nightie and you know, was like trying to entice him off the bed, to get him away from her. You know, that sort of thing. She [grandmother] was insanely jealous of the attention that her father gave her [mother].

Mitch idolized his father and did not admit the severity of his father's alcoholism nor family violence. He denied his father's criminal involvement and the financial problems this caused for the family. We found these details in supporting documentation. In his account, Mitch gave us his own version of life at home and how his father's problems impacted on it.

Mitch: I can only remember one time it was by accident; Dad got a little too aggressive, he'd had a few beer and he got me good, but I was asking for it. We were play fighting and squaring off ... and got carried away. He's a trained boxer. I was fooling around with him and he kicked me. He apologized and everything, it was an accident 100 per cent.... Oh yeah he drank, but he wasn't a raging alcoholic or anything.

Int.:   What kind of work is he or was he in?

Mitch: At the [work site] I believe in [city]. He was a [low-skill occupation] too.... He ended up getting laid off.... He was getting paid under the table for being a [same occupation]. At the [work site] he ended up getting laid off....

Int.: How about your mom, did she ever work outside the home?

Mitch: Oh yeah… [service sector job].… We moved a lot actually. We lived in a house in [city] when we were young, then moved to [a second city] and lived in a house.… Then we moved again to a different part of [second city], to a townhouse, and then after that, that's when my parents divorced. We ended up in another townhouse, not very far from that one.

The supporting documentation indicated that Mitch's father had significant problems. He was an addict. His drinking and drug use contributed to family instability, interfering with his ability to keep a job, and he spent too much of the money his wife earned on liquor and drugs. He was physically aggressive and had been arrested for assault. This aggressive behaviour became more understandable to us when contextualized by his upbringing. He came from a long line of boxers. In his family, the masculine attributes of toughness, violence, self-protection, and non-emotionality were highly valued. Criminal behaviour was also a source of status. His family had a history of financial problems, criminal activity, and working on the margins of the economy.

A final dimension of parenting in context was that some parents chose or developed maladaptive strategies for coping with their children. These parenting styles may have been well intentioned, but they likely contributed to the negative behaviours in their children. Nancy described an incident in which she got into trouble at school, then assaulted the principal, and noted that her mother's response to this was to take her shopping. Why? Because her mother knew that she would be upset about the incident and wanted to make her feel better. Nancy laughingly noted that her mother always did this. Johnny's mother knew about his aggressive risk-taking because he confided in her, but she did not attempt to stop him from doing these things, only warned him that he would get into trouble, sooner or later. Nigel was teased for being overweight. His mother tried to help him deal with it, but her strategy wasn't helpful.

Nigel: Um, well when I got suspended there, I was sent down to talk… a bit. Like I guess they just dismissed it as, you know, kids being kids kind of thing. I mean, my mother is a bigger person. She told me, well, "I was a big kid when I was growing up. I had to put up with some of the same teasing that you

have to put up with now, kind of thing, so you know, just forget about it. Don't listen to what they are saying, kind of
thing." It's like, well yeah, maybe, but it's not really the same.

As Nigel noted, his mother's support didn't help him to deal with being
called fat or the nasty jokes he heard. His mother tried, but did not or
could not find a better strategy to help Nigel deal with his pain.

Families in Summary
The family experiences of our participants cover a wide range from positive, healthy families to dysfunctional, violent, and abusive families. Some
young people were physically and sexually abused, some were emotionally
abused, and others were simply ignored and neglected. Parents left them in
care, ignored them after divorce, or deserted them altogether. Some participants lived with both parents, untouched by divorce, poverty, or other
harmful circumstances.

While families provided young people with a base from which to begin
life, the diversity of family experiences reflects the multiple paths that can
lead young people to become involved in homicides. It is not simply that
"bad kids" come from "bad families": families provide children with positive *and* negative experiences. Positive experiences are not a guarantee that
young people will not become involved in homicides, and negative experiences are not a sure road to involvement either.

Early Institutional Experiences

As participants moved out into the world, a variety of social institutions
became involved in their lives. All our participants went to school, and
many had contact with the child welfare, social welfare, and/or mental
health systems. In addition, we asked participants about their involvement
in recreational and religious activities and about their communities. These
institutions can be important in providing young people with positive
experiences that decrease the likelihood they will become involved in
crime and other risky activities; they may also provide young people with
negative experiences. Negative experiences were defined as experiences
within institutional settings that harmed children emotionally or physically,
along with inaction or failure to identify or to respond effectively to their
problems. As with negative family-based experiences, negative institution-
ally-based experiences left some of these young people with feelings of

anger, frustration, shame, and humiliation—all precursors to anti-social behaviour.

Positive experiences were defined as experiences that increased participants' sense of ability, self-worth, or value, and actions taken within institutions that responded appropriately to the problems these young people were experiencing.

School-Based Experiences

School-based experiences, like family-based experiences, were both positive and negative. We found that problems began very early in the school careers of some offenders; for others, this did not happen until after the age of 12. Some problems were related to bio-physiological factors, such as learning disabilities; other problems were related to social interactions. Some of our young people did very well in school, which led to positive feelings about themselves and their abilities. Some were average students with few scholastic problems, and some struggled academically.

School Achievement School is a testing ground for young people. The most obvious test is assessing their intellectual ability compared to their peers. Two participants (Steven and Susan) did exceptionally well at school. They had above-average intelligence and achieved excellent grades during primary school. Others had average ability and performed at adequate levels in grade school, passing grades successfully. However, as we discussed above, seven of our participants were diagnosed with serious learning disabilities and/or ADHD. These conditions contributed to school failure and other negative school experiences. One participant, Bruce, was never diagnosed; indeed, his learning disability was only identified after his conviction. George was 10, Paul was 12, and Johnny was in high school when they were diagnosed with learning disabilities. As a result, these young men received no treatment until late in school. They had to struggle with poor grades and the accompanying frustration. Four participants (Phillip, Kyle, Scott, and Walter) were diagnosed early with both learning disabilities and ADHD, which led to them acting out in school. In some ways, their ADHD diagnoses led to the early identification of their learning disabilities.

When learning disabilities were identified early, our participants were placed in special classes. For some, this began as early as kindergarten. Nigel was placed in a special class.

Int.: Were you ever in any special class?

Nigel: Um, when I was in grade one or something, it was, I guess you would call it, speech impediment or something like that. Had trouble reading so I, when I was in grade one or something, for an hour or two in the day I'd go to a special class for just learning reading. I guess my reading skills were just pretty....

Int.: So what was going on back then?

Nigel: Dunno. Just had trouble reading. Pronunciation of words and like spellings and stuff, like long "a"s, and different kind of "a" sounds, kind of thing, and stuff....

Int.: Ever diagnosed as having any learning disabilities?

Nigel: No. Never had any learning disabilities there.

Int.: What about as having behaviour problems?

Nigel: Well I guess that's when my school fighting started, kind of thing. When I started going to this special class, I was made fun of there, too. So....

All of the participants who were placed in these special learning settings reported feeling ashamed and being stigmatized. They were known as the "school dummies" and were subjected to ridicule, teasing, and bullying. This is consistent with research that suggests that special needs children are more likely to be bullied.[9] It also highlights the difficulty schools have in addressing special needs in the context of a peer setting that is hostile to children identified as different.

The difficulties are further highlighted by the negative consequences experienced by some of our participants when their learning difficulties were not identified until quite late in their academic careers. This is what happened to George and Paul. George performed poorly at school and was disruptive. Finally, the school refused to accept him back until he was tested for learning disabilities. He was found to have ADHD, was prescribed Ritalin, and allowed to return to school. The Ritalin calmed him down so much that he could barely function. Thus, while his disruptive behaviour declined when he took his medication, his school achievement did not improve. Eventually, his father took him off the medication without seeking medical advice. His disruptive behaviour returned, and he was once again in conflict with the school authorities. Paul had problems with reading; dyslexia and auditory processing problems were not identified until grade seven, when he was 12 years old. These problems limited his achievement at school; he was frustrated and felt stupid. Bruce's learning difficulties were never diagnosed, and he, too, suffered feelings of failure and low self-esteem.

Bullying Bullying—physical, verbal, and psychological intimidation[10]— was a common problem. Swarming, a form of bullying, occurs when a group of two or more youth use physical and verbal intimidation to inflict physical or emotional harm, or steal articles of clothing, money, etc.[11] Thirteen of our participants reported being bullied or swarmed in school. Estimates of the proportion of all children who are bullied range from 15 per cent[12] to 25 per cent.[13] Research suggests that victims of bullying are more likely than non-victims to also be victims of parental emotional and physical abuse and are more likely to be victims of sexual assault.[14] Parental relationships with children are also predictive of risk for being bullied. Two groups of young people have been found to be at higher risk for being bullied—children with low levels of parental care (neglected children) and children with over-protective parents.[15] Ken Rigby found that boys who had negative relationships with absent fathers and girls with negative attitudes towards their mothers were more likely to be victims of bullying.[16] Young children who are bullied are also more likely to have low self-esteem[17] and to have psychological problems. Thus, many young children who are bullied are often vulnerable before they enter school. Other young children become vulnerable once in school if they are stigmatized because they have special needs (such as learning disabilities), which are identified and labelled or which are unidentified but impede their functioning in school.[18] Their peers recognize that these young people are different and so they are vulnerable.[19]

Young people in our study were bullied for a number of reasons. As noted above, some were bullied when they had and/or were identified as having learning disabilities. But there were other reasons as well. Steven was bullied because he was poorly dressed. No one intervened until he beat up his tormentor (a friend's older brother). Steven was suspended, and the other boy's parents forbade their sons to play with him. Nigel reported that his "school problems" began when he started to fight the children who teased him. Note that the "problem" according to Nigel was his retaliation, and *not* the bullying. The school apparently shared this definition—they punished his aggression and not the teasing. Allan and Ian said that they were bullied and teased and had virtually no friends in their childhood. Ian was overweight and the butt of many jokes. Allan was sensitive, had poor interpersonal skills, and was unable to cope with the verbal repartee at school.

Bullying has negative impacts on young people and these impacts are felt for a long time.[20] Research has shown that bullying can lead young people to involvement in gang activity, to have mental health and psychological problems, and to feel unhappy and lonely at school.[21] It is important to note that the negative consequences of bullying are mitigated by other supports young people have (both other peers and within their families) and by non-abusive familial relationships.[22] The emotional impact of bullying was experienced by our respondents. Both Allan and Leo referred to themselves as "losers" and "social outcasts" at school. Other participants identified themselves as being slow, stupid, or dumb, accepting the negative labels their peers applied to them. Nigel noted how hard he worked to get out of his grade one special class to avoid further bullying by his peers.

What is missing from our participants' accounts of experiences with bullying at school is any reference to the schools acting to stop the bullying. Likely the schools did nothing. Although bullying is a serious problem for young people, for far too long schools have not intervened. Our participants who experienced bullying were left with negative feelings and to find their own solutions—usually fighting back with fists rather than words. Nine of the 13 participants who were bullied (George, Phillip, Steven, Bruce, Johnny, Ian, Mitch, Walter, and Nigel) reported at least one incident of fighting back before the age of 13. For some, retaliation began early. Walter slammed another child's head into a desk at age five. At age seven or eight, Steven knocked down an older bully and began kicking him in the face. Ian reported being increasingly aggressive towards others from about age nine up to age 13 or 14. Our participants said they were pushed to defend themselves. They also reported that, when they did so, they were punished by their schools.

Another common solution these young people found to stop bullying was to attach themselves to an aggressive peer group. George, Steven, Bruce, Johnny, Ian, Mitch, and Walter took this route. These peer groups provided them with positive emotional support and, as we shall see in

Chapters 4 and 5, contributed to continued aggression and to their involvement in the homicides.

Four participants—Allan, Leo, Paul, and Nigel—responded to being bullied by becoming increasingly withdrawn and by isolating themselves socially from their peers. Allan described his strategy as "trying to blend into the woodwork." Leo physically separated himself from other children by going to little-used areas of the playground. Nigel, Scott, and Phillip found themselves isolated by their peers. Scott said he did not like the company of others; other children likely feared him because of his irrational violence. Phillip was physically removed to mental health facilities. Nigel was isolated because of constant school changes; he found being the "new kid" a problem.

Positive School Experiences   As with family-based experiences and individual traits, not all our participants had negative school experiences. School also afforded opportunities for positive experiences and helped to build their self-esteem. Some recalled a range of positive school-based experiences: involvement on sports teams, a special teacher who made a difference in their lives, or scholastic achievement.

Susan, Steven, Johnny, and Connor (until age 10) all appear to have had very positive experiences at school. They were all in regular classroom settings, did not demonstrate behavioural or learning difficulties, and participated in extra-curricular sporting activities. In addition, Susan and Steven had excellent grades and were identified by their teachers as having exceptional ability.

David had exceptional athletic skill. He played on a number of school teams and excelled. His skill on the basketball court earned him both praise and status at school. However, he valued only the athletic opportunities and had little interest in scholastic activities. Frank, too, reported that sports were a positive aspect of school for him. He had ability, but, more importantly, sports allowed him to spend time away from his abusive foster home in a positive environment.[23]

Mental Health

Given the emotional and physical harm suffered by some of our participants in their families and schools, we wondered how—or if—these problems had been addressed by mental health professionals. In order for young people to be connected with supportive services, their problems have to be identified *as* problems. It is difficult, however, to identify emotional harm in younger children—especially when these children are not behaving in inappropriate ways. Further, when parents are neglectful this often extends into disregarding the health needs of their children. Too often, no one paid much attention to the problems experienced by participants in their childhood. Did anyone care? As our participants got older and their negative behaviour had more serious consequences, the system began to respond. We will discuss this in Chapter 4.

Only Phillip, Frank, and Nancy received mental health intervention prior to age 12 in spite of the fact that most of our participants were exhibiting problematic behaviour and most had experienced serious emotional harm. By grade three, Phillip had been diagnosed with serious learning disabilities, including dyslexia. Before age 12, he was diagnosed as having ADHD, early-onset conduct disorder, and bi-polar disorder. He reported that he always felt like a social outcast, the school dummy, and had few friends. His "rages" started in kindergarten, as did the incessant bullying and teasing by older peers.

Phillip: It started about age seven, or slightly before, whenever people start kindergarten, somewhere in that area, about seven. It was school-related. I had trouble dealing with school, coping with schoolwork. Feeling inadequate, I guess, and at first it started off that I was a very passive person. I was just withdrawn and quiet. It went from being withdrawn, I guess, to not being able to hold all that. From being withdrawn to blowing up. Throwing things around, screaming at teachers, that type of behaviour.... I can't really identify what it was. I was frustrated that I was feeling not equal to everyone else, and not being treated equal to other people. As I said, I started off being very withdrawn, and having feelings that there was nothing about this, and I just had to take the stress of what was happening. That evolved to finally blowing up and saying "no one is going to put me in this position, nobody's going to hurt me. Nobody's going to put me in a position that I can't cope with. I'll deal with it. I'll teach them," type of attitude.... I was not able, or I felt that I wasn't doing it [schoolwork] at the same speed as everyone else, or getting the marks; that kind of thing. I felt that the teachers weren't giving me adequate help with the work; that I was just sort of handed the book or the schoolwork and told "do this," and not explained how to do the work. That was my perception of things.... I was teased a lot, and I remember these older girls, they were probably only 11 or 12, when I convert it to my age now. They used to throw me down and beat me up all of the time, at school. The school wasn't doing anything about it. My sisters tried to get in, and they couldn't do anything about it. Actual cause? I don't know. I was very young, I was about seven years old. Reasoning is a little different then. You don't understand things, per se.

Int.: Yeah. But was it because you looked funny or you had trouble?

Phillip: That was always what I thought it was, anyway. About my looks or who I was. That really played a part in self-esteem later on.... I just remember them always punching me and throwing me down and kicking me.

Phillip spent much of his early childhood in mental health treatment centres. All the attempts to reintegrate him upon discharge failed. He was subjected to a variety of different therapists and to several changes in diagnoses. This pattern continued after age 12, and we discuss it in more detail in the next chapter. Nancy was also diagnosed with mental health problems and was placed in a psychiatric ward at age 12. There was no clear diagnosis in her medical records. Frank was sent for mental health counselling because he frequently ran from care and then lied about what happened. Frank refused to tell psychiatrists why he ran away. He knew that reporting the abuse in his foster home would mean that he and his brothers would be split up. Frank said he would have preferred an Aboriginal counsellor and did not trust white psychologists and psychiatrists.

The ability of the mental health system to respond effectively to these young people was limited. Identification of their problems was likely difficult in the context of their abusive or negligent parents, some of whom reportedly were resistant to treatment.

Social and Child Welfare

We employ the term social welfare (SW) to include income-support programs, social housing, and the range of other community-based counselling and prevention services, excluding child welfare (CW) intervention. Nine of our participants came into contact with one or the other system prior to the age of 12 for a variety of reasons. Five (George, David, Kyle, Steven, and

Frank) were from single-parent, female-headed households on welfare. Two (Scott and Walter) were from intact families. Scott's family lived in social housing. They first came to the attention of CW officials when an aunt called to report that the children were being abused. Walter grew up on a reserve, and his family lived in poverty. Their contact with a variety of native and non-native CW agencies centred around Walter's negative behaviour. Two participants (Connor and Bruce) came into contact with the system because of school truancy. This was under the JDA and was not related to family-based problems, although both young men were experiencing significant problems at home.

Five participants (George, Johnny, Allan, Mitch, and Leo) were victims of or witnessed family violence, yet had no contact with the CW system.

We found that the system interacted with our participants in four ways.

1 No contact with the CW system. This was true for ten of our 19 participants. Two (Phillip and Nancy) had contact with the mental health system and had mental health placements. The other eight (Susan, Johnny, Allan, Ian, Mitch, Leo, Paul, and Nigel) had no contact with the CW system prior to age 12.

2 Contact with SW through financial support of the family or social housing, but no child welfare investigation. This was true for two participants (George and David).

3 Contact with CW due to allegations of abuse or neglect followed by an investigation, but participant was not taken into care. This occurred in one case (Scott).

4 Contact with CW due to allegations of maltreatment resulted in child(ren) being taken into care. This occurred in six cases. In four of these cases (Walter, Kyle, Frank, and Steven) the focus was on abuse. In two cases (Connor and Bruce) the concern focussed on school attendance. The length and number of placements varied.

The ten participants who had no contact with the social or child welfare system prior to age 12 shared some common features. All came from families who were supporting themselves (i.e., they were not receiving social welfare support). Some were living fairly well. Susan, Johnny, Allan, Nancy,

Phillip, and Paul had middle- to upper middle-class families. Susan and Phillip reported no family problems prior to age 12; Johnny, Allan, and Paul's families had problems, and there was abuse at home. Although Nancy denied any problems, the truth status of her account was low. The remaining four young people (Leo, Nigel, Ian, and Mitch) also escaped the notice of the SW system. Though their families were poorer than others, they were self-supporting nonetheless. Mitch's mother worked steadily, although his father worked only sporadically and pushed them to the edge of poverty with his drug abuse and alcoholism. Nigel's parents were not wealthy, but they worked and owned their own home. The family was broken by divorce, but this is hardly unusual. They appeared functioning at an acceptable level. This was also true of Ian's family. They were not well-off, but they appeared to be fine.

Of the ten participants who had no contact with either system, eight had serious family problems for which they received no support. Why were they invisible? There were only two routes to contact these systems. Parents could have self-referred, yet none did this. Professionals who knew the family and suspected maltreatment had to report it to CW authorities by law. Either no one saw the signs of maltreatment, or they were unwilling to report their suspicions.

Three participants (George, David, and Scott) had family problems and contact with either the SW or CW systems, or both. These contacts were ineffective. George and David came from single-parent families living in poverty. George's mother had grown up in care, was a cocaine addict, and had become a mother at age 14. She was at significant risk for maltreating her children. She had a succession of boyfriends who were abusive towards both her and George. Apparently, no one noticed George's problems. He was not diagnosed with ADHD until age ten, despite serious school-based problems. He slipped through the cracks. David's case was more difficult to assess. He would not share his records, so we could not verify if he was ever taken into care prior to age 12. He said that he was not. His mother worked at times and received welfare at other times. The family lived in social housing. David was abused physically, but again the abuse may simply have not been severe enough to be noticed. He, too, slipped through the cracks.

In Scott's case, contact with the CW system was initiated by a call alleging abuse. There was an investigation, which resulted in his older autistic brother being made a Crown ward. Concerns were apparently raised over the years, and another younger sister was also permanently removed from the home. Allegations that Scott was being abused were investigated, but he said he lied because he was afraid of being taken into care. Without his disclosure, the worker could apparently do little except monitor the situation.

Six of our respondents were investigated by the CW system and were taken into "care." We use quotation marks here, because what happened to them away from their families was hardly a matter of caring. Bruce and Connor ended up in custody as a result of truancy — they were locked up with youth who had committed crimes and with young people who had run away. Four others were taken into care and placed in a variety of settings. Steven was first taken into care at age two because he had been severely beaten with a coat hanger. The records indicate that it was not clear who had beaten him. His mother insisted it was a babysitter. He was returned home, then taken into care a second time at age five when his mother was arrested for shoplifting. When she had served her sentence her children were returned to her. Steven described what happened.

> Steven: Well, umm, basically my father left when I was about two years old; I'm not sure about the details around that, I do know that at about that point I was placed into foster care, apprehended by [CW]; I had been hospitalized because I had been beaten severely.... So when I was five, I was in a foster home for about two years, and that wasn't too bad and they had their own kids as well, and I could certainly feel the difference. Then I was five, my mother was hooked up with this other guy [name] whom she married just as I was being released from the foster home to live with them.... Other than being too strict, he wasn't too bad to be around except when he was drinking. Which over the years increased a great deal, and he became a violent alcoholic, and he used to beat my mother and beat us, so there were some traumatic problems. My mother, she has a lot of problems too, she's basically, right now she's living in mental health housing and she's mentally ill. Over the years she was a compulsive liar, she encouraged me to steal... she wasn't accessing the system that much.... I think it was ingrained in me right from when I was five not to be discovered by [CW] or any people. I know at five the worker came around to possibly apprehend me, and my mother and a few other adults were saying "Don't let her take you, don't let her take you. She's gonna take you, and you'll never gonna see me again." They

got me all worked up, and when the [CW] worker came in, I
bit her in the arm as hard as I could; never saw her again. So
that mentality was ingrained since I was a kid, so I don't know,
that was my family upbringing in a nutshell I guess....

In Steven's case the authorities tried to get him to report abuse, but he
was afraid what his parents would do if he told. Though there was continued contact with the family and his sister was taken into care on allegations
her stepfather had sexually abused her, Steven was never again taken into
care.

Kyle was taken into care at the age of 12. He was accused of sexually
abusing his younger siblings, and his mother was unable to stop the abuse as
long as he remained at home. This was Kyle's first experience in care,
despite a childhood marked by violence, neglect, poverty, and an alcoholic
stepfather. He was sexually abused by his cousin, but no one noticed. He
had many school-based problems; again, no one noticed. When he became
a danger to others at age 12, someone did notice. By then, it was too late.

Frank was abandoned by an alcoholic mother and stepfather. He was
made a Crown ward. His foster home had one positive feature—he could
be there with his brothers. This was the only placement at the time that
would take all three children. Apart from that positive aspect, Frank
described the home as emotionally and physically abusive. The foster parents were racists and cruel. No one noticed. Frank did run away occasionally, but he lacked the trust to tell anyone about what was happening in
care. He believed, as his foster family and the CW authorities apparently
had told him, that he would be separated from his brothers if he left the
foster home. Frank endured. Caught up in a racist system that was far from
child-friendly, he coped the best he could. He stayed in care from the age
of six or seven until age 16, when he could no longer stand the abuse and
felt his brothers were old enough to take care of themselves.

Walter had several placements over the years. He was taken into care
from both his mother's and father's homes by CW authorities. He was sent
to a residential placement he described as being in chaos. He said that drug
use was widespread and that he used substances heavily there. Despite
efforts to help Walter, nothing seemed to have worked.

The CW and SW systems failed some participants, were unaware of the
problems that most were facing, and struggled to meet the complex needs
of those participants who, along with their families, resisted help. Both the
private nature of much of the abuse and neglect that our participants expe-

rienced and the unwillingness to reach out for help to authorities probably contributed to no one seeking help for family-based problems. Young people drifted along in dysfunctional families and coped as best they could with their feelings of rage, shame, humiliation, and fear.

Community Supports and Recreation

There is controversy in the sociological research about whether young people (especially high-risk youth) who participate in recreational activities are less likely to become involved in crime.[24] We explored with our participants whether they had been involved in community-based recreational activities and what experiences they had with these activities. We recognize that for high-risk youth, recreational activity may not be sufficient to mitigate against the other negative influences in their lives. Indeed, if these recreational experiences are negative, they may compound existing problems.

Six of our participants said that they had had no involvement with recreational activities up to age 12. Phillip, David, Leo, Nigel, Johnny, and Bruce did not belong to any clubs, groups, organized sports teams, or other activities. Phillip did try Cubs, but he lasted for only one month before he had one of his rages and was asked to leave. Johnny reported participating in sports only after age 12, when he was extensively involved. Leo wanted to take karate, but said that his father forbade the children from doing sports. Nigel did no sports inside or outside of school, nor did he participate in any other organized activity. He reported doing "nothing," as did David and Bruce. Fourteen of our participants did participate in recreational activities, mainly school sports.

Susan, Mitch, Ian, and Nancy were involved with organized community-based sports activities. Susan played t-ball and soccer for local recreational teams. Mitch played hockey from the age of eight or nine until he was 11 or 12. Ian played one year of community softball. He said he was not allowed to play ball or join any other team sport after this because he was so much larger than the other children. We could not confirm this. Nancy was very active in community sports. She played rugby, tennis, soccer, badminton, and volleyball at school. She also attended summer tennis camps.

In addition to sport, participants had a variety of other activities. Scott spent a year and a half going to a local recreational facility, his only reported activity outside of school and home. He reported that he didn't like it, preferring to be alone. Allan reported his only recreational activity as going places with his Big Brother. Paul joined Scouts, but this may have begun after age 12. Both George and Susan went to camp for two summers. Steven participated in a chess club at school, was involved in a church-based group, and began playing structured (and violent) war games with his friends. Frank was forbidden by his foster family to participate in any community-based recreational activities.

These groups offered our participants positive community-based experiences. For the most part, they enjoyed these activities and reported that they made them feel good about themselves. For some, they were also a source of frustration. Scott disliked going to the recreational facility. He did not like the other children, had problems interacting, and felt that his mother sent him there just to get him out of the house. Ian reported that he liked playing baseball. Although he insisted that he was banned from community and school teams because of his size, his records suggested that he was banned because he was aggressive towards the other children. The experience left him frustrated and angry.

Religion

The role of religion in people's lives is complex. Ongoing research suggests that cultural institutions, such as organized religion, can mediate psychological and familial harms, because these institutions provide positive role models and moral values. Some research indicates that religion is positively related to pro-social behaviour and negatively related to delinquency, drug use, and suicide.[25] Others caution that the influence of religious beliefs is impacted by attachment between children and parents and the influence of peers.[26] Thus, while religion may provide some protection from engagement in anti-social activities, its importance can be strengthened or weakened by other factors in a young person's life.

We asked our participants about spirituality. Most separated their experiences with organized religions from their personal beliefs. David and Walter did not directly answer questions about their experience with religion while they were growing up. Six of our participants (George, Susan, Kyle, Bruce, Ian, and Mitch) reported they had no contact with religious institutions; they did not attend religious services or Sunday school.

Eleven of our participants were involved with religion growing up. Seven (Nancy, Leo, Allan, Phillip, Paul, Walter, and Frank) attended church on a weekly basis. Leo and Scott were both brought up in strict religions. Both their fathers were lay preachers, and both fathers were severely abusive towards their children. Leo reported that he accepted much of the religious teaching, but that he came to despise church because of his father's abusive behaviour. Scott said he had lost his faith altogether and blamed it on his father's violence towards him and other family members.

Frank's foster family required that he and his brothers participate in another strict Christian church, which was the basis of the family's social life. He reported that this laid the foundations of his persistent belief in a Creator. He was excommunicated from the church when he left his foster family and was accused of stealing from the church. Phillip reported a positive relationship with a Pentecostal church. He attended services and a youth group. He also developed a close personal relationship with the youth pastor, who provided him with emotional support. Finally, Paul, Nancy, and Allan all attended church with their families while growing up. Nancy said she was forced to go church and Sunday school with her mother; she said she felt no connection to the faith. Paul attended church services regularly with his family. Like Nancy, he said he had no spiritual connection to the teachings. Allan attended church and Sunday school, until he realized that he didn't "believe that crap."

Four participants had more limited contact with religion. Steven went to services and attended a youth group at a Baptist church for about three years when his first stepfather was involved with the family. He indicated that this experience laid the ground for his core values, which he still practised at the time of the interview. Johnny was raised Catholic, but was not required to attend church regularly. However, he indicated that after age 12, he went most Sundays with his mother. At the time of the interview, he told us that he regarded church as a holy place, although it did not play a significant role in his life. Connor was also raised Catholic, but had no contact with the church after his mother's death. Nigel reported he had some contact with religion, but was never forced to go to church.

For most of our participants, religion did not provide even the potential of being a buffer against the other negative aspects of their lives. It failed to provide them with core values, and for some, their negative experiences led them to despise it. But for Frank, Phillip, and Steven, religion did provide them with positive core values. Although these values did not prevent them from committing homicide, they did help them in dealing with the aftermath of what they had done. We will explore this matter further in Chapter 6.

Conclusion

The 19 young people we interviewed came from diverse family backgrounds and had widely disparate experiences. These experiences are illustrative of their multiple pathways to involvement with the criminal justice system and to homicide.

Some reported severe abuse and/or trauma in their early lives. Steven grew up in severe poverty. His parents were divorced, his biological father absent. His stepfathers were alcoholics and abusive to both the children and their mother. He was living virtually on his own by the age of 12. His mother and her third husband spent most of their time at another residence. Steven, clinging to his positive involvement in school, lived in social housing and had to steal to feed himself. He lived in constant fear that someone would realize he was on his own and would call child welfare services. Despite this terrible litany of abuse and neglect, at age 12, Steven was functioning exceptionally well. He was succeeding in school, was active in extra-curricular activities, and had many friends.

Frank, too, had experienced multiple stresses in his life. Taken into care at a very young age, he moved from a household with physical abuse, addictive parents, and neglect to a foster home that was racist and emotionally, sexually, and physically abusive. He was functioning well at school, but by age 11 he had already begun to drink, steal from his foster parents, and experiment with drugs.

Walter had a similarly desolate childhood. He grew up in chaos, surrounded, as he put it, by "poverty, violence, and drugs." His parents fought frequently and eventually separated. The family had problems with physical and sexual abuse. Parental substance abuse contributed to a lack of supervision. Walter was exhibiting serious behavioural problems in kindergarten. These increased over the course of his first 11 years of life.

Scott also came from an extremely negative family situation. Unlike Steven and Frank, he had no positive school experiences to bolster his confidence. He was unable to function in the regular system, and his biological father was extremely abusive towards all family members and people in the community. While CW had some contact with the family, Scott was never taken into care. He exhibited many behavioural problems in school and in the community. His learning disabilities were identified, and the school attempted to respond to them. The attempt was unsuccessful, and Scott found himself passed from grade to grade, although he was virtually illiterate.

George had less serious physical abuse and exposure to violence than Scott, but he, too, had an extremely disruptive family experience. There was ongoing substance abuse by his mother and her many partners. He was physically and emotionally abused, and there was ongoing abuse between the stepfathers and children, and between George and his older brother. Like Scott, George was functioning poorly at school, the result of ADHD and other learning disabilities. George's problems remained undiagnosed until age ten, when he was placed on medication. His parents unilaterally discontinued the medication when he was about 12. The result was a return to both aggressive and disruptive behaviour.

Leo experienced severe abuse. Beatings and sexual abuse started prior to age six, and behavioural problems in school began by age seven. He was referred to counselling and went for more than two years, never revealing the abuse to his counsellor. He also had other family problems — his biological father controlled the family despite being separated from his mother, and there was poor supervision by the parents. The biological father was addicted to prescription drugs.

Here we see six young men. Prior to age 12, each has suffered serious, long-term maltreatment. Each was coping in different ways. Steven seemed highly resilient and was functioning well. Frank was functioning fairly well, but was beginning to become involved in anti-social activities and with anti-social peers. Scott and Walter were functioning very poorly — each had few positives in their lives, and both were already using violence (both intra-familial and in the community) to vent frustration and rage. George had early problems that medication helped, but the drug had negative side-effects. Going off the medication without medical consultation at age 12 began his descent into serious ongoing criminal activity and drug abuse. This early engagement in aggressive and violent behaviour is illustrative of the documented literature on early pathways leading into serious and violent juvenile offending.[27] Leo was becoming increasingly withdrawn.

Most of our participants (13 of 19) had experienced less abuse than this first group, yet they too suffered from the physical and psychological consequences. The number and extent of their problems varied.

Bruce reported no intra-familial abuse. Supporting documentation indicated that both parents were alcoholic, although both were working and functioning relatively well. He appeared to have been somewhat neglected and poorly supervised. He had serious learning problems and negative school experiences. His attempts to avoid school led to a truancy arrest. He tried to run away from home and was sent to a juvenile detention centre.

He was angry and frustrated. By age 12, he was already acting out in an aggressive fashion and was in conflict with the police. Ian also reported some emotional abuse in his family, but generally things were reported to be manageable. His description of his parent's parenting style suggested they used reason to deal with conflict and were generally good parents. Yet, before age 12, he too was acting out aggressively. He was bullied from a young age and teased about being severely overweight.

Nigel reported no familial problems. The supporting documentation raised questions of substance abuse by the father and mother and also suggested poor parenting skills (although these observations were made posthomicide). He had experienced familial disruption—divorce and several moves that seemed to be related to job instability for his stepfather. By age 12, Nigel had broken into a neighbour's home and was caught. This was the home of his homicide victim, and, despite the seriousness of his actions, the family dealt with the break-in without police involvement. He was a victim of some bullying at school, a loner, and was very overweight.

Mitch was also teased, about being poor. In addition, he experienced emotional abuse and witnessed physical abuse in his family. However, he was not manifesting any evidence of serious problems—he was in school, attending, and passing. He was not involved in any fights prior to age 12. Paul was similar to Mitch. He, too, reported being emotionally abused and witnessing physical abuse in his family of origin. He was teased and bullied at school because of his learning problems and poor interpersonal skills, but he was attending school and passing.

Allan, too, had experienced more severe abuse than the others in this second group, both serious emotional abuse and some physical abuse related to discipline. In addition, he had poor peer relationships and was yet another victim of bullying and teasing. His parents were divorced, and both exhibited poor parenting skills. By age 12, Allan had serious problems in school and was exhibiting signs of depression.

David's case was difficult to assess. Although he reported few family problems, supporting documentation indicated that there were problems related to physical abuse in the family. There was also some evidence of neglect. By age 12, David was spending considerable time with an older brother who had anti-social peers and was involved in serious criminal activity. David was attending school and had no contact with the youth justice system despite his ties to his brother's gang. Kyle reported physical abuse in the family and sexual abuse by a male cousin. This was a single-parent household, with minimal supervision. Neither David nor Kyle had stable father-figures. By age 12, Kyle had a range of problems: he was sexually abusing children, exhibiting behavioural problems at school, and increasingly was involved in fighting and criminal activity. Finally, Johnny had many family problems, but none severe enough to raise the interest of CW authorities. His father was an alcoholic with emotional problems who was occasionally physically and frequently emotionally abusive to his wife and all the children. Johnny was given considerable freedom, and his activities were not closely monitored. He was engaging in risk-taking behaviour by age 12, including games of "chicken" with friends on the back roads.

In contrast to these young people who were suffering from the consequences of moderate to severe abuse prior to age 12, Connor had little abuse. His life began to fall apart at age ten, when he was traumatized by the sudden death of his mother and by his older brother's suicide. His father, though present, sober, and working, seemed quite uninvolved in Connor's care. Connor was barely attending school. By age 11 he had begun using drugs, and by age 12 he had moved out of home.

For other participants, the pathway to crisis was related to mental health problems. Nancy seemed to have few negative experiences prior to age 12. Her parents were together, although there were some concerns that they lacked good parenting skills. There was no physical or sexual abuse, but there was verbal abuse. Yet, by age 11, Nancy had been taken into psychiatric care because of her uncontrollable aggression. Phillip had a similar history—no familial abuse, parents were married and supportive. Yet, he had serious mental health problems and interventions began by age eight or nine. He too was institutionalized, but for a much longer period than Nancy. While Nancy was institutionalized for about two years in total (in hospital and CW placement), Phillip reported spending from age eight to 12 in and out of mental health facilities. For both these young people, the system struggled to identify their mental health problems and to respond effectively.

Finally, one of our participants seemed to lead a charmed life prior to age 12: Susan was in school and doing well. She was active in extra-curricular activities. Her parents were together, and there was no emotional, physical, or sexual abuse within or outside the family, nor was there any alcohol or drug abuse at home. She had some problems with racism, being the only visible minority child in an all-white, middle-class school.

These experiences resulted in very different outcomes for these young people. By age 12, some appeared to be thriving, others were in crisis, and some were engaging in violent and criminal behaviour. Some were involved in the mental health system. These divergent responses can be understood in terms of the supports that these young people had to help them deal with trauma and with their individual resilience.

Young people who perform well in school are somewhat protected from their negative family experiences. Steven and Frank both reported that positive school experiences helped them deal with the negative realities of their home lives. Susan had no early family problems and positive school experiences up to age 12. Two of our young people (Johnny and Leo) had few problems prior to high school. They were attending school, passing, and generally not experiencing any school-based problems. However, neither described their school-based experiences as positive.

In contrast, failure at school compounded the family problems experienced by most participants. Scott and Walter both had severe learning disabilities, which their schools were unable to accommodate. Bruce had serious problems related to learning, but was never tested for learning disabilities. School became an increasingly frustrating experience for him. Phillip and Nancy both had mental health problems, which resulted in negative in-school behaviour, conflict, and repeated assessments and placements. Nigel and Ian both experienced school as a location of bullying and teasing related to their weight. Allan, Phillip, Paul, and Walter were also victims of school-based bullying. Learning and social problems at school increased the emotional pressure on these young people, exacerbating existing problems.

These young people also differed in the personal supports they had to cope with adversity. Some told no one about their problems. They said that they didn't expect anyone to be able to help them. Often, the help that was offered was directed at the obvious problems—failing math, not going to school, advice to ignore teasing and bullying. Parents struggled with the problems of homework not being done and behavioural problems, but didn't seem to link them to cries for help and/or sources of harm. They dismissed problems as youthful exuberance or "normal" behaviour. In some cases they were aware of problems, and these became the focus of conflict within the family. Some participants were defined as "causing problems" for the family and came to see themselves as "black sheep."

Few participants got counselling to deal with their personal and family problems. Those that did receive treatment said that it didn't help. Ian received counselling from the age of seven in response to school-based behaviour problems. The focus was on management of his behaviour; the issue of sexual abuse was not dealt with. Phillip had ongoing contact with the mental health system from age seven or eight. There were numerous diagnoses in the accompanying files; some completely contradicted previous diagnoses. His mental health problems continued to interfere with living in the community and with schooling. Nancy was brought into the mental health system about age 12. She too was sent because of behavioural problems. Reports noted that Nancy functioned best in a structured setting. Ultimately, she was released to her parents' care, and they ignored the follow-up treatment plan. They explored other options, and Nancy ended up in unstructured settings. Frank was involved in counselling on several different occasions, because he ran away from his foster home. The therapists all asked him for his trust and pushed him to reveal why he ran. But, as Frank noted, he had no trust. He was constantly threatened with being separated from his brothers if the foster care arrangement broke down, so he did not tell about the physical, sexual, and emotional abuse, or about the racism. He told us that the risk was too high that he would be separated from his brothers. Scott was sent to counselling at about age 12 for the sexual molestation of a young child, as an alternative to a criminal sanction. His parents failed to follow through with the counselling. Thus, there were no consequences for his actions, and no support for his mental health problems. He drifted.

Among all the factors that did help, resilience was the most important in achieving positive outcomes. Steven had many negative social experiences. He grew up in poverty in a family split by divorce and replete with physical abuse and neglect. He was virtually abandoned by age 11 and was forced to feed himself by stealing. He had few positive supports — no family support, no mental health or child welfare support. It seemed that only his school offered early positive support. Yet, he seemed to thrive. He attended school, functioned well in the school setting, and got good grades. He was extremely resilient at age 12. Other young people had few negative experiences, such as Susan. Her greatest stress was the break-up of her parents. This divorce sent her into a whirl of anger and defiance. From being a good student and well integrated into her community, she spiraled into drug use and crime. She was not resilient.

Most of our participants were average kids dealing with serious stresses. It was not surprising that they had limited ability to deal with these pressures. They also had few supports in their lives. It was this combination of problems, supports, and resilience that allowed them to function well prior to age 12. After age 12, their lives took on new dimensions.

Notes

1 Canadian Institute of Child Health, 2000.

2 Hawkins, 2000; Miller, 1999; Pallone and Hennessy, 2000.

3 Totten, 2001c.

4 Totten, 2001c.

5 Latimer, 1998, 2.

6 Trocme *et al.*, 2001.

7 Bass and Davis, 1988; Lew, 1988.

8 Trocme *et al.*, 2001.

9 Torrance, 1997.

10 King *et al.*, 1999.

11 Totten, 2001c.

12 Sourander, Helstela, Helenius, and Piha, 2000.

13 Duncan, 1999a.

14 Duncan, 1999b; Schwartz, 1998.

15 Rigby, Slee, and Cunningham, 1999.

16 Rigby, 1994.

17 Sourander *et al.*, 2000.

18 Salmivalli, Kaukiainen, Kaistaniemi, and Lagerspetz, 1999.

19 Sourander *et al.*, 2000.

20 Sourander *et al.*, 2000; Duncan, 1999a.

21 Knox, 1998; Rigby, 2000; Duncan, 1999a.

22 Rigby, 2000; Duncan, 1999b.

23 Unfortunately we do not have complete information on the school experiences of all of our participants. The school experiences of David, Allan, Mitch, Leo, Frank, and Nancy were not as clear, due to a lack of school records.

24 Rietschlin, Pearson, and Kierkus, 1996.

25 Donahue and Benson, 1995.

26 Brent, and Whiteside, 1995; Brent and Flynn Corwyn, 1997.

27 Tremblay *et al.*, 1995, 1996; Schumacher and Kurtz, 2000; Hawkins *et al.*, 1998; Loeber and Farrington, 1997.

Lessons Learned in Adolescence

Introduction

By the age of 12 our participants had had a range of negative experiences. Most were dealing with the impact of bullying, poverty, neglect, abuse, or racism, which was reflected in feelings of shame, humiliation, powerlessness, and low self-esteem. A minority were in good shape emotionally, with school success and solid family situations providing them with support. As our 19 participants moved into their teen years, they had new positive and negative experiences, and increasingly they struggled with negative feelings. These experiences and related responses by our participants played a critical role in their involvement in the homicides.

As children reach adolescence, peers play a more and more important role in their lives. While this is true of most young people, patterns of involvement with peers vary. Some young people become increasingly withdrawn as they grow into adolescence. Most establish intimate peer relationships, but retain close ties to their families as well. Youth with negative family situations are pushed to make connections with others, most commonly their peers, and these relationships become central to their lives.[1]

Peer relationships can be positive when the group is pro-social. However, if young people become connected to groups that are anti-social and violent, these close ties may be quite dangerous.[2] This happens to many adolescents who have suffered trauma from bullying, abuse, neglect, failure, and turmoil. They attach themselves to marginal groups because they themselves are marginal, or to violent peers because violence offers them a means for expressing their anger and frustration and establishing social status.[3]

The young people we interviewed were at high risk in adolescence for involvement with violent and aggressive peer groups. Some of these groups had norms that led our participants to engage in dangerous or risky behaviours. Others had norms that legitimized the use of violence and required participants to resolve problems with others outside traditional normative structures (e.g., school, the criminal justice system, etc.). These peers also played a role in some of the homicides. Only six of our participants were the sole accused persons in their homicides. The other 13 had between one and six co-accused. It is important to note that not all of our offenders were part of peer groups. Some described themselves as loners; they were outside both a support network and normative behaviour.

School involvement declined for most participants in adolescence. Suspensions, expulsions, dropping out, and skipping school meant many were rarely in school. Once young people are out of school, they often drift with few pro-social ties and few checks on their behaviour. The ties of these young people to other social institutions (mental health and social welfare organizations, child welfare authorities, and the criminal justice system) continued or began to play a role. Physical and mental health problems continued to present serious concerns for most of our participants. Yet, while they had a range of personal stresses and often abused drugs or alcohol, they actually had little contact with the public health system. It became more difficult for the health care system to reach them because they and/or their families chose to have little contact with it. Involvement with the criminal justice system was common for most participants, but not for all: for some, their first contact was a result of the homicide. This group was perhaps the most difficult for institutions to identify and help. For those who had previous involvement in the youth justice system, their involvement was due typically to serious assaults, similar to the homicides they would ultimately commit. These contacts were not successful in addressing the risks these young people posed to themselves and others, nor were they successful in identifying their complex needs.

Finally, as most participants reached age 16, their contacts with the social welfare, mental health, and education systems changed again. Some were supported on welfare as they moved to independent living away from home or child welfare, youth justice, or other facilities. Others were already on the street, living in shelters, rooming houses, or with friends. Turning 16 marked a significant loss of pro-social support for almost all of them.

Peers

Our participants had a wide range of peer activities between the age of 12 and the commission of the homicide. While most had some positive inter-actions, all moved into increasingly anti-social relationships. Some became involved in violent sub-cultures in which physical aggression conveyed sta-tus and power. Others rarely, if ever, used violence, but became engrossed in violent fantasies. In these alternate planes of reality,[4] violence was used symbolically to express their feelings of rage and frustration, which were eventually acted out on convenient victims. Finally, other participants became socially isolated, which, when combined with their other prob-lems, contributed to their violent behaviour.[5]

Many of our young people had poor peer relationships after age 12. Ten of the 19 described themselves in their teens as loners (Phillip, Bruce, Allan, and Leo) or as having few friends (Kyle, Connor, Paul, Scott, Frank, and Nigel). For some, isolation from peers was a continuation of earlier prob-lems (Phillip, Allan, and Nigel). Some grew increasingly isolated, often withdrawing in response to maltreatment at home (Kyle, Connor, Allan, Paul, Scott, Frank), problems at school (Bruce, Scott), and frequent family moves (which resulted in Leo and Nigel losing ties to peers).

Social isolation created stresses for participants, leaving them without emotional support and with low self-esteem; it was also a symptom of the social problems they experienced. Many were isolated by and from their peers through bullying and teasing; they experienced shame, humiliation, and low self-esteem. Many said that they did not fully understand what made them both the target of this abuse and vulnerable to such attacks. Bruce, for example, was stigmatized due to learning problems. He reported feeling ashamed, isolated, and frustrated.

Other participants isolated themselves from peers and the outside world by withdrawing into fantasy worlds. This was the case for Paul, who began playing war games glorifying male violence, as a means of gaining approval and respect from his parents. Allan retreated further and further into him-self as the pressures at home became intolerable. In his fantasy world vio-lence made him powerful, and his feelings of anger and rage at his mother were expressed in homicidal scenarios. He made friends with others who were marginal and angry and who considered violence as a viable means of expressing their social outrage. Leo also retreated into a violent fantasy world, an escape from the traumatic maltreatment he suffered at home. Phillip developed an obsessive, dependent relationship with his girlfriend, who was on the run from a child welfare facility. In their LSD-induced fantasy world, he envisioned himself as Romeo and she as Juliet. He reported that they perceived the external world as hostile and threatening, and had a suicide pact should they ever be separated.

For some participants, social isolation began in early childhood. As they entered adolescence, they responded to their isolation by seeking friendship with anybody, through any means possible. Peers, no matter how marginal to mainstream society, provided them with a sense of "fitting in" and normalcy. They attached themselves to a number of marginal groups, including criminal and drug subcultures and gangs. Ian was teased about his excessive weight and size. He dwarfed other children his own age; his solution was to make friends with older youth who were not in school, who abused substances, and who were involved in violent criminal activity. Ian was valued by them for his size, strength, and fighting ability. Likewise, Mitch noted that he felt valued by his peers for being tough; accordingly, he acted violently. He also began selling drugs and found this to be very lucrative. It did not matter to him that he had been permanently expelled from school for truancy, fighting, and drug use. In fact, expulsion solved his problem of being constantly teased about his "welfare" clothing. Dealing drugs brought him into contact with other young criminals and justified his violent behaviour (he reported using violence mainly to enforce drug debts).

These peer groups were commonly focussed on substance use and abuse. Leo moved to a new community at age 13. He had significant problems fitting in because of his appearance: he had been badly burned in a house fire and was small for his age. His new "friends" were a group of young people involved in gas sniffing. He said that they were the only group open to him, and "belonging" required no more than joining them in sniffing gas. Similarly, Phillip became connected to a peer group through drug abuse; he and his "acquaintances" spent their time partying at the home of an older drug dealer who preyed on young girls. Bruce, too, found friends in a group of much older, marginal addicts who engaged in serious crime.

Isolation was not the only route to involvement with anti-social peers. Some young people lived in communities with both high crime and high substance abuse problems. Eight (George, David, Kyle, Steven, Ian, Mitch, Scott, and Walter) grew up in areas of extreme poverty, where drug use among teens was common, and involvement in violent, criminal, and high-risk activities was part of the local teen culture. They reported having many friends and solid, supportive, peer relationships. The problem was that these close friends were dealing drugs, committing break-and-enters ("b-and-e's"), stealing cars, vandalizing property, and engaging in interpersonal violence. Their normative commitments included not revealing information about criminal activity — not to "rat" on others — and to settle scores within the group rather than through criminal justice or other mechanisms. Being part of the group required that they buy into these values. These peer group activities were quite closed. Violent exchanges occurred within the peer group or with youth involved in other peer groups. Their activities were linked to the wider society through crime.

These peer sub-cultures were, too often, worlds without adults. Adult supervision was either not available (due to neglect) or not able to penetrate the reality behind the normative social masks presented by the participants. Some parents reportedly had no idea with whom their children were "hanging-out," nor what they were doing. In some cases, the participants' parents either were not present or did not care. Steven's parents abandoned him by age 11, and he had no adult supervision. He supported himself by stealing food and breaking into night safety-deposit boxes. Connor had no supervision past age 12, when he left home and dropped out of school. His father, a single parent working shifts, was unable to pay much attention to his self-destructing adolescent son. Connor quickly spiralled into addiction, depression, and serious drug dealing by age 13; no one was there to intervene. Other participants said that they were able to hide their substance abuse, violence, and crimes from their parents. Bruce reported that he mainlined cocaine and stashed large amounts of money in his room, yet his parents never noticed. Even when some parents became aware of the negative activities of their children, they reportedly viewed them as "healthy" teenage rebellion. Johnny told his mother about his risk-taking and aggression towards others; apparently, she responded by telling him that he was going to "meet his match some day." Leo's mother was aware that he was sniffing gas and apparently simply told him to stop. She believed that he had stopped on his own. On the day he killed two neighbours, records indicate that he sniffed before the homicides.

Specific features of peer relations and social isolation posed particular risks for our participants. Three of these features are discussed below: peer groups and violence; peer groups and silence; and social isolation (the loners). Each of these had a role in some of the homicides. It is important to remember that most young people who engage in these behaviours or have these experiences do not kill. When these high-risk behaviours were combined with the immediate context of the homicide and their personal choices, our participants committed murder.

Peers and Violence

For most of our participants, adolescent peer interactions involved violence. This does not mean that all always used violence. Rather, violence was accepted and valued as an inevitable part of peer relations. Typically, violence was a means to an end, including:

- increasing social status (George, Ian, Scott, Mitch, Walter);

- self-protection (Bruce, Leo, Walter, Nigel);

- release of rage, anger, and frustration (Phillip, Kyle, Bruce, Johnny, Connor, Allan, Paul, Scott, Nancy, Nigel);

- enforcement of drug debts (Susan, Steven, Mitch, Walter);

- a necessary part of criminal activities (George, David, Kyle, Frank, Walter);

- source of power: ensuring others "did as they were told" (Ian, Mitch, Scott, Walter).

In describing the "goals" of violence, our participants suggested that it was a tool. This utilitarian view indicated a process for assessing whether or not violence was necessary and appropriate, and to what degree. The process seems quite rational at face value, but is in reality more complex. Once these young people began to act out violently, they were not always in control of their behaviour.

Steven: With me, it's not quick to get into it, but once in, there's almost like a line you crossed, and once you cross that line you know. With me, it's been the apprehension and the fear of being violent disappears because you've crossed that line. Something has been initiated seriously, and it's like your adrenaline is able to let go.

Int.: Is it a rush?

Steven: I call it more of a relief than a rush.... I think there's a point if you cross that line.... At least with me when that line gets crossed, then it's almost like there's no other choice, but for the adrenaline to take its course. Sort of like lightning striking the ground—when it goes, it's gonna hit the ground. It's not really a rush, I wouldn't call it a rush, I would call a relief, it's like this violent act happens, but I don't feel uptight about it, I don't feel anything. It's like it runs its course.

This violent acting-out became more dangerous as these adolescents grew older. Ian realized that, while his violence gave him social status, once he reached his full size he had the potential to seriously harm someone.

Int.: Do you think your violence has increased over the years?

Ian: Decreased.

Int.: Even going up to the homicide?

Ian: No, up to the homicide? Yeah, it did decrease.

Int.: So when was the peak of your violence then?

Ian: Grade eight or seven.

Int.: Why would you say that's your peak?

Ian: That's when I was fighting the most, just doing stupid stuff, destroying property, didn't really think of the consequences of hurting people.

Int.: So then what happened after grade eight to have it decreased?

Ian: I just realized. Grade eight is when you realize your strength, and I knew when I was hitting those windows, I was hitting them with such force that if I hit somebody's face, they'd really get hurt. It didn't bother me at all when I was hitting glass obviously, putting holes through them.

Int.: So something went off, and you said "holy shit."

Ian: I'd better slow down. That's when I got into the heavy drugs.

Int.: Oh … so do you think that's the reason you started getting into the drugs, because you were scared.

Ian: Not really, it was just a way to get away from the fights. If you're high, you're not gonna fight that much. I can't, anyway.

Ian attempted to control his use of violence, but was unsuccessful. He continued to use violence against others to deal with problems, and ultimately was convicted of a brutal assault that led to a frail man's death.

Violence was linked not only to peer group interactions, but also to the construction of normative masculine identity. There is evidence that the male participants negotiated their identities and compensated for their perceived masculine deficits through the use of violence.[6] Sources of these perceived deficits included victimization by sexual abuse (Leo, Kyle, Ian); perpetrating sexual abuse on young children (Kyle, Scott); feelings of humiliation and low self-worth due to maltreatment (George, Kyle, Steven, Johnny, Allan, Leo, Paul, Scott, Frank, Walter); living in poverty and having limited employability (George, David, Kyle, Steven, Mitch, Scott, Walter); chronic enuresis (Scott, George, Walter); victimization by bullying (all but David, Connor, Frank); and serious learning disabilities, which resulted in being labelled as stupid (George, Phillip, Bruce, Paul, Scott, Walter).

The participants made sense of challenges to their masculinity by using resources available to them in their social setting. Most compensated for and masked their fears. The lives of the 17 young men in our study were characterized, in varying degrees, by a pursuit of the traditional male attributes of toughness, competitiveness, and dominance. They were not a homogenous group and likely did not define their masculinities in the same way. Some adhered to a patriarchal–authoritarian model of gender, something closely linked to extreme violence perpetration in marginal male youth.[7] Many of these young people did not view their behaviour as harmful. Although they were engaging in very dangerous behaviours, they interpreted their actions as moral and righteous. Evidence suggests the existence of two interrelated value sets or planes of reality for most participants. The first was characterized by boredom, drudgery, powerlessness, and a preoccupation with daily living. The second was defined by a hierarchy of the powerless:[8] feelings of moral superiority evoked in the participants when harming the less powerful.

Their descriptions of when and why they used violence are full of references to protecting the weak (e.g., women, smaller friends) and defending their social status. It is interesting that some reported being proud of their role of protectors of the vulnerable, while at the same time, they used violence against victims who were obviously weaker.

> Mitch: Some of the other fights were unavoidable. I have a couple of friends who are smaller than me, and when we'd go out they'd get picked on, and because they were so scrawny I would stick up for them. A couple of times that happened when somebody tried to pick on them, I'd step in and say "fuck off," and I'd end up getting into a fight.

> Int.: How many fights would you get into in a week?

> Mitch: A lot of them weren't intentional.

> Int: Weren't intentional?

> Mitch: A lot of them were bar fights, sometimes I'd stick up for my brother. My brother's a drinker, he likes to drink, and he gets drunk and gets into fights, so sometimes I'd step in to make sure nothing too bad happened to him. Like if he got into a fight with some guy and he got beat up, that would be his problem, but if he got into a fight with some guy and three others stepped in, then I'm there.

Similarly, Ian's description of motivations for fighting reflects both a normative masculine ideal and a lived experience that challenged this idealized view of fighting.

> Int.: So what did the fighting give you?

> Ian: I don't know, I never did it for power or anything, it was just, if somebody said something about me or one of my friends, I'd stick up for them. Especially if it was a girl. That was my problem, I had to stop sticking up for others and worry about me

and not them. Now if I was out and somebody was getting picked on, I'd tell them to stop, but I wouldn't get into a fight over it, unless that someone was holding a gun or knife and then I'd have to step in, regardless of my probation, I'd have to step in. They could charge me if they wanted, but they wouldn't.

Int.: Did that happen?

Ian: No, not to that extent, but I know a girl who was supposed to get punched in the face, and I told "buddy" I'm getting out of here so you better watch it, he backed off right away. That was my best friend, I know if he would have hit her, I would have whacked him.

Others described jumping into fights to ensure that friends were not unfairly outnumbered. Johnny, in talking about his involvement in these kinds of fights, began by noting how anger played a role.

Int.: What triggered those things [violence towards others]?

Johnny: I don't know, just my anger or whatever. Other people's actions triggered them, really. If other people hadn't reacted or acted to what I did, things would have been fine. If I did something and somebody reacted, well I always had to react more violently I guess, I don't know.

Int.: What were they reacting to in your behaviour?

Johnny: Well like I say, something had started the fight, and I was like, "don't bother." He was just standing there and you could see it in his eyes, and I'm like, "don't fucking bother, it's a waste of your time." He just looked like he wanted to get into it, like kick my friend in the head or something, and I wasn't about to let that happen. He didn't heed my warning, and I guess I had to prove something back then. Back then I always felt like somebody owed me something; I wanted to do what I wanted to do.

For Walter, fighting was tied to both masculinity and to experiences with racism. He noted the lessons he had learned about using violence from both being a victim and from victimizing others.

Int.: Okay, so getting back to the worst incident you were involved in?

Walter: I guess I was the bad boy of the family, I got in shit, getting kicked out of school all the time. I got kicked out of school lots, to tell the truth. Like my last real school grade was grade ten, not completed. I got kicked out of school because of fights, there was a lot of racism going on right beside the hick towns. I remember being probably ten or 11, being jumped by about six or seven white guys. These guys were like 17, 18 years old and beating the living shit out of me, so I learned at a young age that violence was, like, connected to everything. If you use enough force on someone and if they don't agree with whatever you're saying, they're gonna respect you, they're gonna give you space. That's what I started to do, that's what I learned, if I want something, or I want something done, I have to take it by force, because if you don't, it's gonna be done upon you. Just like the saying says, "only the strong survive," which is true because if you're weak, then you're done in. If you're weak, you're punched.

Walter was small for his age. He prided himself in his fighting skills and maintained that size had nothing to do with winning a fight. He said that as a teen, being known as a good fighter made him feel good; and, during the interview, he seemed to take great pleasure showing his many scars from stabbings and shootings. He was covered in tattoos, most of which he had done himself. It is interesting that he claims he began carrying a gun at age ten, around the same time he joined his first gang. It is plausible that he did this for self-protection, given his small size.

In the short term, violence worked for our participants. For some it helped them relieve emotional pain; for others, it stopped them from being bullied or got them out of difficult situations. It gave them social status and a reassurance that they were "real" men. But it also brought them into conflict with their families, peers, the school system, and the criminal justice system.

Gangs, Crews, and Criminal Peer Groups

Youth gangs have received considerable attention in the popular media in Canada. In reality, very few gangs exist in Canada, and, of the *bona fide* type, only a minority fit the popularized, stereotypical image.[9] Fred Mathews developed the concept of a continuum of peer group/gangs, spanning from "groups of friends" to "hard-core criminal gangs." Placement on the continuum is based upon degree of involvement in organized, violent, criminal activity.[10] We classified the group activities of our participants using this continuum. When asked about their involvement with criminal peer groups and gangs, ten participants indicated that they were part of organized criminal peer groups, and only Walter said he was a gang member. The rest denied being involved in gangs. However, when we proceeded to explore with them the types of criminal activities and nature of these groups, five more participants fit Mathews's criteria for hard-core criminal gang members (George, Susan, Kyle, Steven, and Ian). They all belonged to organized, identifiable groups immersed in serious criminal activities, of which violence was a regular part. Police reports and court records provided further information, which supported their classification by us as hard-core criminal gang members. Two participants termed their groups "crews" rather than gangs. Both "crews" were involved in regular, serious criminal activities and violence, making them fit with Mathews's description of gangs. David was on the fringe of a gang, and Allan, Frank, and Mitch met the criteria of belonging to organized criminal peer groups. These young people did not fit the stereotypical image of gang members. Although some were involved in violence to protect their geographical territory, most "turf" wars were over control of the drug trade. They were involved in organized auto theft, break-and-enters, "fencing" of stolen property, pimping, armed robberies, and extreme violence. Why would they deny gang involvement? Most likely for social desirability reasons. As discussed in Chapter 2, these participants attempted to present themselves as naive and innocent youngsters who were in the "wrong place at the wrong time" when the homicides occurred. It was not in their best interests to disclose any element of planning or involvement in serious crime preceding the killing, because this likely would have affected their charges and sentences.

While involvement in violent and criminal peer groups had many negative consequences, on the positive side, these groups provided our participants with a range of protective factors. Steven's description of his crew illustrates the ties that brought them together.

Int.: Were you part of a gang? Like did you have names for the groups?

Steven: We sometimes did, but I never really thought of it as part of a gang. Now that I think about it, it could well be considered a gang. A lot of the elements were there, but it wasn't like a big formal gang that you read about in the papers or anything, and we didn't really have a name. It was more of an informal gang but the criminal element was there. More of a crew I would say.

Int.: So you would all be carrying weapons?

Steven: We'd all be carrying weapons, similar mentality, similar home life, shared values, hate society, very angry. We justified just about everything we did. It's not like I didn't have a conscience either going through all this stuff, I mean, the bank things I was doing, I thought, hmm, I've got no money and they got lots of money. They had these big towers in [city] and they're insured, so like this little bit I'm taking is not gonna matter too much. Plus I was so angry at society in general, I thought I felt like I was really ripped off in life.

Kyle also said he was involved in a crew; this group was involved in break and enters, auto theft, and drug dealing.

Int.: Were you ever a member of a gang?

Kyle: I wouldn't call it a gang member, like at [neighbourhood], we were all a crew; we're not saying we were this or that, that impression shit you know....

Int.: So did you ever call yourself a [street or gang] name or something with [two co-accused]?

Kyle: People just knew us as [name]; even to this day, my [alleged place of work], anytime I call up, it's like, "oh what's up [name], you coming today [name]?"

Int.: That's what they call you — [name]?

Kyle: Yeah....

Kyle: Best crew there ever is in [city] man. The tightest set of friends, there's a lot of older guys we hang out with too, you know what I mean. Old people like to talk about like murders and shit that's going on. The older generation, the guys that run the city [the criminal hierarchy], and they look at us, and they can't believe how tight we are as friends. They said to us they never got close to people until they were like 25 or 26, until they actually started trusting people. They can't believe that we've known each other since diapers. Diapers, man, like I've known them since we were kids in diapers, and we're still hanging out to this day. I've been through incarceration, he's been through incarceration, he's grown, and I'm getting out starting a new life, and we're still friends. I don't know too many people like that, and everybody talks about that, basically the respect we have for each other, you know. We're not necessarily a crew or a gang or anything, we're just best buddies, man, and we're solid to each other, you know.

He described the social benefits he received from his involvement.

No, don't get me wrong, like our age we were using [drugs] all of our time. The fights weren't that common, because we didn't really have to fight, we already had a reputation. Once you have a rep, you don't have to do anything, kind of like a Mafia boss; you don't need to do anything, just sit on your ass. We were sort of like that; we didn't have to prove ourselves any more. We did get in a few scuffles here and there.

Kyle's description of his crew is illustrative of how these groups provided participants with much needed emotional support and respect. While serious crime and violence were components of the crew's activities, he glossed over them, stressing instead the positive emotional support. This may reflect his experience with the crew. With some of his crew he committed crimes; with others, he had a primarily social involvement focussed around sports and music. Kyle claimed that he was a gifted athlete and musician.

Ian's involvement with gangs included close social connections and using his size to protect other members and intimidate other gangs. He insisted that his gang was not violent, but fought defensively; he alleged that they did not take part in criminal activity.

> Int.: Were you a member of a gang?

> Ian: At [place], but we never went around shooting at people, just because we didn't agree. If somebody started with us, we'd defend ourselves.

> Int.: Did you have fights with other groups?

> Ian: [One gang], the [other gang]… it's a group, the [name] boys, in [place], there weren't gang fights, it was usually two or three guys that didn't get along with each other from each group that would fight.

> Int.: Were any of them into serious organized crime?

> Ian: There's not much of that in [place]. There's a few right wing extremists and wackos.

Ian was also involved in the organized dealing of large quantities of prescription drugs with his peers, despite insisting that crime was not a key feature of the group's activities. He did not explain how they got the prescription drugs they were trafficking.

Allan was a loner and social misfit, who said that he never had a friend until he met his co-accused at age 15. He spent the better part of his adolescence depressed, out of school, and staying in his room. His co-accused moved in with Allan's family as a boarder. They spent a couple of months developing murder plans, basing their ideas on a violent fantasy comic whose hero used violence to right wrongs perpetrated against himself and others. They enrolled in an alternate school and began widening the group. They fancied themselves as killers for hire. The group had secret meeting places, carried knives, and spent their spare time making plans about killing. They also attempted to keep their "activities" secret. This group was not a gang; though they formed for an "illegal" purpose, they were involved in only two illegal activities: an attempted murder and the murder of another group member. Allan recounted for us how this process evolved.

> And at some point, one of us, probably him [Allan's co-accused], could have been me, I dunno, had said what it would take — sort of as a, at the time more like an intellectual exercise sort of thing. How would you go about putting together a group to become hired assassins? And that's how it sort of began. It just, you know, we'd just sit and talk about it. And just sort of build, and you'd say, you know, would you do this? Well no, what about this? You know, did we want this many people? You'd want to make sure about that. That sort of thing. And you know, you'd read these [violent comics] and get ideas from there — that sort of thing. It just sort of grew. Once we moved to this new school, we started asking people there about whether, you know, if they would like to sort of join, and uh, not a single person we asked ever said, well, they, some weren't interested, but nobody ever said, "Hey what are you talking about?" Nobody ever said, "Are you serious?" Nobody ever questioned it. They just said yes or no and that was it. And uh, that's when we started getting other people involved, including our victim actually. He was with the group for a while, and uh, and [co-accused], and my current girlfriend at the time, and at least two other kids from school, from [name of school] all became involved in the group.

Susan and David were both implicated as members of a gang accused of carrying out a torture-murder and the tortures of several other victims who did not die. Although they both denied it, court records showed that Susan was highly involved and that David was on the fringe of this gang through another family member, who was one of its leaders. The motivation for the murder and tortures was drug- and race-related. The victims were all white, and both Susan and David claimed that their racist comments and drug debts triggered the violence. Susan knew the gang through dealing drugs, and court documents suggested that she actively participated in the murder and tortures and had personal relationships with other mem-

bers. She also had another group of peers, primarily females, who participated in criminal activity. In this peer group, Susan was a leader. Supporting records report that, in the year leading up to the murder, she was a key
player in the forcible confinement and abuse of a developmentally delayed
young male and had a number of people working for her dealing drugs.

Peer Groups and Silence: "Don't Be Ratting on Your Friends"
One recurring theme in the interactions between participants and their
peers was related to silence about group activities. This included keeping
quiet about illegal activities and dealing with conflicts with other young
people (both in and outside the peer group) outside the normative structures of wider society. Assaults by others required retaliation, not involvement by the police. Some violent incidents could not be reported because
they were linked to illegal activities. In particular, our participants could
not report drug debts; therefore, enforcement was up to them. They said
that, if they failed to enforce these debts, they would soon be out of business; yet, enforcement meant risking involvement with the criminal justice
system. Other events were minor by broader social standards, but linked to
individual and group status. Assaults over sexual partners were not uncommon—both our female participants assaulted other young women over
boyfriends, and two young men (Scott and George) recounted violent
assaults triggered by jealous rages.

Ratting (telling outsiders about gang or group activities) brought retaliation by peers, yet keeping silent had serious consequences as well. Maintaining silence could mean being charged with a crime as a co-accused.
David was charged with obstruction of justice because he would not name
his co-accused in an armed robbery.

> Int.: You plead guilty to robbery. Okay, after telling the police an
> acquaintance was responsible for it, so you plead guilty to
> obstruction of justice as well. What was the obstruction piece?
>
> David: It's because they wanted to know another prisoner, and I told
> some fucking bullshit. I told them my real name, but I would-
> n't tell them the other guy's name.
>
> Int.: Why not? Why wouldn't you tell them your friend's name, if
> you wanted to get off?

David: Why would I do that? I wouldn't want him to do it to me if I got in.

Kyle linked not ratting to proof of friendship. He said that he could have got away with manslaughter if his co-accused had stood solid and not told the police what he (Kyle) had done. He placed limits on keeping silence; according to him, you could rat if someone's life was in jeopardy.

Int.: Before the manslaughter, were your best friends the people you were living with?

Kyle: They weren't. Like at that point and time they were like my best friends, but I look at it now, and they're not even close to being friends with me.

Int.: How come?

Kyle: Because they're not people I would consider friends at this point in time in my life. They're not friends that would take the rap for me; like fuck, I could have gotten away with this charge, you know, the manslaughter charge. From the beginning none of them wanted to take ownership for their shit. I'm sitting solid in a cell while they're twiddling their thumbs, you know. I was the one going down for it, the murder charge, and I was in the back seat. To me that's not a good friend, you know. Fuck like if I was in [first co-accused's] position now, if [second co-accused] had ratted on [first co-accused], it wouldn't have happened. Don't get me wrong, I don't agree on ratting on someone, to a point, like if someone's life is in jeopardy, fuck I don't care what anybody says. I don't care about the prison shit, man. Like if someone's life is in jeopardy, fuck I'm more than willing to tell on somebody, man. I'm growing up now, I'm not a little punk anymore. Like if a girl could get hurt, like raped or something, or a child's going to be hurt, I don't care what anybody in here says. If they have something to say about that, then fuck, say it to me, you know. And no one ever will, because I just don't put up with that shit. Like I said, I'd be away from this charge if they'd [co-accused] kept me out of it, man. They [police and Crown] had no proof I was there, you know.

Another interesting feature of Kyle's account was his assertion that the code of silence was a code for children. He said that he had matured during his incarceration and recognized that, if one kept silent about everything, this could have potentially serious consequences for innocent people. It is interesting that he stressed the importance of protecting children from sexual abuse by telling the authorities about it, since he himself had committed sexual offences with children. His "reaction formation"[11] (a socially amplified emotional and behavioural response, which is an attempt to prove that one is very different from the individual being vilified) on this issue was similar to that of Scott, who also demonstrated reaction formation when he attempted to cover up his violent behaviour against his girlfriends, mother, and sisters.

Steven confided in a close friend about the homicide and relied on him to help hide the body. He struggled with his conflict between silence among friends and the factors that impelled his friend to report the homicide.

> Steven: We just took right off, got in the car, and drove away. He took me to my place, and I said, "there may be some heat on for this, give me some time to get away and then I'll call and say I'm the guy, and you'll be off the hook." Soon as he got home, he woke up his parents and told them, and they called the police, which was in some way not a surprise to me. I mean here he's 16, a year younger than me, and here he's implicated in this murder. In that way it wasn't a surprise to me, but in another way, it was, because we had done so much together, and there was always this "don't tell on each other" kind of thing, and we worked through our stories all the time.

These offenders believed that the breakdown of silence made them vulnerable to the sanctions imposed by wider society, not their violent actions. They told us that as long as one maintained in-group solidarity and did not tell, the justice system and other external agents of social control could not act. This gave them considerable impetus to ensure that others kept silent, but it also pulled them deeper and deeper into sub-cultural involvement in crime, placing them at considerable risk for involvement in homicides. Ian's account is illustrative. He was assaulted and stabbed by another young man and retaliated. He recognized that he could have reported the assault, but said if he had:

Back then you'd be considered a rat and you'd get beat up. The reason I'm in so much shit now is because I wouldn't say what happened, I wouldn't give my side of the story [to the police]. That's what gave me the cheating hand. I sealed my own fate instead.

Silence ultimately came with a price. Many of our young people "did not tell" at the time, and some still have not told what actually happened. Instead, they told us that their co-accused and other witnesses ratted, resulting in their (the participants') convictions. Being convicted was seen as distinctly separate from harming another person. Although some participants admitted responsibility, almost none were keen on accepting the consequences. Silence would have protected them, they claimed. However, if they didn't talk and others did, then they could end up doing more time. Conversely, they said that if they did talk and others didn't, they ran the risk of being assaulted. According to these young people, keeping *or* breaking silence could be deadly.

Peer groups provided our participants with positive benefits and negative experiences. They noted that interpersonal ties and protection gave them status and confidence. Many defined themselves as loners and social outcasts before they joined a group. However, group and gang involvement came at tremendous social cost: their activities as part of the group were also focussed on crime and led to homicides. Excluding Steven, all offenders who identified as being involved in gangs or criminal peer groups committed their homicides with these peers. Even for those young people who did not identify themselves as gang or group members, the homicide event typically involved at least one other peer. Only four participants were sole perpetrators of their homicides: Steven, Leo, Nigel, and Bruce. We will explore this issue in more depth in Chapter 5.

Social Institutions: Schools, Mental Health, and Child Welfare

As we noted above, these young people typically came into conflict with a variety of social institutions because of their behaviour and the emotional harm it reflected. How did these institutions respond? They were supposed to have been the "social safety net" for our participants. However, the process for triggering involvement of these institutions was problematic in many cases, and involvement often was reported as being not helpful. Many offenders supported these claims by blaming their homicides in part on institutional failure. We begin with schools, where our offenders spent (or were supposed to have spent) much of their time prior to the homicides.

Schools

Problems in school continued for most participants. These included academic performance problems, attendance problems, conflict with teachers and others, and violence. We noted in Chapter 3 that by age 12, 10 of our 19 participants were experiencing learning disabilities, behavioural problems (rages, defiance), failing grades, attendance problems, and/or fighting. After age 12, these problems continued for these adolescents, and they began for others. By the time of the homicides, all participants had experienced one or more problems at school.

Attendance was the most common source of conflict between our participants and their schools; 13 had such problems. The schools responded in a range of ways. For those who were in high school prior to the passage of the YOA, this typically involved warnings, discussions with parents, and, as a last resort, referral to the courts for truancy under the provisions of the JDA. Bruce, Connor, and Frank were placed into custody for truancy. All three were released when they reached 16, the age at which they could legally leave school.

Under the YOA, arrests for truancy ceased. Young people with attendance problems remained the concern of both the schools and the child welfare system. Different schools responded in a variety of ways to participants who were chronically truant. Johnny was allowed to drive his own car when he turned 16. He skipped school on a regular basis to drink, play pool, and hang out with friends. Before they would readmit him, his school required him to sign a contract, according to which he would attend regularly and maintain a "C" average. Johnny was able to follow the contract for one semester. His attendance then fell off, and he was arrested for the homicides before the school could decide how to deal with his failure to meet his contractual agreement. Susan quit school at age 15. The school was not prepared to have her attend without a contract because of her involvement in a fight. She refused the contract and left school and home for the street. Her mother did not call the police, though Susan was a minor illegally at large and was in breach of the conditions of a probation order. However, the police picked her up and returned her home on a number of occasions. She would run again, and neither the youth justice nor child welfare systems could intervene effectively. Susan's mother resisted any type of intervention; she apparently wanted to protect her daughter from criminalization. Susan remained on the street working as a drug dealer until her arrest for the homicide. Steven was deserted by his mother and stepfather around age 12 and gradually drifted away from school. He found it increasingly difficult to provide for his basic needs while attending school. Substance abuse, crime, guns, and violent war games became an escape from his tragic circumstances. He dropped out of school by age 14. No one tried to track him down; no one called child welfare.

Kyle was in custody by age 12 for sexual abuse, auto theft, and various other criminal offences. He was made a Crown ward and spent the next four years bouncing between child welfare and young offender facilities. He received some treatment and was released back into the community at age 16. His mother and stepfather would not take him back home. He was given welfare assistance on the condition that he attend school and was supposed to be adhering to the conditions of his probation order. He got an apartment with criminal peers. Although he claimed to have attended school, on a daily basis he was involved in break-and-enters — usually done at about 10 a.m. when most people were at work and most children were in school. He was also involved in serious substance abuse. No one intervened.

A relatively common solution for attendance problems was to transfer young people to "alternate" schools; this was the case for both Allan and Ian. They reported that, while this made going to school easier, it did not help them deal with the underlying problems that led to their initial truancy. Ian said he liked his school and trusted his teachers, who were very supportive. Yet he was unable, not surprisingly, to stop his serious drug abuse; school was not a location where his emotional problems and anger were dealt with. Allan also transferred to an alternate school after chronic depression kept him from attending his regular school. He found this school to be a better environment and made friends for the first time. Unfortunately, they were his co-accused and victim. Here again, the response assisted the young person in dealing with his school problems but not with the issues that contributed to them. Phillip had serious mental health problems and was referred at an early age for assessment by the school. He bounced between specialized classes, schools, and treatment centres. Whenever he attempted to re-integrate with the regular school system, he was referred back to the mental health system for his problems.

By age 16, he was out of school, out of his parents' home, and living on the street.

Seven of our participants (George, Phillip, Kyle, Bruce, Paul, Scott, and Walter) had learning disabilities. Most were identified through testing, and their schools attempted to help them. However, this meant putting them in special classes, apparently without consideration of the emotional impact of being labelled "learning disabled." They described themselves as being in the "dummy class" and being called stupid, retarded, and idiots. They also said that they were teased and bullied by their peers because of the special placement. This increased their emotional harm and the likelihood that they would act out in school. While the school's response was positive—most had a teacher who identified the problem and pushed for testing, which provided them with the opportunity to improve their learning—the impact was not.

As we saw in Chapters 2 and 3, nine of our participants reported being bullied and teased for a range of reasons: being overweight, in a learning-disabled class, Aboriginal or black, or poorly dressed. Not a single participant indicated that the school was informed about the bullying or, if it was informed, did anything to address the problem. They had to deal with the bullying themselves, often in ways that ended with them in trouble. Nigel discussed the reaction of others to his fighting and noted that he usually fought when someone else was bugging him.

Nigel: Mostly when a fight would break out people would just sit back and cheer.

Int.: So were they cheering you on?

Nigel: Yeah, 'cuz this guy had got on the nerves of a lot of people.

Int.: That kind of get ya pumped up?

Nigel: Yeah. It would be a good feeling.

Int.: So was this usual when you would fight, people would cheer you on?

Nigel: No. I don't usually fight when there is a big ... I don't hang

out in big crowds, or anything like that. Usually when I was
fighting, it was like a secluded corner of the field or something,
and somebody would come over and start bugging me.

These experiences with the school system indicated a number of things.
First, the institutional response to these young people was not holistic, but
compartmentalized. Schools were responsible for ensuring participants'
attendance, appropriate placement, good behaviour, and the safety of other
students. When participants were identified with learning disabilities, the
schools focussed directly on learning-related issues (testing and placement)
and apparently ignored the social and psychological consequences of these
placements. In cases of bullying and teasing, neither school mandate nor
expertise extended to addressing the root causes of participants' negative
behaviours.

These kinds of responses did not mean that educators were not concerned about our participants; they were not equipped to deal with such
complex needs. Some young people did receive positive help from teachers
and others within the school system, but these interventions were aimed at
responding to their educational problems and challenges. For example, Ian
had a teacher who recommended the alternate school as a solution to his
conflicts in the regular system. Ian liked his new school—his teachers were
supportive—but no one ever addressed his drug abuse problem, although
teachers did take him to emergency at the local hospital following an over-
dose. While several participants indicated that they had teachers who tried
to support them, most said that they received minimal support. These troubled young people were difficult for teachers and school administration to
deal with: they were angry, frustrated, hurt, violent, and unable to do the
required work necessary to succeed in class.

Mental Health
An effective, cost-efficient way to prevent high-risk adolescents from turning to violence is to address the root causes of their behaviour (i.e., poverty,
social disorganization, child maltreatment and poor parenting, emotional
and behavioural disturbances) using a public health approach.[12] Successful
interventions target high-risk neighbourhoods. Nurse home visitation of
disadvantaged first-time mothers is the best strategy to prevent child
abuse.[13] Effective youth violence prevention programs work on individual
risks and environmental conditions, using strategies that develop individual
skills and competencies, train parents, enhance the school climate, and

address peer group problems.[14] In Canada, an array of federal and provincial/territorial programs address child well-being and healthy development. Examples include specialized health, education, and developmental services; programs targeted at Aboriginal families and children (such as the First Nations-Inuit Child Care Initiative and Aboriginal Head Start); prevention and early intervention programs for families at risk (Child Development Initiative, Child Care Visions, Canada Prenatal Nutrition Program, Community Action Program for Children, New Brunswick's Early Childhood Initiatives, Ontario's Better Beginnings Better Futures, Quebec's Centres Locals des Services Communautaires, Saskatchewan's Action Plan for Children, etc.); the network of Community Health/Resource Centres; and recreational programs. However, although these are critical programs, there simply are not enough of them to reach the large number of high-risk children, youth, and families.[15]

Some of our participants had contact with mental health services; many did not. In this respect, they are no different from the majority of Canadian children and youth with emotional and behavioural disturbances. Many simply "fell through the cracks." Although this may appear to indicate a failure of the health system in these cases, the situation was much more complex. The first step to responding effectively to young people such as our participants is identifying the need and assessing the appropriate course of action. Responding effectively requires diagnostic tools, skill, and a variety of prevention and treatment strategies. Some of the participants were never identified as having problems. Others came to the attention of the system at a young age, yet were misdiagnosed or offered ineffective treatment, or their families failed to follow through with recommended strategies to address their problems. Others were diagnosed as having serious emotional and behavioural disorders only after the homicide. It must be recognized that caregivers who maltreat their children are often reluctant to reach out for help, resist treatment, or lie to health care professionals because they do not want to break the secrecy around the violence at home.[16]

Non-Identification of Problems Nine of our participants indicated that, after the age of 12, they had no diagnosed mental health or behavioural problems, although most reported that they had experienced significant emotional harm and/or maltreatment prior to reaching adolescence. The consequences of such harm were either not apparent to those around these young people or were not identified as significant issues. Yet, once arrested for homicide, most were diagnosed with a serious problem, including oppositional-defiant disorder, conduct disorder, narcissistic personality disorder, anti-social personality disorder, and depression.

David, Susan, and Ian's cases are illustrative. David appeared to be generally fine, yet in fact was in trouble. He grew up in poverty with poor parental supervision. He was victimized by racism and involved in criminal activity before age 12. These experiences left him with feelings of anger and shame. His father's absence was a serious and hurtful issue for him. Nevertheless, he was going to school, with minor attendance problems and some defiance. He was involved in a visible, pro-social peer group through sports and in an invisible, anti-social peer group through another family member (who was the leader of a criminal gang). Yet, he seemed to be fine. There was almost nothing that would have triggered any response to deal with his emotional and behavioural problems. Even if this had happened, he indicated that his family was resistant to getting help. He said that he didn't have any problems, and intervention would not have made any difference anyway. He began running away from home and was taken into care by child welfare. He ran again from his group home and lived on the street with a gang before the homicide.

Susan's behaviour was similar. She exhibited some school-based problems at age 12 when her parents separated. Her father returned home, and her problems abated until about age 14, when he left for good. She began acting out at school: her attendance was a problem, and she was violent towards others and defiant in the classroom. The school's response did not address her emotional or family problems; she was identified as an in-school behaviour problem, and she was suspended. No one identified emotional or mental health issues, despite the fact that she was twice sentenced to serve time in custody for drug dealing and breach of probation. She was highly resistant to treatment and returned to the street, dealing drugs and living with anti-social peers. She continued this activity until the homicide and only then got effective treatment in custody. She was quite open about how her pain and frustration over her family's breakdown contributed to her spiral into crime and anti-social behaviour.

Int.:   Tell me about your family background.

Susan: My goodness. I've been asked this question about a thousand times, so I know I'm an old pro, so I'm going to give it to you fast. I had, without a doubt, an awesome childhood... I had two great parents. I still do have two great parents. School was good, I started ruckusing around a little bit in grade seven, grade eight, pre-teen, early teen years, nothing major, nothing that was a really big problem.

Int.: When you say ruckusing, what do you mean?

Susan: Oh, what, I don't know, goodness. Maybe little arguments or goodness, I'm trying to remember. I remember things happening at school, the mailbox got set on fire once, and of course, being most noticeable, we were held responsible, when you know, we had nothing to do with it. Just little things, I can't really pinpoint one thing. Things at school, you know, making out, maybe glue on somebody's chair, little things. So then my father left home when I was 15 I think, and I just didn't cope with it. Everything sort of went downhill from there.

Int.: How come your dad left home?

Susan: He said, I don't know what his reasoning was, goodness. He said my mother pushed him away, but I think he just couldn't deal with the responsibility. I don't know why he left.

Int.: Did you have contact with him after that?

Susan: Yeah, we used to. My brothers and I used to go to my father's house every Tuesday and a weekend; I can't remember the schedule. Then my father and I had a fight, which was almost physical, and I stopped seeing him. I stopped coming to the house after that and we stopped talking for, oh goodness, it could have been for six months. It's so long ago. We stopped talking for a while, I think we started talking again, and then, we went out for coffee a couple of times, and that was it. By then, I was into dealing. I didn't even talk to my mom much, you know. I came home like once a month for a couple of hours and that was it. I never really had much contact.

Ian also reported health problems and a history of emotional harm. He became increasingly involved in prescription drug abuse after age 12. Following a one-week school break, he returned to school still suffering from the effects of these drugs. His teachers took him to the hospital, reportedly agreed not to tell his parents why he was ill, and tried to get him some medical attention. What happened?

> Int.: So you never ended up at Emerg[ency]?

> Ian: I did, but my teachers from [school] brought me in. The teacher and principal called my mom and told her what they were doing but not why, because I asked them not to, and that's what made me trust them. That's why I did so well, because I could trust them with anything. They brought me in, told the doctor what I was taking, and he looked at me and told me I was lying, and he told me to leave. The teachers said not to worry about it, if anything happened they'd take me right back up. They knew I was telling the truth because I was shaking, I was messed up, but this was three days after the March break when I did all those pills. The doctor said if I took that much my brain would be mush. They had me see a psychiatrist or psychologist to see if I was suicidal. I just wanted to get high.

These cases indicate that although some participants were acting out emotional harm through problematic behaviours, systems either did not intervene effectively or simply did not identify the need for intervention. Steven, Johnny, Mitch, Leo, Paul, and Nigel also reported suffering significant emotional harm in adolescence, yet had no contact with the mental health system.

Problem Identification and Response Some of our participants — Nancy, Phillip, Frank, George and Scott — were identified as having emotional and behavioural disturbances, and there were efforts to get them into the health care system. Nancy exhibited serious problems in school around age 12; she was disruptive in class, verbally abusive towards the principal, and aggressive. The school referred her to a counsellor and then sent her for a mental health assessment. Her psychological report on intake to custody for the homicide reported that " ... mental health interventions have not been received in an orderly fashion and have been quite fragmented in their provision." Her medical records indicate that the school requested she be tested for ADHD based on her anti-social behaviour in the classroom.

She was treated for ADHD, but not because she exhibited the requisite problems with concentration associated with this disorder; instead, the drug therapy was supposed to curtail her anti-social behaviour. There were other problems. Following a one-year hospitalization in a psychiatric ward at age 12, she was released to her parents with a recommended community-based treatment plan. Her parents rejected this plan, choosing to pursue another route. Eventually, Nancy just stopped going to the individual counselling sessions they set up. She reported that the problems with her behaviour extended beyond herself and included her parents. For example, she assaulted her school principal when he grabbed her by the wrist in an attempt to restrain her. Her father defended her action, Nancy said, because he thought the principal should not have restrained her. According to Nancy, her mother's response was to take her shopping to make her feel better. On another occasion, she was convicted of assaulting a school secretary. Instead of holding her accountable, her parents again blamed the school. Nancy's records indicated that there was no significant intervention to address problematic parenting.

Phillip was another young person who was identified as having problems and who received treatment. As we have seen, he spent most of his childhood and adolescence in mental health facilities; on some occasions, he was involuntarily held in psychiatric facilities due to the risk he posed to himself and others. He noted that the in-care programs were good, but there was often no follow-up after discharge. When back in the community, his behaviour quickly deteriorated into rages, violence, and suicidal behaviours. Once he was expelled from school and could no longer live at home due to his violent behaviour (age 16), mental health intervention all but ceased. Legally, he was of age to refuse service (which he did on occasion), and, being out of school, his emotional and behavioural problems were less visible to authorities. Spending most of his young life in institutional care had negative consequences for Phillip. He told us that he could not cope outside of care — he found it difficult to manage his day-to-day life and didn't know how to keep a job, manage his welfare money, or find suitable housing. Perhaps the most disturbing feature of Phillip's records was that his diagnosis kept changing. Like Nancy, he was initially referred for mental health intervention by the school. Initially, he was diagnosed with ADHD and dyslexia. Over time this changed to diagnoses of bi-polar, conduct, and anti-social personality disorders. In an assessment done after his arrest for homicide, a psychiatrist reported to the court that Phillip may have had no mental illness whatsoever; it was suggested that had behavioural interventions addressed his rages and violence, he would have learned not to use violence, since violence would not have achieved the desired ends. It was a chilling report given how Phillip's life had unfolded.

Frank was also referred to mental health professionals to deal with problems of running away and stealing from his adoptive family. Frank refused to co-operate with his therapists. He said he did not trust them, because they were all white. Frank's problems were related, in part, to the serious emotional and physical abuse by his foster parents and to his being abandoned by his mother. He told us that his adoptive parents threatened to send his two younger brothers away if he told about the abuse (their biological son also sexually abused Frank's younger brother). Frank was treated with medication, apparently tranquilizers and ADHD drugs. He said that his adoptive family was pleased when he was on this medication, because he slept all the time, was no longer disruptive, and basically acted like a "vegetable." Unfortunately, the drugs interfered with his school performance, and he vacillated between not taking the medication and using street drugs to counter the side-effects.

In George's case, medical problems were only identified at age ten, and even then, there was no long-term intervention plan. George was disruptive in class, and the school refused to readmit him after a suspension (one of many, this latest one being for fighting) until he was assessed by a doctor. He was tested and diagnosed with ADHD. His family doctor prescribed medication. George said he was over-medicated and that his father put an abrupt end to the negative side-effects:

Int.: Your dad took you off the Ritalin?

George: My doctor was fucked. You know, about Ritalin? She was giving me six pills a day. I was taking two in the morning, two in the afternoon, and two at night. I was like a vegetable. I'd be sitting on the couch crying for nothing and my mom would say "what's wrong?" I'd say "I'm bored, I have no friends," and this and that. Meanwhile, I had a whole project of friends, but I was just in that depression mode, you know. I went to see my dad one weekend and he was, he saw me take my normal dosage, and then he saw how I was and told me I didn't [have to do] that shit. He flushed them down the toilet and that was the end of it.

Int.: Like cold turkey?

George: Yeah. I went home on the Monday and told her [mother] what had happened. She said "we shouldn't have done that, but it's good that you're off it 'cause you were like a vegetable on it." Somehow, I think my doctor was a little ... she was a old, old, hunchback. For myself, I've never heard of anybody taking six pills a day.

The medical system could not respond to the issue of over-medication because neither George's parents nor the school informed the doctor. The parents were not on speaking terms (they had separated due to the father's violence when George was young, and the mother received no financial support from him), and both were marginally educated, poor, and substance abusers. The father was involved in criminal activities. These factors influenced their ability to communicate with the doctor. As well, they simply may not have cared. George had suffered long-standing abuse and neglect at home and rarely had seen his father since his parent's separation. Indeed, his mother became "fed up" with George and distanced herself from him once he began to experience conflict with the criminal justice system.

Scott had serious learning disabilities and behavioural problems and at age 12 sexually assaulted a six-year-old on the school bus. Here was a young man with a history of severe maltreatment, who had witnessed horrific violence in his home. The sexual assault triggered a criminal investigation, and the recommendation was that Scott receive mental health counselling rather than being processed through the criminal justice system. This never happened, because Scott and his family failed to follow through on the treatment. There was no monitoring nor follow-up by the child welfare or justice systems. His violent behaviour continued to escalate at home and in the community. At age 15, Scott was victimized by a brutal assault, which required hospitalization for a couple of days. He was jumped and stabbed by four other youth. The trigger for the assault was their claim that Scott was stalking a former girlfriend, who relied on her friends to deter him; there had been a number of violent altercations prior to this assault. Here again, mental health intervention was warranted, yet never happened. It should be noted that Scott lied to doctors about his involvement in this incident, maintaining that he was an innocent victim who just happened to have been jumped. He refused to give any information to the police. Finally, he was convicted of assaulting another girlfriend prior to the birth of their son and was required to attend counselling as a condition of his probation order. He went for one session with a psychiatrist and told us that he refused to go back; apparently, he took offence at being asked if he had been sexually abused. He threatened his mental health outreach worker and seriously injured a peer whom he assaulted at a recreation centre. He believed this young man was making sexual advances to his girlfriend. Therapy was attempted with another counsellor and was not successful; during these couple of months in which he was still on probation, Scott tortured two young men, leaving them with life-threatening injuries, and murdered another person.

It is clear that many participants did not receive required mental health intervention. Some were not identified because, despite their problems, they functioned relatively well. Others were clearly in trouble, but their problems were not identified by parents, teachers, or other professionals with whom they had contact. Some participants were identified and received services, most of which were ineffective. Problems with diagnoses, compliance by offenders and their caregivers with treatment, and a general mistrust of the "system" all impeded services. Finally, for most of these young people, their problems were long-standing and unlikely to have been remedied with intervention this late in their troubled lives.

Child Welfare System

In 1995, the national rate of children and youth in care was 67 per 10,000 (48,343 in care out of 7.1 million Canadian children and youth). Rates ranged from a low of 36 in Ontario to a high of 234 per 10,000 in the Northwest Territories.[17] Does taking children and youth into care work? Much more research is needed in this area. Outcomes for many adolescents taken into care are questionable, and long-term placement can be harmful. Longer-term, intensive community services are associated with better outcomes, no matter what kind of intervention is provided.[18] Many youth who engage in violence have had multiple residential placements and other forms of child welfare intervention preceding their involvement with the youth justice system. Many enter the young offender system as wards of the state.[19] A lack of permanency planning and frequent moves from one residential facility to another aggravate the trauma they have already suffered. This contributes to the social isolation, lack of community integration, and mental health problems experienced by many violent adolescents. Child welfare reforms to address these problems are urgently needed.[20]

How do the child welfare experiences of our sample compare with the findings of existing research? Ten had spent time in child welfare, young offender (YO), and/or treatment facilities in adolescence: George and Susan were in YO facilities; Phillip was in mental health and YO facilities; David, Walter, and Kyle were in child welfare and YO facilities; Nancy was in child welfare, mental health, and YO facilities; Bruce and Frank were in child welfare homes and training schools (under the JDA); and Connor spent time in a training school. Eight had placements in multiple residential facilities totalling more than 12 months; seven had spent at least three years of their adolescence in one or more of these institutions (George, Phillip, Kyle, Bruce, Frank, Nancy, and Walter). Although some benefit was surely accomplished through institutionalization, we have to question the overall outcomes. Problematic behaviours and emotional disturbances certainly escalated following admission into these facilities and definitely continued unabated following release. In fact, these young people said that, during their time in these residential settings, they became friends with other young people who also had serious emotional and behavioural problems and were heavily engaged in crime. It is interesting that seven participants committed homicides with peers they met in these institutions (George, Phillip, Susan, David, Kyle, Nancy, and Walter).

Three young people with serious emotional and behavioural disturbances never had contact with the child welfare system during adolescence: Scott, Mitch, and Steven. We wonder if they would have taken a different pathway had these interventions been made. All three told us that they harboured deep feelings of anger and rage at the "system" for not intervening with the serious problems at home. Scott acknowledged the serious negative effects of his father's violence, yet idealized both his parents. Mitch also put his father on a pedestal, despite his violence and substance abuse; he blamed his mother for kicking his father out on the street, leaving him with no place to live. Steven was the most realistic about his parents: he told us that they were abusive, developmentally-delayed alcoholics with serious mental illnesses, who set the stage for his violent behaviours. He did not idealize them. He reported that his rage against child welfare's failure to intervene fuelled his violence.

Experiences with the Youth Justice System

One common perception about young people convicted of homicide is that they are serial criminals. This was not the case for some of the young people in our study. For three participants the homicide was their first and only contact with the criminal justice system. Two others had a single contact, which resulted in no charges, prior to the homicide. The other 14 had at least one previous charge.

Allan, Leo, and Nigel all had no contact with the criminal justice system prior to their homicide convictions. Allan had a litany of other problems—family breakdown, physical abuse by both parents, emotional abuse by his mother, the absence of his father from his life, and loneliness and isolation from his peers. His primary behavioural problem was severe depression, which led to non-attendance at school and an eventual transfer to an alternate school. He rarely drank and had tried, but was not addicted to, marijuana. At age 15, with the only friend he ever had, he created a fantasy world based on a violent comic book figure. Together, they began planning how to become hired assassins. He bought knives and began carrying them with him. But these behaviours would not have indicated to anyone that he was likely to kill someone. Allan himself reported that he did not believe he was capable of killing someone until the victim was dead.

Leo also had no contact with the police. His life experiences were different from Allan's. His father was physically abusive to him, and his older brother sexually abused him. This brother was himself sexually abused by a friend and boarder and also reported to child welfare authorities that his father had sexually abused him. Nothing was ever proven. The father was financially irresponsible, and the family lived in poverty. Leo had no school-based problems on his official record, although he said that he was bullied. By age 13 he began sniffing gas, in order to make friends when his family moved to a new area. He failed grade eight and had to repeat it. Prior to the homicide, he had never been suspended nor expelled and was going to school on a regular basis. Once again, there is very little on the surface that suggests he would become a murderer. However, he had unidentified and serious emotional problems. He told us that he had had ongoing fantasies about killing people since a young age. He reportedly fantasized about killing a friend and then raping her. His homicide was something he said was inevitable; he reported that sooner or later he knew he was going to kill someone.

Nigel, the only other respondent with no police contact prior to the homicide, had broken into a neighbour's home in the middle of the night prior to the homicide. He was caught, but, instead of being turned over to the police, the matter was dealt with privately between the two families. He later murdered this neighbour. He was bullied at school and responded by fighting back, for which he served almost weekly detentions in grades five and six. He was suspended for two days in grade eight for fighting. That same year he failed English and had to repeat it at summer school. But, by high school, he was fighting less. He reported generally good grades. Yet, he was a loner. He did not drink, nor did he use drugs. Here again, from the outside it did not appear that this young man might kill someone. He seemed to have a few problems, was lonely perhaps, but otherwise was fine.

Allan, Leo, and Nigel were loners, and none had connected to an anti-social peer group until shortly before the murders. This likely accounted for their limited criminal careers; they had no contact with police and no criminal charges prior to the homicides.

Most of our other participants became involved in criminal activities with their peers; yet, their contacts with the criminal justice system varied considerably. Paul reported a single contact with the police, in which dis-cretion was exercised and no charges were laid. He was picked up for shoplifting. His family and the school vice-principal both asked that charges not be laid. They noted that Paul had just got on track with his transfer to his new school and that the shoplifting was unlikely to be repeated. Connor had numerous contacts with police all related to his vio-lent behaviour but was never charged. He went to local bars and dances and got involved in violent fights. The police response was to take him away, let him cool down, and release him with no charges. He described one such incident at a local dance:

Connor: I remember, at a dance, I got in three fights, uh, they asked me to leave, so I said, okay I'll leave. Coming down the stairs, two police officers come down. I punched one, shoved another. I didn't care, it was just weird....

Int.: But they didn't charge you with that?

Connor: I was never like that though, but I just thought ... what the hell are you doing? You don't need this. You don't fight these people. But it happened anyways.

Int.: Did they grab you? Did you take off?

Connor: I took off, and they, they eventually jumped me, they didn't beat me up or anything. They knew, they thought I was very odd or something.

Int.: Did they charge you?

Connor: Nope.

Int.: So you walked.

Connor: Yeah. Actually they brought me back. They took me to the station, made me mellow out for a bit, said okay, you can't go back there, because you got in three fights. Blah, blah, blah. I said, well I gotta go back. I gotta go get my jacket because my jacket was there, so they escorted me on their way.

When Connor told us "they knew, they thought I was very odd or something," he was likely referring to the fact that he lived in a small town where the police knew of his mother's sudden death and brother's suicide. In this case, however, we wonder if the murder Connor committed could have been prevented if the police had dealt with him in a different manner.

The remaining 14 participants had more contacts with the police, yet their charges varied considerably. The most common charges were assault and assault causing bodily harm. Ten (George, Phillip, David, Kyle, Steven, Ian, Mitch, Scott, Nancy, and Walter) were convicted of at least one of these offences. Susan was under investigation for the physical and sexual assault of a developmentally delayed adolescent immediately prior to the homicide. Susan and Frank had been convicted of drug possession; Susan was also convicted of dealing. Seven of our participants (George, Kyle, Steven, Johnny, Bruce, Mitch, and Frank) had been convicted of property offences — theft, robbery, break and enter, car theft, and possession of stolen property. Of the whole sample, George had been convicted of the most offences as a young offender — 14 in all.

This charging pattern differentiates our participants from the typical young offenders in Canada. The most common form of youth crime in Canada is property crime. In contrast, the most common offence for our participants was violent crime. While it would be easy to argue that this tendency to use violence was what led them to become involved in homicide, we must be cautious. First, the vast majority of violent offenders in Canada do not become involved in homicides.[21] Second, not all young offenders convicted of homicide have a history of criminal violence.[22] However, the path to homicide was linked to the use of violence for many of the young people in our study. Most committed unplanned homicides, which were unintended but likely outcomes of their aggressive risk-taking activities. We will explore this issue in more detail in Chapter 5.

How did the criminal justice system react following the charging of these adolescents? It responded in a variety of ways, depending on the number of charges, the seriousness of the offences, and their age. The YOA sentencing principals were used in many of these cases. Young people were incarcerated when they committed violent offences against others. All of our participants who were charged with assault (except one who had not yet been convicted at the time of the homicide) were sentenced to periods of open and secure custody. The length of sentence varied, as did the responses of the young people to their time in custody. However, it was clear that the criminal justice system attempted to send a message to these adolescents that harming others was viewed as serious and the public had to be protected. Given the seriousness of these charges, it is not surprising that interventions differed somewhat compared to the typical YO response in our country. In 1998 to 99, 40,205 youth were admitted into custody, at a national rate of 164 per 10,000 youth in Canada. Over one-half of these adolescents were ordered into open and secure custody facilities for non-violent crimes.[23]

Other sentencing principals were also apparent for our offenders. Of particular concern was ensuring that young people received treatment. For example, two of our participants were charged with sexually assaulting children. Both were quite young when the offences were committed — both Scott and Kyle were 12 years old. Scott had no previous criminal history and was not put in custody. He was identified as having serious emotional problems and referred for community-based treatment. His parents never followed through with this, nor did the criminal justice system monitor this situation. Kyle began stealing cars and doing break-and-enters around age 11 and was made a Crown ward at age 12. His mother and stepfather were unable to control him, and he sexually abused his younger siblings. He was taken into care and required to participate in treatment.

One serious concern that emerged from the interviews was the ability of the criminal justice system to monitor and provide appropriate supports. Most participants had been on probation at some point in their adolescence. Some cleared probation without any further problems until the homicide. For example, Johnny had two convictions prior to the homicide: theft and break-and-enter. He received two separate sentences of probation as a result. Right after he cleared his first order, he was arrested for the second time. He regarded both offences as not being serious. The theft charge was related to what he termed a prank. Along with a friend, he stole a vending machine, put it in his truck, and was planning to leave it on the lawn of a fellow student as a joke. They were caught and charged. Steven also was arrested, he said, about every nine months from the age of 14 until the homicide, which occurred when he was 16. Each time, he completed his probation order and then re-offended violently. He was never caught for dealing drugs nor for breaking into night safety-deposit boxes. Steven was living with a friend and the friend's mother; he appeared to be "supported" in a traditional way, although he relied on crime to meet his basic needs. He told us that sometimes there was a line-up of people extending into the apartment building hall waiting to buy drugs from him. Apparently, none of the neighbours ever called the police about this.

Susan was convicted of drug dealing and possession and sentenced to serve secure and open custody time. She was released on probation with an order not to associate with particular known criminals. She was caught dealing and associating with criminals again. She served more time and was released, once again on probation. She became involved with a gang and committed the homicide while on probation. Apparently, no one was able to monitor her activities while she was on the second probation order. Susan was not the only person to ignore probation conditions. Kyle was also on an order not to associate with certain known criminals, but he, too, was living on his own with his co-accused for a couple of months prior to the homicide. Other probation conditions were also not met in his case (to go to school and abstain from drugs/alcohol and criminal activities). Scott's situation provides another example of the inability of the justice system to adequately monitor cases. His parents did not follow through with treatment for sexual offending. Scott continued to exploit weaker individuals: he robbed a young girl of her Halloween candy and was put on probation. A short while later he was convicted of beating his pregnant girlfriend so badly that she had a miscarriage; for this crime, he received only 12 months probation. During this time, he was supposed to see a psychiatrist on a regular basis and participate in an anger management group. Neither condition was met, and he was still on probation at the time of the murder.

These poor outcomes of YO correctional rehabilitation for many participants are not surprising. Other researchers have raised similar concerns about YO treatment interventions.[24] On a per capita basis, our youth incarceration rate is among the highest in the world.[25] We lock kids up without any compelling evidence that this works.[26] We sentence our most violent young people to lengthy periods of custody, often without comprehensive rehabilitation, nor intensive community supports to aid reintegration following release. Evidence suggests recidivism rates are high, and far too many juvenile delinquents "graduate" to the adult justice system.[27]

We find it heartening that alternative approaches to dealing with violent youth crime in Canada are presently being explored. Initiatives to prevent youth violence have recently been undertaken in two national strategies by the Department of Justice Canada: the Youth Justice Renewal Strategy and the National Strategy on Community Safety and Crime Prevention. The development of national crime prevention strategies in both Canada and the US are based in large part on community mobilization.[28] There are some promising demonstration projects in Canada, but far too many high-risk children and youth do not have access to these critical programs.[29]

Conclusion

In the last chapter, we found that by age 12, Susan and Connor were at the lowest risk of all participants, whereas Scott, Leo, and George had the most negative social experiences and no protective factors. Ten of the participants had many negative social experiences and few protective factors (they were at medium-high risk), and the remaining four had both few negative experiences and protective factors.[30] When we look at their lives prior to the homicides, the picture is very different: risk factors had substantially increased, whereas protective factors had greatly decreased. All but three had been suspended (for most, this happened more than once) or expelled from school, and 11 were not in school for the six-month period prior to the homicide. Only two were not fighting and using violence. Nine said their violence had dramatically increased during adolescence. Only three had not been convicted of criminal offences and were not abusing substances; eight were carrying guns and/or knives. Ten had spent time in child welfare, young offender, and/or treatment facilities. Of this group, eight had been in multiple residential facilities for more than 12 months; seven (George, Phillip, Kyle, Bruce, Frank, Nancy, and Walter) had spent at least three years of their adolescence in one or more of these institutions.

In summary, by the time of the homicide all of these adolescents had serious emotional and/or behavioural impairments; most told us they were "out of control," and nothing could have prevented them from killing at that point in their lives. Although a minority still had some protective factors, these positive influences were powerless to mitigate against the overwhelming risks which had engulfed these adolescents' lives. Neither positive community, family, educational supports, nor individual resiliency could offer enough protection. Again, we cannot paint these adolescents with the same brush. There was tremendous variety in their lives. The pathways they took to homicide were very different, as were the types of killings they would eventually commit.

In Chapter 2, we described how a bio-social-psychosocial, risk/resiliency model contributes to our understanding of these multiple risk factors and pathways, and this model is helpful in analyzing the adolescent experiences of the participants. The multiplicity of risk factors negatively affected their healthy development during this critical stage in their lives. Serious problems were not identified. Effective intervention and prevention practices could have been initiated; this did not happen for a variety of reasons, including resistance and secrecy by participants and their caregivers and ineffective intervention by systems once problems were identified. We know that multi-disciplinary intervention approaches, based upon a risk/resiliency model and targeted at key developmental stages of high-risk children and youth, have the best outcomes for violence prevention.[31]

The literature suggests that preventing the development of risk factors is much more effective in reducing levels of child maltreatment[32] and youth violence[33] than treatment programs. Given the large number of children and youth at risk in Canada, treatment programs alone cannot reduce their "burden of suffering." Universal programs and those that target high-risk groups are therefore necessary.[34] Primary prevention services in childhood (which identify the behavioural, environmental, and biological risk factors linked to violence) may have prevented our participants from engaging in serious violence and homicide. However, this was not possible due to the late identification of problems. Ideally, these services should be initiated with high-risk expectant parents and be continued throughout childhood and adolescence.[35]

Notes

1   Harris, 1998; Garbarino, 1999.
2   Garbarino, 1999; Totten, 2000a.

3 Totten, 2000a.

4 Totten, 2000a.

5 LoPiccolo, 1996. LoPiccolo presents a theory of homicides committed without motive, plan, or even emotion. He argues that some loners who internalize problems (which most of us vent to family or friends) may risk a "mindstorm" that can trigger violent acts.

6 Totten, 2000a, 2001a; Rubin, 1976; Klein, 1982; Connell, 1992; Messerschmidt, 1993, 1997.

7 Totten, 2000a.

8 Totten, 2000a.

9 Totten, 2000a.

10 Mathews, 1993.

11 Cohen, 1955.

12 US Department of Health and Human Services, 2001; Doob *et al.*, 1998; Loeber and Farrington, 1997, 1998; Hamburg, 1998; Elliott, Hagan, and McCord, 1998; Mercy *et al.*, 1993.

13 MacMillan, 2000; MacMillan with the Canadian Task Force on Preventive Heath Care, 2000.

14 US Department of Health and Human Services, 2001; Doob *et al.*, 1998; Loeber and Farrington, 1997, 1998; Hamburg, 1998; Elliott, Hagan, and McCord, 1998; Hawkins *et al.*, 1998; Mercy *et al.*, 1993.

15 Jenson and Stroick, 2000.

16 Statistics Canada, CCJS, 2000b.

17 Statistics Canada and the Federal-Provincial Working Group on Child and Family Services Information, 1996.

18 Ballantyne and Raymond, 1998; Butts and Barton, 1995; Moretti, Holland, and Peterson, 1994; Morrison and Eisner, 1993; Inglehart, 1993; Andrews, Hodge, and Leschied, 1992; Seelig, Goldman-Hall, and Jerrell, 1992; Fuchs, 1990; Kagan *et al.*, 1987; Timberlake and Verdieck, 1987; Pardeck, 1985; Proch and Taber, 1987; Steinhauer, 1996, 1984.

19 Totten, 2000a, 2001a, 2001c; Andrews, Hoge, and Leschied, 1992.

20 Ballantyne and Raymond, 1998; Moretti, Holland, and Peterson, 1994; Proch and Taber, 1987; Timberlake and Verdieck, 1987; Steinhauer, 1984; Hornby and Collins, 1981.

21 Totten, 2001c.

22 For example, this was the case for five offenders in our study.

23 Molden and Kukec, 2000. These data include remand, open, and secure custody admissions.

24 Totten, 2001a, 2001c; Doob *et al*; 1998; Andrews *et al.*, 1990.

25 Doob *et al.*, 1998; Savoie, 1999; Stevenson *et al.*, 1998.

26 Doob *et al.*, 1998.

27 Neeley-Bertrand, 2001; US Department of Health and Human Services, 2001; Totten, 2000a, 2001a, 2001b; Stevenson *et al.*, 1998; Blanchette *et al.*, 1998; Shaw, 1994b; Statistics Canada, CCJS, 1997; Sampson and Lauritson, 1994.

28 National Crime Prevention Centre, 2000a, 2000b, 1998; Sherman *et al.*, 1997; US Department of Justice, 1996.

29 Totten, 2001c.

30 See Chapter 3, Table 3.3.

31 US Department of Health and Human Services, 2001; Wasserman and Miller, 1998; Loeber and Farrington, 1997, 1998.

32 MacMillan, with the Canadian Task Force on Preventive Health Care, 2000; Wachtel, 1999; Offord *et al.*, 1998; MacMillan *et al.*, 1996; MacMillan *et al.*, 1994; Wekerle and Wolfe, 1993; MacMillan, MacMillan and Offord, with Canadian Task Force on the Periodic Health Examination, 1993.

33 US Department of Health and Human Services, 2001; Wasserman and Miller, 1998; Loeber and Farrington, 1997, 1998; Cook and Laub, 1998; Hamburg, 1998; Elliott, Hagan and McCord, 1998; Mercy *et al.*, 1993.

34 Offord *et al.*, 1998.

35 MacMillan, 2000; US Department of Health and Human Services, 2001.

Homicides in Context

Introduction

As we have shown, the young offenders we interviewed had diverse experiences in their families, with their peers, and in their communities. They had a range of contacts with the educational, mental health, child welfare, and criminal justice systems as they were growing up. These experiences, combined with their feelings of anger, rage, shame, and humiliation, and the youth sub-cultures to which they belonged, all contributed to their involvement in the homicides. In this chapter we attempt to put the homicides into context. We follow the model discussed in Chapter 3, which connects past histories, immediate conditions, and the homicides themselves. This model is not meant to be determinant. We argue that our participants made choices that led to potentially dangerous behaviours; these behaviours put them at risk for becoming involved in potentially lethal situations; they then made choices that led them to commit the homicides.

Offence Profiles

Table 5.1 provides a summary of some features of the homicide events. Eleven of the 19 offenders were 17 years old at the time of the homicide, five were 16, two were 15, and one was 14. This range and distribution fits Canadian youth homicide patterns. Most of the homicides (13) involved more that one person; six involved a sole perpetrator. Of the homicides that involved more than one person, six were committed with one co-accused, three were committed with two co-accused, two were committed with three co-accused, and two with six co-accused.

Offender	Age	Gender	Weapon	Location	# of Co-accused
George	17	male	gun	public street	2
Phillip	17	male	knife, bat	victim's home	0
Susan	17	female	electrical cord, beating	private home	6
David	15	male	electrical cord, beating	private home	6
Kyle	16	male	gun	public street	2
Steven	17	male	gun	isolated public area	0
Bruce	17	male	gun	isolated rural area	0
Johnny	17	male	car	highway	0
Connor	17	male	blunt instrument	isolated rural area	1
Allan	16	male	knife	isolated urban spot	2
Ian	16	male	beating	isolated public area (alley)	1
Mitch	17	male	metal cylinder, victim burned	victim's home	1
Leo	14	male	gun	victims' home	0
Paul	17	male	gun	isolated rural road	3
Scott	17	male	stomping, beating	isolated public area	1
Frank	17	male	gun	offender's home	2
Nancy	16	female	knife	isolated public area	1
Walter	17	male	gun	business	3
Nigel	16	male	knife	victim's home	0

Table 5.1: Offence Profiles (George and Kyle were involved in the same homicide, as were Susan and David.)

The methods used to commit the homicides also varied. Fifteen of the homicides involved weapons. Guns were used in eight of the killings, knives were used in four, a blunt object was used in two, and in one a car was used as the weapon. The four remaining homicides resulted from severe beatings. In two of these cases, the victim died as a result of strangulation administered during the assault. In a third, the victim died later of pneumonia following injuries that caused serious brain damage and a coma; in the fourth case, the victim bled to death after a broken rib pierced his heart.

The murders happened in a variety of places. Seven of our perpetrators killed their victims in private homes: four in the victims' homes, two in another person's residence, and one at the perpetrator's home. Two homicides took place at a business. One was the killing of an employee during an armed robbery, and the other was the murder of a taxi driver. Seven of the murders took place in isolated public places, including alleyways, public parks, a schoolyard late at night, rural lanes, and a group hideout. The remaining three homicides took place on public streets: two perpetrators were involved in a drive-by shooting and one in a vehicular manslaughter.

Victim	Age	Gender	Relationship to Offender	Victim Marginal/Weaker
victim #1	23	male	stranger	no
victim #2	39	male	friend	no
victim #3	17	male	acquaintance	no
victim #4	17	male	acquaintance	no
victim #5	23	male	stranger	no
victim #6	17	male	friend	no
victim #7	38	male	acquaintance	drug addict
victim #8a	18	male	acquaintance	no
victim #8b	18	male	acquaintance	no
victim #8c	18	male	acquaintance	no
victim #8d	17	male	acquaintance	no
victim #9	41	male	stranger	no
victim #10	16	male	friend	youth in care
victim #11	68	male	acquaintance	elderly alcoholic street person
victim #12	32	male	stranger	drug addict
victim #13a	49	male	neighbour	no
victim #13b	39	female	neighbour	no
victim #14	35	male	stranger	no
victim #15	45	male	stranger	mentally ill street person
victim #16	25	male	acquaintance	no
victim #17	16	female	friend	no
victim #18	18	male	stranger	no
victim #19	39	female	neighbour	no

Table 5.2: Victim Profiles

Victim Profiles

Our 19 participants killed 21 people (see Table 5.2). Whom did they kill? Most of the homicide victims were male (18 of 21). Nine of the victims were other young people between the ages of 16 and 18 years, two were in their early 20s, six in their 30s, three in their 40s, and one was in his late 60s.

The relationship between the participants and their victims also varied. Some of our participants' victims were strangers (six), some were acquaintances (eight), some were friends (four), and some were neighbours (three). Seventeen of the homicides involved single victims. One of our interviewees killed two people, and the youth that committed a vehicular homicide was responsible for the deaths of four people. Again, this fits with national patterns for youth homicide in Canada.

Most of the victims were ordinary people rendered vulnerable by the presence of weapons and/or multiple assailants. But some were particularly vulnerable. These included one senior citizen, three addicts (drugs/alcohol) living on the margins of society, and one mentally ill street person. The victimization of these weaker individuals is particularly troubling.

Classifying the Homicides

The young people in our study engaged in different types of homicides and reached the moment of killing another person by diverse paths, which we have detailed in the previous chapters. These paths connected the roots of violent behaviour, to the goals these young people had when they used violence, to the immediate trigger(s)—the context of the murders. While some of our offenders intended to kill, most were engaging in dangerous, violent behaviour where death was an unintended, though perhaps not unforeseen, consequence of their actions. These were termed *unplanned* homicides and consisted of two types: homicides that resulted from "ordinary" violence, and homicides that resulted from risk-taking aggression. Some of the homicides were *planned*. Although they had similar root causes of violence and motives for using violence, the planned homicides had a somewhat different character than the unplanned ones. They were, in part, the result of the adoption of a coping strategy in which the participants developed an intense fantasy life focussed on killing and violence: we call this fantasy-based violence. Let us examine each of these types of homicides in turn.

Ordinary Violence

In 12 of the 19 cases, the participants reported being surprised that a death resulted from an "ordinary" violent encounter. As we noted in the previous chapter, in the sub-cultures in which they lived, to these participants the use of physical violence towards others was a normative part of day-to-day life. They knew when and why violence should be used, who should use it, and against whom. They also described to us how they came to use violence as a way of dealing with victimization by bullying, abuse, and violence in their communities. These homicides had three important components: the root causes of using violence, the goals of using violence (what these young people sought to achieve by using violence), and the immediate homicide context.

Roots of, Routes to Violence   The routes leading young people to use violence included feelings of shame, fear, and humiliation resulting from bullying, abuse at home, poverty, and neglect. Further, for our male participants, the use of violence was linked to their social construction of masculinity.[1] Some of our participants also had feelings of powerlessness. For some, these resulted from negative events (e.g., the sudden death of Connor's mother and his brother's suicide; Susan's parents' divorce); for others, they were the result of negative social conditions that they could not control (e.g., Steven struggling with poverty and abandonment). Participants involved in these situations reported that they felt unable to prevent harm to themselves or others. As well, some of these young people may not have been able to control their violent impulses due to brain injuries and mental disorders. Scott, for example, had a severe brain injury at age two and had a long history of violence and poor impulse control.

Goals of Violent Behaviour   The reasons why participants used violence varied. They included fighting to achieve power or status as a part of criminal activities and as gang or peer group activities (e.g., enforcing drug debts, silencing others). One important factor in the use of violence was masculine identity. By responding to challenges from others through violence, male participants achieved a normative masculinity, which meant being tough, muscular, aggressive, successful, and in control. It also included, for some, using violence to resolve conflicts and to maintain others' role expectations. Participants *chose* to use violence to deal with these situations, although it was not the only choice available to them. Walter and George, for instance, grew up in communities where violence was common. For others, such as Mitch and Ian, violence was encouraged by other (male) family members, and training in the ability to fight was part of their growing up. Ian described how he retaliated against an older teen who challenged his power.

> Ian: I never broke any bones or anything, maybe broken noses, a
>   few bruises and stuff like that....
>
> Int.: Nothing that sticks out in your mind? Like one fight that ...
>
> Ian: I never used a weapon on anybody and still haven't. I've had it
>   used on me before, but —

Type of Homicide: Ordinary Violence

Roots of Violence	Goals of Violence	Triggers for Homicide
► Feelings of shame, humiliation, low self-worth resulting from bullying and maltreatment and linked to hegemonic masculine identity (for the male participants).	► Achieving and maintaining power/status; responding to challenges by peers.	► Attempting to establish power or status or to assert masculinity.
► Feelings of powerlessness resulting from negative events and social conditions that offenders could not control; offenders reported they were unable to prevent harm to themselves or others.	► Releasing feelings of anger and frustration.	► Challenges to offenders' power, status, and/or masculinity.
	► Enforcing perceived normative structure by punishing norm violations (e.g., not paying drug debts, paybacks for assaults on weaker individuals, "ratting," violating traditional gender roles).	► Alleged norm violations.
► Brain injury and mental illness reduced inhibitions against using violence.		► Victim was available, and offender was extremely angry or frustrated.

Type of Homicide: Aggressive Risk Taking

Roots of Violence	Goals of Violence	Triggers for Homicide
► Feelings of shame, humiliation, low self-worth resulting from bullying and maltreatment and linked to hegemonic masculine identity (for the male participants).	► Thrill seeking, excitement, creation of alternate plane of reality where offender was omnipotent.	► Anger or conflict with victim.
► Feelings of powerlessness resulting from negative events and social conditions that offenders could not control; offenders reported they were unable to prevent harm to themselves or others.	► Source of status and identity linked to hegemonic masculinity and particular youth sub-cultures.	► Challenges or encouragement by peers to participate and/or to continue with assault.

Type of Homicide: Violent Fantasy-Based

Roots of Violence	Goals of Violence	Triggers for Homicide
► Feelings of low self-worth resulting from physical, sexual, or emotional abuse.	► Alleviating feelings of powerlessness.	► Murder plan completed.
		► Opportunity (victim present and weapon available).
► Feelings of powerlessness resulting from negative events and social conditions that offenders could not control; offenders reported they were unable to prevent harm to themselves or others.	► Personal thrill for sociopathic offenders: others' lives have no value.	► Victim identified (anger towards victim, victim had something offender wanted, victim randomly chosen and available).
		► Peer pressure.

Table 5.3: Type of Homicide Described by Roots of Violence, Goals of Violence, and Triggers for Homicide Event.

Int.: What happened?

Ian: I was stabbed in my right shoulder.

Int.: When was this?

Ian: When I was 14 or 15.

Int.: What happened there?

Ian: I was walking in the alleyway between the subway and the [place] in the city, you know where that is, and a black fella from the [place] drove it right into my shoulder—a buck knife, it wasn't a hunting knife or nothing, and he didn't kill me or anything, but it hurt.

Int.: What did you do?

Ian: Didn't do nothing that night, couldn't swing or anything, but my buddies grabbed hold of him, threw punches at him, and I saw him a couple of weeks later and got into a fight and that was it and it was all done with. After that I knew him to talk to him.

Mitch frequently used violence as a means for releasing feelings of anger and frustration. He assaulted two different people who were, as he acknowledged, doing nothing. They just happened to be around when he was feeling angry and needed a release. Violence was valued in his household, and Mitch told us that he was proud of his prowess as a fighter. Physically assaulting others gave him a feeling of powerfulness in a world in which he felt he had little control. He had been abandoned by his mother who only offered to take him back because she wanted social services to provide her with a larger home. She needed to have all her children with her to qualify for a larger welfare allowance.

Some participants used violence as a mechanism to punish norm violations such as not paying drug debts or assaulting weaker individuals. Steven described an incident in which he beat up a young man who had ratted on a friend. He also used violence to enforce drug debts. Susan and some other young women were involved in the forcible confinement, sexual assault, and battery of a vulnerable young man over a drug debt.

Immediate Triggers Unplanned murders occurred because of the combination of a traumatic history, a choice of violence as a strategy to cope with trauma, and a normative structure that advocated using violence. The triggers identified for using violence, not surprisingly, matched the factors our participants used to justify their use of violence. These were:

- attempting to establish power or status or to assert masculinity;

- challenges to the person's power, status, and/or masculinity;

- alleged norm violations;

- victim available when person is feeling extremely angry or frustrated.

Phillip had a long history of using violence as a mechanism to cope with stress and frustration in his life. He described two incidents of serious violence prior to the homicide. In the first he smashed a garden shed with a sledgehammer and then chased his sister's car down the street and attempted to assault her. In the second he felt threatened and lashed out in anger by slamming a hatchet through a door on the other side of which was a police officer. Neither incident resulted in serious injury to the intended victims. The homicide was different. Phillip began his assault on his victim by beating him with a baseball bat, injuring him so severely that death was inevitable. To avoid further suffering by the victim, Phillip cut his throat.[2] Phillip appeared surprised that this assault resulted in serious harm and suffering.

Ian also used violence as an ordinary technique for getting what he wanted. He reported that group norms for his peer subculture included using violence to settle scores, rather than reporting them to the authorities or walking away. He said his violence was never used against a girl or someone weaker, although he and his friends killed an alcoholic senior citizen. He clearly believed that violence was not only the normal way to deal with problems, but also that it was required. He argued that he could not have stopped the homicide assault because his co-accused was defending his girlfriend against an alleged assault by the victim. He assisted in the assault because he would have wanted help if it had been his girlfriend in question.

> Ian: [Co-accused] grabbed him and gave it to him. [Second co-accused] came over and gave it to him, and I hit a few times. I'm not going to say I didn't, I'm not innocent, I didn't mean to hurt Mr. [victim]. I didn't think he'd get hurt; all my other fights nobody got hurt. He got hit quite a few times, I hit him maybe four or five times, I didn't hit him that hard.

This account was in stark contrast to the police report, which listed the injuries to the victim as several broken ribs, a ruptured spleen, and brain damage so extensive that had he lived he would have been a "vegetable." The report claimed that Ian and his co-accused repeatedly kicked the victim in the head, presumably after he had fallen to the ground. Ian insisted he didn't witness this part of the assault, nor does his account include the fact that six other young people witnessed it. None of these young people intervened to stop the beating.

Mitch also used violence as an ordinary part of "doing business." His account of an assault on a guy who ratted on a friend is illustrative of how his peer subculture used violence.

> Int.: Apart from the homicide, what's the most violent act you've ever committed? Is it the one where you left the guy with 13 stitches?

> Mitch: That was pretty bad, but I'd say that'd be it. I look at that as just being a stupid kid doing bad, I mean it was violence, but there was times when I hit a guy a couple of times where I was ruthless. There was this guy who ratted on my friend and I ran into him, actually I went up to his house. My buddy had a knife on him and he saw it and called the cops and told the cops he had it, and I'm looking at him like, you're ratting on him right in front of him? The next day I went to his house and I punched him in the face, he thought I was a gangster the way I talked to him.

> Int.: What did you say to him?

Mitch: I told him not to rat, that it's stupid and he shouldn't have. I just told him not to rat. He wouldn't admit it. I hit him until … I had to hit him three times until he would admit he did it. Then I had to ask him, oh, I cut him on the forehead, I was wearing leather gloves, I broke my knuckle and I was telling him not to rat on me. I'd ask him who hit him and he'd say "you did," so I hit him until he said "I don't know." That's the way I do things, unfortunately.

Mitch downplayed the brutality of the beating death. He and his co-accused gained access to the victim's apartment on the pretext of selling him some cocaine. They robbed their victim of his drugs, then proceeded to beat and torture him to death in an effort to extort $7000 from him. Mitch's description was quite detailed, although its truth status was low. Official reports indicated that Mitch, not his co-accused, delivered the fatal blows and burned the victim while he was still alive. However, this was not what Mitch told us.

Mitch: He [co-accused] just whacked him, and whacked him a couple more times and the guy's on the ground, he's drunk and high and he's just moaning…. Somehow we ended up tying him up; I don't know who did it, me or him, but he ended being tied up…. It seemed like a good idea. This crackhead, if he comes upstairs with a gun or something, and he wants his dope back. Anyhow, he's tied up and when we're leaving he says, "let me go, I'll give you seven grand." As soon as my co-accused hears that, he doesn't want to leave. He starts beating this guy and kicking him and saying "where's it at, where's it at?" He goes and starts searching the house again. By this time the guy on the floor is screaming and hollering, and I just looked at him and I'm thinking this is a three-middle and we're on the bottom. So he's hollering, and I go over and hit him twice. That's the guy who ratted on my buddy, and I hit him in the forehead. I had a broken arm, and the cast was just taken off that day because I was sick of it and it didn't heal properly. I hit him twice with this hand, and now I'm hollering because it fucking hurt like a bastard. I tell him to shut up after I hit him and he's telling me to let him go and he'll give me seven grand, he's still saying this. I back off a little bit, and my co-accused comes back and can't find it, so he's like "where's it at, where's it at?" The guy starts screaming, so I kicked him, instead of hitting him. I kicked him twice I believe, and he finally shuts up.… I'm drinking this guy's beer and I finish my beer, he looks at me and says, "what are you doing?" I say, "I'm not finished drinking yet." It's a big joke to me. I'm drunk. I was hammered… The guy's not saying anything now, he's either asleep or unconscious, he's snoring, right, he's breathing loud, whatever he's doing. My co-accused, there's a [burning appliance] on the table, he takes it and turns it on. He takes it down by the guy's face and he's grazing it so the guy can feel the heat. He's saying "where's the money, where's the money?" The guy's not responding, so he takes the flame and burns him on the arm, and the guy didn't even move. No, actually, I got that wrong. Before he turns it on, he grabs the [metal cylinder], and he's whacking him with it, asking him where the money is. The guy's just saying "leave me alone," and he's just beating him. He beat him so bad the [metal cylinder] was dented, that's when he … does the burn thing. I remember he burned him on the arm. This is where I started remembering. He didn't even move, the guy; if you burn someone on the arm with a [burning appliance], they're gonna flinch or something.

This detailed account left out important details and minimized the brutality of this torture-murder. Police reported that the beating took place over a period of three and a half hours. All the bones in the victim's face were broken, all his ribs were cracked, and he was badly burned. Despite Mitch's claims that the victim was yelling, the victim was found bound and had a cloth wrapped around his head to prevent blood from getting on the accused; it acted as a gag. Mitch suggested that the victim was not alive when the burning took place, but official reports said otherwise. Mitch did not see the use of violence, in and of itself, as problematic. He, too, tried to normalize what happened by insisting that the victim was a crackhead, caused Mitch to hurt his hand, and was making too much noise.

Scott had a long history of using violence against others as well. Brutality was an integral part of his life. He noted that he was immune to feeling pain after all the abuse he had experienced. He under-reported the brutality of the murder of a marginal, mentally-ill street person. Scott described the initial assault by himself and his co-accused as a "fight" — a fight in which the victim was attacked by two younger and stronger men.

Scott: But anyways, um, then my fiancée at that time which was my son's mother ended up going to the water fountain to get a drink, and he was mumbling some words to her, you know like, what are you doing with these losers. Ah, I took an insult to that, you know what I mean. Uh, so I started a conflict with him. Like, who the fuck are you calling a loser? They're [his co-accused and another person] pestering you, I'm not bothering you, why are you categorizing me with them, you know? So I took offence to it and he turned around and I'm yelling at him like you know, "why are you calling me a fucking loser, I didn't do anything to you," know what I mean? So he says if you want to deal with it, we'll deal with it. So I ended up being in a fistfight with this guy I don't even know. It was like, I don't want to fight you. First of all, I'm just not going to sit there while you're calling me a loser — why are you telling her that I'm a loser. Anyways it ended up being a fistfight, and I knew right before I was getting into it that you don't stand a chance. I'm a lot younger than you first of all, second of all you're clearly out of shape — I'm not, and third of all I don't know what your past history is, but I can take one hell of a beating. So…. Yeah. So it was a mistake. I should have known better and to stop, but I didn't stop. [Scott and his co-accused left the scene to eat dinner and returned later.] So we go back and see how the guy's doing and the guy's lying on a bench and we say hey, are you all right? and he's like fuck this. I'm not looking at why the guy's mad, but now you look at it ten years later — the guy just got punched, of course he's gonna be pissed off, you know.

Int.: Yeah.

Scott: So, but I'm not thinking of that, as a kid, you know, and I'm like "you haven't had enough," you know what I mean…. My [co-accused] started beating him. Next thing you know, the next morning I find out the guy's dead….

Int.: So you didn't know this guy at all, and the second altercation—did you take part in it at all?

Scott: Yeah I did, I did. I kicked him, punched him.

Here, too, like Mitch, Scott suggested that the death was an unfortunate
result of a normal "fight." He downplayed his involvement in the second,
fatal assault. The police report said that both accused young men jumped
from an elevated location on to the chest of the victim and later tortured
him with a sharp tool while he was still alive. A fractured rib eventually
punctured his heart, killing him.

Connor was uncertain of his role in the beating death for which he was
convicted. He was high at the time of the murder and said that he remembered nothing about the homicide. He described what he thought happened, based on his co-accused's statements and his memories immediately
after the murder.

Int.: So you think that what happened is that [co-accused] beat this
guy to death, and you …

Connor: Yeah.

Int.: And you didn't intervene? To be fair.

Connor: No. No. I didn't say anything … just, if you say that's what
happened, [co-accused], that's what happened.

Int: You … Did you dump the body?

Connor: No. Nothing.

Int.: Well, if you are in the middle of a swamp…

Connor: The car was still running, the driver was still in the driver's seat.
Uh, um, I ended up, uh, at my girlfriend's. Actually, I remember
coming to the door, the door of the back seat, the back door of
the [car] on [co-accused's] side was open, and I came through
into the swamp, into the water. And that's where I got mud
and…

Int.: You were in the swamp?

Connor. Yes. And I get up and I uh, [co-accused's] not around, and I know [co-accused] is supposed to be with me. So I am yelling for [co-accused]. All I see is the driver sitting there, and I had no idea there was anything wrong with him really, so I walked. I walked.

Int.: You walked away from it?

Connor. Yup. Walked up to where my father lived, which was a farm half an hour from there and I got my step-brother, I got a ride to my brother's and I said to my brother "You have to come with me. I think I'm in trouble." So away we went to the [car] and he said, "Yeah, you're in trouble," and so I told him, "Well, call an ambulance," and I got him to drive to my girlfriend's place, and I said "I'll be here. And uh, you know, whatever happens, happens. Send the police here. Whatever has to happen, has to happen."

The account contained some contradictions. While Connor claimed that he had no idea there was anything wrong with the victim, the fact that he sought help and came back to the scene of the crime suggests he did know something serious had happened. He left out any description of the victim's injuries, and there were few details about what actually killed the victim (although he did tell us that a blunt object and knife were used). Connor had a history of aggressive violence; he had had confrontations with the police before. Because there were no other records of this homicide available to compare to Connor's account, it is unclear if the motive for the homicide was robbery as he suggested. Connor, however, insisted that he did not commit the assault, since the weapon and crime scene had only his co-accused's fingerprints on them.

Although "ordinary" violence was a part of the lives of these young people, in these cases it suddenly became lethal. The reasons for this varied. For some, it was because they used a weapon—Steven had access to a gun, and Phillip used a bat and a kitchen knife. For Ian and Mitch, the murders were different from previous assaults only in the extent of injury they inflicted. They took their "ordinary" violence a bit too far: as Ian put it, "no one ever died before."

Aggressive Risk Taking

Aggressive risk taking is the second category of unplanned homicides. In these deaths, participants were involved in risk-taking behaviour that, when combined with aggressive anger, led to fatal results. These behaviours provided them with excitement and thrills through engagement in potentially dangerous activities. There were only three offenders in this category.

Roots of, Routes to Violence Risk-taking provided both adrenaline-based thrills and status for the three young men in this category. However, it was also linked to feelings of anger, shame, and humiliation resulting from emotional, physical, and/or sexual abuse; neglect; and a life of poverty. It was also linked to how the young men defined their manhood: taking risks meant being powerful and was a proof of their masculinity. Perceived threats to their masculinity made them vulnerable and provided triggers for violent and dangerous behaviour.

Goals of Violent Behaviour This risk-taking behaviour provided participants with thrills, excitement, feelings of power, and an escape from their daily troubles. According to existing research, there is a seductive quality to these intoxicating activities.[3] Risk taking also provided our participants with social status, as peers encouraged, challenged, and applauded them.

Johnny's risk-taking behaviour involved aggression towards others, but its main expression was in playing high-speed "chicken" with friends on back roads. He described driving up behind other cars at stoplights and using his car to push them into the intersection, simply for the thrill of the danger.

> Johnny: Just like I never thought driving like an idiot was a problem, to me it was normal. It was nothing different, nothing new. Even making contact between cars, like my friends and I used to run into each other, like at 75 mph, touching sides on corners. Like going around the corner, trying to get in just before the other car came around the corner. That was a routine thing, we drove between [place] back to [another place], a 25-minute drive, if you didn't almost get killed five times, it had to have been because there were no cars on the road.

> Int.: Like playing chicken or something?

Johnny: Playing chicken or you know, going to pass your buddy and you getting over this hill and you're saying "I'm not gonna let him in, so he better back off," but are we gonna back off—no, we're not, so we're gonna go faster to beat him over the hill; if there's a car then we're all gonna get smoked, but maybe we'll go in the gravel or something—see what happens. Somehow we made it, it was ridiculous.

Int.: But you'd play games and you'd actually touch each other?

Johnny: Yeah, like I said, we'd be going around a corner and if the guy was faster than you, maybe you'd be trying to touch his back end and get him loose, so he'd start to lose control and you could get ahead, to be able to get into or out of the corner before him. This was my favourite. We used to stop at stop-lights in the city and I used to push the other guys out into the traffic, because I had a heavier car; it sounds rather ridiculous, but it was just funny as a kid, because you'd see buddy "oh no," trying to go into reverse and the tires are smoking.

George fought often. He reported not taking his medication for ADHD in order to increase his aggression. He described this as fun and would laugh when his friends told him not to take his medication, so he would be more "out-of-control." He also learned to drive by stealing cars, and was proud of the risks he took learning to drive.

Int.: Okay. So where'd you learn how to drive? You were locked up most of the year.

George: Yeah, that just. Actually, just stolen cars in my project.

Int.: So you didn't have a licence, then?

George: Oh no. To this day I don't have one. I was just in the project, driving. I backed into a house one day by mistake, but eventually, I learned how to drive. [He laughs.]

Int.: How many cars do you think you've stolen?

George: Myself, I'd say I stole about 50. A lot of cars.

For the most part, these risk-taking behaviours had not resulted in serious consequences prior to the homicide. There had been no serious injuries and only limited conflict with school authorities and the police. However, it was when risk taking went too far that our participants ended up killing others.

Immediate Triggers   Often, the participants were challenged or encouraged by peers to continue these activities as the risks mounted. These young men reported that just prior to the fatal risk-taking event, they were feeling angry. Johnny's case of vehicular homicide is illustrative. He was drunk and enraged with the victims (all acquaintances) when he caused an accident that killed them. He told us that he played out his anger with his car and that his car was a weapon. He had been involved in risk-taking activities involving aggressive driving for years. There was little difference the night of the homicide — except that the teens in the other car died.

Int.:   You had to have been feeling something when you were driving that car, like you said, you were pretty angry.

Johnny: I was beyond angry, I can't explain it, but probably like a mad dog. Like if I were a dog, I probably would have been frothing at the mouth. I don't remember the music or what the guys were saying, I know they were talking and stuff and music was playing, but I remember none of it. I was gone.

Int.:   Was that because of the alcohol or the anger?

Johnny: No, because I was so fucking angry, I was so mad; like the true meaning of a mad dog would be, was probably what I was. At that point in time nothing was going to stop me — the only thing that ended the anger was when we crashed; that's when I snapped out of it. From that point on, I remember everything.

The second example of aggressive risk taking was a drive-by shooting. Neither of the young men we interviewed was the shooter in the homicide. One drove the vehicle, and the other shot the gun a number of times, but did not kill anyone. They were angry after losing out on a chance to participate in an armed robbery. Kyle told us that shooting out windows on an urban street, laughing as people ran for cover, vented his frustration and made him feel "like a movie star." The fatal shot apparently was supposed to hit the victim in the buttocks. It missed the mark and killed him. Kyle described the events:

Kyle: Basically, we were just a couple of young punks you know what I mean? Hungry for money, we went to do a break-and-enter, the people came home, and we wanted to get out of the house without hurting anybody. We were confined to a room and [he] locked us in, but we left the room, I was wielding a knife, trying to scare the guy to get back, and eventually we got out, jumped into the [car] and we left. Then we went to a friend's house ... they actually had one of our guns there, without us knowing. [We] flipped a coin to see who'd take the gun, 'cause they wanted to do an armed robbery and [co-accused] was pissed off 'cause we didn't make any money that day. So he wanted to join in but there were already too many men ... as we're driving, I shot out the window at a restaurant and everybody was like "down!" and shit and we got a good laugh out of it, you know what I mean. It was funny; you know what I mean? Shit, to see them move, you know. It was crazy because I coulda hit anybody in there. Then we stopped at [co-accused's] house for a few minutes and after leaving, [co-accused] shot out to show off for his brother, you know, shot his next door neighbour's house, whatever....

Then we all took turns shooting at restaurants and shit, all the way down the strip. We came to the last one where [another co-accused] pulled out the gun, oh yeah, I loaded it up for him, and we're trying to persuade him "fuck, no more, let's get outta here" you know; he's like, "just one more, just one more" and then he ... rolled down the window and he pointed out and shot him, fuckin' idiot; then we went around the block and I looked out and I thought I saw the guy, you know, and that was it.

Int.: So, did you mean to hurt the guy?

Kyle: Well, fuck yeah, he said he was aiming for his back you know, that's what he says, you know. I still don't know, you know what I mean?

Kyle and his friends felt they had power and status (no matter how fleeting) because they had a gun and were willing to use it. They had total control over the people on the street who ducked and scattered to avoid being shot. Kyle said that it was payback time for all the people and institutions that had let him down. His account shows how, for these young men, masculinity was a tenuous thing: it was constructed and defined on a daily basis and was always at risk.[4]

Violent Fantasy-Based Killings

Four of the homicides were planned. In these killings the perpetrators glorified the use of violence, and most fantasized about killing others. Some thought about and planned killing specific others. Some were involved in "war games," in which they played out scenarios of using violence and killing.

Roots of, Routes to Violence Four young men (Allan, Leo, Paul, and Nigel) took part in planned homicides. They had had disparate negative experiences. Allan and Paul both suffered severe emotional abuse at home. Leo was physically and sexually abused. Divorce and frequent moves disrupted Nigel's home life, but he reported no physical, emotional, or sexual abuse. However, as we noted in Chapter 4, he told us that a serious fall had resulted in head injury and that both his parents were recovered alcoholics who had stopped drinking ten years before the homicide. Leo, Allan, and Paul experienced feelings of low self-worth and powerlessness, due to maltreatment at home; they also felt powerless to change their circumstances. Leo could not stop the abuse by his father and brother, Allan could not stop his mother's emotional abuse, and Paul could not stop his family from calling him stupid and treating him as if he were an imbecile. Although Nigel denied maltreatment at home, having two alcoholic parents must have resulted in some negative social experiences. His brain injury also raises questions about both reduced impulse control and inhibitions against using violence. As Leo himself said, the harm suffered by these young men was "almost invisible". Most were in school at the time of the homicide, had few school-based problems, and did not have a history of violent aggression towards others.

Goals of Violent Behaviour   For Paul and Allan, being able to kill someone made them feel powerful and in control. For Leo, the killings were a personal thrill—as if the lives of his victims had no worth and taking them was of little consequence. Nigel claimed that his murder was not planned, although police reports indicated otherwise. He brought a hunting knife to the scene, although his goal was likely to sexually assault his victim.

None of the four had had contacts with the criminal justice system prior to their arrests for murder. Their frustration and anger was channelled into violent fantasies, which, in the end, they played out. Leo had planned how to kill others for years and fantasized about killing and raping. Paul played war games and envisioned himself as a soldier, saving his country and others, and for the first time making his family proud. Allan and his co-accused developed a detailed plan, based on a violent comic, of murder for hire.

Immediate Triggers   The immediate triggers that moved these young men from fantasy to action varied. While Allan reported that his plan was implemented only after one group member (of the seven teens involved in the "murder-for-hire" fantasy) had transgressed group rules and was thereby identified as the victim, Leo said he "just knew it was the right time" to start killing. Paul was brought into a planned murder as the "trigger-man." He agreed to participate because it made him feel powerful and because his normative structure allowed him to see the killing as protecting a weaker person—in this case, a woman who alleged she was a victim of spousal abuse, whom the police apparently could not protect. He said that two women manipulated him into doing the killing for them. Nigel denied planning the homicide, but police reports suggested he both planned it and watched the victim's home for an opportunity to break in when she was home alone.

Leo described moving from fantasy to a double homicide.

Int.: How come you murdered them? What was going on there?

Leo: Well at the time, I don't know, I really had ah, really kind of messed up... it wasn't like you could physically tell. My actions were always the same as they've always been. I was just like fascinated with killing people. I was thinking about it constantly.

Int.: When did that start?

Leo: I don't know. I've always kind of enjoyed the violent stuff and always imagined it, in a daydream kind of way.... But then I started thinking about it in a more realistic way, because I kind of got to know their patterns.... So I kind of got to know their patterns and things, without trying to learn it, it just happened. Then I started thinking about that. One morning ... I woke up ... and kind of knew almost instantly, that yeah, I could do that today.... I kind of thought about my plan.... I started dressing up when I got home, like black jeans, black t-shirt, and I used a black t-shirt like a mask over my face, and I knew [person] had shoe polish, black shoe polish, because she was in the navy cadets or something. So I took some of that and put it on areas of my body that were still undarkened. I put on these camouflage gloves with grips on them, and then I just waited for them to leave. Then I saw them leave, and I took my step-father's crowbar and snuck out around the back of the house, because there's neighbours and stuff across that could see over, you know. I went to their house and I knocked on their door first to see if anyone may have been inside, and nobody was, so I smashed the window, got their gun and just waited for them to come home.

Int.: So help me understand something. At what point did you decide it was going to be them?

Leo: Well actually it was, I wasn't only really planning on just killing them. I kind of had this idea in my head that I would kill all kinds of people and the only weapon I knew was around was at their house. So I thought that if I took their rifle and left their house, they would come home, see that it was stolen, and call the police, so I figured I had to get rid of them. It was that problem, so that's why I killed them.

Int.: So who else were you going to kill?

Leo: Like I said, I was kind of thinking I would kill everybody, like in a daydream kind of way I would kill everybody and do this, and work my way up the hill, all around and then go hide off in the woods somewhere. After they were dead, I couldn't believe it, I didn't enjoy killing them. At the time I didn't really feel anything, I was in a state of shock or some sort of thing. I just couldn't do it, so I cleaned myself up....

Leo developed his violent fantasy world as a child as an escape from the physical and sexual abuse he suffered at the hands of his father and older brother. It is quite common for abused children to dissociate from reality to avoid pain.[5] Leo maintained that he was morally blameless for the murders. He admitted feeling guilty about the few seconds during which his victims suffered, but told us that he had done nothing wrong. He said that the victims were "good people," and, since good people go to heaven, he had done the victims a favour by delivering them there. He was very careful to explain that if he had killed "bad people," he would have been responsible; bad people go to hell, he reasoned.

Allan and his co-accused planned the murder for a couple of months, then went back to school to engage five other students in the planning. The victim was a ward of the state; he was originally part of the murder plan, but became the target after a conflict within the group. Allan described his planning of the murder:

Allan: Yeah. That sort of thing, yeah. But not, you know, well let's kill this guy, that sort of thing. It was just like, well "what if" sort of thing. You know, what if you were going to do this and you know, uh, what kind of weapon would you use, and where would you take him and how would you get rid of a body. You know? That sort of thing. But not any sort of specific thing about who was it going to be, and when it was going to be, and that sort of thing. That came up much later because uh, [victim] ... began telling other people about it, which was like, our one sort of like rule, which was, you know, don't tell anybody about it. And [first co-accused], uh let's see, ... one of the other guys, I forget what his name was, who testified against us, they got really furious at him about this.... But these two were just really mad about it, and so they said no that's it. He's gonna be the one. He's gonna be the victim. Ok, whatever. And everybody just accepted that. And you know, we would set a date, and then it would get put off and get put off. You know, ridiculous things, like somebody didn't bring the right shoes or, you know. Nobody really seemed to take it seriously, you know? And then one day, I was actually getting [second co-accused] really pissed off, 'cause he was, "when are we going to do this? Are we really going to do this? You know, let's do it." Then, like I say, I didn't know about this. This came in through the court proceedings. The day before, he passed a note to [first co-accused], that was the kid's name, the one who was pissed off at [victim], uh that just said "tomorrow" on it, and that was when the final date was decided, and that was it for everybody else.

The truth status in Allan's account was low. He denied being a leader, but all other records indicate that he was one of two ringleaders. He bought a "Rambo"-type knife for the murder, he assisted in getting the victim to the murder site, and he actively participated in the stabbing. His account is replete with attempts to minimize his role and to deflect blame on to both his co-accused and the victim. He recounted the planning and execution of the murder as if it were a game. He accepted little, if any, responsibility for his actions.

Paul was brought into a murder plan as the "trigger man." Although he indicated in the interview that he committed the murder to protect an abused woman, supporting documentation suggested it may have been a murder for hire.

Paul: Yeah, and we went over to [first co-accused]'s basement apartment and that's where [second co-accused] was. That's when they fed me stories — asking what they should do and I — the first thing I said was they should go to the police and what not. They said they'd done that and the police wouldn't help them — couldn't do anything. And from there progressed to — somehow progressed to [second co-accused] asking how to kill — how she could kill him, and they told me about a couple of ways they had tried but not succeeded. And then, I'm not sure where it happened, but somehow it turned to me shooting him and somewhere along the line I just basically, my thought process shut down, and it was kind of like I was in a dream and watching it from a distance — it wasn't really going on, it wasn't really happening.

Int.: Over what period of time was this?

Paul: Over about an eight-hour period. And through the whole
        thing [first co-accused] kept saying how evil he was. How he
        was doing things ... they took me over to [second co-
        accused]'s house where she got it. And I remember them say-
        ing they needed a car, and so I went to see [third co-accused]
        and I said—and something in the back of my head was saying
        this is a dream, this isn't really happening, I'll go see [third co-
        accused] and he'll wake me up. This will all go away and this
        isn't real, this isn't happening. This is a bad dream. And I went
        over to see [third co-accused]. I saw [third co-accused], and he
        basically said yeah, sure, I'll help you.

Nigel's homicide was perhaps the most difficult to understand. He gave
us very little information, insisting that it was the unintended outcome of a
break-in. The police reported that Nigel watched the victim's home, waited until she was home alone, broke in, and then cut the phone lines before
assaulting her in her own bedroom. She resisted, using a small pair of
sewing scissors to try to protect herself; in the ensuing struggle Nigel took
out his hunting knife and slashed her throat. Nigel insisted that he carried
the knife with him at all times because the woods behind his house were
dangerous. He maintained that he did not know that anyone was at home
and that he killed his victim in self-defence. He also insisted that he cut the
phone lines after the homicide to ensure his escape, not before. The police
claimed that Nigel would have known that no one would be coming home
until the children returned from school late in the afternoon.

These planned murders were chilling, but they can be understood as the
ways these youth coped both with the trauma in their lives and with the
negative feelings they had about themselves and others. Their creation of
fantasy worlds allowed them to cope with their feelings of inadequacy and
self-loathing. They escaped into an alternate plane of reality, where they
enforced a superior moral code. At these times, they were masters of their
own universe, omnipotent, and in complete control.[6] The triggers for their
violence were quite different. It is not clear what triggered Leo or Nigel's
assaults: they said "it just seemed like the right time." Paul happened across
two women planning a murder who claimed they needed a protector. This
image fit with his violent fantasies of himself as an avenging hero. Allan's
violent fantasies became increasingly elaborate with the help of his friends;
because one of them violated group norms, he became a victim.

Level of Involvement in the Homicides

What role did these offenders play in the homicides: primary, secondary, or tertiary (see Table 5.4)? Participants were classified as having primary responsibility if they played a major role in the killings, such as pulling the trigger or delivering the fatal blow(s), planning the murder, and luring the victim to the site. If our offenders did not plan the assault or killing and they did not lure or bring the victim to the site, but took part in the assault, they were classified as playing a secondary role. If the perpetrator was present, but did not take part in the assault nor try to stop it, they were classified as having tertiary responsibility. Finally, two offenders claimed that they had no involvement (i.e., they were falsely convicted).

As Table 5.4 indicates, we classified level of responsibility in two ways. The first was based on the level of involvement admitted in the interview. Seven young people admitted primary responsibility, five admitted secondary involvement, five admitted tertiary involvement, and two claimed they had no involvement. The second assessment was derived from the account of the homicide in supporting documents. According to these "official accounts," 15 offenders had taken a primary role, two played a secondary role, and two had a tertiary role. None were identified as having no role; they had all been convicted. Clearly there is a gap between "official" and offender accounts, as the offenders accepted less responsibility for their involvement than the official record assigned them. Five of the seven young people who admitted primary responsibility were sole perpetrators and could not blame anyone else. Two who admitted to primary responsibility (Frank and Walter) had co-accused, but accepted responsibility. This leaves eight people who had primary responsibility, according to the official record, but who admitted to less involvement.

The five participants (Allan, Ian, Mitch, Paul, and Scott) who admitted secondary involvement in the crime placed primary responsibility for the killing on a co-accused. The official records indicated that all five downplayed their responsibility for the homicides. All participated in the assaults, and all were held to have contributed or directly caused the victim's death. Of the five, Ian was the only one convicted of manslaughter, since the courts were unable to sort out which of many blows had led to death, because the victim ultimately died of pneumonia.

Although five participants (George, Connor, Nancy, Susan, and Kyle) admitted to tertiary responsibility, only one—George—was clearly a bystander. He admitted his involvement, although this admission was not

	Method	Role	Admitted Guilt?	Accepted Culpability?
George	gun	Tertiary—drove car. Admitted to tertiary.	yes	Yes—could have stopped car when shooting began, before homicide. No—said they were just young kids, told co-accused not to shoot.
Phillip	knife, bat	Primary—sole perpetrator. Admitted to primary.	yes	Yes—he killed him, he decided to do it. No—mitigating circumstances included drug abuse; victim's assault of girlfriend; fatal stabbing to end suffering. Also, mitigation was supported by official reports and media accounts (victim a predator, perpetrator mentally ill).
Susan	electrical cord, beating	Secondary—held victims, tried to cover up crime. Admitted to tertiary.	no	No—claimed was "caught up in the moment," intimidated by primary co-accused, did what everyone else did, might not even have assaulted the victim.
David	electrical cord, beating	Secondary—beat, tied up victims. Admitted to nothing.	no	No—claimed he was victimized by the criminal justice system; was young; said victim died not from strangulation but because he had asthma.
Kyle	gun	Secondary – shot weapon, joked with main shooter about shooting a person. Admitted to tertiary.	yes	No—claimed youthfulness, was out of control kid, unable to take gun away, would have violated group norms, shooter was "half crazy" and dangerous.
Steven	gun	Primary – sole perpetrator. Admitted to primary.	yes	Yes—said felt guilt, wanted to confess, apologized to family. No—angry because of past; because victim robbed and lied to him; fatal shot was to end victim's suffering.
Bruce	gun	Primary – sole perpetrator. Admitted to nothing.	no	No—claimed he was falsely convicted.
Johnny	car	Primary – driver. Admitted to primary.	yes	Yes—didn't stop after crash; didn't walk away from conflict. No—claimed tried to avoid fatal crash; was angry beyond reason; victims provoked conflict.
Connor	blunt instrument	Uncertain. Admitted to tertiary. Primary – planned murder, lured victim to site, stabbed him with knife.	yes/no	Yes—moral responsibility because someone was dead. No—claimed was high; blacked out; physical evidence suggested co-accused did the killing.
Allan	knife	Admitted to secondary – claimed he did not deliver fatal slashes.		Yes – said he could have walked away from it. No – claimed did not deliver the fatal slash, without which victim would have lived; was on automatic pilot; would not have done this without the influence of his co-accused.

Table 5.4: Participants' Role in Homicide and Reports of Culpability (continued on facing page)

	Method	Role	Admitted Guilt?	Accepted Culpability?
Ian	beating	Primary – beat and kicked the victim. Admitted to secondary – claimed didn't hit him as hard as he could, nor kick him.	yes	No – claimed was high; victim provoked the assault; did not hit victim hard enough and hadn't killed anyone else in his other fights; group norms required revenge.
Mitch	beating with metal cylinder, victim burned	Primary – beat victim, tied him up and gagged him. Admitted to secondary – said co-accused delivered fatal blow.	yes	No – claimed was drunk; co-accused delivered fatal blow; co-accused blamed the murder on him which led to his conviction; "it's a shame."
Leo	gun	Primary – sole perpetrator. Admitted to primary.	yes/no	Yes – said felt bad about inflicting pain on the victims. No – claimed victims were good people, and he "sent" them to heaven (a better place).
Paul	gun	Primary – shooter. Admitted to secondary – said was manipulated/conned into killing.	yes	Yes – said felt guilt, shame, depressed by what he'd done. No – claimed was acting "automatically"; was young and gullible.
Scott	beating kicking	Primary – full participant in the assault; began the assault. Admitted to secondary – said co-accused delivered fatal blows.	yes	No – claimed co-accused primarily responsible; death was an accidental outcome of a "fight," a mistake; he was a kid, didn't intend to kill him.
Frank	gun	Primary – shot victim in head. Admitted to primary.	yes	Yes - said he could have just walked away from the situation. No – claimed had to get rid of the victim because victim was threatening him.
Nancy	knife	Primary – got weapon, lured victim to site, held her during the assault. Admitted to tertiary – claimed did not know what co-accused was going to do.	no	Yes – said made her own decisions. No – claimed was doing time because of her boyfriend's actions; was in a subconscious state; it "just happened"; shouldn't be in for second degree.
Walter	gun	Primary – shooter. Admits primary.	yes	No – claimed intended to rob, not kill; it was co-accused who suggested robbery; it just happened; was in the "wrong place at the wrong time"; made bad choices.
Nigel	knife	Primary – sole perpetrator. Admits primary.	yes/no	No – claimed victim assaulted him and he responded; did not intentionally bring knife to the scene, he just always carried knife; didn't want to kill her.

seriously damaging. Connor admitted to tertiary involvement, specifically being present and not helping the victim, but he claimed that he had blacked out and believed that it was his co-accused who beat the victim to death. He was held primarily responsible in court and received a murder conviction, while his co-accused was convicted only of manslaughter. From the limited records we cannot tell whether Connor was more involved than he admits to. Nancy admitted to being present at the murder, but insisted she was not actively involved. Official records indicated that she planned the assault with her co-accused, obtained the murder weapon, and lured the victim to the murder site. Susan said that she was present at the murder and delivered a single kick to the victim. However, official records placed her in the room where the murder occurred and stated that she played a lead role in the torture of two other victims, who were not killed. Her involvement was closer to secondary than tertiary. Kyle was present at the homicide and admitted that he had loaded the gun and handed it to the shooter; also, he had fired at other people prior to the murder. He refused to accept that he had a role in the killing and felt that his actions did not contribute to the death, since shooting out windows was "all in good fun." What classified his role as secondary was that he loaded the gun and handed it to the shooter.

Two young people denied any responsibility. Bruce alleged he was falsely accused, and David insisted that he knew nothing about what had happened and was unfairly convicted of involvement in the events. If Bruce committed the murder, the evidence suggested that he was the sole perpetrator and would, therefore, have primary responsibility. David seems to have had tertiary involvement in the homicide, since he was involved in some of the abuse of the victim, but not directly in the murder.

Why would our participants' accounts tend to reflect less responsibility than that attributed to them in the official records? There are a variety of reasons. First, they sought to make themselves and their behaviour less repugnant to us as interviewers, to criminal justice system officials (e.g., parole boards, case officer), and to their family members. Furthermore, their version of events helped them to reconcile their behaviour with their sense of themselves as "good" people who had been marginally involved in terrible events. Minimizing involvement was not an option for all our participants. When they were the sole perpetrators, they had no one else to blame for the murders.

A variety of processes are at work here. First, most of our participants were "putting the best face" possible on themselves and their actions. In some cases, they justified their actions by arguing that what makes a person primarily responsible is not involvement in the crime, but delivering the fatal blows. This is true in Allan's case. Although he was involved in planning the murder, luring the victim to the crime scene, and stabbing him, he argued that he was a secondary player because he did not deliver the fatal throat slashing. In other cases, offenders justified their actions by arguing the exact opposite: although they delivered the fatal injuries, they did not plan the homicide. This was what Paul claimed limited his responsibility. Thus, though he shot the victim, others had planned the crime; he believed he was manipulated into doing the killing. These examples illustrate how offenders used features of their crime to attempt to reduce their roles.

One of the dilemmas we faced in assessing the homicide accounts was how to "make sense" of what occurred. In some accounts, participants expressed anger with their victims and said that this anger, as an immediate determinant, provoked the attack. In others, there was no reason given: the murders were described as "just happening."

Popular press coverage and criminal justice system accounts provided some reasons for why the victims were attacked, and some revealing details of the events. Accounts of other witnesses and court transcripts came closer to describing everything that occurred. In the end, it is clear that, although some perpetrators have clear motives for their homicides, others do not. We shall now examine how participants interpreted the events of their homicides and if and to what degree they felt culpable.

Accepting Responsibility (Culpability)

Admitting culpability for a homicide requires that a person identify himself or herself as a murderer. Our society offers two different social constructions of murderers: they are either portrayed as evil, cold-blooded, predatory, and bad—and, therefore, as completely responsible—or as "sad" cases with problems (such as mental illness), which limit their culpability.

Hazel May's study of relatives of people convicted of homicide explored how family members reconciled the offenders' status as murderers with their own understanding of the offenders as good people. The relatives' accounts either referred to factors that mitigated guilt or they accepted that their family member was guilty.[7] In examining our participants' accounts of their homicides, we sought to assess whether or not they admitted culpability for their actions. However, we felt that there might be considerable differences between our participants' perceptions of their crimes and those of

relatives examined in May's study. First, admitting guilt may be more difficult when referring to one's own actions than when referring to the
actions of others. Second, our participants probably had more information
on the nuances of the social interactions that led to the homicides.

Mitigation of culpability allows people to resolve the contradictions
between being a murderer — by definition a "bad" person — and their
sense of themselves as "good." According to May's research, explanations
that mitigate responsibility portray the perpetrator as being unable to control his or her actions, these actions are seen as unusual or irregular, and/or
the victim is "blamed" for the homicide. A person cannot be a murderer if
he or she is not fully responsible or culpable for the actions which led to it.
Accounts claiming unusual actions as the cause of murder are termed
"vocabularies of excuse." They appeal to cultural scripts of accident and illness, such as intoxication, being high, or experiencing a temporary break
from reality. The second option is to blame the victim. May termed this
technique "vocabularies of justification," an attempt to establish that the
victim, to some degree, victimized the offender in the assault through
provocation. Thus, the victim had a significant role in the chain of events
that led to his or her own death. The victim is seen as contravening social
norms, knowing that such violations will cause a negative response, and,
therefore, making him or her at least partially responsible for the consequences.

These mitigating factors — vocabularies of excuse and vocabularies of
justification — may not be mutually exclusive. Indeed, as we shall see (Table
5.5), most of our participants' accounts included use of or reference to both
sets of factors. In contrast to May's findings of the accounts of perpetrators'
relatives, this reflects the perpetrators' more nuanced sense of the homicides
and their need to present themselves as "good."

Mitigation of Culpability: Vocabularies of Excuse
Seventeen participants employed vocabularies of excuse in their accounts
of the homicides. The wide range of excuses offered can be classified into
three categories. In the first, homicides were presented as a negative outcome of diminished responsibility. These participants claimed that alcohol,
drugs, fear, adrenaline, and/or youthful inexperience impaired their judgment. In the second, homicide was presented as a result of a "bad" choice, a
mistake that any person might make. In the third, perpetrators insisted that
they were convicted of homicide because of an incorrect court decision.
The decision was incorrect either because the accused claimed to be

innocent or because they claimed they were guilty of a less serious criminal act.

Diminished Capacity   Excuses that limited the offenders' ability to make "good" decisions or to intervene to stop the killing included being young, being unable (physically or for normative reasons) to stop their co-accused, being drunk or high, and being manipulated by others. George reflected on his involvement in a drive-by shooting:

> George: I was there and I know we were being idiots and being stupid kids, but I know we weren't out to kill. So I can't really say, "[co-accused], you're a fucking idiot, I'm not your friend anymore." I know he didn't want to kill the guy, he just wanted to be a stupid idiot and shoot him in the ass. [He laughs.]

George blamed the death on being "stupid kids," an appeal to a lack of experience and a resulting inability to make reasonable decisions. He also insisted that he could not intervene in the actions of his co-accused as this would be a violation of normative behaviour.

Allan blamed his involvement on his companion. Although he was actively involved in planning the murder, he said it only escalated into action because of his co-accused.

> Int.: Looking back on the homicide, what could have prevented it? Little picture, big picture...

> Allan: Well, that's kind of hard to say because looking back on it from now, if I was who I am now, obviously I could have prevented it, but what could have prevented it at the time?... If [co-accused] had never moved in, if ... well, see there's another thing. There are certain things. I can only know what I could have done. Things like if I had killed myself, I know it wouldn't have happened. I just know that I wouldn't have been involved with it. You know, that sort of thing. I mean, I don't know if removing myself from the situation would have been enough to stop it happening. Now at the time of the offence, if I had turned around and walked out, that probably would have stopped it right then. But that doesn't mean it wasn't going to happen again later. You know, that sort of thing. Um, I mean,

left to my own devices, it probably wouldn't have happened, not because [co-accused] is like worse or more violent or something. I was just so … um, bogged down, you know, so I could have gone the rest of my life without doing a single thing about anything, so having this, probably never would have. I didn't have any sort of … there is too much inertia, you know. I wasn't doing anything, or going anywhere, I didn't care about anybody. Left to my own devices this [planning and carrying out a murder] never would have come to anything, but talking about it.

Allan presented himself as an inactive person. Although he admitted to having a fantasy about being a killer, he insisted that on his own he would not have acted. He was not responsible for giving in to peer pressure to commit murder; his co-accused was responsible for exerting that pressure.

Mitch and his co-accused were planning on robbing their victim of his drugs and $7000 in cash. Mitch also attributed primary responsibility for the homicide to his co-accused. Six times in his account he indicated that he was drunk, an appeal to diminished responsibility. To Mitch, being drunk meant he did not care, as he normally would, about his and his co-accused's actions. As we saw earlier in this chapter (p.153), Mitch claimed that it was a "big joke to me. I'm drunk, I was hammered." A number of our participants (Phillip, Johnny, Nancy, and Scott, as well as Mitch) were high or drunk at the time of the homicide and said that this contributed to the killing. Only Nancy noted that intoxication was no excuse for her actions.

Some participants (Susan, Steven, Johnny, Allan, Paul, and Nancy) said they were out of control—driven by anger or fear or caught up with the adrenaline of the moment—during the homicide. Susan described a slow build-up to increasing violence in the days before the murder and what led her to continue her involvement as events became more and more brutal, culminating in a situation beyond normal understanding. She explained this in physiological terms.

Int.: Help me understand, from your perspective.

Susan: It was to fairly, safely explain, you could never understand it unless you've been through a similar situation. Not a murder, but a situation that involves consistent adrenaline; adrenaline to the point that you're not seeing properly or you're not thinking properly; you're ... it's completely go with the flow. There's not even a better saying for it. It was just go with the flow. You're just so caught up in the moment, so much adrenaline, nobody was thinking, and it just got hectic. Actually now, reflecting back, ... those of us that are smart, or regretful, were happy the police came when they did because, had they not, you know, maybe the rest [would have] died. It was a definite good thing they did come.

Int.: So, was it like you were in a different world when this was going on?

Susan: It's not a different world, it was a time zone. It's not about the world, it's about time. I can't, watching a movie, you know when you see a slow motion, that's exactly what it was like. Everything I was seeing was moving like that, even when I was alone in the bathroom, it was like going to the washroom took me five minutes, where it was only 30 seconds, 'cause we were only in there 16 minutes. So it was a definite time lapse; it was just so fucked up that it's hard to explain. Shit, I should have known better, I should have called the police, I should have tried to stop it. There's so many things I should have done, but I didn't. There's so many things everybody else should have done, but they didn't. Nobody did. Everybody was involved and everybody got caught up in it. Some were more involved than others, and some of them were just sort of followers. Some were just present. You see there's the leaders, the followers, and the present. I was in between the present and the followers.

Susan and Ian argued that group norms meant they could neither interfere nor walk away. Ian was involved in a beating death. According to him, the victim provoked it by throwing a bottle and almost hitting his co-accused's girlfriend. The norm, said Ian, was to defend one's woman. So his co-accused was required to attack the victim, and Ian had to help, or at least not intervene. The victim was a homeless alcoholic in his 60s, and the assailants were teenaged boys.

Ian: The thing is I couldn't stop [co-accused] because what would I have done if that had been my girlfriend. I would've stopped that fight there and then, but it's not, if it was over a lighter, yes, I'd jump in and beat [victim's] head up, yank him off. If somebody smashed my girlfriend's face, I'd smash him, I know I would. I wouldn't let it get too far, I didn't think it had gone too far.

The participants presented their actions as temporary aberrations, which should, therefore, be excused. Indeed, this theme of their behaviour as "temporary" was emphasized when they said they would not allow themselves to get back into such situations. Some said they were now "grown up" and beyond the risk of youthful high jinx; some said they had been manipulated and were now "stronger" people and immune to such pressures; others said they were no longer using drugs or alcohol.

Two perpetrators could have used the excuse of mental illness to diminish their culpability, but did not. Nancy and Phillip had both spent time in psychiatric hospitals. In fact, Phillip's mental illness and the victim's history of being a sexual predator were used in newspaper coverage of the crime to mitigate his responsibility. But Phillip did not accept this.

Int.: The papers certainly pulverized him [victim].

Phillip: For three or four days they did papers on the guy. I was surprised by that too. They weren't doing a whole lot of bashing of me, and they were doing a whole lot of bashing of him, which made me very uncomfortable. 'Cause here I'm sitting in my guilt, and they make him out to be the felon, and sort of blaming my side of it as falling through the cracks of the system. Saying I should've got more help in these institutions, why couldn't they help him [Phillip], why did it have to come to this?

Why did these two not use this excuse? Probably they wished to avoid the stigma of mental illness, a stigma more lasting than the conviction for homicide. Being labelled "mentally ill" suggests that they are likely to be dangerous throughout their illness, perhaps throughout their lives. This could result in indefinite confinement to a psychiatric hospital. Nancy's past experiences with the mental health system were quite negative, and she was distrustful and disdainful of psychiatric diagnoses. Phillip felt that his mental condition was not a factor. He clearly linked the death to his violent behaviour.

"Bad Choices" Other offenders indicated that their *choices* resulted in death. They qualified this, however, by claiming that they had made one or more *bad* choices: what under the circumstances seemed correct proved in hindsight to be wrong. Steven and Phillip reported that they chose to kill their victims in order to end their suffering after the initial assault.

> Steven: I went over to where the water was and I had the gun, and I sort of realized he was caught because he was stuck in the water and mud. So then he turned towards me and started walking out of the water, saying "no I didn't do it," and on and on. That was the worse thing to do because I've got this gun, and I just shot him at that point in his general direction, and I guess I got him in the chest. He went down, and then it was a weird sort of transition at that point, the anger's gone out, and I'm in shock at this point. Like what has happened and what I've done and the series of events and I'm still not quite comprehending it, and then he's down and I can hear that he's still alive. He's just taken the shot blast, and we used to play with this gun, so I knew what it was capable of. It was a 12-gauge shotgun and that close can do some real damage. So he's down and he's sort of talking to himself, and very quiet, and I'm thinking "holy shit, what the hell am I gonna do?" I didn't think too much about it though. I thought a little bit, but at that point, and this isn't a justification or whatever, in my mind I had already shot him and killed him, but I realize he's still alive and probably gonna die. They said that the second shot was fatal. So I figure wow, he's hurt, I'm just gonna end it real quick, and so I shot him again in the head, and that was it.

Phillip's account, detailed at the beginning of Chapter 1, was quite similar. After the initial assault had caused serious injury, he decided to kill the victim to prevent further suffering; as far as he was concerned, his murder was an act of mercy.

Walter shot a store clerk in the head during an attempted robbery. In his account he attributed blame to everyone (note his use of "we" when refer-

ring to firing the first shot), although he was the sole shooter. He concluded his account of the killing by describing it as a "mistake":

> Int.: So tell me what happened?

> Walter: What at the verdict? You don't want to hear this.

> Int.: You don't want to tell me?

> Walter: Well I'll tell you this, there were four of us, we had a feeling
> something crazy was gonna happen that day. We ended up at
> [place] ... and one of my co-accused walked into the [store]
> and decided to rob the place. I pulled up and said "give us the
> fucking money." He [victim] didn't know what to do, he's in
> shock, so we tell him "give us the fucking money." He's still in
> shock, so we pop him in the head and he falls down, so I
> popped him again. We jumped in the car and went to the
> [place]. We passed out for a while and some of them went back
> to [place] where we got arrested.

> Int.: How come you decided to do an armed robbery ...?

> Walter: It was just one of those things. We talked about it a few times
> and next thing you know it happened.

> Int.: That particular [day]?

> Walter: No, it just happened, just like that. Something you wish you
> could change but you can't. It's just one of those things in my
> life that I made a mistake in.

What these accounts have in common are references to decisions as bad
choices — and we all know that everyone makes bad choices. Making a bad
choice is a culturally acceptable explanation for excusing someone of
responsibility for negative actions. The different accounts here show how
this script was stretched. It must have been difficult for these offenders to
sustain a belief that choosing to shoot someone in the head was a "mistake." It might be possible to accept that killing someone to end their pain
and suffering is an understandable, if still wrong, choice. However, it is

difficult to accept such a rationalization when the person who caused the suffering then uses it as an excuse for murder.

The participants also excused their behaviour as "bad choices" by insisting that they had no prior intent to kill. Someone died, but, since they didn't mean to kill, they were not really responsible for the death. What led up to the killings was a series of bad choices with unexpected ends. Nigel's account reflected this rationale; it was particularly chilling.

Int.: How did you break in?

Nigel: The door was unlocked. It was. So, I just walked in and I was going around, and uh, looking in jars on the kitchen counter, you know, where people might hide cash kind of thing. Uh, I went upstairs, checked the rooms out up there, uh. Found some, you know, peanut change, you know, 10–20 bucks, was downstairs searching bedrooms down there, and I walked into one bedroom and um, she was lying in the bed, and she woke up and started yelling, "what the fuck you doing here?" kind of thing. "Get the fuck out of my house!" And, [I] was just oh, froze, you know. Didn't know, you know, what the fuck to do. And then she reached on to her night table and grabbed a pair of scissors and came at me. And uh, I was trying to block off some of the holes. I got scars from being stabbed. Uh, I just happened to have a knife in my pocket, so I pulled it out and I stuck her in the throat, and she backed off a bit. I tried to get up, and I tripped. Fell down again. She came at me again, tried to stab me, and that's where I got this scar from. It was cut deep, down to here, down to the bone. There is a little mark here actually, where it went in through there and came out, started to come out through the other side.

Int.: What kind of knife did you have on you?

Nigel: It was a hunting knife with a blade where you bring it up, uh....

Int.: Okay.

Nigel: She was still trying to stab me and she was clawing at my face, and I was on the floor trying to get up, trying to get out, and stabbed her a few more times. I don't remember quite all of it to be honest with ya, and the next thing I know I am standing there and she is dying in front of me, and I am all covered in blood, and I panicked and ran over and cut the line to the phone. I don't know why. It was some kind of panic thing. I'm in deep shit now, kind of thing. I cut the phone, so I can get away. If I can get far away, they won't get me kind of thing. I mean, I didn't mean to kill her. It's, I don't even like the sight of my own blood. Uh, just panicking…. Ran into the bathroom and threw up all over the fucking place and I jumped in the shower and tried to wash the blood off me. It's uh, don't know why, but it's all I could think of to do.

Later, Nigel explained that his knife was for general protection in the woods outside his home and that he always had it with him. Why did he offer this information? He could not retain the image of the homicide as unintentional when he came to the house armed. Nigel went over in minute detail the small scars on his hand, injuries he claimed to have suffered from his victim's "attack." Her "weapon" was a pair of very small sewing scissors.

In these cases, our participants said that they could be excused from responsibility either because they made a bad choice that led them to kill or because they acted incorrectly but had formed no intent to kill. In other words, their bad choices led to the immediate circumstances that resulted in the death.

Incorrect Court Decisions   Four participants claimed that the criminal justice system had made a mistake either in convicting them at all (Bruce and David) or in convicting them of homicide (Susan and Nancy). Both our female participants were in this latter category. These young women presented themselves as adjuncts to the killings — they claimed that they were not in control of the situation, but at the mercy of decisions made by others. They admitted they did something "bad," but did not take responsibility for the charge for which they were convicted. Nancy insisted that she and others who were familiar with the criminal justice system felt she was incorrectly convicted of murder.

Int.:   Was it fair that you got convicted of second [degree murder]?

Nancy: Um, I think I should be in jail. I agree that I should have been sentenced to jail, yeah. There has to be consequences. I believe in the justice system, I believe in laws, and I believe in rules and stuff. 'Cause I think if there were no rules there'd be chaos. However, upon speaking with different court ... like people like that and stuff and people who know the story, they say that I should not have been convicted of second degree murder, and that if the lawyer that I had would have spent the time on my case that he should have, that I never would have been convicted of second degree murder.

Int.: What would you have been convicted of?

Nancy: They said maybe manslaughter or aiding and abetting.

Yet, Nancy was clear earlier in the interview that she was responsible for her own actions.

Nancy: Um, I think when I first came to jail I was mad because I blamed him [co-accused]. I thought it was all his fault that I was here. But now I don't blame him for anything, 'cause really — I make my own decisions and nobody can force me to do anything.

Int.: So if that's the case — that you make your own decisions, and nobody can force you to do anything — it seems to me, what you're telling me is you still don't know much about your involvement in this.

Nancy: I know what I did.

Like the others in this category, Nancy did not see her actions as constituting second-degree murder. The official account contradicts this. According to it, Nancy held the victim down, baring her throat so her co-accused could slit it.

David was extremely angry about his conviction. Originally charged with manslaughter and a slew of other offences, he was convicted of lesser charges, including kidnapping and forcible confinement. He said the system punished him unjustly. He told us that although he was present, he

Excuse		Participants who used excuses
Youthfulness	▶	George, David, Kyle, Paul, Scott
Couldn't stop co-accused	▶	George, Susan, Kyle, Allan, Mitch, Scott
Drunk or high	▶	Phillip, Connor, Ian, Mitch
Mentally ill	▶	Available to two (Nancy and Phillip); used by neither
Manipulated by others	▶	Phillip, Paul
Out of control	▶	Susan, Steven, Johnny, Allan, Paul, Nancy
Criminal justice system made a mistake	▶	Susan, David, Bruce, Nancy
End victim's suffering	▶	Phillip, Steven
No intent to kill	▶	Ian, Paul, Nancy, Walter, Nigel
Made bad choices	▶	Paul, Walter
Group norms	▶	Susan, Ian

Justification		Participants who used justification
Victim was sexual predator	▶	Phillip - noted in interview but did not use it as defence. Paul gave it as a reason he agreed to kill victim.
Victim provocation	▶	Johnny, Ian, Frank, Scott, Nigel
Victim robbed/lied to perpetrator	▶	Steven
Victim harassed perpetrator	▶	Mitch

Reasons given for accepting culpability		Participants who accepted culpability
Made a choice which resulted in death	▶	George, Phillip, Johnny, Allan, Nancy
Felt remorse or admitted murder was wrong	▶	Steven, Connor, Paul

Table 5.5: Vocabularies of Excuse, Justification, and Acceptance of Culpability

didn't participate in any way in the tortures or murder. However, official records clearly show that he joined in the beating of the murder victim and the torturing of another young person who did not die.

David spent 26 months in custody prior to his conviction and claimed that he got no credit for his remand time. It is unclear from the official records if this was, indeed, the case. David was focussed on what had been done to him, not what he was convicted of doing. Like the other offenders in this category, he had an external locus of control: the "system" was always out to get him, and there was nothing he could ever do to change this.

Bruce was the only participant who claimed he was completely innocent. While we have included his case in vocabularies of excuse, it is important to remember that he might indeed *be* innocent. Bruce attributed his conviction to the actions of the police.

Int.: Looking back on it, what could have prevented you from getting involved in the death of [the victim]? Like does it all go
back to school and not going to school or ...?

Bruce: It comes back to cops I think. There was a problem with
school, I agree with you there. You know what I mean? Growing up in a biker's household let's say, and the cops beating up
on you, then was the clincher. I may have had a disability. I
may not. I can't prove it so I can't really say for sure. I know
what I went through and I know I couldn't retain anything,
and you had to go to school, you know what I mean? I wanted
to get out and get away from school, find out something to
earn money with. You know what I mean? It's not a legal job,
legal jobs get taken away from you, so I went the drug route.
Popularity, hey I'm not dumb anymore, I'm not stupid. You
know what I mean?

Bruce had been offered a job, but failed to pass a criminal records check;
he blamed the police for this. This led, from his perspective, to his becoming involved in drug dealing with the homicide victim and his availability
as a suspect. He insisted that witnesses changed their statements and were
allowed to collude with one another to create a stronger case for the prosecution.

Mitigation of Culpability: Vocabularies of Justification
Eight participants employed vocabularies of justification: their victims were
blamed for provoking the assault that resulted in homicide. In seven of
these accounts, this blame was tied to normative understandings of violent
youth subcultures, such as seeing the victim as a sexual predator and an
abuser of women.

Paul was involved in a murder for hire. Two adult women convinced
him to kill an alleged wife abuser. Paul was told that the police refused to
help, leaving one of the women (a co-accused) with no other option. As
we saw earlier in this chapter, Paul came to her rescue and killed the alleged
abuser. After describing the killing, Paul said, "My thought process shut
down, and it was kind of like I was in a dream and watching it from a distance. It wasn't really going on, it wasn't really happening." The interview
continues:

Int.: When you first killed this man you thought that he had sexually assaulted someone and, I can't remember, a whole bunch of
other things....When did you find out that it wasn't true?

Paul: I don't know. I didn't want to believe that it wasn't true for a
very long time. I think I finally actively consciously admitted
to myself that it was all a bunch of lies probably when I was
arrested.

As well as citing rules that allowed violence in response to an attack on
oneself, someone weaker, or a woman you felt responsible for protecting,
participants believed that violence could be used against someone who lied
to you, stole from you, owed you drug money; or who verbally attacked
you by calling you a "goof," or "stupid"; or who questioned your "honour"
or integrity. In all these cases the "victim" had broken the rules, and the
offender—who was injured or accepted responsibility for the person
injured—had the right to use violence. In some cases, the use of violence
was deemed more than acceptable; it was necessary. The offenders said that
refusing to fight, walking away, or calling the police would have resulted in
a loss of status and/or expulsion from the peer group. In this superior
moral code, status and honour ruled: one could not be physically and
socially vulnerable. The need to use violence was re-enforced by a rule of
not ratting on others to out-of-group authorities.

Scott and his co-accused killed a mentally ill person living on the street.
Scott said the victim had a pair of panties in his pocket, suggesting he was a
sexual pervert. Scott initiated the "fight" to protect his honour because the
victim provoked him, calling him stupid in front of his girlfriend and other
peer group members. This made Scott feel bad and signalled, in his opinion, a challenge to fight, although Scott was clearly younger and fitter than
the victim. Scott found more and more ways to excuse and justify his
behaviour. Although he said that assaulting the murder victim was a "mistake," he blamed the death on the victim for continuing to fight, on his co-
accused, and on his own (Scott's) youthfulness.

Scott: Yeah. So it was a mistake. I should have known better (and) to
stop, but I didn't stop. So, and I kept telling the guy "stay down,
stay down" and he kept trying to get back up and he kept taking swings and everything else. It was embarrassing. It was real-

ly embarrassing because a cat and dog fight, you know like who's gonna win — you know the dog's gonna win. So it ended up we left, he was alive and my [co-accused] — he just got out of jail and he's getting all nervous. "Oh the guy's going to identify us," and blah, blah, blah, and I said " listen we'll go back and see how he's doing", that's it. So we go back [after eating dinner] and see how the guy's doing and the guy's lying on a bench and we say "hey, are you all right?" And he's like fuck this. I'm not looking at why the guy's mad, but now you look at it ten years later — the guy just got punched, of course he's gonna be pissed off, you know?

Int.: Yeah.

Scott: So, but I'm not thinking of that, as a kid, you know, and I'm like "you haven't had enough?" You know what I mean. So when I left, when we were leaving again, and my [co-accused] picked up the bike … it was my bike actually, he picked it up and he just threw it on the [victim]. Now I used to always carry a [heavy tool] on the back or someplace, then I notice halfway home my [tool is] missing. So I went back and my [co-accused] … started beating him.…

Int.: So you didn't know this guy at all and the second altercation — did you take part in it at all?

Scott: Yeah I did, I did. I kicked him, punched him.

Scott left out a few details. Official records indicated that it was Scott, not his co-accused, who took the lead in the beating and tortured the victim with a sharp tool as he lay dying. These details made his role less socially acceptable and the murder victim more pathetic.

Frank shot his victim in the head while he slept. While he admitted that he could have just "walked away," Frank told us that, at the time, he felt the victim got what he deserved. The three co-accused had just discovered that the victim had been stealing from them; they were all involved in organized criminal activity, and he threatened to go to the police if Frank and his co-accused did not give him a portion of their share of the criminal proceeds.

The night of the homicide, the victim attacked Frank and his co-accused in their apartment. He tied them up, ransacked the apartment, and eventually went to sleep on the couch. Frank managed to get free.

Int.: So you got free, the other two were still tied up.

Frank: Well, I got them loose. I just grabbed my gun. As soon as I got them loose I grabbed my gun, went to the living room to see if anything was there. He was there. I shot him, the other guy shot him, and that was it.

Int.: He still had a weapon?

Frank: No, he was laying down sleeping. I think he was sleeping any ways, I don't know.

Int.: So you shot him....

Frank: Shot him in the head.

Int.: And the other guy shot him.

Frank: Yeah.

Int.: In the head too?

Frank: Yeah.

Int.: Then what happened?

Frank: Then we went and ate.

Int.: You went and had breakfast?

Frank: Went and had breakfast 'cause we was hungry. People thought in the court that that was weird. I said how can that be weird 'cause we're smoking the joints and on acid all that night and by the time you get hungry, you get hungry. And as far as I'm concerned like what was going through my mind when I had to get rid of the problem, he was the problem. And how I got rid of it was to get it eliminated completely. I couldn't deal with the threat of the guy holding this information over my head and coming to me any other time and saying well, if you don't give me this I'm going to the cops about this and this.

Frank saw the victim as a threat, as a problem that had to be "gotten rid of." Had the victim not assaulted Frank and not threatened to tell about their mutual illegal activities, there would have been no need to kill him. The truth status of Frank's account was high. Official records supported his version of events.

Conclusion

Homicides are complex events. Our participants arrived at the point where they murdered someone through diverse paths. In the unplanned homicides, the immediate context provided triggers for young people's use of violence or for their reckless behaviour. But the choice to use violence at the time of the homicide was tied to their adoption of violence and aggression towards others as a strategy for coping with their circumstances.

Participants used violence, in part, because for them it worked. This is an instrumental understanding of violent behaviour. In the short term, violence provided them with a means to control their situation, to force others to comply with their wishes, and to improve their individual circumstances. Violence worked because it prevented them from being bullied by others, or it gave them status and power; it allowed them to have some control over their lives. To some it gave pleasure (Scott and Leo reported that they enjoyed hurting or imagining hurting others). Choosing to use violence was also, for some participants, a component of how they viewed masculinity. That is, violence was part of their cultural understandings of how men should act in particular situations: physically tough, aggressive, and in control. Yet, they lived lives where they had been victimized, were vulnerable, and were unable to control what happened. Using violence, as men, was one option for creating at least the illusion of control and power, one way to assert that they were "real" men. Finally, the thrill of using violence was also a component of risk-taking, an example of what Jack Katz termed the seduction of crime.[8]

Involvement in violent sub-cultures and using violence or risk-taking aggression towards others put some participants in unsafe situations. The use of violence, in and of itself, put them at risk for injuring and perhaps killing others. Their code provided situations where they felt that using violence was justified. For some, like Scott, violence was his only tool for dealing with the challenges of the world. He used violence in most situations in which he felt threatened or sought to feel powerful. For others, violence was used more narrowly, to settle drug debts or other scores. In all these cases, the use of violence meant the potential of serious injury to or the death of someone. The histories of violent acting were warnings of that risk. All too often, the behaviour was responded to with suspensions, expulsions, and arrests, but the root causes were not addressed.

Some young people coped with the problems in their lives through violent fantasies. Here they could be powerful heroes or seek revenge on others. For these young people, the extent of their personal trauma was almost invisible to the outside world. The decision to use violent fantasies as a coping mechanism did not inevitably lead to the actual homicides. Participants chose to put their plans into action, and they were responsible for these choices. What pushed them into acting out their violence was linked to their specific fantasy world. Paul sought to play the hero, and others exploited this belief; Allan and his co-accused had a plan and then a suitable victim; Leo simply thought that it was time to act; and Nigel had opportunity to get to his victim when she was alone. These participants appeared to be less dangerous to others; indeed, most seemed to be quiet, well-mannered people. Some evidence of personal problems was present, but, for the most part, they did not appear to have serious problems or to pose a risk to themselves or to others.

Most participants were reluctant to admit complete responsibility for the homicides. Those who were not sole perpetrators chose to blame their co-accused and to claim that they had had a minor role in the deaths. They also sought to excuse and justify their behaviour. Victims were blamed for provoking assaults or were vilified as being "bad" people not worthy of sympathy. Participants indicated that they were drunk or high or too young to be fully responsible for their actions. These excuses and justifications represented their attempts to deal with being identified as murderers and hence as "bad" people themselves, in contrast to their self-image of being "good." They were, very simply, not stereotypical murderers. But, as this study indicates, it seems that the stereotype we have of murderers is incorrect.

Notes

1   See Totten, 2000a, 2001b.
2   See the quotation at the beginning of Chapter 1.
3   Totten, 2000a, 2001b; Katz, 1988.
4   Totten, 2000a, 2001b.
5   Bass and Davis, 1988; Lew, 1990.
6   See Totten, 2000a; Katz, 1988.
7   May, 1999.
8   Katz, 1988.

Charged and Convicted: Experiences in Custody and the Community

Introduction

In this chapter we examine the custodial and release experiences of our participants. Sentencing and custodial experiences were affected by the legislation that young people were convicted under and the type of crimes committed. Custodial assignments, particularly whether young people were tried as youth or adult offenders and whether they were held in youth or adult facilities, were also important in shaping their experiences, as were remand time (time spent in custody prior to conviction), sentence length, and treatment and programs received in custody.

Legislation: The Legal Response to Youth Crime

The legal response to young people in conflict with the law and in particular to those who commit homicide has changed dramatically over the past 150 years. The earliest legislation on youthful offenders dealt only with the separate incarceration of youth, defined as persons younger than 16 years of age. Youthful offenders were subjected to the same legislation as adults and hence to the same penalties; for murder, this included capital punishment. The 1908 Juvenile Delinquents Act (JDA) shifted the focus away from the criminal responsibility of youthful offenders to their social welfare needs. It covered a diverse group, including youth in conflict with the law, youth experiencing abuse and neglect, runaways, and children truant from school. This focus on social welfare needs was not extended automatically to youth charged with homicide. Children as young as 14 years of age were eligible for transfer to adult court for this crime. In 1984, the Young Offenders Act

(YOA) came into effect. The YOA began a return to a legalistic response to youth in conflict with the law, while still focussing on their social needs.

The Juvenile Delinquents Act

Legislation specific to juveniles emerged in Canada in the middle of the nineteenth century. John Hylton notes the passage, in 1857, of two federal acts on juvenile offenders.[1] The first, "An Act for the Speedy Trial and Punishment of Juvenile Offenders," instituted bail provisions and limited pre-trial detention time. The second, "An Act for the Establishment of Prisons for Young Offenders," provided for the construction of two youth reformatories (one in Upper and one in Lower Canada). Youthful offenders were charged with the same offences as adult offenders, tried in adult courts, and subject to the same penalties as adults. In 1894 the Criminal Code was amended to provide separate trials for "young persons apparently under the age of sixteen years," and for "their incarcerations, prior to sentence, separately from older persons."[2]

The JDA defined a child as "... a boy or a girl apparently or actually under the age of sixteen years[,]" with a lower age limit of seven years. The JDA also had a provision allowing the provinces to raise the upper age limit for juvenile delinquents to 18. As a result, the upper age limit varied from province to province. It was set at under 16 years in Prince Edward Island, Nova Scotia, New Brunswick, Ontario, and Saskatchewan; under 17 years in Newfoundland; and at under 18 years in Quebec, Manitoba, and British Columbia. In Alberta, the age limit was higher for girls (18 years) than for boys (16 years) for some period of time.[3]

The Act included criminal offences, but also non-criminal status offences such as truancy and incorrigibility. The inclusion of status offences created a problem for legislators. They had the power to legislate responses to criminal offences, but not non-criminal status offences, which were under the jurisdiction of the provinces. The solution was to create a new criminal offence of "delinquency," which included acts committed by young persons between the ages of seven to 15 who were in violation of the Criminal Code and federal and provincial statutes covered under the JDA. The legislation provided for the establishment of separate juvenile courts and the requisite juvenile detention facilities. It initiated the practice of holding hearings that were closed to the public to protect the child's identity in the belief that juvenile delinquents were "... not criminal[s] [but] misdirected child[ren] ... needing aid, encouragement, help and assistance."[4]

Children charged with homicide offences were included under the JDA. However, the JDA allowed for children 14 years of age or older charged with indictable[5] offences (including murder, manslaughter, and infanticide) to be transferred to adult court, tried, and punished as adults. The provisions for transfers to adult court are contained in Section 9 of the 1929 Act (previously section 7):

> 9 (1) Where the act complained of [the crime the offender is alleged to have committed] is, under the provisions of the *Criminal Code* or otherwise, an indictable offence, and the accused child is apparently or actually over the age of fourteen years, the Court may, in its discretion, order the child to be proceeded against by indictment in the ordinary courts in accordance with the *Criminal Code* in that behalf; but such course shall be in no case followed unless the Court is of the opinion that the good of the child and the interest of the community demand it.
>
> 9 (2) The Court may, in its discretion, at any time before any proceeding has been initiated against the child in the ordinary criminal courts, rescind an order so made.[6]

Children transferred to adult court under Section 9 were treated as adults — they were subjected to adult penalties and incarcerated in adult penal facilities.[7] For the three youth in our study tried and convicted of homicide as adults when the JDA was in effect, this meant life sentences. The adult system had a set of provisions related to early release and parole that were not available to children held under the JDA.

Parole is an important component of sentencing. Parole is defined in the Corrections and Conditional Release Act as allowing an offender to be "at large" during the period of the sentence. When offenders are released on parole they must report to their parole officer and must abide by specific conditions. If they breach parole conditions (violate parole) they are returned to custody to continue serving their sentence. Thus a "life" sentence is indeed surveillance for life, although this may occur in the community if parole is granted. Eligibility for release to the community is variable. The current parole ineligibility periods for life sentences are 25 years for first-degree murder and a minimum of ten years to a maximum of 25 years for second-degree murder. There is provision in the Criminal Code for offenders sentenced to a 25-year ineligibility period to apply for parole after 15 years in custody — the so-called "faint hope" clause.

The Young Offenders Act (YOA)

The YOA marked a significant shift in the philosophy guiding Canadian juvenile justice legislation from a child-welfare approach towards a legalistic approach.[8] Under the YOA the focus is the youth's violation of the Criminal Code, although the response to the young person continues to reflect the "special" needs of the adolescent offender. The YOA also modified the age of criminal responsibility, excluding children under 12 years and setting the upper limit at 17 years.[9] It also includes provisions for due process rights—affording young people the rights and freedoms guaranteed to adults and requiring that they be informed of their rights. On the positive side, these due process guarantees ensure that children are protected from arbitrary interference in their lives.

The provisions of the YOA covering homicide offences have been of particular concern since it was first enacted.[10] It is important to note that these provisions apply only to young offenders who are tried as young offenders, not for those who are transferred to adult court, where they are subjected to adult sentences with some modifications of the parole provisions. The YOA also has provisions (modified in 1986) for transferring young people to adult correctional facilities when they reach 18 years of age. If they have two years or more left to serve, they may be transferred to a federal penitentiary; if they have less than two years, they may be transferred to a provincial adult correctional facility.[11] The legislation does not require automatic transfer to adult facilities at age 18. Some of our participants were transferred to adult facilities before the age of 18; some were transferred at a later age.

Under the original provisions of the YOA, a young person tried and convicted of homicide in youth court was subject to a maximum sentence of three years. Concern was raised that the sentence length was too short to provide either adequate rehabilitation or to act as a deterrent to others, so the sentencing provisions were reviewed and modified in 1991.[12] The new provisions extended the period of custody for young people tried in youth court to five years less a day (three in custody and two years less a day under community supervision). The amended YOA also included a provision for holding a youth in custody for more than three years if he or she was deemed to be a threat to the public. The maximum youth court sentences were increased again in 1995.[13] These changes increased the sentence for first-degree murder convictions in youth court to ten years—six years in custody and four years of conditional supervision. The maximum sentence for second-degree murder was seven years: four years in custody and three years of conditional supervision. The penalties are different if a young offender is transferred to adult court. Nicholas Bala writes that:

> The result of a transfer order is that the young person will thereafter be dealt with in the adult court (or "ordinary court" as it is referred to in the YOA). In the event of conviction in the adult court, the youth may face penalties imposed under the *Criminal Code* rather than the more limited dispositions found in section 20 of the YOA, as well as the possibility of incarceration in an adult correctional facility, though there are provisions that may result in a youth facing a less severe punishment than an adult even after transfer.[14]

Under the 1984 YOA, youth transferred to adult court faced adult sentences of life imprisonment with no eligibility for parole for 25 years for first-degree murder and for ten to 25 years for second-degree murder. Youth transferred and convicted served their sentence in adult facilities. Sandra Bell notes that under the YOA "... judges could choose only between the extremes of a three-year sentence or a life sentence in adult court."[15] In response to this concern, the 1991 revisions remained the same, but the parole eligibility criteria were lowered from an automatic ten years for second-degree murder and 25 years for first-degree murder to five and ten years respectively. Judges could set parole eligibility limits at the time of sentencing. In addition, the court could now determine whether a sentence was served in an adult or a youth facility or in both systems. Finally, in 1995, the provisions were modified to provide for automatic transfer for 16- and 17-year-olds charged with serious crimes of violence. Though these young people were to be automatically transferred to adult courts, they were not to be treated as adults; they would have a parole eligibility of ten years for first-degree murder and seven years for second-degree murder. Parole eligibility for offenders who were 14 or 15 years old was set at a minimum of five years for second-degree murder and seven years for first-degree murder.

How are determinations made about whether young people will be tried as young offenders or adults? In 1984, transfers to adult court required application by the Crown and consideration of both the needs of the youth and protection of the public. In 1991, these provisions were clarified, so that protection of the public took priority when the two interests (the needs of youth and public protection) could not be reconciled. The onus remained on the Crown. The 1995 legislation required automatic transfer for youth 16 and 17 years of age, and the possibility for transfer, with the onus on the Crown, for youth 14 and 15 years of age. Youth automatically transferred to adult court could apply to be tried as young offenders. The criteria for a successful application was to establish that public protection and rehabilitation could be better achieved in youth court. Transfer hearings occur before trial. This often results in lengthy delays; during this time most young people charged with homicide are remanded to custody. This time spent in custody (on remand) prior to going to trial is known colloquially as "dead time."

Charges, Trials, and Sentencing

The custodial experiences of our 19 offenders varied according to:

- the legislation under which they were charged (JDA and YOA);

- whether or not, if charged under the YOA, there was a transfer hearing;

- the length of time they were detained in remand and credit (if any) for this;

- whether they were tried and sentenced as an adult or young offender;

- the type of conviction (manslaughter, first degree, second degree);

- where participants were sentenced to serve time, age of transfer to adult system (if applicable), length of sentence, and availability of treatment programs.

Legislation
Three offenders were charged with homicide under the JDA. All were automatically transferred to adult court. At age 17, Bruce was convicted of second-degree murder and was sentenced to life with no parole eligibility for ten years. He served all his time in adult prison. At the time of the interview, he had served 14 years. Connor was convicted of second-degree

murder at age 17. He served the mandatory minimum of ten years before his successful release on day parole. Frank, 17 years old, was convicted of first-degree murder and sentenced to life in prison without parole eligibility for 25 years. His sentence was reviewed, and his parole eligibility was reduced to 16 years. He had served 24 years at the time of the interview.

Sixteen participants were tried under the YOA. The Crown applied for transfers to adult court for all 16. Twelve participants were tried as adults, and four (Ian, Susan, Johnny, and David) were tried as young offenders. All four were convicted of manslaughter charges (the least serious of homicide offences). Sentences for those convicted as young offenders ranged from two years and two months for David (who was ultimately convicted of aiding and abetting) to four-and-a-half years for Susan. Ian received a sentence of three years and three months in custody and two years probation. Johnny received a three-year sentence and a ten-year prohibition on driving.[16]

Of those tried as adults, three were convicted of manslaughter (Kyle, George, and Phillip). George and Kyle committed their offences prior to the 1995 changes to the YOA. George was sentenced to four-and-a-half years. He served two years and nine months in youth remand and, at age 20, was transferred to an adult facility, where he served ten months. Kyle was sentenced to five years and eight months for manslaughter. Despite turning 18 two years after his conviction, he was allowed to serve his complete sentence in YO facilities.

The remaining nine participants were convicted of the more serious homicide offences of first- and second-degree murder. All were convicted in adult court and received life sentences. However, their parole eligibility varied. Paul received a life sentence and the earliest parole eligibility — five years. Mitch, Leo, and Nigel received life with seven years before eligibility for parole. Two participants, Allan and Nancy, were ordered to serve eight years before eligibility for parole. Steven, Walter, and Scott received sentences of life with ten years before parole eligibility. The differences in parole eligibility reflect the changes in the YOA. Most participants convicted of first and second degree murder under the YOA served more than their minimum parole eligibility period, because parole is not automatic.

All offenders who were convicted of first- or second-degree murder (those convicted under the JDA and those convicted under the YOA) received life sentences. How different were their sentence lengths? In Table 6.1 we list the sentences that all our participants received. The three participants convicted under the JDA were all convicted as adults of first- or second-degree murder. Two received parole eligibility times similar to YOA offenders. Bruce and Connor each had to serve a minimum of ten years for second-degree murder. Frank, however, was sentenced to serve a minimum of 16 years for first-degree murder.

The key distinction in sentence length was whether participants were convicted as adult or youthful offenders. Transfer to adult court meant that participants were subjected to longer minimum sentences. It is important to note that a life sentence, no matter what the parole eligibility, means that a person may spend the rest of their life in custody. Although offenders have a right to apply for parole, they are not guaranteed release; if they are released, they can be returned to custody if they violate their parole conditions. Had these participants been convicted as young offenders, they would have done their time and been released.

Transfer Hearings

Most of our participants (13 of the 16 charged under the YOA) had transfer hearings. Two (Phillip and Mitch) waived their right to a hearing in return for a plea bargain. Phillip agreed to stand trial for a manslaughter charge in adult court, because a conviction would not carry a life sentence — a sentence he would have faced if his transfer to youth court was unsuccessful.

Int.: How old were you at the time?

Phillip: At the time of the offence? 17.

Int.: Were you tried as a young offender or as an adult?

Phillip: Originally, I was charged as a young offender, and I was most definitely going to be bumped up, there was pretty good darn odds that I was going to be transferred. Part of that was because I had an extensive history of emotional and anger problems. The other way they classified it was "can he be rehabilitated within five years (three years closed; two years open)? I'm not sure what they have now. But, the likelihood was that they'd say no, I couldn't be rehabilitated in that time. Now the crown attorney came up with a manslaughter plea, which involved me waiving my rights to stay in young offenders, in return for lessening the sentence. I felt at the time that I wasn't going to gamble with a life sentence over the odds of trying to stay in young offenders. So that's how that came about.

Mitch also waived his hearing and pled to the lesser charge of second-degree murder. He insisted he was tried as a young offender, but was confused about the distinction between the court in which he was tried (adult or youth) and the special parole provisions granted to young offenders tried in adult court. His sentence of life (minimum seven years before parole) proves that he was tried in adult court.

George, Kyle, Steven, Johnny, Allan, Paul, Scott, Walter, and Nigel were all tried prior to 1995. At that time the onus was on the Crown to establish that offenders should be transferred to adult court. All but Johnny lost their transfer hearings and were tried as adults. Johnny expressed his feelings about not being transferred to adult court.

> Int.: So you weren't bumped up to adult?

> Johnny: No, they tried at the start in court, for a Section 16 transfer and that didn't work, so thank God.

Paul remained bitter about his transfer hearing, which he felt he should have won.

> Int.: Tried as a youth or an adult?

> Paul: Adult.

> In.: So there was a hearing?

> Paul: There was a transfer hearing, yeah. I don't know how that judge made all the decisions he made, he was snoring the whole time.

> Int.: He had made the decision before?

> Paul: Oh, he did, because the evidence he quoted was the opposite of what was given.

> Int.: Sorry, I missed that. You were bumped up to adult?

Paul: Yes. In [year].

Int.: So you were bumped up to adult ... so you got sentenced as an adult.

Paul: Yes.

Int.: Was there evidence given at the transfer hearing?

Paul: Some, yeah. The evidence regarding... The judge – his reasons for bumping—his stated reason I should say, for bumping me were ah, he didn't give any regard to the three psychological reports that were given because even the Crown psychological report was favourable for me.

Int.: What did the report say?

Paul: Ah, they all said that I should remain in the YO system.

Int.: Why?

Paul: 'Cause they felt that it would be very detrimental putting me in the adult system because I was so easily led and susceptible to negative influence.

Int.: So there was a risk?

Paul: Yeah, there was a big risk. Which is from the lack of self-esteem and the gullibility. So he disregarded those and evidence was given that the prison system was 25 per cent over-populated—the adult system—and that there were no proper school or educational facilities in the adult system. Which is quite true. And that there were educational, proper schools, and education facilities in the YO system, that there was counselling available, and that I should be treated. Of course, when he made his decisions it was that there were no schools in the Young Offender system whereas the adult system had them and the adult system was 25 per cent under-populated and had more than enough room and abilities for treatment.

The implications of the transfer were life altering. The life sentence will follow Paul forever. He will be on parole for the rest of his life. Had he stayed in youth court, he would have served a maximum term of five years less a day, and then he would have been free.

Five participants (Susan, David, Ian, Leo, and Nancy) were charged in 1995 or later. Three offenders (Susan, Ian, and Nancy) were 16 or 17 at the time of the offence, and they were automatically moved to adult court. They had hearings to try to get a transfer back to youth court. Susan and Ian were both successful in their transfers. Both were convicted on manslaughter charges, and both had fixed youth court sentences; they have completed their sentences and are now free. Nancy failed in her attempt for transfer to youth court; she was convicted in adult court of second-degree murder with parole eligibility in eight years. She seemed to have taken little notice of the transfer hearing:

Int.: And were you tried as an adult?

Nancy: Yes.

Int.: And did your lawyer fight that or try and change you to YO?

Nancy: They had a trial thing, but I don't think it did much.

Two of our participants (David and Leo) were 14 or 15 at the time of the offence, and the Crown applied to transfer them to adult court. David was not transferred, but he was angry about the attempt to transfer him. In Leo's case the Crown was successful, and he was transferred to adult court and sentenced to life with parole eligibility in seven years.

Transfer hearings were protracted, and these offenders were not tried until a determination had been made. As a result, they spent considerable time remanded to custody (on remand).

Remand to Custody
Remand is the time an accused person is held in custody after being charged until they are sentenced (or acquitted). During this time, offenders are in a kind of legal limbo: they have not yet been convicted, and anything they disclose to custodial staff, including counsellors, can be used against them at trial. This limits the psychological and interpersonal support available to them. Some lawyers even caution clients not to discuss their alleged

	Age at Homicide	Tried as Adult or YO	Conviction	Sentence	YO Time Served (including Remand)
George	17	Adult	Manslaughter	4 years, 6 months	2 years, 9 months
Phillip	17	Adult	Manslaughter	7 years	2 years, 7 months
Susan	17	YO	Manslaughter	4 years, 6 months	3 years, 2 months; 2 years probation
David	15	YO	Manslaughter	2 years, 2 months	2 years, 2 months; 2 years probation
Kyle	16	Adult	Manslaughter	5 years, 8 months	5 years
Steven	17	Adult	2nd Degree	Life (10)	3 years
Bruce	17	Adult (pre-YOA)	2nd Degree	Life (10)	none
Johnny	17	YO	Manslaughter	3 years	2 years, 6 months
Connor	17	Adult (pre-YOA)	2nd Degree	Life (10)	none
Allan	16	Adult	1st Degree	Life (8)	3 years (1/2 YO, 1/2 pre-conviction)
Ian	16	YO	Manslaughter	3 years, 3 months; 2 years probation	2 years, 3 months
Mitch	17	Adult	2nd Degree	Life (7)	none
Leo	14	Adult	2 counts of 2nd Degree	Life (7)	3 years
Paul	17	Adult	1st Degree	Life (5)	10 months
Scott	17	Adult	2nd Degree	Life (10)	1 year, 1 month
Frank	17	Adult (pre-YOA)	1st Degree	Life (16)	none
Nancy	16	Adult	2nd Degree	Life (8) (minimum 6.5)	3 years, 9 months
Walter	17	Adult	1st Degree	Life (10)	1 year, 4 months
Nigel	16	Adult	2nd Degree	Life (7)	2 years

Table 6.1: Homicide Remand, Trials, and Sentences

crimes with family and other visitors. Remand experiences are also shaped by where young people are held. Young people are, ideally, held in youth facilities, which are set up to be "youth friendly," with school, recreational, and counselling programs.[17] However, some facilities have few programs, and some jurisdictions have no facilities. Procedural revisions to the YOA in 1986 allowed for youth to be incarcerated with adults if there was no youth facility available.[18] This includes provincial jails. Youth not remanded in custody can be released to a responsible person, with or without the posting of bail. These releases are usually conditional and may include curfews and orders to reside in a specific place, to attend school, and to not associate with particular individuals (e.g., co-accused). Remand experiences can be quite diverse in terms of their length and location. For our participants, there was considerable variation in the length of time spent in remand and credit given in sentencing for time already served.

Two participants (Ian and Johnny) were released to the community while awaiting trial. Johnny spent a year in the community on bail prior to his trial. Ian was on bail for 23 months and on remand for three months prior to trial. Both young men lived with family members and were

Adult Time Served	Age at Time of Transfer
10 months (2 months max., 8 months med.)	20
3 years, 4 months (3 months max., 24 months med., 13 months min.)	20
none	not transfered
none	not transfered
none	not transfered
5 years, 9 months (7 months max., 44 months med., 18 months min.)	20
14 years (2 years max., 10 years med., 2 years min.)	16
none	not transfered
10 years (30 months max., 66 months med., 24 months min.)	17
5 years, 6 months to date (36 months max., 30 months med.)	17
none	not transfered
3 years to date (6 months max., 30 months med.)	18
3 years, 6 months to date (7 months max., 35 months med.)	17
7 years, 2 months (20 months Provincial Holding, 6 months max., 3 years med., 2 years min.)	20
8 years to date (4 years max., 4 years med.)	18
25 years to date (6 years max., 12 years med., 7 years min.)	17
2 years to date (4 months max., 20 months med.)	20
4 years, 9 months to date (40 months max., 17 months med.)	18
4 years to date (8 months max., 40 months med.)	18

required to attend school. They also had strict conditions including curfews. They made significant progress on their high school diplomas, stayed away from negative peers, and engaged in structured recreational activities. Their remand times were the shortest of all participants in the study. The remaining 17 were remanded in custody until they were tried.

The three young men arrested when the JDA was in effect (Bruce, Connor, and Frank) were charged as adults and were held in adult (provincial) facilities awaiting trial. These facilities housed adult offenders serving provincial time (sentences of less than two years) for a variety of crimes. All three described these centres as crowded, noisy, dirty, and dangerous. Bruce described his first experience being held in a provincial jail:

Int.: What jail were you at?

Bruce: [Name], right in the population.

Int.: That's the real jail?

Bruce: That's the real jail.

   Int.: How old were you then?

Bruce: 15. There I waited 9 months, finally the charges were dropped
and I was let out before the sixteenth birthday or whatever, and
I was re-charged. Thrown back in jail, under other headings,
like they didn't charge me with arson or anything like that, but
all of a sudden I had "b-and-e"'s up the ying-yang. It's crazy,
but there was a lot of creepy people in jail, man, just like that
fucking principal. I think I was 70, 80 lbs soaking wet, maybe 4
feet nothing, when they first threw me into jail.

   Int.: What happened to you in jail, when you got thrown in with
the general pop[ulation]?

Bruce: You had to fight, you got the shit kicked out of you, you got
your food fucking taken away from you, you know what I
mean? You had to fight.

Bruce did six months on remand in the same facility before he was convicted of the homicide, and Frank did four months remand in an adult
facility before his conviction. Connor was convicted on circumstantial evidence and was on remand for a year before he was found guilty and
received the mandatory life sentence.

For the remaining participants charged under the YOA,[19] custodial
remand times varied from seven to 28 months. George, Steven, Mitch, Leo,
Nancy, and Nigel all spent one year or less (seven to 12 months) in remand.
Phillip, David, Allan, Scott, and Walter were remanded for between 13 and
18 months. Susan and Kyle were held for 28 and 24 months respectively.
All did their remand time in youth custody. Paul was held on remand for
30 months. He did ten months in a YO facility; when he turned 20, he was
automatically moved up to an adult facility for another 20 months.

Participants reported a number of problems while on remand. Some of
these were related to being on remand itself, others were related to being in
custody. Two participants (Steven and Paul) reported that they found
remand difficult because they could not discuss with others the emotional
problems that led to the homicide and the trauma of its aftermath. Their
lawyers had cautioned both these young men not to discuss any aspect of

the homicide prior to the determination of guilt or innocence. Steven reported that this was difficult, although he tried to talk around it. Allan reported he received excellent support in remand custody. He identified his problems as being related to his family, and thus he could deal with this when on remand. He noted that he, too, had been cautioned not to talk about the homicide and other charges, and so he could not deal with all his issues.

> Int.: Like you couldn't until you were convicted, right, you couldn't like take part in counselling or anything or ...?

> Allan: Oh well, I could to a point. Once I was, once I knew I was gonna be there for a while. The thing with Dr. [name] was that, her, there were two psychologists in the young offender unit, one for half the alphabet and one for the other half of the alphabet, and she normally doesn't do any real therapy there. It's mostly crisis intervention kind of stuff, like maintenance sort of things. But when there are people who are going to be there for a long time, and know they are going to be there for a long time, she is willing to start if they are willing, and we began, we just didn't discuss the offence itself. You know, it was more about family life, and that's when things started to turn around. Because when I was first arrested, I was so out of it that I was honestly surprised that everybody was so upset. That's how messed up I was. I was thinking, well I don't get it. Why is everybody so upset about all this? I mean, obviously I look now, but when I first came, the first really six months.

Nigel relied on group programs and noted that there were some programs in which he could not take part because of being on remand.

> Int.: Now when you were in remand did you do, get any counselling, or like groups, or programs, or anything apart from the education?

> Nigel: Well there would be group sessions where, every once in a while, where you'd sit around in a circle and talk, kind of thing, whatever.

Int.: Not about the offence, though? You hadn't been convicted.

Nigel: I hadn't, yeah, I was, there was some I couldn't participate in 'cause I hadn't been sentenced yet, so I was, well like you're saying, don't talk about anything.

Most of our offenders (15 of 19) were placed in segregation when they were admitted to youth facilities while awaiting trial. Segregation meant being locked up for most of the day — in some institutions some offenders spent up to 23 hours a day in their cells alone. They had no access to television or family, but did receive other support visits (e.g., chaplain, youth worker). While segregation is often used when offenders are first admitted to these facilities, it was the violent nature of their offences that led institutions to keep these young people segregated. While male participants had some (very limited) contact with other segregated inmates during recreation, Susan and Nancy were particularly isolated. They were considered to be violent girls in a system without institutions to deal with them. Susan was housed in an otherwise all-male unit and had to be segregated. Nancy was segregated from a non-violent youth population and was completely alone in her wing. The only other available segregated unit was an all-male facility, which was deemed inappropriate.

Susan found segregation difficult.

Susan: Well the first month was living hell. They treated me inhumanely. I was locked in a cell for a month, pretty much 24 hours a day. I got yard for about an hour once a week, and I got to shower every other day. I got to clean my cell every three days, no TV, no human contact. I couldn't have visits, but I could use the phone, but that was it. I was in this metal cell about 5 ft by 8 ft with a bed and a metal toilet, no window, no anything. I was fed through a latch in the door; sometimes they'd forget to feed me so I'd get two meals a day as opposed to three meals. They called me every name in the book.

Nigel described his experience in much more positive terms than Susan did.

Int.: Were you in seg[regation] when you actually got there?

Nigel: The lockdown unit, yeah.

Int.: How long were you locked down?

Nigel: Uh, a year and a half.

Int.: How come so long?

Nigel: It was the only place they could put young offenders charged as adults. There was five or six of us there.

Int.: At the same time?

Nigel: Yeah.

Int.: You had a full house?

Nigel: Yeah. But after about a year and a half, they moved me up to the education level, to get my education....

Int.: So overall it was a positive experience then?

Nigel: Uh, yeah. Uh, I mean, counsellors there were always willing to talk. They never talked down to ya. I had many sessions with the chaplain there. Went to church regularly. It's all mandatory group action, so everybody had to go to the gym, and partici-pate, so it was like...

Int.: In sports?

Nigel: Uh, floor hockey or basketball or something.

Int.: So even while you were in seg[regation] you got to do this?

Nigel: Every day you got exercise.

Offender Experiences in YO: Remained in YO

	Behavior	Education	Recreation	Spirituality
Susan	Segregation, violence, medium motivation	Finished High School, started Post Secondary	Sports, Crafts	—
David	Low motivation	Finished Grade 12	Sports, Crafts	—
Kyle	Segregation, violence, low motivation	Finished High School	Sports, Crafts	—
Johnny	High motivation	Finished High School, started Post Secondary	Sports, Crafts	Organized Relig
Ian	Segregation, violence, medium motivation	Finished Grade 11	Sports, Crafts	Organized Relig

Adult Transfers' Participation in YO Programming

George	Violence, segregation X4, infractions, poor motivation	Finished Grade 9 (Grade 5 level literacy)	Sports, Crafts	Organized Relig
Phillip	Violence, segregation X2, suicide, high motivation	Finished Grade 10	Sports, Crafts	—
Steven	Violence, segregation X2, high motivation	Finished Grade 12	Sports, Crafts	Organized Relig
Allan	Suicide, self harm, medium motivation	—	Refused	—
Mitch	3 months segregation, poor motivation	Completed High School	Sports, Crafts	—
Leo	3 months segregation, poor motivation	Some work on Grade 8	Hated it	Chaplain
Paul	Violence, high motivation	Finished Grade 11	Sports, Crafts	—
Scott	Violence, segregation, poor motivation	Upgrading for illiteracy	—	—
Nancy	13 months segregation, violence, self injury poor motivation	Finished Grades 10, 11	Sports, Crafts Post-segregation	—
Walter	13 months segregation, violence, suicide, 40 infractions, poor motivation	Upgrading for illiteracy	—	—
Nigel	18 months segregation, 12 infractions, poor motivation	Poor motivation, no credits	Organized Daily Post-segregation	Chaplain

Table 6.2: Offender Experiences in YO: Remained in YO; Adult Transfers' Participation in YO Programming

Mandatory "Rehabilitation" in Young Offender Custody

One of the dilemmas facing the penal system is how to assist young offenders in a custodial setting. Is rehabilitation possible under these circumstances? Does counselling work in a punitive, coercive environment? Many researchers and clinicians have questioned treatment effectiveness under such conditions.[20] Although the prison environment is not conducive to therapeutic treatment, professionals working both within and outside the criminal justice system have recognized that young offenders, generally,

Treatment

Substance Abuse Programs	Psychological 1:1	Life Skills/Problem Solving Group	Violence/ Anger Group	Family Counselling	Youth Worker Counselling
Denied was problem	Weekly individual counselling	4 Groups	4 Groups	Few sessions with Mother	Weekly, Community Worker
Denied was problem	Refused	Daily	1 Group	Refused	Weekly
Weekly Groups	Weekly individual counselling	7-Step Group	1 Group	Few sessions with Mother	Weekly, Community Worker
Weekly Groups	Weekly individual counselling	7-Step Group, Problem Solving	Many Groups	Many with family	Weekly, Community Worker
Weekly groups	Weekly individual counselling	Weekly Groups	Many Groups	Many with family	Weekly
Weekly groups, 1:1	48 sessions	7-Step Group	—	—	Weekly
Weekly groups	Weekly	Groups	1	—	Weekly
Weekly groups	Weekly, Art Therapy	Groups	1	No contact	Weekly
—	12000 hours, 15h./week	Many	1	3 sessions	Weekly
—	—	—	—	—	Weekly
Weekly	Weekly	Groups, little work	Weekly, hated	No contact	Weekly
Remand	Remand	Remand	Remand	Remand	Weekly
Remand	Remand	Remand	Remand	Remand, no contact	Weekly
Weekly Post-segregation	Weekly Post-segregation	Weekly Post-segregation	Weekly Post-segregation	—	Weekly
—	—	—	—	No contact	—
Weekly Post-segregation	Weekly Post-segregation	Weekly Post-segregation	Weekly Post-segregation	No Contact	Weekly

have serious personal problems that contribute to their involvement in criminal activities. The result is a "catch-22" — counselling is essential, but is being provided to clients who may be resistant and in a setting that is far from ideal. In the YO system, counselling, educational, and recreational programs are integral to the custody regime. Compared to the adult system, YO facilities are program intensive. Table 6.2 summarizes the custodial experiences of the five participants who served all their time in YO, and the YO custodial experiences for the 11 participants who were transferred up to adult facilities.

Susan, David, Kyle, Johnny, and Ian served only YO custody time. All five, no matter what their level of motivation, were required to participate in sports and recreation, schooling, and group treatment, which included sub-stance abuse treatment, life skills, problem solving, and violence and anger management. Offenders were also provided with weekly (at minimum) meetings with their "key" youth worker and psychologist or psychiatrist.

The outcome of these programs was largely determined by the offen-ders' level of motivation to succeed and reintegrate successfully back into the community. Official records indicate that David and Kyle demonstrated little motivation to rehabilitate themselves. In Kyle's case, this may have been related to his arrest at age 12 for sexually abusing his younger half-sib-lings. He may have been unwilling to discuss the abuse and worried that, if it became known, he would become the target of abuse by other inmates. Yet, despite his resistance to treatment, he did find through sports a positive source of self-esteem. He was an excellent athlete, and the sports program gave him an opportunity to shine. So, despite the official record, Kyle did find some positive features in his YO experience.

Int.: So was there anything positive of your experiences in the YO system?

Kyle: [Name]Youth Center that was it.

Int.: What was so good about [centre]?

Kyle: They actually fucking gave me a chance, man. They believed in me, and I took advantage of everything they had to offer me, you know what I mean? It's not the programs or anything like that. They talked to me like a normal human being, man. They talked to me like buddies, like I'm a friend of theirs, like I was always welcomed in their home. Fuck, these people, a lot of them, I've been in their houses and shit. One of the staff, I've even held their fucking son, a little baby, man. I was on a pass and we stopped at their house, and I was holding her baby and everything. Name one institution that would ever, ever let a young offender at their house. None guaranteed. I also go to [name of school] for my education, and that's on my own, you know what I mean? I do that on my own.

Int.: So you basically got your high school there.

Kyle: Yeah I got my high school diploma. I graduated and shit. I played for every sports team they have. I played in the community against other regular high schools.

Int.: So you played on the team?

Kyle: Yeah the team, we played after school.

Int.: Oh really, eh?

Kyle: Oh yeah, I'm telling you, I was in newspapers and everything up there. I had my jersey, had it retired and everything.

Int.: So what sports were you playing?

Kyle: Basketball, volleyball, ice hockey, soccer, badminton, tennis, what else, swim club, fuck, I went on canoe trips, went camping.[21]

Although Kyle was reluctant to participate in the YO counselling programs, he reported making close contacts with people in the system. These contacts provided him with a source of self-esteem, and he felt he had been respected. He appeared to be unimpressed with his achievement in finishing high school, glossing over his graduation to focus on sports. He had little interest in the programs and took them only because they were required

Johnny, who did all his custody time in YO facilities, was anxious to participate in programs, which he saw as opportunities to gain insight into what had led him to commit homicide. He appreciated the support he received from others in custody.

Johnny: I got tons of help.... There were guys in there with charges not as serious as mine, but pretty close, they never got the kind of service or attention I did. Now I don't know if it's because they didn't put a lot of the effort in that I did either, but I know that when I was booked to see a social worker for one hour, we probably do two hours. I worked my ass off trying to figure out why I went wrong and what was wrong and what I did wrong and the effects of what I did wrong, not just for me, but for my family, and everybody in general. I figured out that every day with the staff at the place and outside help that I had, I probably had like 13 people helping me every day, and that's a lot of help. If you want it, and somebody who goes in there and truly wanted help, you don't even need to know how to get help, just that you can be helped. If you want the help, there's a way to get help and there are a lot of ways for people to help you. You don't even have to go to counsellors, like just the staff alone will help you in a huge way...[I did] 7 Steps... AA, and two other substance abuse groups to deal with alcohol. I did another volunteer group which was Solution Focussed Problem Solving—figure that one out. It was phenomenal. It was like 15 or 20 weeks, it was long enough. I was in everything I could possibly be in, more or less. Plus I had a specific social worker who was great.

He did exceptionally well at school, excelled in athletics, and developed a sound plan for his reintegration into the community.

Susan's approach to treatment was more utilitarian. She saw participating in the programs as earning her a positive assessment and possibly assisting her early release. With the exception of one good counsellor, she reported that she got nothing out of the treatment programs.

Susan: I didn't have a choice, for one thing, you know. I went to counselling, I tolerated, forgive me, counselling, so that I could get an earlier review, nothing else. I did everything I could in my favour, and I was shot down every time. There's no way they were going to let me out a day earlier! Even though, by then, it was disgusting. I'd done how many high school credits, done every single group I was supposed to do, done counselling for as long as I was supposed to do, was accepted in university and was supposed to start. Everything was in my favour and there's no way. So yeah, I did every program, every anger management group. I think I did about four anger management groups, life skills, problem solving, victims of violence. The only thing I never had to do was the drug abuse or alcohol abuse because it wasn't prevalent [sic] or it wasn't a problem.

Int.: Did you get anything out of either group or individual counselling?

Susan: Yeah I can remember one counsellor.... She was awesome, and
I actually liked going to talk to her. I could tell her anything,
especially after I got involved in this one relationship. She'd
take me and the guy for relationship counselling. She was really great.... By then I had been so analyzed and had so many
assessments and got so much counselling, after that, it was like
just do it because I had to. I didn't get anything out of it, I did-
n't like going, I didn't want to go, but I had to. I go to counselling now, once a month. I don't want to go, it's a waste of
time. I re-schedule any chance I can get.

Doing what you have to do to get through the system, to get early
release or a positive report, is one way that young people in a coercive situation may respond to counselling. There is a choice to be made here, and
Susan's was to passively resist the process. This may be related to her rejection of culpability for the homicide and her need to minimize her participation in it. It may have been difficult for her to maintain these fictions in
counselling sessions.

Ian's programs focussed on two issues: his addiction to prescription
drugs and anger management. He began counselling when he was held on
remand for nine months. While on house arrest for a year, he began, at the
request of his lawyer, individual counselling with a private therapist. He
described some of the anger management programs he did in custody and a
problem he had with group therapy.

Int.: So the anger management, what did that do? What did it con-
sist of? What did you do there, was it like a group thing?

Ian: No. That was one on one. Did you ever read *Men and Anger*?[22]

Int.: Yeah.

Ian: I did that one, *What Color Is Your Parachute*?[23] All kinds ... all
kinds.

Int.: It [counselling] was all individual. So you didn't do any group stuff?

Ian: We did group, but it [individual counselling] was mostly where I got most of my stuff.

Int.: So you found that individual worked better for you?

Ian: Yeah.

Int.: How come?

Ian: Because I could actually get my feelings out without any of the troublemakers in the unit playing on it to get me in shit.

Group therapy can make individuals more vulnerable since they disclose information and feelings to other inmates, as well as to counsellors. Ian found that others used information revealed during group sessions to torment him. He would retaliate and then would be in trouble with the custodial authorities. He struggled with anger management, relating it to how he dealt with his frustration about events in custody. He had to learn to acknowledge the feelings and the consequences of expressing them in unacceptable ways.

Int.: So when you were doing this individual stuff, what were the feelings, like what did you actually learn?

Ian: I learned my true feelings, how to express myself, and know what I'm doing. Like I can't tell them I feel like punching their head off, just because I'd get a three for something or two for something [disciplinary action], or I'd get [sent to a more secure unit], so I had to be really careful. Even though I've been told over and over again that I'm not a bad guy, I'm a good guy, and I care about people and about what I do, but, one little word can ruin it all, even now. I'm going up for review, if I don't get out in six months, I'm going down the crack.

What Ian was not forthcoming about in group therapy was the sexual abuse he had suffered as a child, abuse which contributed to his prescription pill addiction, violent behaviour, and emotional problems. He was able to be more open in individual therapy, although he noted that he was careful to test the staff many times to ensure that he could trust them before he confided in them.

Clearly, when our participants were ready and motivated to change, the variety of support groups found in the YO system were beneficial. When they were not motivated—because they lacked trust, because the therapy process was not suited to their needs, because they weren't ready to deal with the issues—then they were less likely to benefit from therapy in custody.

George, Phillip, Steven, Allan, Leo, Paul, Mitch, Scott, Nancy, Walter, and Nigel did time in both the youth and adult systems, giving them—and us—a perspective on both. Because they were on remand, four participants (Walter, Scott, Paul, and Mitch) were transferred to adult custody without receiving treatment in YO. Walter was in segregation, in the same block with two co-accused (both had agreed to testify against him), and for security reasons he was kept on lockdown. Not surprisingly, he found the YO system extremely frustrating. He found it too restrictive, but he also knew staying in YO meant doing less time.

Int.: Would it have been better for you to stay in YO?

Walter: In some way yes, in some ways no. You get more humane treatment in adult than the YO. You get a stereo, you get to smoke, hang. You don't get treated like a little kid. I didn't have to be in for the long haul [if he remained in YO], but they kept me in [he was denied transfer down to the YO system and thus got a life sentence as an adult]. They didn't give me a chance.

Walter was not the only participant to have been held without treatment in YO facilities. How can the YO system best support young people who are held on remand in anticipation of being transferred to adult prisons for committing serious violent crimes? For Walter, the problems were related both to the limited availability of institutions and to the particulars of his case; he had few options. Mitch was on remand in the YO system for eight months. He was transferred out of YO remand for breaking the rules and was incarcerated in a provincial jail where no programs were available. Paul received no treatment because he was on remand. However, he did receive educational support.

> Paul: I spent ten months of it in juvie [young offenders' facility], and the rest of it in the dungeon [provincial jail].

> Int.: So the ten months that you were in the youth facility, you say you were in [name of facility], how was that?

> Paul: That was pretty good. I was going to the school there.

> Int.: And were you receiving counselling at [facility]?

> Paul: No. Because I hadn't gone to court yet, so nothing could be talked about.

> Int.: You were in school though.

> Paul: I was in school.

> Int.: Getting any help with the learning disability?

> Paul: Yes. There were only six kids in the class and one good teacher there, so I got a lot of help.

He was transferred after ten months because he had turned 20 and was no longer eligible to be held in a young offender's facility. Scott was in custody, originally, for aggravated assault. He was held on remand for the entire 13 months in YO custody and on conviction was transferred immediately to an adult maximum-security facility. Because he was on remand, staff were limited in the kinds of treatment they could offer him. Anything he might have revealed in therapy prior to his trial could have been used against him at trial. As noted above, getting youth immediate treatment when they are charged with a crime is a common problem. He provided no details of how remand impacted on him. His primary concern was explaining how his co-accused made deals that led to his (Scott) becoming the focus of the case and ultimately, in his view, to receiving a life sentence.

Several participants did receive support in the youth system prior to transfer. Leo's experiences with the YO system were complex. He participated in the mandatory treatment and programs as required. However, he was frustrated because he believed that none of the programs were suited to his particular needs. He did not believe he needed anger management, a program he was required to take, because he was not (in his own words) violent. Rather, he wanted help with his attachment to violent fantasies. He did try to work with one psychologist and confided in him about a violent fantasy.

Int.: Have you talked about this with a psychiatrist or psychologist?

Leo: Yeah I actually did, there was a new psychologist in [YO facility]. I kept it secret [a planned rape and murder] for years right?

Int.: Yeah, that's a big secret.... So what did this psychologist say... about it?

Leo: Well when I told him, because like I said, it was eating away at me, it was a secret I kept for years. I always thought that because I'm a spiritual person, that this would hold me back [going to Heaven], if I suddenly got killed or I died, this would hold me back because I never told anybody. So I said, "I have to tell the truth because I've been lying about this for years." So I went in and told him. I tell you today like I'm very calm and things, but when I told him, I was a wreck. I was crying, but I felt good afterwards. It felt good that I had finally told someone.

Int.: And what did he say?

Leo: He said that my remorse showed. The shame I felt, he felt it was genuine and he believed [it]. Shortly thereafter I got transferred up here. We could have gotten, well we were starting to get into some really deep therapy, but then I got transferred.

Int.: Why did you get transferred?

Leo: I don't know. My parole officer said he likes it when young people are transferred in the adult system as early as possible. I

was expecting to have to stay in [name of facility] for another
five or six months, like I was only 17.

Whether or not his transfer to an adult prison shortly after this disclosure
was related to concerns that he was dangerous, the result was that it ended
his access to the support of the psychologist. There seemed, in this case, to
be a difficult tension between the needs of the offender and managing the
risk he was perceived as posing.

In YO, prior to sentencing, Nigel had found the staff and the chaplain
supportive. His experiences underlined the differences in accessing programs between the YO and adult system.

  Int.: Think it was a good thing you got transferred up? Back then?

  Nigel: [Sigh] I dunno. Uh, I would, I probably would of liked it better
    at the young offenders facility, 'cause it's non-stop programs. I
    mean, there is no waiting list. It's programs are programs, and
    it's every day, there's something. I mean, here, it's just, they are
    just warehousing ya for however long, until ya, you know, you
    complain enough to actually get something done.

  Int.: Ok. So is there any treatment here?

  Nigel: No. There's nothing here resembles treatment.

Nancy spent her time in YO in segregation because of the violent
nature of her crime and because she attempted to escape. She attended
many programs while in YO custody.

  Int.: So when you were in the secure unit, did you get any help for
    any violence or any counselling?

  Nancy: I took anger management programs.

  Int.: Okay.…What else did you take?

  Nancy: Um, reasoning and rehabilitation, life skills, substance abuse,
    drug education enrichment program, self-esteem, [anger man-
    agement program], and I think that's it.

Int.: Did you learn anything from these at all?

Nancy: Some things, yeah.

Int.: Like what?

Nancy: Um, I don't know really. I can't really name off the top of my
head what I learned about myself, but I know that I didn't
know how to handle the emotion of anger, so, and now I'm
better at handling the emotion of anger, but I can't say that I've
perfected it. It's healthy to get angry, if pushed people should
get angry. It's all in how you deal with it and handle it. And
the majority of the time now I know how to handle my anger
without losing control, but sometimes I get mad and yell. I still
throw things sometimes.

Nancy seemed to receive some benefit from the programs. She felt she
had more insights into herself and her feelings of anger. She also took programs in the adult system, and for her the adult system was better.

Nancy: Doing my time here at [adult facility] is much better than
doing time at a youth facility.

Int.: It's better than doing time at a youth facility? Why?

Nancy: Because you had to learn things for yourself here. Like you
don't ... people don't wait on you, people don't clean up after
you — and you can't just... You have to take responsibility for
the things you do. Like nobody's gonna wake me up to go to
work. I have to get out of bed myself, I have to set my alarm, I
have to pack my lunch if I need to take a lunch with me and
whatnot.

For Nancy, the adult system was a time for her to begin to take responsibility for herself. In the YO system she felt that she was treated as a child.
She resented the mandatory programs. They helped, but she preferred the
choices the adult system required of her. Steven also came to a point where
transfer to adult custody "made sense" for him. He received psychotherapy
in the YO system, which, given that he was highly motivated, was very

helpful to him. He described the programs he received and the transfer to adult custody.

Int.:   Did you get any other kind of counselling when you were in?

Steven: I was also part of a therapy group for a good year or so, and we did a lot of art therapy, and that was very good. Just being in a group of my peers and mostly guys that I liked, you know there's a trust level built up, and that was another part of it as well.

Int.:   Was the psychotherapy specifically targeted at violence or was it general?

Steven: It was specifically targeted at me, and whatever problems I had. It wasn't necessarily violence, it was the problems I had as an individual that led to violence. I'm not saying it all worked. I remember the first guy I saw, I didn't see him for very long because we just didn't get along, so it took a few people to go through until I was able to make a couple of good connections and work on the issues.

Int.:   What was the worst thing about your young offender time?

Steven: Probably the worst thing was knowing I was going off to adult prison, and seeing other guys who I felt were no different than I was, same age as me, in for homicide or whatever, and like I said, after a year or two they're out. I'm going on 'cause I got life-ten. I didn't sense any justice in that. Although I did feel a great deal of remorse for my crime and that helped me. This is where the cards are laid, and I will face this music. That was one of the things, the other thing was, after a while being treated like a kid, like I was 20 years old when I left there, some of the new staff coming were my age, so that's one of the reasons I asked to leave. That's not just with me, that's with a lot of the kids in there, they really supervise you in a lot of ways, but they overdo to some extent, and they treat you too much like a kid. For a kid to learn responsibility, you have to be given some responsibility. So that was another big problem as well.

Steven's experience also highlighted the need for young people to learn responsibility, to make a transition to being an adult.

Transfer to Adult Custody

Fourteen participants were transferred to the adult system. Those transferred under the JDA—Bruce, Connor, and Frank—served all their time in adult custody, which included provincial jails and minimum-, medium-, and maximum-security prisons. As with the group who remained in YO custody, experiences and motivation levels varied in adult custody.

Introduction to the Adult System

Integration into the adult system is a complex process. Offenders are assessed and classified for the necessary level of security – minimum, medium, or maximum. Assessment also assists prison officials in identifying problems, needs, and strengths. On arrival, the offender is usually placed in one of two units—either the general reception area, or, if deemed to be at risk to themselves or others, in segregation. The processing of inmates can be quite protracted (ranging from two to eight months). It includes medical examinations and psychological testing, but little in the way of orientation to the adult prison setting. Most participants said that they learned about the rules and prison culture on their own or with the assistance from other inmates. They had varying reactions to the assessment process. Generally, the level of custody was key in shaping their experiences. However, all 14 participants who were transferred to adult facilities were first sent to maximum-security reception units to await their assessments. They were then classified and moved to the appropriate unit.

Three offenders (Scott, Frank, and Walter) were sent to maximum-security custody after reception. Eleven (George, Phillip, Steven, Bruce Connor, Allan, Mitch, Leo, Paul, Nancy, and Nigel) were sent to medium-security. Most participants reported few problems in reception. Leo was transferred to an adult facility at age 17. He was assessed in a YO facility and integrated into the general youth population. Then, after revealing a plan to rape and kill another person, he was put back on lockdown[24] and transferred to a maximum security reception unit of a combined maximum- and medium-security adult facility. Despite his fear, Leo did not find the transfer so bad.

Int.: What was it like when you got transferred up here?

Leo: I was nervous for a few hours, and then I started telling myself it wasn't going to be that bad. Because the entire time in [YO facility], even the staff members were saying go to adult, getting raped, getting beaten, so I was expecting to have to fight for my life when I came up here. I've had reports from other people who have been in jail and have said it's not that bad. I got up here and I didn't exclude myself from anybody else. If they gave me the choice now, I wouldn't go back to [YO], I'd stay here.

Int.: You prefer this place to [YO]?

Leo: Yeah.

Int.: How come?

Leo: There's more freedom. In [YO] it was driving me nuts with all the restrictions they had.

Leo gave no indication that he had had any conflicts, been threatened, assaulted, or otherwise targeted by other inmates since arriving in the adult system. Allan had spent time in a provincial jail prior to going to the penitentiary. He found transfer to reception positive because he was allowed to have his possessions back. However, he reported that he hated the prison culture—the diverse rules about who was "acceptable" and who was not. Nigel's transfer experience was somewhat different. He spent two weeks in a holding facility prior to going to maximum-security. He met other inmates and developed a sense of the kind of offenders with whom he would be held.

Phillip, Scott, Nancy, and Walter all reported being afforded some protection from other inmates because they had murder convictions. Phillip was welcomed into a lifers' group, which provided him with guidance and assisted in settling conflicts with other inmates. Scott and Walter had long histories of violence and were well able to take care of themselves. Nancy was sent to maximum security, but found the transition positive. She noted no intimidation or conflict.

Mitch was transferred at age 18, and found the transition difficult. He reported feeling he had to grow up over night, but also that he was accorded some respect because he had a homicide conviction. He may also have been feared because he had been violent in both YO custody and in the provincial jail. After our interview was finished, the correctional officers said that Mitch was very violent in custody and ran with a prison gang.

It is difficult to know if the transition to adult custody was as smooth as these participants suggested. We noted previously that the truth status of these accounts was often low. Steven's interview had a very high truth status and his description of transferring to adult custody is in sharp contrast to the accounts thus far. Steven reported finding his experience was intimidating for a number of reasons: the appearance of the prison, the diverse mix of prisoners on the unit, the constant moving of people in and out of reception, and the value placed on violence.

> Steven: Then I went to [maximum-security penitentiary] for seven or eight months; that was quite a place. Reception where they've got guys going to maximum, medium, minimum, all over, all in one, all kinds of charges and sentences, 500 or 600 guys, just a total zoo. You're locked up 23 hours a day, I had about ten different cell partners in there, a whole variety of guys.

> Int.: At once?

> Steven: No, at different times while I was there, like two to a cell, a very tiny cell. You get your yard, an hour, hour and a half, like that was a big thing. Fortunately I had made a few friends in the [other facility], and they had been transferred, so they were like, "hey come on over, you want to work out." They have all the weights and everything. My very first day going into the place, looking at all the barbed wire, gun tower, it was quite a bit different than anything I had seen. You think this is the big time, you know? The guard takes you in and says, "welcome to [name], folks, the tour begins." It's a whole other world. I had three very serious confrontations there where I had to stand up for a few things like the phone again, and a few other things. I ended up basically getting through there without getting hurt or picked on, because I stood my ground real firm, and I knew it could be life or death with these guys, but there was no way that I was going to be a victim. This is actually a place where violence and aggression was not shunned; it was respected. So, I just made a stand for myself.

Paul also reported having no trouble on transfer to reception, because of the time he had spent in adult jail prior to his conviction. He found being in jail traumatic, and he feared for his safety. He witnessed considerable violence directed at other inmates. The transfer to the penitentiary system brought more of the same, but he knew people from his time in provincial jail, and he found that, because he had been convicted of murder, some inmates were nervous around him. The truth status of his account was high. George reported no problems on being transferred to reception. He indicated that another inmate befriended him and helped him out. However, the supporting documentation indicated that he had considerable trouble. He was hospitalized and placed on a suicide watch for the first three weeks.

The three participants sentenced as adults when the JDA was in effect were all put directly into prison populations. Frank, whose account also had high truth status, reported he was in shock. He had to fight to prevent exploitation by a sexual predator, and he quickly attached himself to supportive peers.

Int.: How long were you in [first penitentiary]?

Frank: Four and a half years.

Int.: And you were assaulted how many times?

Frank: No, I wasn't assaulted [sexually]. I was, ah, this guy from [a different penitentiary] come there, and he kept on saying bad things to me and how he wanted to screw me and stuff like that, and I didn't know what to do, so I asked the other boys, what am I supposed to do.

Int.: And they said hit him.

Frank: They said you do one of two things. You either give into him or you fight. So I said I'm gonna fight, what do I fight him with, and they gave me a weight bar.

Int.: You can do a lot of damage with a weight bar.

Frank: Yeah, I broke his collarbone.

Bruce found his time in reception difficult. For him, the issue was his denial of guilt and ongoing appeal. He also reported concerns with violence directed towards inmates by guards and with fellow inmates lying about others to gain transfers or other benefits. It is not clear what Connor experienced. By his own admission, he was so detached from reality due to his drug abuse that the reception process was a blur.

The amount of time spent awaiting classification ranged from two to eight months. This period of time was in many ways the most difficult for our participants. Lockdown was stressful for most; they feared being assaulted and/or sexually exploited. In addition, they were still trying to cope with the homicide and its aftermath. This process was not all negative, however. The classification time did provide for a more gradual integration into the adult system.

Transfer Coping Strategies
It is interesting to explore the coping strategies utilized by our offenders during their transfer to the adult system. We have identified three coping strategies: alignment with older, supportive inmates; removal of self from the group; and status protection. It is clear from Phillip's account that his supportive relationships with older inmates serving life sentences were key protective factors during his time in maximum reception.

> Phillip: I've been under the wings of the lifers the whole time, and their groups and socials. The lifers are the ones who are the easiest going, and those are the guys who are looking out for one another and the people they're living with. Anybody who knew me, knew I was affiliated with the lifers and they backed off like the plague. If they had a beef with me or a problem with me, they would go talk to the lifers' group first, to justify they had any problems.

Paul was so terrified for his first three months in provincial jail that he spoke to no one and spent his days hiding in what he felt was the safest place on his range. This strategy, combined with a later supportive relationship with another older inmate (after his transfer to the penitentiary system), emerged as a key protective factor for his survival in maximum.

> Paul: I walked onto the range and I looked down the range and there was 20 cells and two to a cell, but they usually triple bunk

the cells, sort of. Between 20 and 30 people — it was a scary range. I did not know that at the time, and I looked down the range, and at the very end of the range I see this really big Indian and I say to myself, "oh fuck, what have I gotten myself into." I found a corner and I sat there for three months in that corner.... The cells — they would go three cells and pop out a little bit, and three cells and pop out a little bit, so I just sat in one of those — where it popped out, and my back was to this thing, and there's a picnic table on my right — there's a picnic table on my left — and the only way, if someone was coming after me, was straight up front. No one could sneak up on me. They knew who I was, and they just watched me, saw what I was doing — saw me just sitting there, minding my own business — keeping my mouth shut and watching things.... I'd see a lot of people carried off the range ... because they were unconscious. Most of them were either informants or rapists. There were various people that would knock them out.

Bruce employed the third strategy, status protection. Supporting documents showed that he was involved in numerous fights, all of which he claimed were in self-defence. He had many strikes against him: he was an illiterate cocaine addict, seriously learning disabled, and was sentenced under the JDA. He found only one way to protect himself— with his fists.

Bruce: You had to fight, you got the shit kicked out of you, you got your food fucking taken away from you, you know what I mean? You had to fight.... Well see, back then it was, if you stood up for yourself instead of taking it dry, people would step out for you, you know what I mean? "Hey the kid told you dah, dah, dah." Somebody takes your food, you walk up and you smack him. Now if you get the shit kicked out of you, you still smacked him, you see what I mean? Hopefully he wouldn't do it to you again, right, and then people would step in.... I was lucky, because when I came in, there were a few good men. You know, teach you the ropes, tell you what to do and not to do, simple shit you want to know on the street. You don't look into somebody's house, you don't ask fucking questions, and you keep your mouth shut. That's prison.

Prison Warehousing—Experiences in Adult Custody

"Warehousing" has been commonly used to describe the typical adult prison experience in Canada. The Oxford Dictionary defines warehousing as "[t]he depositing of goods etc., in a warehouse whether under bond or otherwise."[25] We employ this term to mean the incarceration of young people in adult prison settings unlikely to support rehabilitation and community reintegration. The experiences of most of our participants in adult custody suggest that these warehouses actually increased risk factors and cut off access to protective factors. In effect, penitentiary time was harmful to the majority of our offenders. For some, their violent behaviour, substance abuse, mental health problems, or criminogenic beliefs increased in prison. Others became increasingly frustrated at their inability to access support and resources that would assist them in dealing with their problems. Table 6.3 summarizes these experiences in prison.

George and Phillip were not serving life sentences. This meant that unless they re-offended, they would be released even if they did not participate in rehabilitative programming. Both did participate, as much as they were able to do so. George became involved in a program for Aboriginal inmates, but reported that no other programs were available to him. He said he needed drug counselling, educational support, life skills training, psychotherapy, and community reintegration guidance. Phillip was identified as having bi-polar disorder prior to his arrest, and he received medication for this condition in custody. He finished grade 10 and took computer and electronics courses. He also did life skills and community re-integration groups and participated in a program addressing substance abuse. Can the different experiences of these two inmates be explained by the length of time spent in custody? Time served is an important factor in accessing programs. There are often waiting lists for these programs. Inmates serving short sentences may find that they are still on waiting lists when they reach their release date. This is not the case here. George served a longer sentence, the majority of which was in a medium-security setting. In contrast, Phillip served 13 months in minimum after serving his medium time. Inmates in more secure facilities generally have more complex needs, and program waiting lists may be longer for these inmates. Of course, another explanation could be that George was not motivated. Phillip, who had better family support and was more intelligent, may have been better able to organize himself to complete these programs. Finally, George reported that he continued to abuse drugs while in custody, whereas Phillip stopped using street drugs.

Ten participants were serving life sentences — three were sentenced under the JDA, and seven were sentenced under the YOA. Bruce, Connor, and Frank were convicted under the JDA. Connor was released after serving his minimum parole eligibility, while Bruce and Frank were still in custody long after their eligibility dates. Why? They all reported that access to counselling services and programs was limited in the adult system and required persistence and commitment. For instance, Connor only sought help after serving seven years of his sentence, and it took a further two years of demands to see a psychologist. He ended up with one session in his final year in prison, in which the psychologist told him that he was fine!

> Connor: ... I had to fight to get some counselling. I had to actually call [authorities], my wife did actually, 'cause they kept telling me, you need to take this program, you need to get some psychological help.... I said, "Well I'd like to. Please let me do it." And in fact, it took me two years. Well, I'd been in for seven years by then, but it took me two years after to get some. And I had to fight for it before they, and the only reason I got it was [wife] called and sent letters to parliament and everywhere else. You better do something. So they did.... Did it help me? No, okay, like there was no counselling. It was okay, you're okay. All right, thanks.

As the quote illustrates, accessing needed programs and support in the adult system requires an inmate to be motivated and persistent. This is in contrast to the required treatment, often of unmotivated youth, in the YO system. While choosing to seek help is a positive feature and is likely to contribute to rehabilitation, it may be difficult for some offenders to access help if they require the kind of persistence Connor demonstrated. Without this help, opportunities for release on parole are limited. Bruce and Frank were much less motivated and were less successful in accessing help once they were interested in doing so.

Further, all three men were involved in drug use in prison. Bruce was a cocaine addict prior to custody and continued his drug use while in custody. This led to conflict with the system, because he refused to provide mandatory urine samples. His rehabilitation was limited, because he never admitted to being guilty. He appealed his first conviction, but was convicted of second-degree murder at his second trial. The appeal and retrial process took ten years, and Bruce reported he got no treatment or programs during this time. He had been working on programs since his second conviction. Frank became an addict in prison and developed hepatitis-C from intravenous drug use. Because he failed drug tests, he was cited for infractions of the rules. Frank insisted that he took drugs, in part, as a means of self-medication for migraines. He reported that he got no medical care for the migraines and was forced to use drugs to cope with the pain. In contrast, and with the support of his wife, Connor stopped using drugs after seven years in prison.

Finally, neither Frank nor Bruce expressed remorse for the murders. Frank acknowledged that he could have walked away instead of killing his victim, and Bruce claimed that he was an innocent man. Connor, on the other hand, was remorseful. He attempted suicide while in custody, got himself off drugs, and, finally, fought for the mental health care he felt was required for him to be successfully rehabilitated. Connor also had outside support to assist him in gaining access to counselling. Frank had no family to support him. He lost contact with his brothers when he was convicted and had had no contact with his mother since he was six. He was serving 16 years to life and seemed to have drifted in despair for the first ten years of his sentence. Bruce also lost contact with his family, since his siblings and his mother had difficulty accepting that he was a convicted murderer. He did marry while in custody, and this marriage was an important factor in helping him work on rehabilitative programs and towards release. Bruce was also angry, and this led to confrontations with others, including with a counsellor in a drug and alcohol treatment group.

The remaining nine inmates serving life sentences (all with variations in their parole eligibility) were convicted under the YOA. Not only did they have to serve a fixed number of years before becoming eligible for parole, they had to persuade a parole board that they were ready to be released; in other words, they had to establish that they had dealt successfully with the problems that had contributed to the homicide. Thus, successful treatment was a critical factor in being released on parole. Participants had a variety of problems that had to be resolved including addictions, violence, and educational deficits. Seven also had mental health problems. These included narcissistic personality disorder[26] (Allan, Nancy, and Nigel,), dysthymia[27] (Paul and Allan), anti-social personality disorder[28] (Steven, Leo, and Scott), sadistic personality disorder (Scott), avoidant personality disorder[29] (Allan), and depersonalization disorder[30] (Allan). Some had begun to deal with these

	Behaviour	Education	Recreation	Spirituality
George	Suicide Substance abuse	Not availabble	—	Native Brotherhood
Phillip	Violence	Finished Grade 10	Computers, Electronics	—
Steven	Violence	Finished High School, Started Post Secondary	—	Organized Religion
Bruce	Substance Abuse	Finished Grade 9	—	—
Connor	Substance abuse 4 infractions, violence	Finished High School, Started Post Secondary	—	Organized Religion
Allan	Physical Health	Finished Grade 12	Refused	—
Mitch	Violence, Gang activity 1 month segregation	Not available	—	—
Leo	—	Not available	—	—
Paul	Violence	Finished High School, Started Post Secondary	Computers	—
Scott	Violence (10 fights) 4 years protective custody	Upgrading for illiteracy	Tattoing	Organized Religion
Frank	Violence, Substance abuse, Physical Health 16 placements, 15 Infractions	Finished High School, Started Post Secondary	Crafts	Native Brotherhood, Spirit of the Eagle, Healing Circle, Sweat Lodges
Nancy	—	Finished High School	—	—
Walter	Substance abuse, Violence, 15 Infractions	Upgrading for illiteracy Poor motivation	Drawing, Tattoing	Native Brotherhood
Nigel	Violence	finished Grade 10	—	—

Table 6.3: Offender Experiences in Adult System

Treatment

Substance Abuse Programs	Psychotherapy	Life Skills/Community Integration Groups	Violence/ Anger Group	Family Counselling	Cognitive Skills Program
not available	Not available	Not available	Not available	Not available	Not available
Offender Substance Abuse Program	Not available	Not available	Not available	Not available	Not available
Offender Substance Abuse Program	Not available	Both	—	—	—
Offender Substance Abuse Program x 2	Not available	Both	—	—	—
—	Not available	Life Skills Group	—	—	—
—	Not available	Life Skills Group	Anger/Emotional Management Programs	—	—
—	Not available	Not available	Not available	Not available	Not available
—	Not available	Not available	Not available	—	Not available
—	Not available	Life Skills Group	Anger /Emotional Management Programs	Not available	—
Offender Substance Abuse Program	After 4 years in Protective Custody	Life Skills Group	1 Violence, 4 Anger Management	—	—
Offender Substance Abuse Program, Native Treatment Centre, many overdoses	Not available	Both	—	—	—
—	Not available	Animal Care, Leisure Education Horticulture, Survivors of Trauma and Abuse Group, 2 Jobs	Anger Management	—	—
Offender Substance Abuse Program, Relapse Prevention Program	Not available	Suspended from 4 jobs	Expelled from Persistent Violent Offender Program On waiting list for Anger Management	—	—
—	Not available	1 job	On waiting list	—	—

Not available = Offender reported s/he wanted to participate in program but either it was not offered or they had remained on a waiting list without receiving service. We verified these reports with participants' institutional records.

issues in the YO system, where they had access to a wide variety of supports, but they were often required to participate. In the adult system they faced access problems similar to those experienced by Bruce, Connor, and Frank.

With this array of mental health problems, it seems reasonable that therapy would be a key component of the treatment provided to inmates. This was not true for our participants. While some showed little motivation to change (e.g., Leo and Nancy), most wanted to get some help, if only to assist them in getting released on parole. They found it difficult, if not impossible, to receive psychological or psychiatric treatment in adult custody. The absence of access to treatment is disturbing, given that the criminal justice system identified these young people as having mental health problems. Paul, like Connor, was able to set up his own counselling support, using his UTAs (Unescorted Temporary Absences) to find help outside. This lack of treatment and opportunity for rehabilitation for these youth in prison is a recognized problem.[31] For our participants, it meant that they were likely to spend more time in custody.

The federal prison support system was built around group programs, not individual psychotherapy. These programs are structured around specific problems, such as addictions, violence, or cognitive skills deficits. Successful completion of these activities was required as part of our offenders' correctional plans, and they did attempt to complete them. Three of the twelve participants serving life sentences had completed between one and three programs (Connor, Walter, and Nigel), and the remaining nine had completed four to seven programs. Motivation levels varied considerably. Three of these young people (Steven, Connor, and Paul) demonstrated a high level of motivation to complete treatment successfully and to work on their schooling. Allan showed a moderate level of motivation in the four programs he completed, but was unmotivated to work on school upgrading. Frank was high on educational motivation but low in his ability to deal with drug addiction. He completed high school and eventually his BA degree. However, he took almost 24 years to do so. He remains a drug addict. The remaining seven demonstrated poor motivation in treatment and schooling. These offenders also had major behavioural problems in the federal system and had incurred serious institutional infractions (e.g., for substance abuse and violence). Some poorly motivated inmates also reported that they had trouble gaining access to programs. For instance, Nigel said that he had difficulty gaining access to a program for violent offenders, although it was required in his sentence plan.

Int.: And what's it been like in here?

Nigel: Uh, here is frustrating.

Int.: Why is that?

Nigel: 'Cause, the guards always have an attitude. Uh, and, you know,
even trying to get something done. Like, trying, I was trying
for the longest time to get myself into the, what was it, the
VOP? Violent Offender Program? And my CMO [Case Management Officer] just kept giving me the run-around, 'til they
don't offer that program here no more. It was two years I was
getting the run-around on that.

Int.: So have you taken any programs?

Nigel: I have taken cog[nitive] skills, and I passed that, with a perfect
score. Five by five on everything. Uh, 'cause the only thing on
my sentence plan was cog skills, VOP, um, completion of education, which I got my GED [Graduation Equivalent Diploma]
for that. And to maintain and hold a job. Which I have. Which
is the range cleaner.

Int.: So you haven't done any other programs?

Nigel: The only one left on my sentence plan is VOP, Violent Offender Program....

Int.: Are you going to do any of that?

Nigel: If they give them to me, ya. Uh...

While group programs did not provide the same individualized support
as psychotherapy, they did provide inmates with some insights into their
behaviour and their crimes. Mitch found the programs helpful, and he
struggled to find the roots of his violent behaviour.

Int.: So what programs have you done inside?

233

Mitch: I've done two: [unclear] and anger management. They helped, but they didn't change me, but I learned a lot from them. If you listen, you'll learn, but a lot of guys don't. They'll go in there and say they've done it, but they can't tell you what happened. The people who want to learn something will, and those that don't won't.

Int.: So what did you get that could be useful?

Mitch: A lot of it has taught me about anger and emotion, and there are different ways other than fighting, the difference between anger and aggression and just little things that matter.

Int.: Did you ever look at your emotions under your anger?

Mitch: Have I?

Int.: They probably did the iceberg exercise with you, eh? The part of the iceberg that's on top of the water is the ice, but the bigger part is under the water. There's gotta be something behind the anger like feeling sad or lonely or not good about yourself.

Mitch: I know when I was young I felt neglected, I know that but, when I was 14, 15, 16, when I wasn't living at home, that was just anger at the world, anger at my mom for kicking me out, things like that.

While Mitch may have got in touch with the emotions that contributed to his use of violence, this did not mean that he had stopped using violence. He was violent in youth custody and continued to use violence in the prison setting.

Despite Mitch's positive comments, our participants did not, generally, see programs as helpful for their problems. Rather, they tended to view them as hurdles that they had to get over in order to have a hope at parole. These offenders were struggling with emotional trauma—trauma from the negative experiences they had growing up and the trauma of the homicide itself. They were also aware that if they did not change their behaviours they were unlikely to be released on parole. Some were frustrated and attempted to find ways to help themselves; others were frustrated and increasingly angry and continued to direct their feelings into aggressive, self-destructive, and dangerous behaviours.

Custodial Pathways

Custodial experiences, both in YO and adult facilities, gave our participants time to stop and reconsider their actions.

Mitch: It's a fucking shame, like, but at the same time, I think it's the best thing that happened to me because of the way I was going. If I hadn't killed someone, someone would have killed me. I've gotten in a lot of fights, I've made a lot of enemies, and I thought I had a lot of friends but ... the way I look at it, if it didn't happen then, it was someone else or me.

Int.: Did you want to die?

Mitch: No, no far from it, but I didn't give a fuck at the time, you know. Now like I said, I have a different look on life. Back then I didn't care about nothing or no one, now it's a lot different. Just being in here seeing people who have 38 years in or 20-something years in, I'm just thinking if I'm old when I get out, I don't want to be that old when I get out.

Participants followed a number of pathways throughout their custodial experiences, but they ended up or were at risk for ending up in one of two places—an institution or in the community. Successful community reintegration requires, at a minimum, the end of negative behaviours, the necessary educational skills for getting work, and community-based support. This must be qualified in a number of ways. For offenders doing life sentences, the persistence of negative behaviours (e.g., drug abuse, violence) is likely to limit their ability to be paroled. Without successfully achieving parole, no matter how skilled an inmate is or how many community-based supports he or she has, they will remain institutionalized.

Persistent Negative Behaviour
Not surprisingly, for most of our participants (13 of 19), negative behaviours persisted after their arrest and conviction. The impact of these actions on their custody pathways depended on the type of sentence they were

serving and whether negative behaviours persisted over the course of their incarceration. For offenders sentenced to fixed sentences, continued negative behaviours created problems while in custody, such as loss of privileges and citations for institutional infractions. Dealing with these negative issues was not, ultimately, a condition for release; however, their persistence put the participants at risk for re-offending. Five of the seven young people given fixed sentences (George, Phillip, Susan, David, Kyle, Johnny, and Ian) continued to engage in some or all of the negative behaviours that contributed to their homicide. George persisted in drug use, and, on release from custody, he immediately went off prescribed medication and back on street drugs. David persisted in his defiant behaviour and continued to blame his incarceration not on his actions but on a racist criminal justice system. Kyle continued to use violence and showed poor motivation to recognize or change his behaviour. Ian also continued to use violence in custody. On the positive side, Johnny had no violence or other problems in custody and reported that he had reduced his risk-seeking behaviour; he was complying with a driving ban. On the negative side, he continued to drink heavily. Phillip and Susan were able to end their involvement in negative behaviours. Phillip was off drugs and had worked to deal with his violent outbursts. Susan was also off drugs and had no reoccurrence of violent behaviour in custody. Whether their negative behaviours persisted or not, all seven were released once they finished their sentences.

For the 12 participants with life sentences, the persistence of negative behaviours meant that they would be ineligible to apply for parole and would continue to be institutionalized. Some did manage, over the course of their time in custody, to stop these behaviours. Paul had little negative behaviour prior to or in custody. He addressed some of the pre-homicide behaviours he identified as contributing to his involvement in the crime. Early in his incarceration, Steven had infractions for drugs and for violence. He stopped using both and became a leader in the YO system. Connor used drugs for some time while in custody, but he was able to get off drugs and to address his problems arising from the deaths of his brother and mother.

Bruce, Mitch, Scott, and Walter all continued to be violent and to be involved in drug use. Bruce had served the longest, 14 years, without changing his behaviour. Mitch had served only three years, but reports indicated that he was involved in gangs and drugs in the adult system. Scott was extremely violent in custody and was placed in protective custody for four and a half years to protect other inmates. Walter was also violent and was involved in serious substance abuse.

One participant (Frank) became an addict in prison. Continued failure of mandatory drug tests will keep him ineligible for parole. Leo had no behavioural problems in custody. Like the other fantasy-based participants, he had had few problems in the community prior to the murder. What persisted for Leo was a belief that in killing his neighbours he had not done anything wrong, because they were good people and he had sent them to heaven. He expressed remorse that they suffered on the way.

We were uncertain about the behavioural risks for Allan, Nancy, and Nigel. Allan had few behavioural problems prior to or in custody. However, he remained extremely withdrawn and somewhat detached from others and had low affect. While his reports suggested that he was better grounded in reality, the persistence of these other behaviours makes him, in our minds, an uncertain risk. Nancy had a history of defiance and non-compliance with authority. She was not engaged in her therapy in the YO facility and insisted that the psychologists, not her, were responsible for fixing her problems. Nigel had served four years at the time of the interview. His behaviour in prison was acceptable, but he had numerous infractions in the secure YO facility. Prior to custody he was a withdrawn and angry young man who rarely acted out. He did not consider himself to be violent and maintained that he killed his victim in self-defence.

Educational and Job Skills

Education is an important component in a successful transition from custody to the community and, more importantly, in establishing a legitimate base on which to build a life. Without education, job opportunities are limited. In the current economy, a high school education is barely enough for most jobs. Our participants had achieved a range of educational levels and had varying abilities and commitment to pursuing post-secondary education. We considered their level of education (including whether they had other employment skills, such as a trade, to assist them in getting a job), their motivation to pursue education, and whether they had learning disabilities that would impede their learning.

Ten participants had weak educational skills. Five of these (George, Kyle, Bruce, Scott, and Walter) had learning disabilities that significantly impaired their ability to complete high school. They also had no trade skills. Leo, at age 19, was still completing grade eight and had low motivation and seemed to drift. Nigel had completed no credits during the two years he spent in YO custody and had only managed to complete grade ten after four years in the adult system. David and Allan had successfully completed high school, but had low motivation. Three of those with weak skills (George, David, and Kyle) had been released after completing their homicide sentences and reported having few skills to secure adequately paying jobs.

Five participants had moderate skills. Phillip, Connor, Mitch, Ian, and Nancy had all completed or were in the process of completing high school or were working on trade skills. Because neither Connor nor Phillip had completed their education, we classified them as moderately rather than highly skilled. Connor has been released and is working full-time. Despite his long history of learning problems, Phillip was learning computer electronics with the aim of becoming a computer technician. Connor had completed high school and some post-secondary education. Mitch and Nancy had completed grade 12, but had not yet begun any post-secondary education. Ian had finished grade twelve and was continuing his high school education upon release.

Five participants had good educational skills. Susan had completed high school and was pursuing a university degree. She was of above-average intelligence and highly motivated. Johnny had completed high school and was training on the job in a trade. He was motivated and had worked for this company for a number of years. He had also begun a post-secondary program. Frank ranked high on education, having completed his undergraduate degree with an interest in pursing either a second degree or an advanced degree. Paul had completed high school and taken some post-secondary courses. He had also taken training in computers and was successful in getting a job in this field. Steven was the most successful of all our participants. He had completed high school and was in third-year university full-time. In addition, he had been living successfully in the community for three years.

Community Support

One of the dilemmas facing the criminal justice system is the reintegration of offenders upon release: how are supportive networks developed in the community? Prisoners released on parole typically are given a non-association order—an order not to associate with criminal peers. Unfortunately, many participants had criminal peers as their sole core support before and throughout incarceration. Thus, a non-association order required them to establish new ties in the community and, potentially, left them without support. The families of young offenders ought to play an important role in providing a non-criminogenic environment. However, histories of family-based abuse, neglect, abandonment, and conflict made returning to their families a problem for some participants.

Seven of our participants had strong community support. Five (Susan, Phillip, Johnny, Ian, and Paul) had support from one or both of their parents, who provided them with somewhere to live and/or with emotional and financial support. Johnny also had support from his employer and from pro-social peers. Two participants, Steven and Connor, had married while in custody. Their wives were able to provide them with places to live and much needed emotional support. Both attempted to expand their support networks by connecting themselves to a number of groups — they were involved in local churches, support groups for lifers, and had developed pro-social peers in the community.

Bruce, Allan, and Frank had moderate support. Bruce had no contact with his family, but he was married to a family friend. However, his wife was quite ill, so her support was limited. Allan had the support of his mother. While this would normally place him in the high support group, their relationship had been quite negative, and a number of issues remained unresolved between them. Frank had had no contact with his family for a number of years. His two brothers were both functioning poorly. However, Frank had married and had made contact with Aboriginal elders.

Nine participants (George, David, Kyle, Mitch, Leo, Scott, Nancy, Walter, and Nigel) had weak support. Those involved in intimate relationships reported them to be unstable; none had positive relationships with their parents. George had been released and had re-entered the adult system; he had been supporting himself and his partner's drug use on welfare and through theft. David and Kyle were not welcomed back home; both were in custody at the time of the interview, their second period of incarceration since having been released for the homicides. Mitch's mother had deserted him prior to custody; he had some contact with his father, who had a criminal career. Leo's mother and stepfather refused to have any contact with him following the homicides; his biological father had been out of the picture for a number of years. Scott and Walter came from extremely abusive families. Walter insisted that he could return home, but it is unlikely that his family would welcome him. Nancy did not want to return home to her parents, because she felt that they would attempt to control her behaviour. Without accepting this support, she presented a high risk not to reintegrate well.

Considerations of Risk

In determining risk, we continue to use a similar classification system as in previous chapters. Participants were classified as high, medium, or low risk based on five areas: experiences in custody, whether or not negative behaviours and/or mental health problems persisted, educational and job skills, level of community support, and motivation. Offenders classified at high risk were negative in at least four of these areas. Those classified at medium risk were negative in two or three of these areas. Low-risk offenders were negative in one or none of these areas. When we classified cases, we recognized that participants could have both positive and negative features within these areas. In deciding what the total score was, we used the ratio of negatives to total items in each category.

High Risk   We identified four different custodial pathways for the high and moderate risk groups (see Figure 6.1).

- Dangerous and Violent Offender Pathway — persistent engagement in violent behaviour with a lack of empathy for victims.

- Entrenched Criminal Pathway — persistent engagement in serious criminal activity and adherence to a criminogenic belief system.

- Substance Abuse Pathway — addicts who continue to use in prison.

- Mental Health Pathway — persistent mental health problems that bring offenders into conflict with the law or prison authorities.

The nine offenders in the highest risk group are likely to remain in custody or to return to custody after release. George, David, Kyle, Bruce, Mitch, Leo, Scott, Walter, and Nigel had persistent negative behaviour in custody (and, for some, after their release), low education or few job skills, and poor community-based support. All were rated as having low motivation based on correctional reports and on their lack of, or resistance to, participation in available programs.

Of this highest risk group in custody, those who had already served their manslaughter sentence prior to our study (George, David, and Kyle) quick-

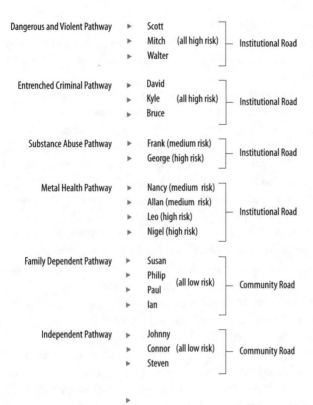

Figure 6.1: Custodial Pathways and Risk

ly re-offended. George was a crack addict at the time of the homicide and had a long history of engaging in serious violence. He reported that despite taking part in YO treatment services (see Table 6.2), he was not motivated and that no programs were available to him in prison (see Table 6.3). In the two-year period between his release for the manslaughter sentence and the interview, he had been incarcerated on two separate occasions. His addiction problems continued. He had spent only five months in the community over this 24-month period. David and Kyle were likewise poorly motivated to participate in rehabilitative or educational programs while in custody. Both reported that they only participated in treatment when forced, and even then it was superficial at best. Kyle completed his high school in custody. David only worked on school when compelled to do so. Both were quickly apprehended and incarcerated for new crimes upon their release for their manslaughter-related convictions. A short time following their second release, they were again apprehended for committing additional crimes and incarcerated yet again. They did not know each other, nor were their criminal activities related. Both were in custody at the time of the interview.

Bruce, Mitch, Scott, and Walter had used violence prior to their homicides, and all four continued to use violence in custody. The persistence of their violent behaviour puts them at high risk to be denied parole because it suggests they would be a risk to others in the community. Mitch, Scott, and Walter had no positive features. They lacked motivation, were resistant to programs, had no community support, and had low education/job skills. Bruce also had few job skills, a frustrating problem linked to his learning disability and the absence of access to trades training. Bruce had continued his violent behaviour in prison, a result of his frustration at being convicted of a crime he insisted he did not do. He had limited community support from his wife, who was ill and elderly. Bruce was somewhat motivated to do programs, but only as a means of getting parole.

Leo and Nigel are our final high-risk offenders. Both committed violent fantasy-based murders. Leo had no history of violence prior to the homicides. As he realized, his persistent belief that killing his victims was positive because he "had sent them to heaven sooner" would not sit well with a parole board and likely would result in continued incarceration. These beliefs were linked to his mental health problems, which were ongoing and not being treated. He had no family or community support, a grade eight education, low motivation, and was resistant to doing any programs. Nigel was still early in his sentence at the time of the interview. He had very little contact with his family, and they offered little chance of support. He was unlikely to be able to return to the small town where he committed the murder. He was still working on completing high school, and it was not clear what types of educational or training opportunities he would pursue. He was not a model prisoner, having acted out violently in YO custody. He was open to programs, but had persistent mental health problems, which were not being treated.

Moderate Risk Three participants were rated as having a moderate risk of re-offending, although they were likely to be denied parole. Allan had a mixture of positive and negative risk factors. He was not a behaviour problem in custody, but he remained withdrawn, a factor that had contributed to his committing homicide. His mother had mental health problems, and she was verbally abusive. Allan had concerns about her being his primary community support. On the positive side he had finished grade 12 and completed programs. He had no history of violence and substance abuse/use. If he can resolve his mental health problems—and he is trying—he may be able to achieve reintegration.

Like Allan, we also placed Nancy on the Mental Health Pathway. She had numerous problems in custody including violence, self-injury, and poor motivation. Correctional staff struggled to define her problems and to identify their source. She had limited support from her family and was not interested in returning home. She was hostile towards her mother and her view of her father seemed over-idealized. She completed grade 12 and was considering plans for post-secondary education.

Finally, although Frank had strong community support and excellent educational achievement, he remained an addict. This behaviour will keep him ineligible for parole. He has taken every program available, but has not been able to stop his drug abuse. His motivation is low. We placed him on the Substance Abuse Pathway.

Low Risk Seven of our participants were low risk and all had been released back into the community. Four had been released at the time of the interview, and three have since been released. Susan, Phillip, Johnny, and Ian were released on time-limited probation or parole conditions. Steven, Connor, and Paul were released on parole for life. We placed them on either the Family Dependent or Independent Pathway (see Figure 6.1).

Susan went home to live with her mother, was in university, and got off drugs. She was working a couple of part-time jobs and had a steady boyfriend. She had been open to educational programming in custody but was resistant to therapy. She had developed pro-social attitudes and was highly motivated. Phillip, Johnny, and Ian had good supports and job skills. They also had some weaknesses. Phillip was about to be released on parole from a minimum-security prison. He was highly motivated. His mother was active in assisting him to set up a plan for the future, using his marketable skills, and both parents were providing him with emotional support and financial aid. However, having spent most of his life in institutional settings, there are some concerns about his transition into the community. Johnny had done his time and had moved back into the community. He was working and had not re-offended after three years; however, he continued to abuse alcohol, behaviour that led to the homicide. He admitted to drinking excessive amounts on weekends and that alcohol abuse interfered, occasionally, with his work. He was motivated to stay out of prison, but did not relate his continued use of alcohol to being a risk factor for re-offending. He had addressed his issues related to violence and had been a leader in an anti-violence group. Ian had moderate motivation and educational achievement. His family was supportive and was planning to move to accommodate his release. He had no substance abuse problems, and his violence had decreased. He had been open to programs in custody and was exhibiting pro-social behavior.

The three low-risk participants on parole for life faced a somewhat different risk of returning to custody. While all three have very positive features, being on parole for life means that they can be returned to custody for minor infractions, such as failure to report to their parole officer or drug use. Connor had been working full-time in the community for seven years at the time of the interview. He had married in prison, had a daughter, was in therapy, and was functioning very well. Steven had dealt with his violent behaviour, was in university full-time and working part-time, married, and was residing in a half-way house. Paul had dealt with his emotional problems and had matured considerably in prison. His job skills remained weak, but his full-time job in the computer field should allow him to develop further skills. Paul's father had helped him to get this job and provided both support and a place to live (see Figure 6.1).

Conclusion

Custody experiences are ongoing for many of our participants. Whether or not they will ever be paroled will depend on both the prison system and on them. These offenders remain involved in violent and/or high-risk behaviours. Their ability and willingness to change is uncertain. For some, their emotional harm may always impede their ability to function safely in the social world. For others, addiction may never be overcome, and they may spend the rest of their lives in prison. Finally, some may continue to be violent, preying on others in custody. Those who do survive the experience of serving sentences for committing murder do so because they have family support and the intelligence and willingness to face their problems and actively pursue education and job-skills training.

Notes

1 Hylton, 1994.
2 Leacy, 1983.

3 Wilson, 1982; Leacy, 1983.

4 Leacy, 1983.

5 Indictable offences are serious in nature, and the minimum sentence is two years or more.

6 Canadian Welfare Council, 1941, 70.

7 If a child was convicted under the JDA, he or she could not be incarcerated in an adult facility unless he or she could not be safely confined in any place other than a jail or lock-up.

8 Bala, 1997, 34.

9 This means that the youth court statistics pre- and post-JDA are not comparable because of who is included and excluded. Specifically the inclusion of older youth is likely to increase both the overall crime rate for juveniles and the murder rate.

10 Bell, 1999.

11 Bala, 1997, 287; Bell, 1999, 185.

12 The provisions came into effect at the end of December 1991.

13 These provisions were contained in Bill C-37 and came into force on December 1, 1995 (Bell, 1999, 186).

14 Bala, 1997, 264.

15 Bell, 1999, 185.

16 This meant that he could not apply for a driver's licence for ten years; after that, he could apply to have a licence, but approval would not be automatic.

17 Bell, 1999, 219.

18 Bell, 1999, 185.

19 Ian and Johnny's cases have already been discussed above.

20 Hawkins et al., 1998; Lipsey and Wilson, 1998; Cunningham et al., 2000; Totten, 2000a, 2001a; Andrews et al., 1990.

21 It should be noted that the truth status of Kyle's interview account was low. In the quote here, he indicated that he was permitted to leave his secure facility to go to school and play sports and even go to the home of a staff member. We doubt that these things ever happened.

22 This workbook, by Murray and Freeman-Longo (1996), has been widely used with offenders in North America.

23 This career guide manual, by Bolles (2001), has been widely used by youth and adults.

24 Lockdown is a term used to describe the situation when an offender is held in their cell for 23 hours a day and only released for segregated recreational activity for one hour per day.

25 The Oxford English Dictionary, 1971, 3687.

26 In the DSM IV, Narcissistic Personality Disorder is identified as an all-pervasive pattern of grandiosity (in fantasy or behaviour), need for admiration or adulation, and lack of empathy. Although it usually begins in early adulthood, symptoms can be present in adolescence and include feelings of grandiosity and self-importance which have no basis in reality, obsession with fantasies of fame and fortune, and a belief that one is superior to others.

27 Dysthymia: chronic, i.e., daily, disturbance of depressed mood enduring for at least one year, associated with the presence of at least two of the following symptoms: poor appetite or overeating, insomnia or hypersomnia, low energy or fatigue, low self-esteem, poor concentration, difficulty making decisions, feelings of hopelessness (DSM IV).

28 Antisocial Personality Disorder is defined by a long-standing pattern of disregard for and violation of the rights of others including the following symptoms: failure to conform to social norms, deceitfulness, impulsivity, irritability and aggressiveness, reckless disregard for safety of self and others, consistent irresponsibility, and lack of remorse (DSM IV).

29 Avoidant Personality Disorder manifests by early adulthood and is identified by a long-standing pattern of feelings of inadequacy, extreme sensitivity to the thoughts about self by others, and social inhibition. Symptoms include avoidance of occupational activities, unwillingness to get help unless convinced self will be liked by helpers, fear of ridicule or shaming in interpersonal relationships, preoccupation with rejection and inhibition in social situations, perception of being socially inept, and reluctance to try new things due to potential personal embarrassment (DSM IV).

30 Depersonalization Disorder is manifested as a feeling of detachment from reality and behaving like an automaton or as if in a dream (DSM IV).

31 Hawkins et al., 1998; Lipsey and Wilson, 1998; Cunningham et al., 2000; Totten, 2000a, 2001a; Andrews et al., 1990.

seven

Conclusion

This book has explored the lives of 19 young people who were convicted of homicide. Although their lives and experiences were diverse, they have one thing in common: they were all victims of harm. Some had been severely traumatized and had multiple sources of harm; others were relatively unscathed. Those who were less resilient suffered more severely.

What were the sources of harm? They included factors that most people recognize as damaging—child abuse and neglect, exposure to parental violence, and parents who were addicted, mentally ill, or involved in crime. But they also included features such as learning disabilities, which limited school success and resulted in labels of "dummy," "retard," and "stupid." The effects of FAS and brain injuries were also significant. Bullying, too long considered as only teasing, also harmed many of our young people. Victims of bullying were socially marginal—they were unattractive, less intelligent, from visible minority groups, or failed to meet gender standards for either males or females. Family breakdown was another factor—divorce, abandonment by parents, and the failure of parents to visit children after the parents separated or children were removed and placed into care. Harm was also caused by negative community environments—poverty, community-based violence and disorganization, and exposure to drug use and crime.

Some participants had quite bleak lives. Others had positive features that made their lives less difficult: intelligence which assisted them at school, physical attractiveness so that others viewed them more positively, health, and (for some) resiliency to the stresses and strains in their lives. Some had positive family experiences and a parent or parents who loved and cared for them. But these positive features were unable to redress the harm our participants had experienced.

Trauma left them with a terrible emotional legacy. Feelings of shame, anger, fear, frustration, hatred, and powerlessness were shared by our offenders. These feelings are not uncommon in the general population. Many young people are harmed as children—some severely—and they do not turn these emotions into homicidal behaviour. Our participants turned their negative feelings into a variety of behavioural responses. They sought to protect themselves, to increase their social status, to improve self-esteem, to feel powerful, to escape their horrible situations, or to make sense of their worlds—all through the use of violence to one degree or another. They *chose* antisocial behaviour, but their choices were constrained. Some modelled the behaviours of people around them ——family members, community members, peers—and others emulated masculine ideals or the social value placed on violence. Others had limited ability to make pro-social or positive decisions because of mental illness, brain injury, and low intellectual capacity.

Their behaviours varied – although they all had violence as a component. Most became violent towards others, although some became involved in aggressive risk taking. They took dangerous personal risks, and they were aggressive towards others when they took such risks. Violent fantasies about rape, murder, and being a hero through the use of violence helped some to cope. They also sought to self-medicate against their pain – drug and alcohol abuse was common. Substance abuse offered them momentary release from their problems, but addictions often involved them in crime to meet their needs. These activities included drug dealing, violence to enforce drug debts, and break-and-enters, all of which put them at further risk. Many developed a lack of empathy for others, and mental health problems became more severe as they grew into adolescence. School failure and behavioural disorders contributed to participants quitting or rarely attending school. Once out of school and away from any supervision, these young people drifted into crime and violent subcultures and deeper into addictions.

Most participants developed antisocial reactions to their troubles. Most were bullied and some were bullies; many demonstrated self-hatred and routinely engaged in self-destructive behaviours; and many defied authority, unable to trust or bond with adults. Others withdrew into themselves. They exhibited few problems and were generally in school and not in conflict with the law.

How did the social safety net respond? For those whose strategy was to internalize their problems and who used violent fantasy to cope, it was almost impossible for authorities to respond effectively. These participants did not seem to have many, or indeed any, serious problems. For others numerous attempts to respond to their problems were not successful for a number of reasons. Some refused to disclose what had or was happening to them. They feared being taken into care or getting into trouble. Some had multiple diagnoses and treatments that were ineffective. Parents or legal guardians often failed to seek support and failed to follow through with appropriate interventions. Participants were also resistant to getting help. They did not want to be treated – to be viewed as "problems."

Their behaviour and the failure of the safety net to effectively intervene put participants at risk. While they were at risk for committing the homicides, they chose to kill, and this is what distinguishes them from other young people in similar situations. Their choices were constrained and not always well informed. Some had the intent to harm, others were careless and ignored risks, and still others were simply indifferent. Their pathways to homicide varied. Participants adhering to criminogenic beliefs and involved in deviant subcultures used violence as an ordinary part of "doing business." This ordinary violence went too far, and they ended up killing someone. They were, in the course of the assaults, indifferent to their victims. Most argued that their victims deserved this treatment. Others blamed their actions on being high, drunk, or young and foolish. Some insisted there was nothing they could have done to stop the killing.

Did they accept that they made choices that led to the murders? Homicides are complex events and our offenders varied in how they expressed responsibility. While some did admit culpability, most sought to deny or mitigate their responsibility. They blamed the victim, society, and immediate circumstances; they minimized their own responsibility.

Custody was, in part, an opportunity to pause and consider what they had done, where they had been, and where they would go in the future. Generally, they viewed incarceration as putting a brake on their out-of-control lives. But for some, custody was viewed as another oppressive assault by society. Here again they had to make choices — constrained choices. Would they accept responsibility and work towards addressing their problems? Could they develop the skills and support they needed to reconnect to the community?

Custody experiences varied. Some participants seem to be on the path to successful reintegration and to useful and productive lives while others appear to be on a pathway to continued incarceration or to re-offending and returning to prison. Failures were rooted in a complex mixture of individual, institutional, and community factors. Individual motivation was an important factor in moving towards successful community reintegration; however, even motivated individuals faced difficulty in making a transition to the community when they had serious mental health problems and were unable to access necessary treatment. Inmates who lacked educational ability and those who remained addicted had negative prospects. Finally, participants who had weak community support also remained at risk. For some, their impoverished and broken families remained their only community support and were inadequate to helping them make changes. Marriage offered one method of increasing family support—and four of our participants married while in custody. Overall those with earlier onset of harm, more negative experiences and fewer protective factors, and with the least community support were the most likely to persist in offending or remain in prison.

Directions for Research

The summary of events that led our participants from birth to the present provides some insights into the reasons why young people kill. However, it is essential to remember that we cannot generalize from these 19 cases to all youth convicted of homicide. What we have presented is a snapshot of their lives at the time of the interview. As a result, there are a number of areas related to youth homicide that we have identified for future research. First, the life-course model of harm-based violence needs to be tested against larger and representative samples of youth convicted of homicide. Our life-course approach requires us to consider what happens to young people over the long term. A longitudinal follow-up would assist us in better understanding the complex processes involved when adolescents kill; in particular, whether youth tried as adults do better, worse, or the same as youth tried as young offenders. Our study had limited information on young women, Aboriginal youth, and visible minorities. There was not enough representation by these groups to develop even tentative conclusions about their special issues and concerns. We deal with these issues in more detail below.

Researching homicide using a representative sample would allow researchers to test and refine the models presented in our study. We could begin to assess whether the models are complete and identify the gaps that need to be addressed. However, access to a representative sample of youth convicted of homicide is difficult, and translating our in-depth interview approach into a tool appropriate for a representative sample would require careful consideration.

Longitudinal tracking over the life course with a sample of high-risk children would be of tremendous benefit. Our participants were at very different stages in their custody experiences. Some (e.g., George, David, and Kyle) returned to custody for violent offences after they had served their homicide sentences. Others are still in the community, but may be returned. Still others have been in the community for years and appear to be successful. We would like to follow these young people over time to see who succeeds, who does not, and why this difference might exist.

There is a paucity of data regarding young women's role in homicide. Very few girls kill. For the decade of 1988 to 98, females represented only 13 per cent of all youths charged with homicide in Canada.[1] With only two females in our study, our sample was reflective of this Canadian trend. However, we are not in any position to draw conclusions based upon these two interviews, nor can we usefully compare these two participants with the 17 young men in our study. Both Susan and Nancy claimed to have played tertiary roles to older co-accused males in their homicides. The truth status in both accounts was low when comparing their accounts with those in the media and official records. This raises many questions. Are young women more likely to have a secondary role in homicide? Do young women use social understandings of women as followers and men as leaders to reduce their sentences? Past research on young women and crime has struggled with whether the courts deal less punitively with young women because they are women (the chivalry thesis). Meda Chesney-Lind concluded that women involved in violent crimes are actually dealt with more punitively than men.[2] This raises questions about the official accounts of women's involvement with homicide: are they gender-biased? Clearly more study is needed.

A study of female homicide offenders should also be undertaken because risk factors and pathways for violent young offenders vary by gender. Compared to violent young men, violent girls report having experienced significantly higher rates of physical and sexual violent victimization in their childhood. Adolescent girls' violent behaviour is closely related to abuse and trauma suffered at home. Substance abuse is commonly used by female victims of child maltreatment to cope with these negative social experiences, and violent girls abuse substances at a significantly higher rate than violent boys. Among adult women who are involved with the criminal justice system, a high number have survived physical and/or sexual violence in their childhood and have youth court convictions. Many of these women cope by slashing themselves and other forms of self-injurious behaviour. Thus, while we have included young women in our model, we need to test the model for gendered differences. These may be significant to responding to young women who are violent.[3]

More detail is also required on the involvement of Aboriginal and visible minority youth in homicide. Although we had five participants who identified as visible minority or Aboriginal, we do not know if this reflects the national trend. It is not possible in Canada to track offending behaviour by ethnic or racial origin, so we simply do not know what proportion of youth homicides are committed by minorities in Canada. However, US data clearly indicate that minorities are substantially over-represented as both victims and perpetrators of youth homicide.[4] Canadian research has suggested that minorities are over-represented in prisons and young offender facilities.[5]

A Final Word

This research has provided us with many insights into youth who engage in extreme violence and many ideas about where to go from here. We are trying to arrange a follow-up study so that we can track our 19 participants over the next few years. We are also hoping to add more youth convicted of homicide to our sample. We are particularly concerned with speaking to more young women, Aboriginal youth, and visible minority youth. While this study supported our pathways hypothesis, we need to test the theory more completely through continued research. We also need to refine our model to consider the differences (if any) that gender, race, and culture may make on how young people become involved in violent crime.

This book has sought to demonstrate for readers how complex homicides are. It challenges the stereotype of "the" murderer and replaces it with an understanding of the factors that harmed and helped our participants. We have sought to demonstrate how constrained choices are made by children who kill and how their adolescence, their personal histories, and immediate circumstances contributed to what they did. We hope that these findings will contribute to an enhanced understanding of adolescent engagement in extreme violence and to the growing chorus for co-ordinated early intervention and prevention programs.

Notes

1 Statistics Canada, CCJS, Homicide Survey.
2 Chesney-Lind, 1998.
3 Budnick and Shields-Fletcher, 1998; Totten, 2001a; Chesney-Lind, 1998; Shaw and Dubois, 1995; Miller and Downs, 1995; Peters, 1998; Leschied and Cunningham, 1998; Kelly and Caputo, 1998; Fisher, 1998; Shaw, 1991, 1994a; LaPrairie, 1996; Wortley, 1999; Heney, 1990; Swern, 1995.
4 US Department of Health and Human Services, 2001; Garbarino, 1999; Heide, 1999b; Beasley *et al.*, 1999; Zimring, 1999; Elliot, Hagan, and McCord, 1998; Hagan, 1997; Ewing, 1990; Katz, 1986; Wolfgang and Ferracuti, 1967.
5 Royal Commission on Aboriginal Peoples, 1996; Commission on Systemic Racism in the Ontario Justice System, 1995; Shaw, 1994a, 1994b, 1991.

Appendix A: Youth Homicide Study Questionnaire

First or Pseudo-name:
Interview Number:
Interviewer:
Date:

Section 1: Demographic Profile

1.1.   Age:
1.2.   Gender:
1.3.   Sexual Orientation:
1.4.   Ethno-Racial Origin:
1.5.   Income Level (Mark One):
    1   None
    2   Below the Poverty Line
    3   Low
    4   Moderate
    5   High
1.6.   Before the homicide were you supporting yourself?
    1   Yes
    2   No, If NO go to question 1.8.
1.7.   If yes, how did you support yourself?
    1   social assistance
    2   disability
    3   employment insurance
    4   part-time paid work: kind of job
    5   full-time paid work: kind of job

6   other (specify)

1.8.   Before the homicide were your parent(s)/guardian(s) supporting you financially?

1   Yes

2   No, if NO go to question 1.10.

1.9.   If yes, how did they support you?

1   social assistance

2   disability

3   employment insurance

4   part-time paid work: kind of job

5   full-time paid work: kind of job

6   other (specify)

1.10.   Before the homicide did anyone else (friends, etc.) support you?

1   Yes, if YES who?

2   No, if NO go to question 1.12.

1.11.   If yes, how do/did they support you?

1   social assistance

2   disability

3   employment insurance

4   part-time paid work: kind of job

5   full-time paid work: kind of job

6   other (specify)

1.12.   Living Arrangements: Before the homicide did you live with:

1   Both Parent(s)

2   Mother only

3   Father only

4   Mother & Partner

5   Father & Partner

6   Guardian (Relative)

7   Foster Care

8   Group Home

9   Friends

10 Alone

11 Partner

12 Other (specify):

1.13.   Prior to homicide what was your usual daytime structure (Check all that apply)?

1   In School

2   Working

3   Training Program
4   Nothing
5   Other (specify)

Section 2: Family Background

2.1.   Could you tell me a little about your family background?

2.2.   When you were growing up was there any abuse between your parents/guardians?

    1   Yes

    2   No, If NO go to question 2.4.

2.3.   If yes, can you tell me about this abuse? Probe for: type of abuse, how often the abuse happened, whether respondent witnessed the abuse, and over what period of time it occurred.

2.4.   When you were growing up did you experience any abuse from your parents or guardians?

    1   Yes

    2   No, If NO go to question 2.7.

2.5.   When you were growing up did you experience abuse from any other family member? Probe for who was abusive: brother/sister, grandparent, aunt/uncle, cousin, other.

    1   Yes, specify who

    2   No, If NO go to question 2.7.

2.6.   If answered yes to 2.4 or 2.5, Tell me about the abuse. Probe for type of abuse, how often happened, and over what period of offender's life it occurred.

2.7.   Were you ever involved with the child welfare system?

    1   Yes

    2   No, If NO go to question 2.9.

2.8.   If yes, were you ever brought into care by child welfare system?

    1   Yes

    2   No, If NO go to question 2.10.

2.9.   If you were in care can you tell me why you were taken into care, how long you were in care and where you were in care?

2.10.   When you were growing up, did your parent(s)/guardian work?

    1   Yes

    2   No.

2.11.   If yes, what type of job; for what period of time; approximate salary. If no, what kind of financial support did your parent(s)/guardian have?

2.12.   Were any of your family members ever arrested and/or convicted for crimes?

1   Yes

2   No

2.13.   If yes, please tell me who and for what reasons?

Section 3: School Experiences

3.1.   Before the homicide, how were you doing at school?

3.2.   What is the highest grade achieved prior to the homicide?

3.3.   When you were in school did you have regular attendance or were you frequently absent? (If absent — why were you absent?)

3.4.   Were you ever suspended from school?

1   Yes

2   No, If NO go to question 3.6.

3.5.   If yes, how many times and what for?

3.6.   Were you ever expelled from school?

1   Yes

2   No, If NO go to question 3.8.

3.7.   If yes, how many times and what for?

3.8.   Did you ever drop out of school?

1   Yes

2   No, If NO go to question 3.10.

3.9   If yes, how many times, when, why?

3.10   Generally, how good a student were you?

3.11.   What were the positive aspects, if any, of school?

3.12.   What were the negative aspects, if any, of school?

3.13.   Were you ever identified as having any behavioural or learning difficulties?

1   Yes

2   No, if NO go to question 3.15

3.14.   If yes, can you tell me what they were:

3.15.   Are you in school now?

1   Yes

2   No, If NO go to question 4.1.

3.16.   If yes, how are you doing at school now?

258

Section 4: Mental/Physical Health

4.1   Have you ever been hospitalized for a serious health problem?

        1   Yes

        2   No, if NO go to question 4.3.

4.2.   If yes, tell me about it. Probe for: what, when, number of admissions, number of different service providers, how long hospitalized.

4.3.   Have you ever been hospitalized for a psychological or psychiatric problem?

        1   Yes

        2   No, if NO go to question 4.5.

4.4.   If yes, tell me about it. Probe for what diagnosis, when, number of admissions, number of different service providers, how long hospitalized.

4.5.   Do you currently have any medical problems?

        1   Yes

        2   No, if NO go to question 4.7.

4.6.   If yes, please tell me about it/them?

4.7.   Are you on any medication prescribed by a physician for physical or mental health reasons?

        1   Yes

        2   No, if NO go to question 5.1.

4.8.   If you are on medication, what and why?

Section 5: Drug and Alcohol Use

5.1   In the six months prior to the homicide, had you used (without a prescription) any drugs?

        1   Yes

        2   No, if NO go to question 5.3.

5.2   If yes, which drugs, through what route (i.v., nasal, oral), and how often?

5.3   In the six months prior to the homicide, had you used alcohol?

        1   Yes

        2   No, if NO go to question 5.5.

5.4   If yes, how often did you drink, how much did you consume, and under what circumstances?

5.5   Do you smoke cigarettes?

        1   Yes

        2   No, if NO go to question 5.7.

5.6   If yes, how much do you smoke?

5.7   Have you had any bad experiences (trips) from alcohol?

    1 Yes

    2 No, if NO go to question 5.9.

5.8   If yes, can you tell me about this?

5.9   Have you had any bad trips from other drugs?

    1 Yes

    2 No, if NO go to question 6.1.

5.10   If yes, what drugs and what happened?

Section 6: Spirituality

6.1   Does spirituality have a role in your life now?

    1 Yes

    2 No, if NO go to question 6.3.

6.2   If yes, can you tell me about your spirituality and why it is important to you?

6.3   Did spirituality have a role in your life prior to the homicide incident?

    1 Yes

    2 No

6.4   If there has been a change in spirituality, can you explain why this changed?

Section 7: Leisure

7.1.   Prior to the homicide, what did you do for fun (recreation)?

7.2.   Did you participate in any recreational activities at school?

    1 Yes

    2 No, if NO go to question 7.4.

7.3.   If yes, can you tell me what activities you participated in. Probe for what, when, how long, why stopped.

7.4.   Did you participate in any organized sports or other organized activities (e.g., Brownies, Cubs, etc.) outside of school?

    1 Yes

    2 No, if NO go to question 7.6.

7.5.   If yes, can you tell me what activities (when, how long)

7.6.   Did your "fun" (recreational activities outside of school and organized activities) usually involve alcohol?

    1 Yes

    2 No, if NO go to question 7.5.

7.5.   Did your "fun" (recreational activities outside of school and organized activities) usually involve drugs?

1   Yes

2   No, if NO go to question 7.6.

7.6.   Were physical confrontations or fights common when you were engaging in "fun" activities? Probe for: who was involved, what was nature of fights.

7.7.   Did you and your friends ever participate in illegal activities for "fun"?

1   Yes

2   No, if NO go to question 8.1.

7.8.   If yes, what illegal activities did you participate in with your friends?

drug use

under age drinking

b&e's

vandalism

swarmings

other assaults

petty theft (shoplifting)

car theft (joy riding)

other (specify)

Section 8: Peers

8.1.   Prior to the homicide, who were your best friends?

8.2.   How long had you been friends?

8.3.   Do any of your friends have criminal records?

1   Yes

2   No, if NO go to question 8.5.

8.4.   If yes, which ones and for what crimes?

8.5.   When you are with your friends, would you say you were usually:

1   a leader?

2   a follower?

3   neither?

8.6.   Were you ever a member of a gang?

1   Yes

2   No, if NO go to question 9.1.

8.7.   If yes, can you please tell me about your involvement in the gang. Probe for gang name, initiation, gang activities, how long a member, role in gang.

Section 9: Criminal History

9.1.   Are you involved in the youth justice system for any other crimes?
       1 Yes
       2 No, If no go to question 9.3.

9.2.   If yes, please tell us what other charges you are currently involved for:
       Charge(s); Conviction(s); Date(s).

9.3.   Is respondent currently in custody?
       1 Yes
       2 No

9.4.   Prior to your conviction for murder/manslaughter had you ever been in custody?
       1 Yes
       2 No, if never in custody, go directly to question 9.6.

9.5.   If yes, have you been in (check all that apply):
       1 Detention
          Date(s) & Location:
       2 Open Custody
          Date(s) Location:
       3 Secure Custody
          Date(s) Location:

9.6.   Are you currently on probation?
       1 Yes — Dates:
       2 No

9.7.   Have you ever been on probation?
       1 Yes — Dates:
       2 No

9.8.   Do you have any other criminal history?
       1 Yes
       2 No, if No go to question 10.1

9.9.   If yes, please give me the details. Probe for adult or YOA.
       Charge(s); Conviction(s); Date(s).

Section 10: History of Using Violence

10.1.   Excluding the homicide, have you ever committed a violent act?
       1 Yes
       2 No, if NO go to question 11.1.

10.2.   If yes, what are the two most violent acts you have committed?

1st act:

2nd act:

10.3. What triggered these acts?

1st act:

2nd act:

10.4. What kind of harm, if any, resulted?

1st act:

2nd act::

10.5. Were weapons used?

1st act:

2nd act:

10.6. Did you know the person or were they strangers?

1st act:

2nd act:

10.7. How did you feel about these violent incidents?

1st act:

2nd act:

10.8. Has your violent behaviour become more serious as you have grown up (i.e., unprovoked, more frequent, using weapons.)?

1 Yes

2 No, if NO go to question 10.10.

10.9. If yes, can you tell me in what way(s) it has become more serious?

1 more frequent

2 unprovoked

3 use of weapons

4 other

Provide Details:

10.10. When you have been seriously violent, did you think about it ahead of time?

1 usually

2 occasionally

3 rarely

4 never

10.11. When you have used violence in the past were you usually:

1 alone

2 with 1-2 friends

3 with a group or gang of friends?

10.12. Prior to the homicide were any of your friends violence?

1 Yes

2   No, if NO go to question 10.15.

10.13.   If yes, how often were they violent?
1   usually
2   occasionally
3   rarely

10.14.   Please describe a "typical" violent event.

10.15.   Did you use drugs and/or alcohol right before or during your violent behaviour?
1   usually
2   occasionally
3   rarely
4   never, if NEVER go to question 11.1.

10.16   If ever, were you more tempted to be violent when you had been using substances compared to when you were straight?
1   Yes
2   No

Section 11: The Homicide Incident

Now we'd like to discuss with you the homicide you were convicted of.

11.1.   What were you convicted of?
1   murder
2   manslaughter
3   criminal negligence causing death
4   other (specify)

11.2.   Who did you kill?

11.3.   How old were you at the time of the homicide?
1   12 years old
2   13 years old
3   14 years old
4   15 years old
5   16 years old
6   17 years old
7   18 years old

11.4.   Were you tried as a young offender or as an adult?
1   adult
2   young offender

11.5.   What was your sentence and where did you serve it? Probe for: sentence length, all institutions, and whether they were YOA or adult facilities.

264

11.6.   Please describe the killing — what happened. Probe for: whether this occurred alone, with a single friend, with a group of friends (how many), with a gang; if homicide occurred while respondent was engaged in another crime (what crime); location of homicide; relationship to victim; weapon(s) used; substance use involved; reasoning?

11.7.   What led up to the homicide?

11.8.   Can you describe the events immediately after the homicide (what did you do, what did the others do, how did you feel, what were you thinking at the time of the homicide?

11.9.   How does/did it feel to kill someone? Probe for: emotions you experienced at the time of the incident? For example, did you get a kick, high, rush, thrill out of doing this? Did you get any pleasure out of killing? Did you have any feelings of regret? Probe to ascertain type of account: denial, justification, minimization, victim-blaming, excusing, admitting, and taking responsibility.

11.10.   How did your parent(s) respond to your involvement in the homicide?

11.11.   How did your friend(s) respond to your involvement in the homicide?

11.12.   How did other(s) — kids at school, neighbours — respond to your involvement in the homicide?

11.13.   What, if anything, could have prevented you from killing?

11.14.   Tell us about your experiences with the Youth Justice System after the homicide?

11.15.   While you were in custody did you get any help for your violent behaviour?
    1   Yes
    2   No, if NO go to question 11.17.

11.16.   If yes, what kind of violence counselling did you receive? Probe for type of program, whether they completed program, and if not why.

11.17.   While you were in custody, did you get any other kind of counselling?
    1   Yes
    2   No

11.18.   If yes, what kind of counselling did you receive?

11.19.   While in custody did you get counselling or treatment for any emotional or psychological problems?
    1   Yes
    2   No

11.20.   If yes, tell me about that counselling. Probe for reason(s), type of counselling, did they finish the program?

11.21.   If respondent has been released from custody: Tell us about your experiences outside since you got released from custody? Probe for responses of family, friends, peers, neighbours, employers.

Provide relevant referral information.

Appendix B: Youth Homicide Study Informed Consent Form

Our names are Katharine Kelly and Mark Totten. We are doing a YSB/Carleton University study on youth homicide. You understand that we will be interviewing you about your childhood and adolescence, family life, the homicide you were convicted of, your experiences in the justice system, and your life now. Please answer each question as honestly as you can. All of your answers will be kept strictly confidential. However, if you tell us that any child under the age of 16 years is being abused or is currently at risk of being abused, we must report this to the child welfare authorities by law. We also have to notify authorities if we believe that you have put someone's life at risk. Also, if we think you are going to kill yourself, we will get you any necessary help. The consent form states that you understand what you are being asked to do in this interview and that you understand that your answers will be kept confidential. Each interview is expected to take about eight hours in total. We will probably do two interviews with you, each about four hours long.

I hereby give my informed consent to be interviewed. I understand the nature of my involvement, and I have been assured that my answers will be kept strictly confidential. I agree that the interview will be audio-taped. At no point during future analysis will I be identified by name. I further understand that all the information recorded from the interview (including that on tapes and computer) will be destroyed after the information has been used in the study for which it was intended. Any quotations from this interview will appear without anything which identifies who I am. I am also aware that I have the right to refuse to answer any questions and that I may withdraw at any time. I agree that the researcher may also terminate this interview with me at any time. Finally, I understand that there is no risk to me, my friends, or my relatives stemming from my involvement in this study.

Please initial or make your mark   Date:_____

Researchers:_____   Date:_____

references

Acland, C. (1995). *Youth, Murder, Spectacle*. Boulder: Westview Press.

Agresti, A., and B. Finlay (1984). *Statistical Methods for the Social Sciences* (2nd ed.). San Francisco: Dellen Publishing Company.

Andrews, D., R. Hoge, and A. Leschied (1992). *Review of the Profile, Classification and Treatment Literature with Young Offenders: A Social-Psychological Approach*. Toronto, Ontario: Ministry of Community and Social Services.

Andrews, D., I. Zinger, R. Hoge, J. Bonta, P. Gendreau, and F. Cullen (1990). Does correctional treatment work? A clinically relevant and psychologically informed meta-analysis. *Criminology* 28 (3): 369-404.

Athens, L. (1992). *The Creation of Dangerous Violent Criminals*. Chicago: University of Illinois Press.

Avakame, E. (1998). How different is violence in the home? An examination of some correlates of stranger and intimate homicide. *Criminology* 36(3): 601-32.

Bala, N. (1997). *Young Offenders Law*. Toronto: Irwin Law.

Ballantyne, M., and L. Raymond (1998). *Effective Strategies for Adolescents at Risk of Out-of-Home Placement*. Toronto: Ontario Association of Children's Aid Societies.

Baron, S. (1997). Canadian male street skinheads, street gang or street terrorists. *Canadian Review of Sociology and Anthropology* 34(2): 125-54.

Bass, E., and L. Davis (1988). *The Courage to Heal*. New York: Harper and Row.

Beardslee, W., E. Wright, P. Salt, K. Drezner, T. Gladstone, E. Versage, and P. Rothberg (1997). Examination of children's responses to two preventive intervention strategies over time. *Journal of the American Academy of Child and Adolescent Psychiatry* 36: 196-204.

Bell, S. (1999). *Young Offenders and Juvenile Justice: A Century After the Fact*. Toronto: Nelson.

Berger, P., and K. Tremblay (1999). Welfare reform's impact on homelessness. *Journal of Social Distress and The Homeless* 8(1): 1-20.

Bessere, S. (1997). Criminal victimization: An international perspective. *Juristat* 18(6). Statistics Canada: Canadian Centre for Justice Statistics.

Blanchette, K., D. Robinson, C. Alksnis, and R. Serin (1998). *Assessing Treatment Change Among Family Violent Offenders: Reliability and Validity of a Family Violence Treatment Assessment Battery.* Ottawa: Research Branch, Correctional Service of Canada.

Bolles, R. (2001). *What Color Is Your Parachute: A Practical Manual for Job Hunters and Career Changers* (rev. ed.). Berkeley, CA: Ten Speed Press.

Borland, C.J. (1996). *Conflict "cans": schoolwide conflict resolution training program for grades K-6, trainer pack.* Oak View, CA: self-published.

Brent, B., and R. Flynn Corwyn (1997). Religion and delinquency: The relationship after considering family and peer influences. *Journal for the Scientific Study of Religion* 36(1): 81–92.

Brent, B., and L. Whiteside (1995). Testing an integrated model of delinquency using LISEREL. *Journal of Social Service Research* 21(2): 1–32.

Budnick, K., and E. Shields-Fletcher (1998). *OJJDP Fact Sheet #84: What About Girls?* Washington, DC: US Department of Justice.

Butts, J., and W. Barton (1995). In-home programs for juvenile delinquents. In I. Schwartz and P. AuClaire (eds.), *Home-Based Services for Troubled Children.* Lincoln, Nebraska: University of Nebraska Press.

Canadian Institute of Child Health (2000). *The Health of Canada's Children* (3rd ed). Ottawa: Canadian Institute of Child Health.

Canadian Welfare Council (1941). *The Juvenile Court in Law* (3rd ed). Ottawa: Council House.

Caputo, T., and S. Goldenberg (1986). Young people and the law: A consideration of Luddite and Utopian responses. Paper presented at the Western Association of Sociology and Anthropology, Winnipeg.

Caputo, T., and K. Kelly (1998). Health risk and homeless youth: Exploring the potential for community-based preventive measures. In National Forum on Health, *Health Action: Building on the Legacy. Volume 1: Children and Youth.* Ottawa: Health Canada: 408–37.

Cardinal, C., and D. Laberge (1999). Le systeme policier et les services de sante mentale. *Sante mentale au Québec* 24(1): 199–220.

Cavadino, Paul (ed.) (1996). *Children Who Kill.* London: Waterside Press.

Cheatwood, D., and K. Block (1990). Youth and homicide: An investigation of the age factor in criminal homicide. *Justice Quarterly,* 7(2): 267–292.

Chesney-Lind, M. (1998). *What To Do About Girls? Promising Perspectives and Effective Strategies.* Arlington, VA: ICCA.

Cohen, A. (1955). *Delinquent Boys: The Culture of the Gang.* New York: Free Press.

Cohen, L. and M. Felson (1979). Social change and crime rate trends: A routine activities approach. *American Sociological Review* 44: 588–608.

Commission on Systemic Racism in the Ontario Justice System (1995). *The Report of the Commission on Systemic Racism in the Ontario Criminal Justice System*. Toronto: Queen's Printer.

Cook, P., and J. Laub (1998). The unprecedented epidemic in youth violence. In M. Tonry and M. Moore (eds.), *Youth Violence, Crime and Justice: A Review of Research* Vol. 24. Chicago: University of Chicago Press: 27–64.

Craig, W., R. Peters, and R. Konarski (1998). Bullying and victimization among Canadian school children. *Workshop Paper for Investing in Children: A National Research Conference, 1998*. Ottawa.

Crutchfield, R., A. Glusker, and G. Bridges (1999). A tale of three cities: Labour markets and homicide. *Sociological Focus* 23(1): 65–83.

Cullingford, C., and J. Morrison (1995). Bullying as a formative influence: The relationship between the experience of school and criminality. *British Educational Research Journal* 21(5): 547–60.

Dekovic, M. (1999). Risk and protective factors in the development of problem behavior during adolescence. *Journal of Youth and Adolescence* 28(6): 667–85.

Department of Justice Canada (1999). *Fact Sheet on Rehabilitation and Reintegration*. Ottawa: Justice Canada.

Denzin, N. (1989). *The Research Act: A Theoretical Introduction to Sociological Methods*. Englewood Cliffs, NJ: Prentice-Hall.

Donahue, M., and P. Benson (1995). Religion and the well-being of adolescents. *The Journal of Social Issues* 51(2): 145–60.

Duff, P. (1997). Diversion from prosecution into psychiatric care: Who controls the gates? *British Journal of Criminology* 37(1): 15–34.

Dukarm, C., R. Byrd, P. Auinger, and M. Weitzman (1996). Illicit substance use, gender, and the risk of violent behavior among adolescents. *Archives of Paediatrics and Adolescent Medicine* 150(8): 797–801.

Duncan, R. (1999a). Peer and sibling aggression: An investigation of intra- and extra-familial bullying. *Journal of Interpersonal Violence* 14(8): 871–86.

———. (1999b). Maltreatment by parent and peers: The relationship between child abuse, bully victimization and psychological distress. *Child Maltreatment* 4(1): 45–55.

Elliott, D., J. Hagan, and J. McCord (1998). *Youth Violence: Children at Risk*. Washington DC: American Sociological Association.

Engler, C., and S. Crowe (2000). Alternative measures in Canada, 1998-99. *Juristat* 20(6). Ottawa: Statistics Canada, Canadian Centre for Justice Statistics.

Eron, L., J. Gentry, and P. Schlegel (1994). *Reason to Hope: A Psychosocial Perspective on Violence and Youth.* Washington D.C.: American Psychological Association.

Ewing, C. (1990). *When Children Kill: The Dynamics of Juvenile Homicide.* Lexington, Massachusetts: Lexington Books, D.C. Heath Company.

Fedorowycz, O. (2000). Homicide in Canada-1999. *Juristat* 20 (9). Ottawa: Statistics Canada, Canadian Centre for Justice Statistics.

Figley, C. (ed.) (1995). *Compassion Fatigue: Coping with Secondary Traumatic Stress Disorder in Those Who Treat the Traumatized.* New York: Brunner/Mazel.

Fisher, J. (1998). Female young offenders: Extent and level of female youth crime. *Briefing Note.* Ottawa: Department of Justice Canada.

Fuchs, D. (1990). Programs for preventing placement of adolescents. In M. Rothery and G. Cameron (eds.), *Child Maltreatment: Expanding Our Concept of Helping.* Hillsdale, NJ: Lawrence Erlbaum Associates.

Garbarino, J. (1999). *Lost Boys: Why Our Sons Turn Violent and How We Can Save Them.* New York: Free Press.

George, M., *et al* (1994). *Population Projections for Canada, Provinces and Territories 1993-2016.* Catalogue no. 91-520. Ottawa: Statistics Canada.

Glaser, B., and A. Straus (1967). *The Discovery of Grounded Theory.* Chicago: Aldine.

Gubrium, J., and J. Holstein (1997). *The New Language of Qualitative Method.* New York: Oxford University Press.

Gutman, L.M., and C. Midgley (2000). The role of protective factors in supporting the academic achievement of poor African American students during the middle school transition. *Journal of Youth and Adolescence* 29(2): 223-48.

Hagan, J. (1994). *Crime and Disrepute.* Thousand Oaks California: Pine Forge Press.

Hagan, M. (1997). An Analysis of Adolescent Perpetrators of Homicide and Attempted Homicide Upon Return to the Community. *International Journal of Offender Therapy and Comparative Criminology* 41(3): 250-59.

Hamburg, M. (1998). "Youth violence is a public health concern." In D. Elliot, M. Hamburg, and K. Williams (eds.), *Violence in American Schools: A New Perspective.* New York: Cambridge University Press.

Harris, J. (1998). *The Nurture Assumption: Why Children Turn Out the Way They Do*. New York: Free Press.

Hawkins, D., T. Herronkohl, D. Farrington, D. Brewer, R. Catalano, T. Harachi, and L. Cothern (2000). *Predictors of youth violence*. Washington, DC: US Department of Justice, Office of Juvenile Justice and Delinquency Prevention.

Hawkins, K.A. (2000). "Frontal lobe dysfunction and aggression: Conceptual issues and research findings." *Aggression And Violent Behavior* 5 (2): 147-157.

Hegar, R., and M. Scannapieco (2000). Grandma's babies: The problem of welfare eligibility for children raised by relatives. *Journal of Sociology and Social Welfare* 27(3): 153-71.

Heide, K. (1999). Youth homicide. In M. Dwayne Smith and Margret A. Zahn (eds.), *Studying and Preventing Violence*. Thousand Oaks, CA: Sage. 175-96.

Heney, J. (1990). *Report on Self-Injurious Behaviour in the Kingston Prison For Women*. Ottawa: Correctional Service of Canada.

Hill, M. (1999). What's the problem? Who can help? The perspectives of children and young people on their well-being and on helping professionals. *Journal of Social Work Practice* 13(2):135-45.

Hindelang, M., M. Gottfredson, and J. Garofalo (1978). *Victims of Personal Crime*. Cambridge, MA: Ballinger.

Hornby, H., and M. Collins (1981). Teenagers in foster care: The forgotten majority. *Children and Youth Services Review* 3 (2): 7-20.

Hornick, J., T. Caputo, R. Hastings, P. Knoll, L. Bertrand, J. Paetsch, L. Stroeder, and A. Maguire (1996). *A Police Reference Manual on Crime Prevention and Diversion with Youth*. Canadian Research Institute for Law and the Family and Solicitor General Canada.

Howard, S., J. Dryden, and B. Johnson (1999). Childhood resilience: review and critique of literature. *Oxford Review of Education* 25(3): 307-23.

Hylton, J. (1994). Get tough or get smart? Options for Canada's youth justice system in the twenty-first century. *Canadian Journal of Criminology* 36(3): 229-46.

Jenson, J., and S. Stroick (2000). *What is the Best Policy Mix for Canada's Young Children?* CPRN Study No. F/09. Ottawa: Canadian Policy Research Networks.

Kagan, R., W. Reid, S. Roberts, and J. Silverman-Pollow (1987). Engaging families of court-mandated youths in an alternative to institutional placement. *Child Welfare* 66 (4): 365-76.

Kahne, J., and K. Bailey (1999). The role of social capital in youth development: The case of "I Have a Dream" programs. *Educational Evaluation and Policy Analysis* 21(3): 321-43.

Kanin, E. (1967). Reference groups and sex conduct norm violation. *Sociological Quarterly*, 8: 495-504.

Karr-Morse, R., and M. Wiley (1997). *Ghosts from the Nursery: Tracing the Roots of Violence.* New York: Atlantic Monthly Press.

Katz, J., (1988). *Seductions of Crime: Moral and Sensual Attractions in Doing Evil.* New York: Basic Books.

Kawachi, I. (1999). Crime: social disorganization and relative deprivation. *Social Science and Medicine* 48(6): 719-31.

Keene, J., and M. Woolgrove (1997). Obstacles and opportunities for multidisciplinary working in drug misuse: A case study. *Drugs: Education, Prevention and Policy* 4(3): 285-95.

Kennedy, B., I. Kawachi, D. Prothrow-Stith, K. Lochner, and V. Gupta (1998). Social capital, income inequality, and firearm violent crime. *Social Science and Medicine* 47(1): 7-17.

King, A., W. Boyce, and M. King (1999). *Trends in the Health of Canadian Youth.* Ottawa: Her Majesty the Queen in Right of Canada, represented by the Minister of Health Canada.

Knox, G. (1998). How to "gang proof" your child: Ten rules to help parents. *Journal of Gang Research* 5(4): 71-76.

Krivo, L., and R. Peterson (1996). Extremely disadvantaged neighborhoods and urban crime. *Social Forces* 75(2): 619-48.

LaPrairie, C. (1996). *Examining Aboriginal Corrections in Canada.* Ottawa: Ministry of the Solicitor General.

Leacy, F. (1983). *Historical Statistics of Canada* (2nd ed.). Ottawa: Ministry of Supply and Services Canada.

Lee, M. (2000). Concentrated poverty, race, and homicide. *Sociological Quarterly* 41(2): 189-206.

Lee, M., and W. Bankston (1999). Political structure, economic inequality and homicide: A cross-national analysis. *Deviant Behaviour.* 20(1): 27-55.

Lee, M., and E. Shihadeh (1998). Labor market structure, unemployment, and crime: The indirect effect of low-skill jobs on homicide and theft in 26 countries. *Sociology of Crime, Law, and Deviance* 1: 49-64.

Leshied, A., and A. Cunningham (1998). Alternatives to custody for high-risk young offenders: The multi-systemic therapy approach. *European Journal on Criminal Policy and Research* 6 (4): 545-60.

Lew, M. (1988). *Victims No Longer: Men Recovering from Incest and other Sexual Child Abuse*. New York: Nevraumont.

Lipman, E., D. Offord, and M. Dooley (1996). *What do we know about children from single-mother families? Questions and answers from the national longitudinal survey of children and youth*. Catalogue no. 89-550-MPE (1). Ottawa: Human Resources Development Canada and Statistics Canada.

Loeber, R., and D. Farrington (eds.) (1997). *Never Too Early, Never Too Late: Risk Factors and Successful Interventions for Serious and Violent Juvenile Offenders. The Final Report of the Study Group on Serious and Violent Juvenile Offenders*. Washington, DC: US Department of Justice, Office of Justice Programs, Office of Juvenile Justice and Delinquency Prevention.

LoPiccolo, Philip (1996). Something Snapped. *Technology Review* 99(7): 52-68.

Lourie, I (1994). *Principles of Local System Development for Children, Adolescents, and Their Families*. Chicago, IL: Kaleidoscope.

Lundy, C., and M. Totten (1997). Youth on the fault line. *The Social Worker* 65(3): 98-106.

Luthar, S., D. Cicchetti, and B. Becker (2000). The construct of resilience: A critical evaluation and guidelines for future work. *Child Development* 72(3): 543-62.

MacDonald, M. (1998). The impact of a restructured Canadian welfare state on Atlantic. *Social Policy and Administration* 32(4): 389-400.

MacMillan, H. (2000). Child maltreatment: What we know in the year 2000. *Canadian Journal of Psychiatry* 45: 702-09.

MacMillan, H., with the Canadian Task Force on Preventive Health Care (2000). Preventive health care, 2000 update: Prevention of child maltreatment. *Canadian Medical Association Journal* 163 (11): 1451-58.

MacMillan, H., J. Fleming, M. Wong, and D. Offord (1996). Relationship between history of childhood maltreatment and psychiatric disorder in a community sample: Results from the Ontario Health Supplement. *Conference Reporting*, International Family Violence Research Conference, Durham, NH.

MacMillan, H., J. MacMillan, D. Offord, L. Griffith, and A. MacMillan (1994). Primary prevention of child physical abuse and neglect: A critical review: Part I. *Journal of Child Psychology and Psychiatry* 35: 835-56.

MacMillan, H., J. MacMillan, D. Offord, with the Canadian Task Force on the Periodic Health Examination (1993). Periodic health examination, 1993 update: 1. Primary prevention of child maltreatment. *Canadian Medical Association Journal* 148 (2): 151-63.

Manion, I., and S. Wilson (1995). *An Examination of the Association Between Histories of Maltreatment and Adolescent Risk Behaviours.* Ottawa: Minister of Supply and Services Canada.

Martin, S. (1999). Police force or police service? Gender and emotional labor. *The Annals of the American Academy of Political and Social Science* 56: 111-26.

McCann, I., and L Pearlman (1990). Vicarious traumatization: A framework for understanding the psychological effects of working with victims. *Journal of Traumatic Stress* 3: 131-49.

Mercy, J., M. Rosenberg, K. Powell, C. Broome, and W. Roper (1993). Public health policy for preventing violence. *Health Affairs* 12: 7-26.

Miethe, T., and R. Meier (1994). *Crime and Its Social Context.* New York: State University of New York Press.

Miller, B., and W. Downs (1995). Violent victimization among women with alcohol problems. In M. Galanter (ed.), *Recent Developments in Alcoholism, Volume 12: Women and Alcoholism.* New York: Plenum Press.

Miller, E. (1999). The neuropsychology of offending. *Psychology Crime & Law* 1999, 5(4): 297-318.

Minor, K. (1993). Juvenile delinquency and the transition to monopoly capitalism. *Journal of Sociology and Social Welfare* 20: 59-80.

Moldon, M., and D. Kukec (2000). Youth custody and Community Services Canada, 1998-1999. *Juristat* 20(8). Ottawa: Statistics Canada, Canadian Centre for Justice Statistics.

Moretti, M., R. Holland, and S. Peterson (1994). Long term outcome of an attachment-based program for conduct disorder. *Canadian Journal of Psychiatry* 39: 360-70.

Morrison, D., and E. Eisner (1993). Child-related dimensions of placement stability in treatment foster care. *Child and Adolescent Social Work Journal* 10 (4): 301-17.

Murray, C., and R. Freeman–Longo (1996). *Men and Anger: Understanding and Managing Your Anger for a Much Better Life.* Brandon, VT: Safer Society Press.

Myers, W. (1994). Sexual Homicide by Adolescents. *Journal of the American Academy of Child and Adolescent Psychiatry* 33(7): 962-969.

National Crime Prevention Centre (2000a). *Draft Policy Framework for Addressing Crime Prevention and Children Ages 0 to 12*. Ottawa: Department of Justice Canada.

———. (2000b). *Draft Policy Framework for Addressing Crime Prevention and Youth Ages 12 to 18*. Ottawa: Department of Justice Canada.

———. (1998a). *Bullying and victimization: The problems and solutions for school-aged children*. Available: http://www.crime-prevention.org/ ncpc.

———. (1998b). *Youth assisting youth*. Available: http://www.crime-prevention.org/ncpc.

Neeley-Bertrand, D. (2001). "What happens after?" *Children's Voice* 10 (2).

Niehoff, D. (1999). *The Biology of Violence: How Understanding the Brain, Behavior, and Environment Can Break the Vicious Circle of Aggression*. New York: Free Press.

Offord, D., H. Kraemer, A. Kazdin, P. Jensen, and R. Harrington (1998). Lowering the burden of suffering from child psychiatric disorder: trade-offs among clinical, targeted and universal interventions. *Journal of the American Academy of Child and Adolescent Psychiatry* 37: 686-94.

Olweus, D. (1991). Bully/victim problems among school children: Some basic facts and effects of a school-based intervention program. In D. Pepler and K. Rubin (eds.), *The Development and Treatment of Childhood Aggression*. Hillsdale, NJ: Lawrence Erlbaum Associates.

Pallone, N., and J. Hennessy (2000). Neuropathology and criminal violence: Newly calibrated ratios. *Journal of Offender Rehabilitation* 31(1/2): 87-99.

Pardeck, J. (1985). A profile of the child likely to experience unstable foster care. *Adolescence* 20 (79): 689-96.

Parker, R.N. (1989). Poverty, subculture of violence, and types of homicide. *Social Forces* 67(4): 983-1007.

Parker, K., and M. Pruitt (2000). Poverty, poverty concentration, and homicide. *Social Science Quarterly* 81(2): 555-70.

Parker, R., and L. Rebhun (1995). *Alcohol and Homicide: A Deadly Combination of Two American Traditions*. Albany, NY: State University of New York.

Peled, E. (1997). Intervention with children of battered women: a review of current literature. *Children and Youth Services Review (UK)*, 19(4): 277-99.

Peterson, R., L. Krivo, and M. Harris (2000). Disadvantage and neighborhood violent crime: Do local institutions matter? *Journal of Research in Crime and Delinquency* 37(1): 31-63.

Pitts J., and T. Hope (1997). The local politics of inclusion: The state and community safety. *Social Policy & Administration* 31(5): 37-58.

Proch, K. and M. Taber (1987). Alienated adolescents in foster care. *Social Work Research and Abstracts* 23: 9-13.

Putnam, R. (2000). *Bowling Alone: The Collapse and Revival of the American Community*. New York: Simon and Schuster.

Rae-Grant, N., B. Thomas, D. Offord, and M Boyle (1989). Risk protective factors, and the prevalence of behaviour and emotional disorders in children and adolescents. *Journal of the American Academy of Child and Adolescent Psychiatry*, 28: 2362-2368.

Rietschlin, J., H. Pearson, and C. Kierkus (1996). Do recreational programs prevent delinquency? Theoretical and methodological issues in evaluation. *American Sociological Association*.

Rigby, K. (2000). Effects of peer victimization in schools and perceived social support on adolescent well-being. *Journal of Adolescence* 23(1): 57-68.

——. (1994). School children's perceptions of their families and parents as a function of peer relations. *The Journal of Genetic Psychology* 154(4): 501-13.

Rigby, K, P. Slee, and R. Cunningham (1999). Effects of parenting on the peer relations of Australian adolescents. *Journal of Social Psychology* 139(3): 387-88.

Roberts, J. (1992). Public opinion, crime, and criminal justice. In Michael Tonry (ed.), *Crime and Justice: A Review of Research*. Vol. 16. Chicago: University of Chicago Press.

Rosenberg, M. (1995). Violence in America: An integrated approach to understanding and prevention. *Journal of Health Care for the Poor and Undeserved* 6(2): 102-10.

Royal Commission on Aboriginal Peoples (1996). *Bridging the Cultural Divide: A Report on Aboriginal People and Criminal Justice in Canada*. Ottawa: Minister of Supply and Services Canada.

Ruzek, J. (1993). Professionals coping with vicarious trauma. *National Center for Post Traumatic Stress Disorder Newsletter* 3(2).

Sacco, V., and L. Kennedy (1994). *The Criminal Event*. Scarborough, ON: Nelson Canada.

Salmivalli, C., A. Kaukiainen, L.Kaistaniemi, and K. Lagerspetz (1999). Self-evaluated self-esteem, peer-evaluated self-esteem, and defensive egotism as predictors of adolescents' participation in bullying situations. *Personality and Social Psychology Bulletin* 25(10): 1268-78.

Sampson, R., and J. Lauritson (1994). Violent victimisation and offending: Individual-, situational-, and community-level risk factors. In A. Reiss, Jr., and J. Roth (eds.), *Understanding and Preventing Violence: Social Influences.* Washington, DC: National Academy Press.

Sanders, R., S. Jackson, and N. Thomas (1996). The police role in the management of child protective services. *Policing and Society* 6(3): 87-100.

Sanders, T. (2000). Sentencing of young offenders in Canada, 1998/99. *Juristat* 20(7). Ottawa: Statistics Canada: Canadian Centre for Justice Statistics.

Savoie, J. (1999). Youth violent crime. *Juristat,* 19(13). Ottawa: Statistics Canada, Canadian Centre for Justice Statistics.

Scott, M., and S. Lyman (1968). Accounts. *American Sociological Review* 33: 46-62.

Schumaker, M., and G. Kurz (2000). *The 8% Solution: Preventing Serious, Repeat Juvenile Crime.* Thousand Oaks, CA: Sage.

Schwartz, D., K. Dodge, G. Pettit, and J. Bates (1998). The early socialization of aggressive victims of bullying. *Child Development* 68(4): 665-75.

Seelig, W., B. Goldman-Hall, and J. Jerrell (1992). In-home treatment of families with seriously disturbed adolescents in crisis. *Family Process* 31(2): 135-49.

Shaw, M., and S. Dubois (1995). *Understanding Violence by Women: A Review of the Literature.* Ottawa: Correctional Service of Canada.

Shaw, M (1994a). *Ontario Women in Conflict with the Law: Young Offenders in the 1991 Survey.* Toronto: Ontario Ministry of Community and Social Services.

———. (1994b). *Ontario Women in Conflict with the Law Subsidiary Report: Young Offenders.* Toronto: Ministry of Correctional Services.

———. (1991). *Survey of Federally Sentenced Women: Report to the Task Force on Federally Sentenced Women.* Ottawa: Solicitor General of Canada.

Shaw, M., and F. Jane (1999). *Family Group Conferencing with Children Under Twelve: A Discussion Paper.* Ottawa: Department of Justice Canada.

Shihadeh, E., and G. Ousey (1998). Industrial restructuring and violence: The link between entry-level jobs, economic deprivation, and black and white homicide. *Social Forces* 77(1): 185-206.

Silverman, D. (1993). *Interpreting Qualitative Data.* London: Sage.

Silverman, R., and L. Kennedy (1993). *Deadly Deeds: Murder in Canada.* Toronto: Nelson Canada.

Smandych, R. (1995). Changing images of childhood and delinquency. In James Chreechan and Robert Silverman (eds.), *Canadian Delinquency*. Scarborough, ON: Prentice-Hall Canada.

Smith M., and S. Feiler (1995). Absolute and relative involvement in homicide offending: Contemporary youth and the baby boom cohorts. *Violence and Victims*, 10(4): 327-33.

Smokowski, P., A. Reynolds, and N. Brezruczko (1999). Resilience and protective factors in adolescence: An autobiographical perspective from disadvantaged youth. *Journal of School Psychology* 37(4): 425-48.

Sourander, A., L. Helstela, H. Helenius, and J. Piha (2000). Persistence of bullying from childhood to adolescence: A longitudinal 8-year follow-up study. *Child Abuse and Neglect* 24(7): 873-81.

Sprott, J., and A. Doob (1997). Fear, victimization, and attitudes to sentencing, the courts, and the police. *Canadian Journal of Criminology* : 275-91.

Straussner, J.H., and S.L.A. Straussner (1996). Impact of community and school violence on children. In Norma Kolko Phillips and Shulamith Lala Ashenberg Straussner (eds.). *Children in the Urban Environment: Linking Social Policy and Clinical Practices*. Springfield, IL: Charles C. Thomas.

Sudermann, M., and P. Jaffe (1997). *Children and Youth Who Witness Violence: New Directions in Intervention and Treatment Across the Lifespan*. Thousand Oaks, CA: Sage Publications

Swern, E. (1995). *Young women as perpetrators of violence*. MA dissertation. Ottawa: Carleton University Department of Sociology and Anthropology.

Statistics Canada, Canadian Centre for Justice Statistics (2000a). The justice fact finder, 1998. *Juristat* 20(4).

——. (2000b). *Family Violence in Canada: A Statistical Profile*. Ottawa: Ministry of Industry.

——. (2000c). *Homicide Survey*.

——. (1999a). Homicide in Canada. *Juristat* 19(10).

——. (1999b). *Family Violence in Canada: A Statistical Profile 1999*. Ottawa: Ministry of Industry.

——. (1999c). Youth Court Statistics 1997-98: Highlights. *Juristat* 19(2).

——. (1997). *Corrections Key Indicator Report for Adults and Young Offenders, 1996-97*. Catalogue no. 85-222-XPE. Ottawa.

Statistics Canada and the Federal-Provincial Working Group on Child and Family Services Information (1996). *Child and Family Services Annual Report*. Ottawa.

Steinhauer, P. (1996). The diagnosis, prevention and management of attachment disorders within the child welfare system. *PRISM*, 6(4): 604-17.

———. (1984). The management of children admitted to child welfare services in Ontario: A review and discussion of current problems and practices. *Canadian Journal of Psychiatry* 29 (6): 473-83.

Stevens, V, P. Van Oost, and I. De Bourdeaudhuij (2000). The effects of an anti-bullying intervention programme on peers' attitudes and behaviour. *Journal of Adolescence* 23(1): 21-34.

Stevenson, K., J. Tufts, D. Hendrick and M. Kowalski (1998). *A Profile of Youth Justice in Canada*. Statistics Canada: Canadian Centre for Justice Statistics.

Sykes, G., and D. Matza (1957). Techniques of Neutralization: A theory of delinquency. *American Sociological Review* 22: 664-70.

Tanner, J. (1996). *Teenage Troubles: Youth and Deviance in Canada*. Toronto: Nelson Canada.

Timberlake, E., and M. Verdieck (1987). Psychosocial functioning of adolescents in foster care. *Social Casework* 68 (4): 214-22.

The Oxford English Dictionary (1971). Compact ed. Oxford: Oxford University Press.

Torrance, D. (1997). Do you want to be in my gang?: A study of the existence and effects of bullying in a primary school class. *British Journal of Special Education* 24(4): 158-62.

Totten, M. (2000a). *Guys, Gangs and Girlfriend Abuse*. Peterborough, ON: Broadview Press.

———. (2000b). *YSB May 1999 Youth Survey: Summary of Findings*. Ottawa: YSB.

———. (2001a, in press). *The Special Needs of Young Women in Canada's Youth Justice System (Technical Report)*. Ottawa: Dept. of Justice Canada.

———. (2001b, in press). Girlfriend Abuse as a Form of Masculinity Construction Among Violent, Marginal Male Youth. *Men and Masculinities*.

———. (2001c, in press). *Maltreated Kids, Violent Adolescents: Is There a Link?* Health Canada Family Violence Prevention Division: Ministry of Industry Canada.

———. (1997). *Youth and violence*. Ottawa: The National Clearinghouse on Family Violence, Health Canada.

Tremblay, R., R. Zhou, C. Gagnon, F. Vitaro, and H. Boileau. (1995). Violent boys: Development and prevention. In James Creechan and Robert Silverman (eds.), *Canadian Delinquency*. Scarborough, ON: Prentice-Hall Canada.

US Department of Health and Human Services (2001). *Youth Violence: A Report of the Surgeon General*. Washington DC.

Wachtel, A. (1999). *The "State of the Art" in Child Abuse Prevention, 1997*. Ottawa: Minister of Public Works and Government Services Canada.

Walker, H.M., S. Stieber, and M. Bullis (1997). Longitudinal correlates of arrest, status among at-risk males. *Journal of Child and Family Studies* 6(3): 289-309.

Wasserman, G., and L. Miller (1998). The prevention of serious and violent juvenile offending. In R. Loeber and D. Farrington (eds.) *Serious and Violent Juvenile Offenders: Risk Factors and Successful Interventions*. Thousand Oaks, CA: Sage.

Wekerle, C., and D. Wolfe (1993). Prevention of child physical abuse and neglect: Promising new directions. *Clinical Psychology Review* 13: 501-40.

Wilkinson, R., I. Kawachi, and B. Kennedy (1998). Mortality, the social environment, crime and violence. *Sociology of Health and Illness* 20(5): 578-97.

Wilson, L. (1982). *Juvenile Courts in Canada*. Toronto: Carswell.

Winship, C., and J. Berrien (1999). Boston cops and black churches. *The Public Interest* 136 (summer): 52-68.

Wolfe, D., et al. (1997). Interrupting the cycle of violence: empowering youth to promote healthy relationships. In D. Wolfe, R. McMahon, and R. Peters (eds.). *Child Abuse: New Directions in Prevention and Treatment Across the Lifespan*. Thousand Oaks, CA: Sage Publications.

Wolfgang, M., and F. Ferracuti (1967). *The Subculture of Violence: Towards an Integrated Theory in Criminology*. London: Tavistock Publications.

Zimring, F. (1999). The hardest of the hard cases: Adolescent homicide in juvenile and criminal court. *Virginia Journal of Social Policy and the Law* 6(3): 437-69.